Honda Accord Owners Workshop Manual

by J H Haynes
Member of the Guild of Motoring Writers

and I M Coomber

Models covered
All versions of Honda Accord Hatchback and Saloon, 1600 cc and 1602 cc.
Also covers USA Honda Accord CVCC models to 1977

Covers manual and Hondamatic transmissions

ISBN 0 85696 991 5

ABCDE
FGHIJ
KLMNO
PQRST

Printed in England *(351-7N4)*

Haynes Publishing Group
Sparkford Nr Yeovil
Somerset BA22 7JJ England

Haynes Publications, Inc
861 Lawrence Drive
Newbury Park
California 91320 USA

Acknowledgements

Thanks are due to Honda (UK) Ltd. for their assistance in supplying certain technical material and illustrations, Castrol Limited who supplied the lubrication data, and the Champion Sparking Plug Company, who provided the illustrations showing the various spark plug conditions. We are also grateful to Shepton Mallet Motors of Shepton Mallet, Somerset, for their assistance in providing a vehicle to enable us to cover later models. Sykes-Pickavant provided some of the workshop tools. Thanks are also due to all those people at Sparkford who helped in the production of this manual.

About this manual

Its aims

The aim of this book is to help you get the best value from your car. It can do so in two ways. First, it can help you decide what work must be done, even should you choose to get it done by a garage, the routine maintenance and the diagnosis and course of action when random faults occur; but it is hoped that you will also use the second and fuller purpose by tackling the work yourself. This can give you the satisfaction of doing the job yourself. On the simpler jobs it may even be quicker than booking the car into a garage and going there twice, to leave and collect it. Perhaps most important, much money can be saved by avoiding the costs a garage must charge to cover their labour and overheads.

The book has drawings and descriptions to show the function of the various components so that their layout can be understood. Then the tasks are described and photographed in a step-by-step sequence so that even a novice can cope with the complicated work. Such a person is the very one to buy a car needing repair yet be unable to afford garage costs.

The jobs are described assuming only normal tools are available, and not special tools unless absolutely necessary. A reasonable outfit of tools will be a worthwhile investment. Many special workshop tools produced by the makers merely speed the work, and in these cases guidance is given as to how to do the job without them. On a very few occasions when the special tool is essential to prevent damage to components, then its use is described. Though it might be possible to borrow the tool, such work may have to be entrusted to the official agent.

To avoid labour costs a garage will often give a cheaper repair by fitting a reconditioned assembly. The home mechanic can be helped by this book to diagnose the fault and make a repair using only a minor spare part.

Using the manual

The manual is divided into thirteen Chapters. Each Chapter is divided into numbered Sections which are headed in **bold type** between horizontal lines. Each Section consists of serially numbered paragraphs and is sometimes further divided into sub-Sections.

There are two types of illustration: (1) Figures which are numbered according to Chapter and sequence of occurence in that Chapter. (2) Photographs which have a reference number in their caption. All photographs apply to the Chapter in which they occur so that the reference figure pinpoints the pertinent Section and paragraph number.

Procedures, once described in the text, are not normally repeated. If it is necessary to refer to another Chapter the reference will be given in Chapter number and Section number. Cross references given without the use of the word 'Chapter' apply to Section and/or paragraphs in the same Chapter eg. 'see Section 8' means also 'in this Chapter'.

When the left or right side of the car is mentioned it is as if one is seated in the driver's seat looking forward. Servicing and overhaul is straightforward and without complication but due to the limitations of space within the engine compartment, it is recommended that overhaul operations of a major nature are undertaken after the engine/transmission have been removed from the vehicle.

The threads of all nuts and bolts are to metric sizes. Torque wrench settings are given at the end of the 'Specifications' Section at the beginning of each Chapter. Where a value is not indicated for a particular nut or bolt, work to the following table:

	lbf ft	Nm
M4 x 0.7	*3*	*4*
M5 x 0.9	*5*	*7*
M6 x 1.0	*9*	*12*
M8 x 1.25	*20*	*28*
M9 x 1.25	*30*	*41*
M10 x 1.25	*40*	*55*
M12 x 1.25	*60*	*83*

Contents

Introduction to the Honda Accord

The Honda Accord was first introduced in 1976 and is the largest and first 'hatchback' car to be manufactured by this famous firm. It has very stylish bodywork and incorporates many interesting, useful and practical features.

The single overhead camshaft, four-cylinder engine of 1600 cc is basically an enlarged version of the popular and well-proven Honda Civic. Located at the front of the car, the engine is positioned transversely and accessibility to the various engine components is excellent.

A CVCC engine model is available for those markets having strict emission control regulations. CVCC (Compound Vortex Controlled Combustion) basically explained, works as follows:

To reduce harmful exhaust emissions it is necessary for the engine to run on a very weak mixture (a relatively small amount of fuel mixed with air in the combustion chamber). This weak mixture can be very difficult to ignite by means of a spark. To overcome this problem, the CVCC engine has two linked combustion chambers for each cylinder. A relatively rich mixture is fed into the small primary combustion chamber which also contains the spark plug; this 'rich' mixture ignites easily. The 'flame' thus produced passes from the primary chamber, which by this time, is filled with a weak mixture and complete combustion takes place.

This system eliminates the need to fit many of the additional components fitted by other manufacturers in order to reduce the exhaust emissions.

The standard transmission is a five forward (all synchromesh) and one reverse gearbox or, as an alternative, the Hondamatic (automatic) transmission is available.

The suspension system is fully independent with MacPherson strut and coil springs fitted front and rear.

Rack and pinion steering gives positive control and the brakes are servo assisted, discs at the front and drums to the rear.

The car is extremely well appointed and the standard of finish is above average.

Honda Accord 1600 cc (1977 UK Specification)

Use of English

As this book has been written in England, it uses the appropriate English component names, phrases, and spelling. Some of these differ from those used in America. Normally, these cause no difficulty, but to make sure, a glossary is printed below. In ordering spare parts remember the parts list may use some of these words:

English	American
Accelerator	Gas pedal
Aerial	Antenna
Anti-roll bar	Stabiliser or sway bar
Big-end bearing	Rod bearing
Bonnet (engine cover)	Hood
Boot (luggage compartment)	Trunk
Bulkhead	Firewall
Bush	Bushing
Cam follower or tappet	Valve lifter or tappet
Carburettor	Carburetor
Catch	Latch
Choke/venturi	Barrel
Circlip	Snap-ring
Clearance	Lash
Crownwheel	Ring gear (of differential)
Damper	Shock absorber, shock
Disc (brake)	Rotor/disk
Distance piece	Spacer
Drop arm	Pitman arm
Drop head coupe	Convertible
Dynamo	Generator (DC)
Earth (electrical)	Ground
Engineer's blue	Prussian blue
Estate car	Station wagon
Exhaust manifold	Header
Fault finding/diagnosis	Troubleshooting
Float chamber	Float bowl
Free-play	Lash
Freewheel	Coast
Gearbox	Transmission
Gearchange	Shift
Grub screw	Setscrew, Allen screw
Gudgeon pin	Piston pin or wrist pin
Halfshaft	Axleshaft
Handbrake	Parking brake
Hood	Soft top
Hot spot	Heat riser
Indicator	Turn signal
Interior light	Dome lamp
Layshaft (of gearbox)	Countershaft
Leading shoe (of brake)	Primary shoe
Locks	Latches
Methylated spirit	Denatured alcohol
Motorway	Freeway, turnpike etc
Number plate	License plate
Paraffin	Kerosene
Petrol	Gasoline (gas)
Petrol tank	Gas tank
'Pinking'	'Pinging'
Prise (force apart)	Pry
Propeller shaft	Driveshaft
Quarterlight	Quarter window
Retread	Recap
Reverse	Back-up
Rocker cover	Valve cover
Saloon	Sedan
Seized	Frozen
Sidelight	Parking light
Silencer	Muffler
Sill panel (beneath doors)	Rocker panel
Small end, little end	Piston pin or wrist pin
Spanner	Wrench
Split cotter (for valve spring cap)	Lock (for valve spring retainer)
Split pin	Cotter pin
Steering arm	Spindle arm
Sump	Oil pan
Swarf	Metal chips or debris
Tab washer	Tang or lock
Tappet	Valve lifter
Thrust bearing	Throw-out bearing
Top gear	High
Trackrod (of steering)	Tie-rod (or connecting rod)
Trailing shoe (of brake)	Secondary shoe
Transmission	Whole drive line
Tyre	Tire
Van	Panel wagon/van
Vice	Vise
Wheel nut	Lug nut
Windscreen	Windshield
Wing/mudguard	Fender

Buying spare parts and vehicle identification number

Buying spare parts

Spare parts are available from many sources, for example: Honda garages, other garages and accessory shops, and motor factors. Our advice regarding spare part sources is as follows:

Officially appointed Honda garages - These are the best source of parts which are peculiar to your car and are otherwise not generally available (eg. complete cylinder heads, internal gearbox components, badges, interior trim etc). It is also the only place at which you should buy parts if your car is still under warranty; non-Honda components may invalidate the warranty. To be sure of obtaining the correct parts it will always be necessary to give the storeman your car's engine and chassis number, and if possible, to take the 'old' part along for positive identification. Remember that many parts are available on a factory exchange scheme - any parts returned should always be clean! It obviously makes good sense to go straight to the specialist on your car for this type of part for they are best equipped to supply you.

Other garages and accessory shops - These are often very good places to buy materials and components needed for the maintenance of your car (eg. oil filters, spark plugs, bulbs, fan belts, oils and greases, touch-up paint, filler paste, etc). They also sell general accessories, usually have convenient opening hours, charge lower prices and can often be found not far from home.

Motor factors - Good factors will stock all of the more important components which wear out relatively quickly (eg. clutch components, pistons, valves, exhaust systems, brake cylinders/pipes/hoses/seals/shoes and pads etc). Motor factors will often provide new or reconditioned components on a part exchange basis - this can save a considerable amount of money.

Vehicle identification number

This is stamped on an identification plate or compliance plate, according to type.

The chassis number

The chassis number is stamped into the bodywork to the rear of the air cleaner case (photo).

The engine number

The engine number is located on the right-hand side of the crankcase at the rear (photo).

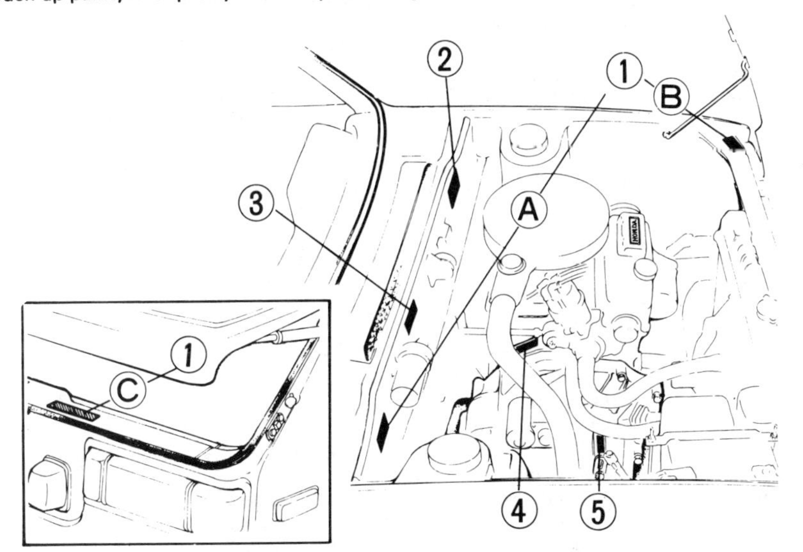

1 Identification plate - Type A, Type B, Type C
2 Compliance plate
3 The chassis number plate
4 The engine number
5 The transmission number

The vehicle identification plate locations

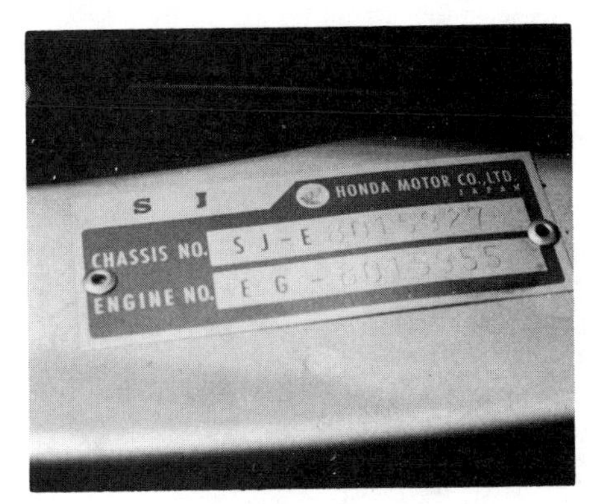

Identification plate

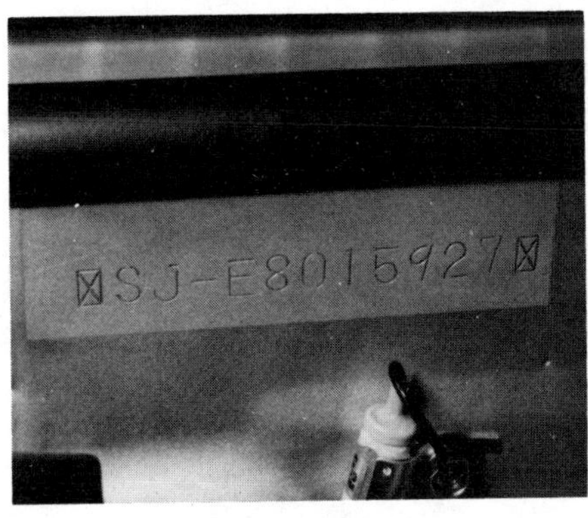

Chassis number

Engine number

Routine maintenance

Maintenance is essential for ensuring safety and desirable for the purpose of getting the best in terms of performance and economy from the car. Over the years the need for periodic lubrication - oiling, greasing and so on - has been drastically reduced if not totally eliminated. This has unfortunately tended to lead some owners to think that because no such action is required the items either no longer exist or will last for ever. This is a serious delusion. It follows therefore that the largest initial element of maintenance is visual examination. This may lead to repairs or renewals.

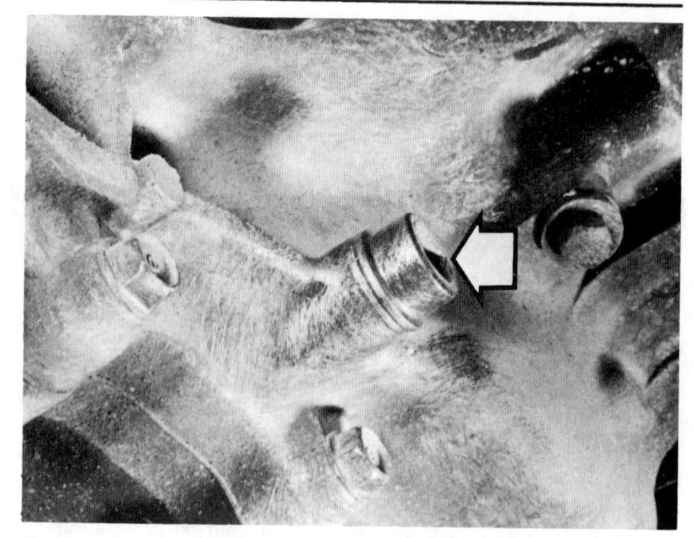

Drain plug - manual transmission

Every 250 miles (400 km) or weekly

Check and top-up the engine oil level.
Check the coolant level in the expansion tank.
Check the battery electrolyte level.
Check the brake fluid level.
Check the tyre pressures (including the spare).
Check lights for bulb failure.
Top-up the windscreen washer reservoir.

Every 5,000 miles (8,000 km)

Inspect tyres for wear or damage.
Change engine oil and renew oil filter.
Clean and adjust spark plugs and contact breaker points.
Check and adjust if required the idle speed and where applicable, the idle CO reading.
Check clutch free movement.
Check transmission oil and top up.
Adjust rear brakes.
Adjust handbrake.
Check the front brake pads for wear and the caliper action.
Check the steering system for wear and grease the steering gearbox.
Check the exhaust system for signs of leaks, deterioration and location mountings for security.
Check the fluid level in the power steering reservoir and top up if necessary.

Every 10,000 miles (16,000 km)

Check the rear brake shoe lining wear.
Renew the brake servo unit filter - this should be entrusted to your Honda dealer.

Every 15,000 miles (24,000 km)

Check valve clearances.
Drain and renew the automatic transmission oil (new cars only), thereafter every 30 000 miles (48 000 km).
Check the coolant level and inspect the cooling system for leaks or signs of deterioration. Ensure all hose connections are good.
Renew the air filter element.
Check the intake air temperature control system.
Inspect the throttle and control valve.
Check the choke mechanism.
On engines fitted with emission control systems, check the charcoal canister, the idle cut off valve and the one way valve for operation.
Renew the distributor contact breaker points. Check the distributor cap and rotor.
Renew the spark plugs.
Check the ignition wiring and ignition timing control system.
Check the front wheel alignment.
Renew fuel filter (new cars only at first 15 000 miles), thereafter every 30 000 miles (48 000 km).
Check drivebelt tension and condition.
Check and adjust ignition timing.
Check the adjustment of the load sensing valve in the braking system.

Every 30,000 miles (48,000 km)

Renew manual transmission oil.
Drain and renew the coolant.
Clean the radiator core.
Renew the fuel filter and check the fuel lines and connections.
Renew the charcoal canister.
Clean the vacuum booster air filter.
Drain and renew the automatic transmission oil.
Renew engine timing belt
Renew the hydraulic fluid in brake circuit.

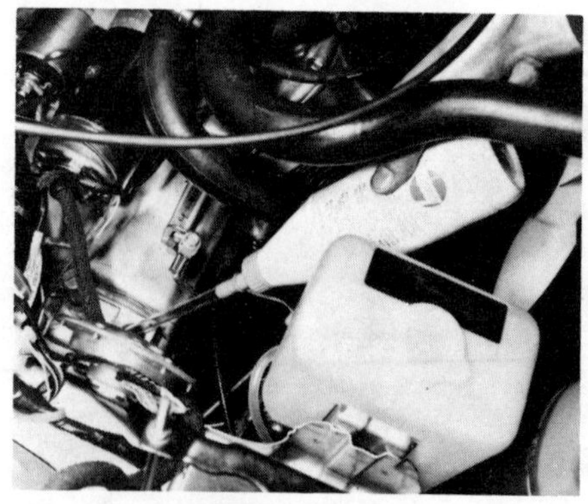

Topping up the transmission fluid

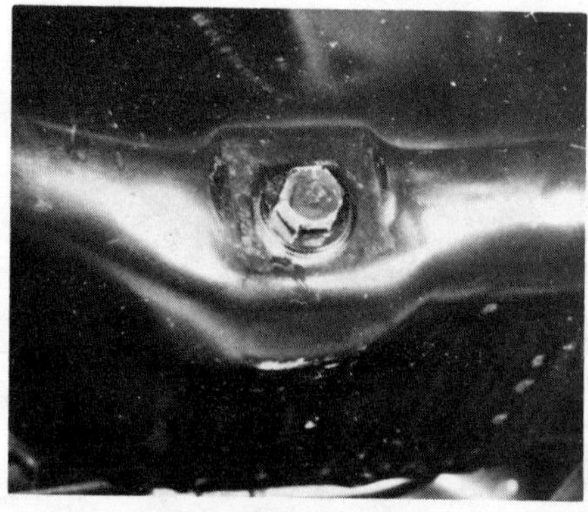

Engine oil drain plug

Removing screw-on type oil filter

Jacking

The jack supplied with the vehicle should only be used for changing a roadwheel. Before jacking up the vehicle ensure that the handbrake (parkbrake) is fully applied and that ground beneath the jack is level and sufficiently firm to support the vehicle weight.

When repairs or overhaul operations are being carried out, the jacking points illustrated must be used and the bodyframe additionally supported by placing axle stands securely under the side sill support points.

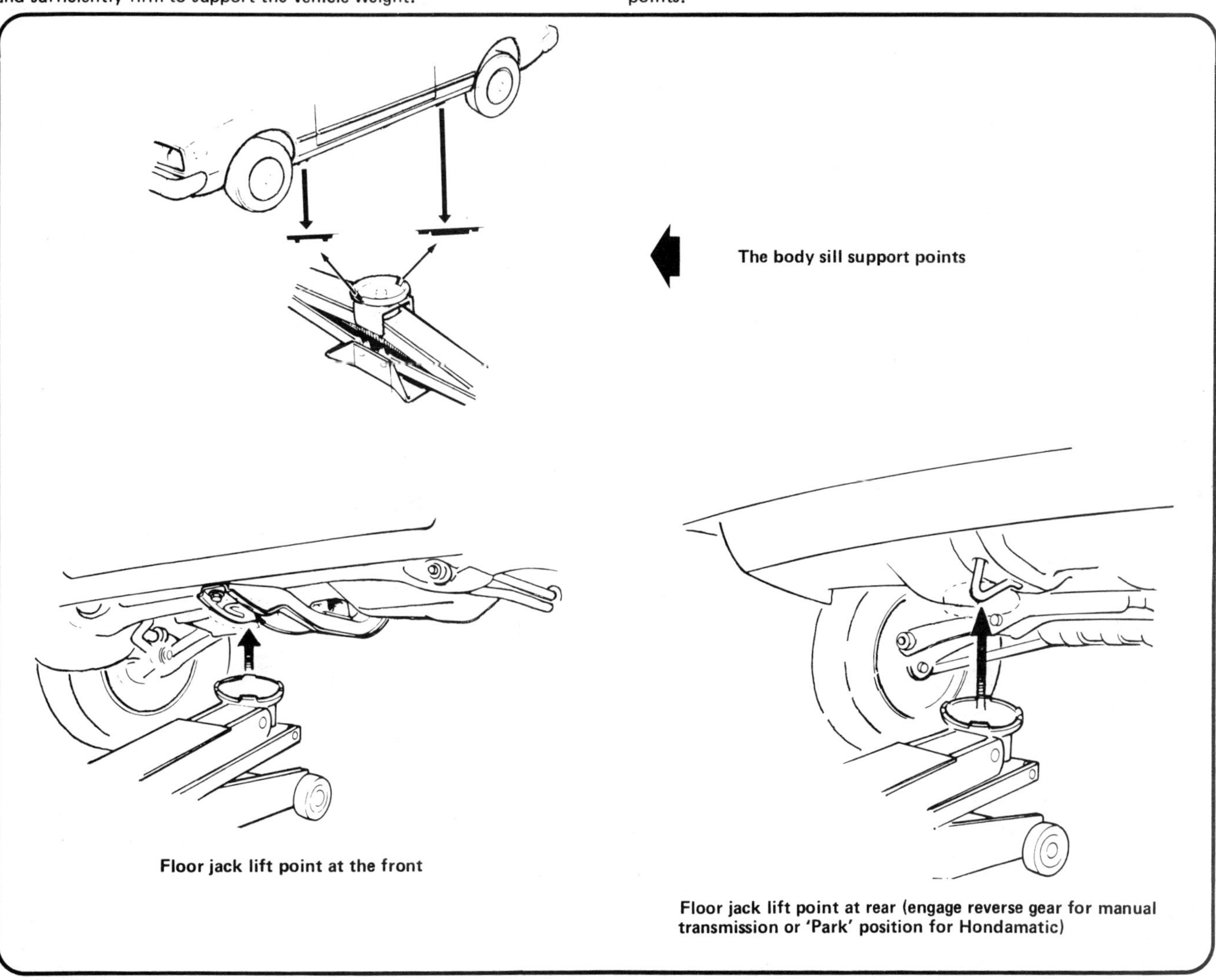

The body sill support points

Floor jack lift point at the front

Floor jack lift point at rear (engage reverse gear for manual transmission or 'Park' position for Hondamatic)

Towing

In the event of a roadside breakdown, the vehicle may be towed using the front towing hook, however, the following precautions must be taken. Check that the transmission is filled with oil. Place speed selector or gearshift lever in neutral position.

Ensure that the steering column lock is unlocked with the ignition key in the 'ACC' position. Restrict the towing speed to 37 mph (59 kph).

When towing another vehicle use the hooks at each side of the underframe.

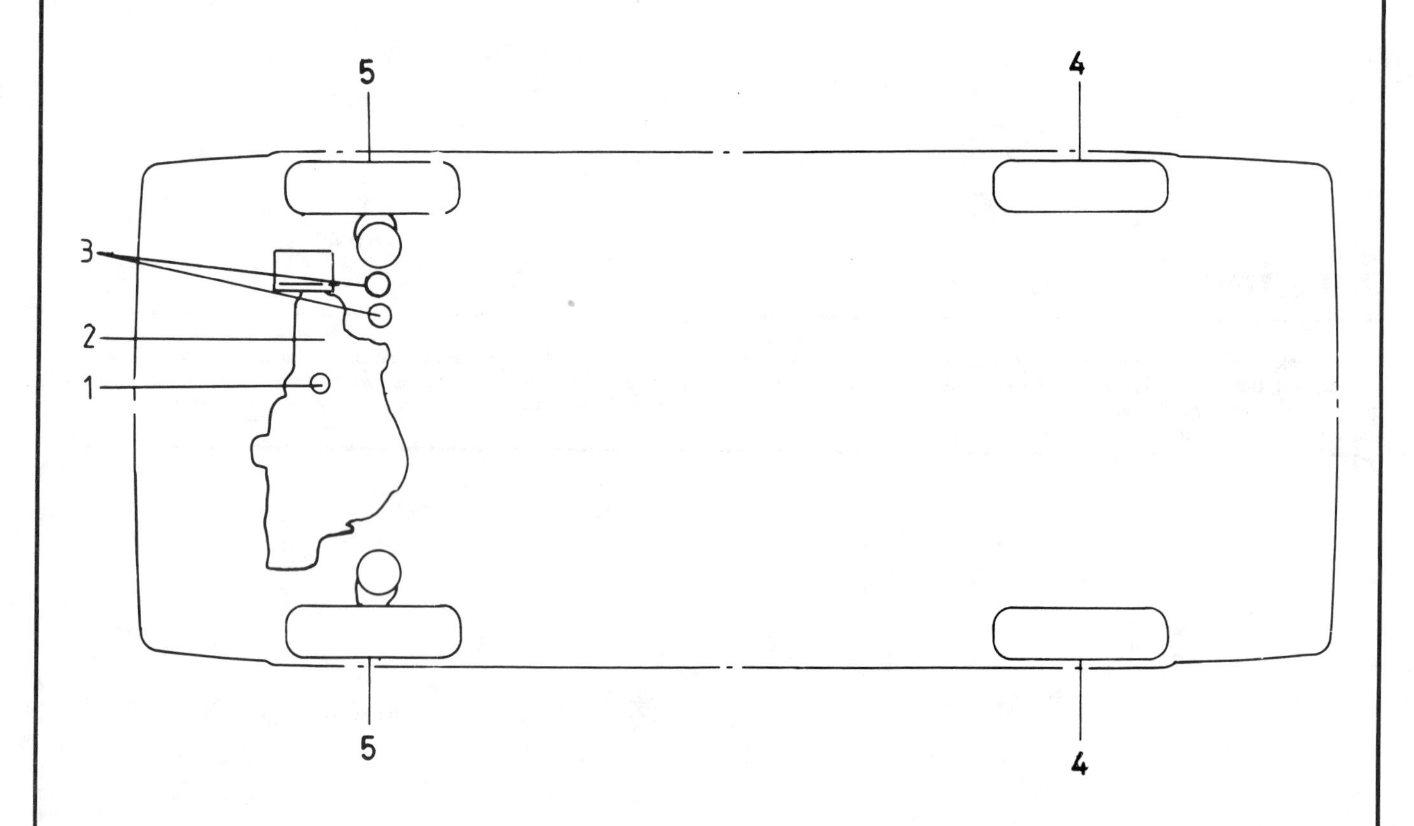

Recommended lubricants and fluids

Component or system	Lubricant type or specification
Engine (1)	Multigrade engine oil SAE 10W/40 20W/40 or 20W/50
Gearbox (2)	
Manual	Multigrade engine oil SAE 10W/30 or 10W/40
Automatic	Dexron ® type ATF
Clutch and brake fluid (3)	Hydraulic fluid to DOT 3 or DOT 4
Rear wheel bearings (4)	Multipurpose grease
Front wheel bearings (5)	Multipurpose grease
Steering box	Multipurpose grease
Steering balljoints	Multipurpose grease
Power steering fluid	Dexron ® R11 type fluid
Driveshaft joints	Molybdenum disulphide grease

Note: The above recommendations are general; lubrication requirements vary depending upon vehicle specification, operating territory and usage. Consult the operators handbook supplied with the car.

General dimensions and capacities

Dimensions:	
Overall length	162.4 in (4,125 mm)
Overall width	63.8 in (1,620 mm)
Overall height	52.6 in (1,335 mm)
Wheelbase	93.7 in (2,380 mm)
Ground clearance	6.49 in (165 mm)
Track:	
Front	55.1 in (1,400 mm)
Rear	54.7 in (1,390 in)
Turning circle	32 ft 5 in (9.8 m)
Weights:	
Curb weight	
Manual transmission	2011 lb (912 kg)
Hondamatic (Australian type)	1995 lb (900 kg)
Maximum laden weight:	
Manual transmission	2800 lb (1270 kg))
Hondamatic (Australian type)	2,937 lb (1,332 kg)
Capacities:	
Fuel tank	11 gals (50 litres) (13.2 US gals)
Engine oil capacity	2.6 qts (3 litres) (3.2 US qts)
Engine cooling system capacity	1.1 gals (5 litres) (1.3 US gals)
Manual transmission oil capacity	2.2 qts (2.5 litres) (2.6 US qts)
Hondamatic transmission oil capacity	2.2 qts (2.5 litres) (2.6 US qts)

Tools and working facilities

Introduction

A selection of good tools is a fundamental requirement for anyone contemplating the maintenance and repair of a motor vehicle. For the owner who does not possess any, their purchase will prove a considerable expense, offsetting some of the savings made by doing-it-yourself. However, provided that the tools purchased are of good quality, they will last for many years and prove an extremely worthwhile investment.

To help the average owner to decide which tools are needed to carry out the various tasks detailed in this manual, we have compiled three lists of tools under the following headings: *Maintenance and minor repair, Repair and overhaul* and *Special.* The newcomer to practical mechanics should start off with the *Maintenance and minor repair* tool kit and confine himself to the simpler jobs around the vehicle. Then, as his confidence and experience grows, he can undertake more difficult tasks, buying extra tools as, and when, they are needed. In this way, a *Maintenance and minor repair* tool kit can be built-up into a *Repair and overhaul* tool kit over a considerable period of time without any major cash outlays. The experienced do-it-yourselfer will have a tool kit good enough for most repairs and overhaul procedures and will add tools from the *Special* category when he feels the expense is justified by the amount of use to which these tools will be put.

It is obviously not possible to cover the subject of tools fully here. For those who wish to learn more about tools and their use there is a book entitled *How to Choose and Use Car Tools* available from the publishers of this manual.

Maintenance and minor repair tool kit

The tools given in this list should be considered as a minimum requirement if routine maintenance, servicing and minor repair operations are to be undertaken. We recommend the purchase of combination spanners (ring one end, open-ended the other); although more expensive than open-ended ones, they do give the advantages of both types of spanner.

Combination spanners - 6, 7, 8, 9, 10, 11 and 12 mm
Adjustable spanner - 9 inch
Spark plug spanner (with rubber insert)
Spark plug gap adjustment tool
Set of feeler gauges
Brake adjuster spanner
Brake bleed nipple spanner
Screwdriver - 4 in long x ¼ in dia (flat blade)
Screwdriver - 4 in long x ¼ in dia (cross blade)
Combination pliers - 6 inch
Hacksaw, junior
Tyre pump
Tyre pressure gauge
Grease gun
Oil can
Fine emery cloth (1 sheet)
Wire brush (small)
Funnel (medium size)

Repair and overhaul tool kit

These tools are virtually essential for anyone undertaking any major repairs to a motor vehicle, and are additional to those given in the *Maintenance and minor repair* list. Included in this list is a comprehensive set of sockets. Although these are expensive they will be found invaluable as they are so versatile - particularly if various drives are included in the set. We recommend the ½ in square-drive type, as this can be used with most proprietary torque wrenches. If you cannot afford a socket set, even bought piecemeal, then inexpensive tubular box spanners are a useful alternative.

The tools in this list will occasionally need to be supplemented by tools from the *Special* list.

Sockets (or box spanners) to cover range in previous list
Reversible ratchet drive (for use with sockets)
Extension piece, 10 inch (for use with sockets)
Universal joint (for use with sockets)
Torque wrench (for use with sockets)
'Mole' wrench - 8 inch
Ball pein hammer
Soft-faced hammer, plastic or rubber
Screwdriver - 6 in long x 5/16 in dia (flat blade)
Screwdriver - 2 in long x 5/16 in dia (flat blade)
Screwdriver - 1½ in long x ¼ in dia (cross blade)
Screwdriver - 3 in long x 1/8 in dia (electricians)
Pliers - electricians side cutters
Pliers - needle nosed
Pliers - circlip (internal and external)
Cold chisel - ½ inch
Scriber (this can be made by grinding the end of a broken hacksaw blade)
Scraper (this can be made by flattening and sharpening one end of a piece of copper pipe)
Centre punch
Pin punch
Hacksaw
Valve grinding tool
Steel rule/straightedge
Allen keys
Selection of files
Wire brush (large)
Axle stands
Jack (strong scissor or hydraulic type)

Special tools

The tools in this list are those which are not used regularly, are expensive to buy, or which need to be used in accordance with their manufacturers instructions. Unless relatively difficult mechanical jobs are undertaken frequently, it will not be economic to buy many of these tools. Where this is the case, you could consider clubbing together with friends (or a motorists club) to make a joint purchase, or borrowing the tools against a deposit from a local garage or tool hire specialist.

The following list contains only those tools and instruments freely available to the public, and not those special tools produced by the vehicle manufacturer specifically for its dealer network. You will find occasional references to these manufacturers special tools in the text of this manual. Generally, an alternative method of doing the job without the vehicle manufacturers special tool is given. However, sometimes, there is no alternative to using them. Where this is the case and the relevant tool cannot be bought or borrowed you will have to entrust the work to a franchised garage.

Valve spring compressor
Piston ring compressor
Balljoint separator
Universal hub/bearing puller
Impact screwdriver
Micrometer and/or vernier gauge
Carburettor flow balancing device (where applicable)
Dial gauge
Stroboscopic timing light
Tacho/Dwell angle meter
Universal electrical multi-meter
Cylinder compression gauge
Lifting tackle
Trolley jack
Light with extension lead

Last, but not least, always keep a supply of old newspapers and clean, lint-free rags available, and try to keep any working area as clean as possible.

Buying tools

For practically all tools, a tool factor is the best source since he will have a very comprehensive range compared with the average garage or accessory shop. Having said that, accessory shops often offer excellent quality tools at discount prices, so it pays to shop around.

Remember, you do not have to buy the most expensive items on the shelf, but it is always advisable to steer clear of the very cheap tools. There are plenty of good tools around, at reasonable prices, so ask the proprietor or manager of the shop for advice before making a purchase.

Care and maintenance of tools

Having purchased a reasonable tool kit, it is necessary to keep the tools in a clean and serviceable condition. After use, always wipe off any dirt, grease and metal particles using a clean, dry cloth, before putting the tools away. Never leave them lying around after they have been used. A simple tool rack on the garage or workshop wall, for items such as screwdrivers and pliers, is a good idea. Store all normal spanners and sockets in a metal box. Any measuring instruments, gauges, meters, etc, must be carefully stored where they cannot be damaged or become rusty.

Take a little care when the tools are used. Hammer heads inevitably become marked and screwdrivers lose the keen edge on their blades from time-to-time. A little timely attention with emery cloth or a file will soon restore items like this to a good serviceable finish.

Working facilities

Not to be forgotten when discussing tools, is the workshop itself. If anything more than routine maintenance is to be carried out, some form of suitable working area becomes essential.

It is appreciated that many an owner mechanic is forced by circumstance to remove an engine or similar item, without the benefit of a garage or workshop. Having done this, any repairs should always be done under the cover of a roof.

Wherever possible, any dismantling should be done on a clean flat workbench or table at a suitable working height.

Any workbench needs a vice: one with a jaw opening of 4 in (100 mm) is suitable for most jobs. As mentioned previously, some clean dry storage space is also required for tools, as well as the lubricants, cleaning fluids, touch-up paints and so on which soon become necessary.

Another item which may be required, and which has a much more general usage, is an electric drill with a chuck capacity of at least 5/16 in (8 mm). This, together with a good range of twist drills, is virtually essential for fitting accessories such as wing mirrors and reversing lights.

Spanner jaw gap comparison table

Jaw gap (in)	Spanner size
0.250	$\frac{1}{4}$ in AF
0.276	7 mm
0.313	$\frac{5}{16}$ in AF
0.315	8 mm
0.344	$\frac{11}{32}$ in AF; $\frac{1}{8}$ in Whitworth
0.354	9 mm
0.375	$\frac{3}{8}$ in AF
0.394	10 mm
0.433	11 mm
0.438	$\frac{7}{16}$ in AF
0.445	$\frac{3}{16}$ in Whitworth; $\frac{1}{4}$ in BSF
0.472	12 mm
0.500	$\frac{1}{2}$ in AF
0.512	13 mm
0.525	$\frac{1}{4}$ in Whitworth; $\frac{5}{16}$ in BSF
0.551	14 mm
0.563	$\frac{9}{16}$ in AF
0.591	15 mm
0.600	$\frac{5}{16}$ in Whitworth; $\frac{3}{8}$ in BSF
0.625	$\frac{5}{8}$ in AF
0.630	16 mm
0.669	17 mm
0.686	$\frac{11}{16}$ in AF
0.709	18 mm
0.710	$\frac{3}{8}$ in Whitworth; $\frac{7}{16}$ in BSF
0.748	19 mm
0.750	$\frac{3}{4}$ in AF
0.813	$\frac{13}{16}$ in AF
0.820	$\frac{7}{16}$ in Whitworth; $\frac{1}{2}$ in BSF
0.866	22 mm
0.875	$\frac{7}{8}$ in AF
0.920	$\frac{1}{2}$ in Whitworth; $\frac{9}{16}$ in BSF
0.938	$\frac{15}{16}$ in AF
0.945	24 mm
1.000	1 in AF
1.010	$\frac{9}{16}$ in Whitworth; $\frac{5}{8}$ in BSF
1.024	26 mm
1.063	$1\frac{1}{16}$ in AF; 27 mm
1.100	$\frac{5}{8}$ in Whitworth; $\frac{11}{16}$ in BSF
1.125	$1\frac{1}{8}$ in AF
1.181	30 mm
1.200	$\frac{11}{16}$ in Whitworth; $\frac{3}{4}$ in BSF
1.250	$1\frac{1}{4}$ in AF
1.260	32 mm
1.300	$\frac{3}{4}$ in Whitworth; $\frac{7}{8}$ in BSF
1.313	$1\frac{5}{16}$ in AF
1.390	$\frac{13}{16}$ in Whitworth; $\frac{15}{16}$ in BSF
1.417	36 mm
1.438	$1\frac{7}{16}$ in AF
1.480	$\frac{7}{8}$ in Whitworth; 1 in BSF
1.500	$1\frac{1}{2}$ in AF
1.575	40 mm; $\frac{15}{16}$ in Whitworth
1.614	41 mm
1.625	$1\frac{5}{8}$ in AF
1.670	1 in Whitworth; $1\frac{1}{8}$ in BSF
1.688	$1\frac{11}{16}$ in AF
1.811	46 mm
1.813	$1\frac{13}{16}$ in AF
1.860	$1\frac{1}{8}$ in Whitworth; $1\frac{1}{4}$ in BSF
1.875	$1\frac{7}{8}$ in AF
1.969	50 mm
2.000	2 in AF
2.050	$1\frac{1}{4}$ in Whitworth; $1\frac{3}{8}$ in BSF
2.165	55 mm
2.362	60 mm

Chapter 1 Engine

For modifications, and information applicable to later models, see Supplement at end of manual

Contents

Specifications

Engine - general

Engine type	Transverse 4-cylinder in-line, overhead camshaft (ohc) water cooled
Capacity	1,600 cc (97.63 cu in)
Bore	2.91 in (74.0 mm)
Stroke	3.66 in (93.0 mm)
Compression ratio	8.4 to 1 (CVCC model - 8.0 to 1)
Firing order	1 - 3 - 4 - 2 (No 1 at timing belt end)

Crankshaft and main bearings

Rotational direction (viewed from pulley end)	Anticlockwise
Main journal diameter	1.9687 to 1.9697 in (50.006 to 50.030 mm)
Maximum journal taper (out of round)	0.0004 in (0.01 mm)
Crankpin outside diameter	1.6526 to 1.6535 in (41.976 to 42.000 mm)
Crankpin max. taper allowable	0.0004 in (0.01 mm)
Axial play:	
Standard	0.0040 to 0.0138 in (0.10 to 0.35 mm)
Maximum allowable	0.0177 in (0.45 mm)
Run out:	
Standard	0.0017 in (0.03 mm)
Maximum allowable	0.0020 in (0.05 mm)
Bearing to journal clearance:	
Standard	0.0010 to 0,0017 in (0.026 to 0.044 mm)
Maximum allowable	0.0028 in (0.07 mm)
Bearing to crankpin clearance:	
Standard	0.0008 to 0.0015 in (0.020 to 0.038 mm)
Maximum allowable	0.0028 in (0.07 mm)
Main bearings and big-end bearing selection and sizes	Refer to Sections 18 and 19 respectively.

Cylinder block

Surface distortion limit	0.0040 in (0.10 mm)
Cylinder bore diameter:	
Standard	2.9134 to 2.9142 in (74.00 to 74.020 mm)
Wear limit	2.9154 in (74.05 mm)
Maximum bore taper	0.0020 in (0.05 mm)
Difference in cylinder diameters	0.004 to 0.008 in (0.10 to 0.20 mm)
Maximum rebore permitted	0.010 in (0.25 mm)

Pistons

Diameter at skirt	2.9114 to 2.9220 in (73.950 to 73.970 mm)
Piston to bore clearance:	
Standard maximum	0.002 in (0.070 mm)
Standard minimum	0.001 in (0.030 mm)
Wear limit maximum	0.004 in (0.100 mm)
Wear limit minimum	0.001 in (0.030 mm)
Compression ring groove clearance	0.0008 to 0.0018 in (0.020 to 0.045 mm)
Compression ring end gap	0.012 to 0.0354 in (0.3 to 0.9 mm)
Oil control ring end gap	0.0079 to 0.0354 in (0.3 to 0.9 mm)
Gudgeon pin diameter	0.6691 to 0.6694 in (16.944 to 17.003 mm)
Gudgeon pin to piston clearance	0.0004 to 0.0008 in (0.010 to 0.022 mm)
Gudgeon pin to connecting rod	0.0006 to 0.0016 in (0.014 to 0.04 mm)

Flywheel

Maximum run out allowable	0.0016 in (0.04 mm)

Cylinder head

Material	Light alloy
Surface distortion limit	0.002 in (0.05 mm)
Thickness	3.56 in (90.5 mm)
Maximum resurface limit	0.008 in (0.2 mm)

Valves

Clearances (cold)	0.004 to 0.007 in (0.12 to 0.18 mm)
Stem to guide clearance (inlet)	
Standard	0.0008 to 0.002 in (0.02 to 0.05 mm)
Wear limit	0.003 in (0.08 mm)
Stem to guide clearance (exhaust)	
Standard	0.002 to 0.003 in (0.05 to 0.08 mm)
Wear limit	0.004 in (0.10 mm)
Stem to guide clearance (auxiliary CVCC)	
Standard	0.0008 to 0.0020 in (0.02 to 0.05 mm)
Wear limit	0.0032 in (0.08 mm)
Inlet and exhaust valve guide inside diameter:	
Standard	0.2602 to 0.2610 in (6.61 to 6.63 mm)
Wear limit	0.2618 in (6.65 mm)
Valve stem diameter (exhaust):	
Standard	0.258 to 0.2599 in (6.55 to 6.56 mm)
Wear limit	0.256 in (6.52 mm)
Valve stem diameter (inlet):	
Standard	0.259 to 0.260 in (6.58 to 6.59 mm)
Wear limit	0.258 in (6.55 mm)
Auxiliary valve stem diameter:	
Standard	0.216 to 0.217 in (5.48 to 5.49 mm)
Wear limit	0.215 in (5.45 mm)

Valve springs

Free length:	
Exhaust inner	1.988 to 2.047 in (50.5 to 52.0 mm)
Exhaust outer	2.118 in (53.8 mm)
Inlet inner	1.583 in (40.2 mm)
Inlet outer	1.573 in (39.95 mm)
Auxiliary CVCC	1.146 in (29.1 mm)

Camshaft

Endfloat:	
Standard	0.002 to 0.006 in (0.050 to 0.15 mm)
Wear limit	0.0197 in (0.5 mm)
Camshaft bearing running clearance	0.002 to 0.006 in (0.050 to 0.150 mm)
Cam height:	
Inlet	1.4856 to 1.4951 in (37.735 to 37.975 mm)
Exhaust	1.4856 to 1.4951 in (37.735 to 37.975 mm)
Auxiliary	1.7316 to 1.7410 in (43.982 to 44.222 mm)

Lubrication system

Oil pump displacement	9.25 gal (35 litres) at 3000 rpm
Inner to outer rotor clearance	0.005 in (0.15 mm)
Pump body to rotor clearance (radial)	0.003 to 0.007 in (0.10 to 0.18 mm)
Pump body to rotor clearance (side)	0.0012 to 0.0039 in (0.03 to 0.10 mm)
Pump drive gear back lash	0.001 to 0.003 in (0.04 to 0.10 mm)
Pump drive gear side clearance	0.002 to 0.011 in (0.05 to 0.30 mm)

Relief valve

Type	Plunger
Pressure setting	54.05 to 59.74 lb/in^2 (3.8 to 4.2 kg/cm^2)
Engine oil capacity	2.6 Imp qts (3.0 litres) (3.2 US qts)
Engine oil type:	
−20°F (−28.9°C) to 20°F (−6.7°C)	5W - 20 or 5W - 30
0°F (−17.8°C) to 60°F (15.6°C)	10W - 30 or 10W - 40
20°F (−6.7°C) to 100°F (37.8°C)	10W - 40, 20W - 40 or 20W - 50

Torque wrench settings

	lb f ft	kg f m
Main bearing cap bolts	30 - 35	4.2 - 4.8
Connecting rod bearing cap bolts	20	2.7
Oil pump unit retaining bolts	7 - 10	1.0 - 1.4
Oil pump cover bolt	7 - 10	1.0 - 1.4
Sump retaining bolts	12 - 14	1.6 - 2.0
Sump drain plug	29 - 36	4.0 - 5.0
Oil filter	18 - 21	2.5 - 3.0
Flywheel bolts	34 - 38	4.7 - 5.3
Hondamatic drive plate bolts	34 - 38	4.7 - 5.3
Cylinder head bolts (Cold)	40 - 42	5.5 - 6.5
Rocker shaft pedestal bolts (6 mm)	7 - 10	1.0 - 1.4
Rocker shaft pedestal bolts (8 mm)	14 - 17	2.0 - 2.4
Crankshaft pulley bolt	58 - 65	8.0 - 9.0
Timing belt adjustment bolt	29 - 33	4.0 - 4.6
Timing belt pivot bolt	29 - 33	4.0 - 4.6
Timing cover bolts - upper and lower	6 - 9	0.8 - 1.2
Splash guard bolts	13.7 to 18.1	1.9 - 2.5
Exhaust down pipe/manifold nuts	28.9 - 36.2	4.0 - 5.0
Engine support bolts - front (left side)	18.8 - 23.1	2.6 - 3.2
Engine support bolt - front (left side) large	25.3 - 31.1	3.5 - 4.3
Engine mounting nuts - RH & LH side	8.0 - 11.6	1.1 - 1.6
Engine to bar bolts	25.3 - 31.1	3.5 - 4.3
Thermostat housing bolt	7 - 10	1.0 - 1.4
Auxiliary valve holder nut	54 - 61	7.5 - 8.5
Front sub-frame centre beam bolts	13.7 to 18.1	1.9 to 2.5
Exhaust pipe/manifold bracket bolt	14 - 18	1.9 to 2.5
Inlet/exhaust manifold bolts - initial	7	1.0
Inlet/exhaust manifold bolts - final	16	2.2
Inlet/exhaust manifold to cylinder head nuts	14 - 17	2.0 - 2.4
Timing belt sprocket to camshaft bolt	18 - 22	2.5 - 3.0
Inlet/exhaust valve locknuts	13 - 16	1.8 - 2.2
Auxiliary valve locknuts	9 - 12	1.2 - 1.6

1 General description

The 1600 cc (97.63 cu in) engine is of a four cylinder, in line, overhead camshaft type. The engine is mounted transversely and is inclined at an angle of 15° to the front.

The manual gearbox (or automatic transmission) is also mounted transversely in line with the engine and the final drive to the front roadwheels is via the differential unit which is integral with the gearbox.

The cylinder block is of cast iron and the cylinder head is aluminium. The single piece forged crankshaft has eight counterweights and is supported in the cylinder block by five main (shell) bearings. The cylinder head design differs according to the sales market. Although the valves are operated by a single overhead camshaft universally, in markets having strict emission control regulations, a CVCC advanced stratified charge type engine is fitted. Basically, explained, the CVCC (Compound Vortex Controlled Combustion) is designed to reduce the quantity of carbon monoxide (CO), hydrocarbons (HC) and oxides of nitrogen (NOx) which are normally produced and emitted in the exhaust gas. This type of engine differs from standard versions by having four auxiliary valves and the necessary operating gear incorporated in the cylinder head. The principle of operation is based upon the progressive ignition of the fuel mixture in two chambers instead of a single combustion chamber as usually employed. A relatively rich mixture in the auxiliary combustion chamber is ignited by the standard spark plug and in turn ignites the main charge, which is of a weak mixture, in the main combustion chamber. This stage ignition or charge stratification ensures stable and complete combustion under all engine operating conditions. An additional benefit from the system is that the high exhaust gas temperature warms the inlet manifold to provide quick engine warm-up and optimum intake mixture temperature.

The camshaft is driven by a toothed belt located over the camshaft and crankshaft pulley wheels and the belt is adjusted by a tensioner in the timing case.

The oil pump and distributor are driven by respective gears on the camshaft. The engine and transmission oil systems are separate.

The engine is water cooled and incorporates a water pump and thermostat. Although the coolant radiator is conventionally mounted, the cooling fan is electrically operated.

2 Operations possible with the engine in the car

1 Removal and installation of the cylinder head assembly and engine ancillaries can be carried out with the engine in the car. The sump, oil pump, piston/connecting rod assemblies can also be removed and the timing belt removed.

2 Any other major operations to the engine will necessitate removal

of the engine from the car.

3 Method of engine removal

1 The engine should be removed from the car complete with transmission for later separation.
2 It should be noted that the transmission unit can be removed from the car leaving the engine in position (see Chapter 6).

Warning - vehicles equipped with air conditioning

Whenever overhaul of a major nature is being undertaken to the engine and components of the air conditioning system obstruct the work, some items of the system may not be unbolted and moved aside sufficiently within the limits of their flexible connecting pipes, to avoid obstruction. The system should therefore be discharged by your dealer or a competent refrigeration engineer.

As the system must be completely evacuated before recharging, the necessary vacuum equipment to do this is only likely to be available at your dealer.

The refrigerant fluid is Freon 12 and although harmless under normal conditions, contact with the eyes or skin must be avoided. If Freon comes into contact with a naked flame, then a poisonous gas will be created which is injurious to health.

3 To ease engine removal, remove the bonnet (hood) with the aid of an assistant and store in a safe place.

4 Engine/manual and Hondamatic transmission - removal

On cars equipped with air conditioning, unbolt the compressor and secure it to one side of the engine compartment. *See Warning note in Section 3.*

1 Disconnect the battery earth (ground) cable.
2 Drain the coolant from the radiator as described in Chapter 2. If the engine had been run directly prior to draining, take care when removing the radiator cap to release the pressure slowly and prevent possible scalding.
3 Unscrew the sump drain plug and drain the oil into a suitable container.
4 Remove the transmission drain plug and drain the oil into a suitable container.
5 Disconnect the radiator top and bottom hoses, detach the electric fan lead and remove the radiator securing bolts. Carefully lift the radiator from the car.
6 Remove the carburettor air filter (photo) - see Chapter 3.
7 Disconnect the carbon canister to carburettor pipes.
8 Disconnect the carburettor to distributor vacuum pipes.
9 Disconnect the choke and throttle cables from the carburettor. Undo the outer cable retaining nuts from the brackets and place the cables out of the way.
10 Detach the carburettor solenoid valve lead from its connector.
11 Unclip and remove the distributor cap, disconnect the HT leads from the spark plugs and coil (photo). Remove the coil low tension lead, and remove the distributor caps and leads.
12 Disconnect the leads from the starter motor.
13 Disconnect the lead from the water temperature sender unit on the thermostat housing.
14 Disconnect the reversing (back up) light leads from the switch to gearbox.
15 Disconnect the earth (ground) cables from the gearbox (photo) and cam cover.
16 On cars fitted with the Hondamatic transmission, remove the fluid cooler hose.
17 Detach the brake booster vacuum tube.
18 Disconnect the heater hoses from their respective engine feed pipes. Detach and remove the top and bottom radiator hoses from the engine.
19 Remove the clutch slave cylinder unit leaving the hydraulic line attached.
20 Pull back the rubber boot from the speedo drive connection to the gearbox and prise the spring retaining clip from the cable. Withdraw the cable (photo) and position it out of the way.
21 Detach the respective leads from the alternator and the wire to the oil pressure switch unit (to the left of the engine oil dipstick) which is incorporated in the same wiring loom as the alternator leads.
22 On cars fitted with emission control equipment, disconnect the

4.6 Remove the air filter unit

4.11 Remove the HT lead and LT lead from the coil

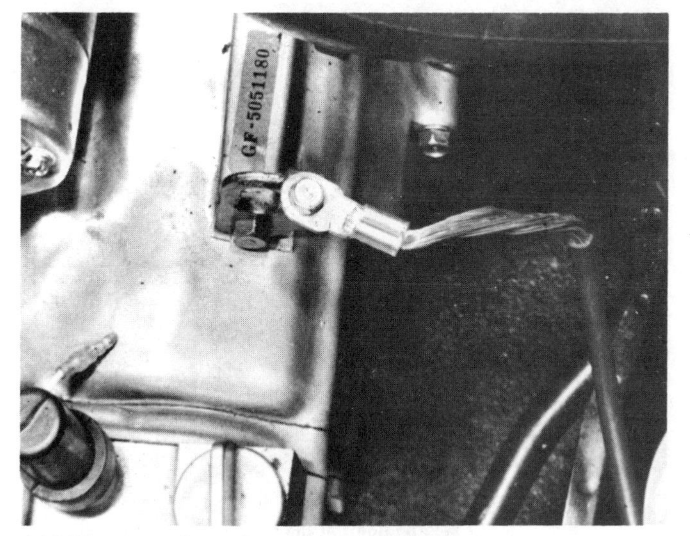

4.15 Disconnect the gearbox earth (ground) cable

4.20 Withdraw the speedo cable

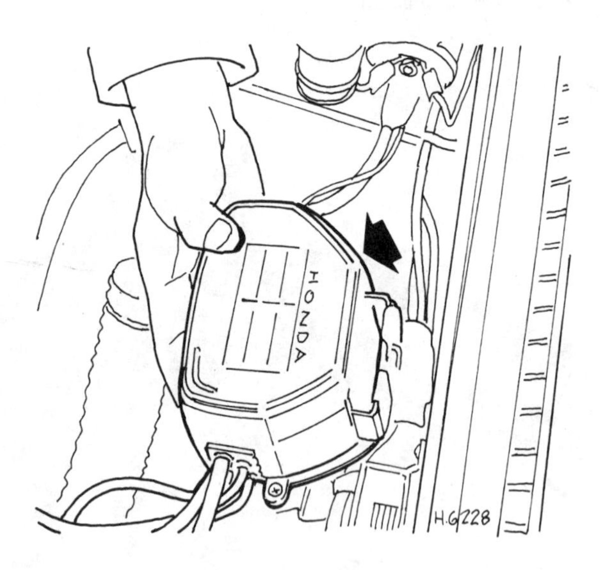

Fig. 1.1. Lift and remove the control box (arrowed) and remove it from the stay (Sec. 4)

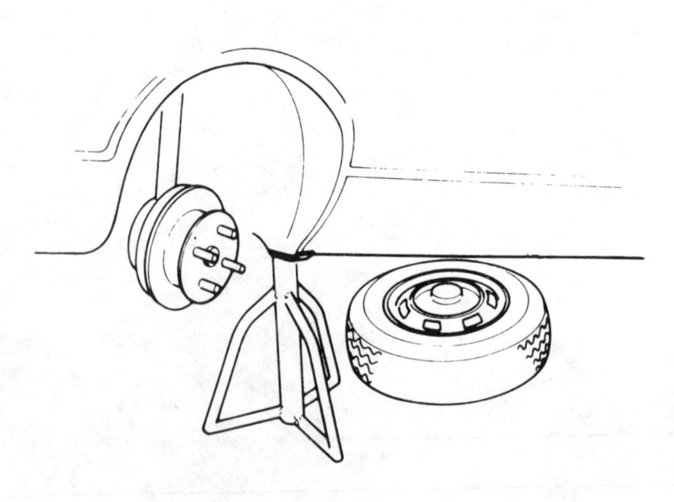
Fig. 1.2. The jacking point at the front side sill (Sec. 4)

4.24 Disconnect the exhaust down pipe and remove it

4.25 Disconnect the brake pipe from the shock absorber clamp and the caliper unit

4.26 Carefully withdraw the respective driveshafts

vacuum hoses - noting their respective positions - and remove the control box unit by lifting and detaching from stays (Fig. 1.1).
23 Push the car over an inspection pit or jack it up at the front end and place chassis stands or blocks in position to secure (Fig. 1.2). Check that the handbrake (parking brake) is fully applied and remove the front roadwheels.
24 From underneath, disconnect the exhaust pipe to manifold and the support bracket retaining nuts. Support the down pipe and disconnect it from the silencer pipe at the flange and remove it (photo).
25 Withdrawal of the respective driveshafts can be accomplished in three ways. The first method is to disconnect the left and right lower arm balljoints and the tie rod end balljoints. A balljoint separator may be required to release the taper joint. The second method is to unscrew and remove the lower control arm inner bolts and the radius rods from the control arms, leaving the balljoints attached. The third method is to unbolt and remove the disc brake caliper unit, and the hydraulic fluid line from its location on the clamp (photo) attached to the shock absorber. Place and support the caliper and line out of the way. Disconnect the lower suspension arms from the steering knuckles. Disconnect the balljoint on the end of each track rod. Remove the clamp bolt from the upper steering knuckle and pressing down on the knuckle, disconnect it from the shock absorber. When withdrawing the driveshafts, remove them together with each hub assembly.
26 Carefully withdraw the respective driveshafts, (photo) taking care not to damage the oil seal indicated in Fig. 1.3.
27 Drive the roll pin from the gear selector shift rod to the transmission gear selecting rod. Slide the retaining clip along the rod to gain access to the pin (photo).
28 Unscrew the shift rod joint bolt nut from the gear shift lever and disconnect the rod (photo).
29 Unscrew and remove the transmission extension arm retaining bolt and dished washer from the lower gearbox casing (photo).
30 On models with Hondamatic transmission, disconnect the control cable (Fig. 1.5). Extract the retaining clip, remove the pin, unscrew the outer cable attachment bolt and disconnect the control cable.
31 Place the engine/transmission lifting sling in position locating the lifting brackets on the gearbox and at the front of the engine on the cylinder head as in Fig. 1.6. Raise the hoist sufficiently to take up the sling slack and just support the engine/transmission weight.
32 Unscrew and remove the engine steady bar retaining bolt and bracket, noting the flat washer between the bracket and steady bar bush (photo).
33 Unscrew the steady bar retaining bolt from the bulkhead and remove the bar.
34 Unscrew and remove the front and rear engine mounting nuts and washers. Note that the front mounting has a flat plate located over the two studs (Fig. 1.7).
35 Unscrew and remove the two mounting bolts and plate from the front of the timing case. Remove the large bolt and push the mounting rubber into the bracket.
36 Check that all of the engine and gearbox attachments to the surrounding body and fittings are disconnected and slightly raise the engine and transmission. Disconnect the transmission extension arm from the bottom of the gearcase.
37 The engine and transmission can now be lifted clear taking care not to damage the surrounding fittings (photo).

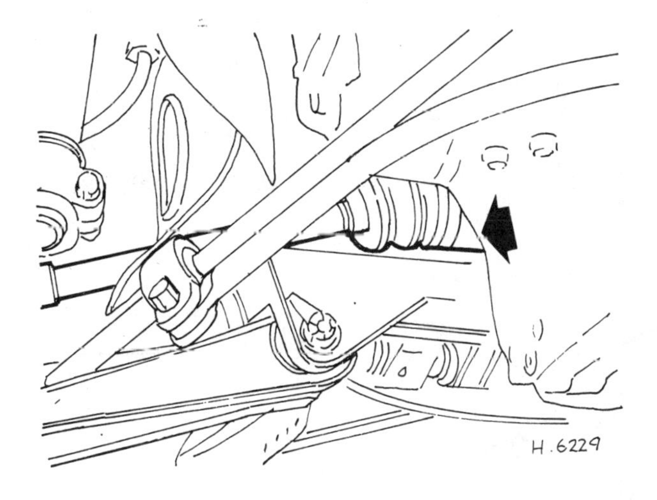

Fig. 1.3. Take care not to damage the oil seal (arrowed) when removing or fitting a driveshaft (Sec. 4)

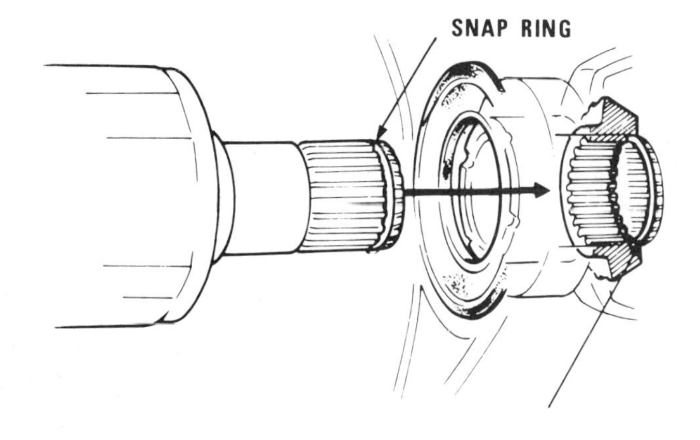

Fig. 1.4. The snap ring position. When refitting the driveshaft ensure that the snap ring clicks into position and retains the driveshaft (Sec. 4)

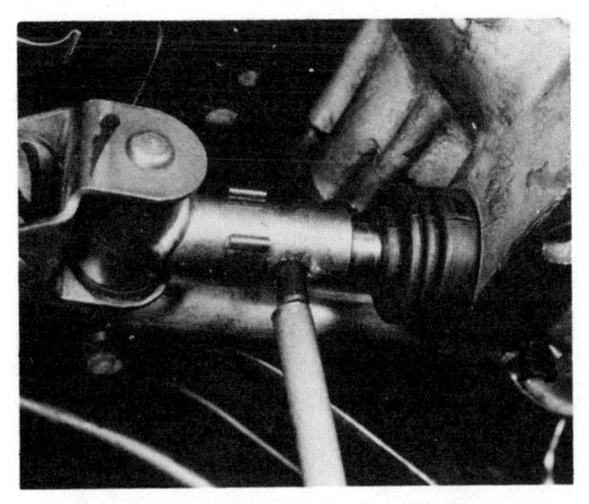

4.27 Slide the retaining clip out of the way and drive out the roll pin

4.28 Remove the shift rod from the gear lever (manual)

4.29 Remove the transmission extension arm bolt and dished washer

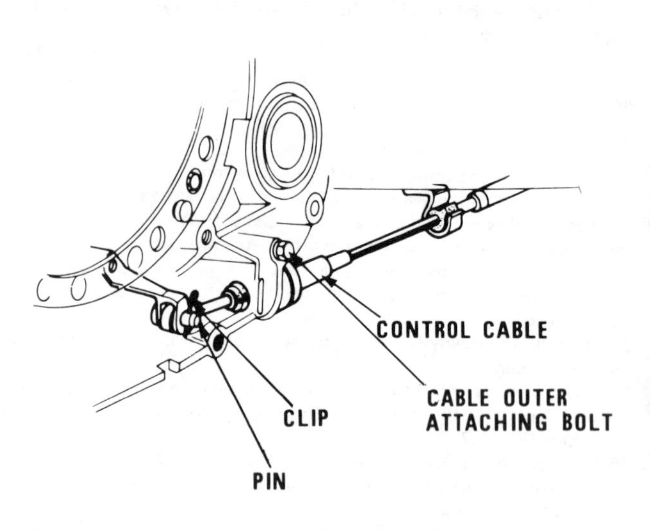

Fig. 1.5. Disconnect the control cable (Hondamatic transmission) (Sec. 4)

4.32 Unscrew and remove the engine steady bar bolt, bracket and washers

Fig. 1.6. The engine and transmission lifting points (Sec. 4)

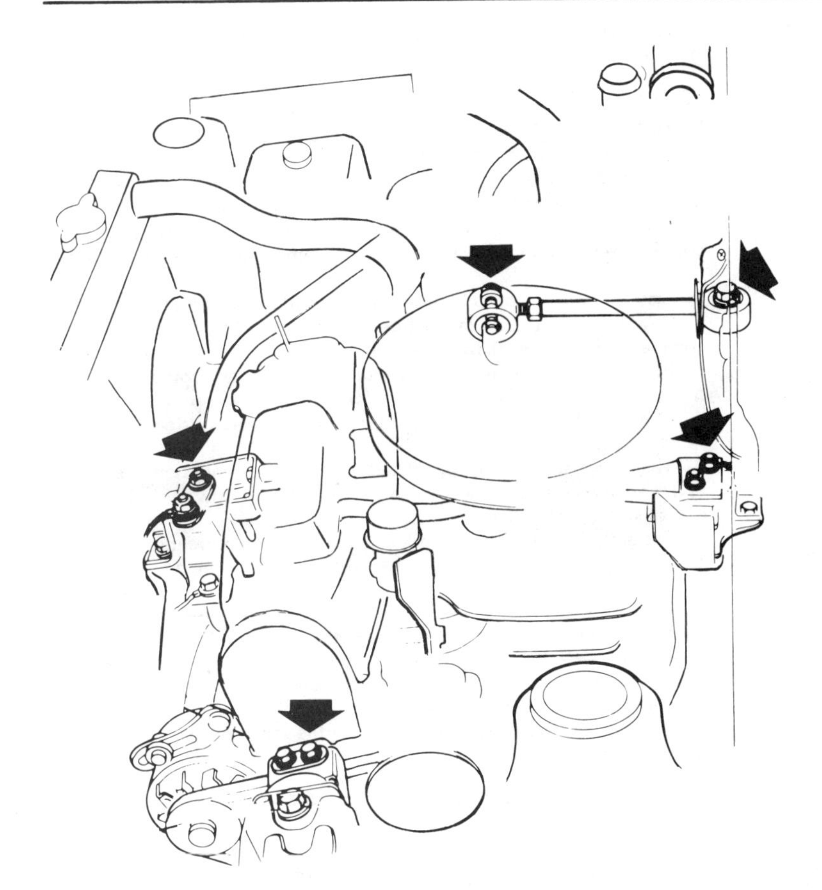

Fig. 1.7. The engine mounting points (arrowed) (Sec. 4)

4.37 Removing the engine and transmission

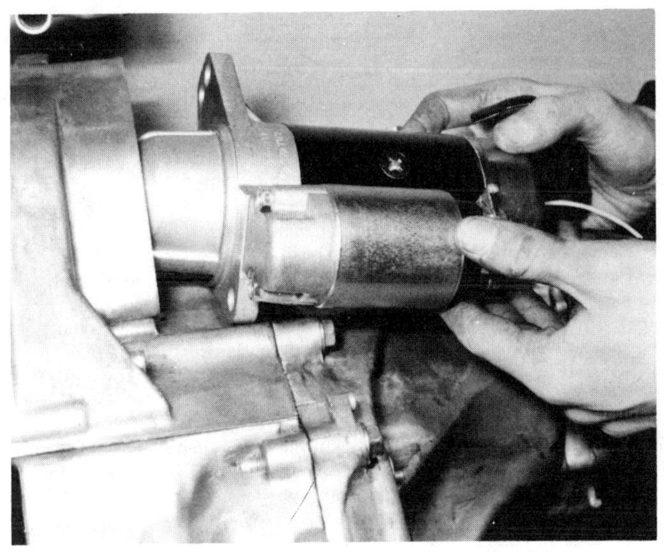

5.3 Remove the starter motor

5 Engine/transmission - separation

Manual transmission

1 Unscrew and remove the three bolts retaining the mounting bracket to the transmission case at the lower clutch housing.
2 Remove the mounting brackets from the cylinder block at the rear.
3 Unscrew the starter motor retaining bolts and remove the starter motor (photo).
4 Remove the remaining transmission to engine retaining bolts and separate the two units by pulling apart in line directly away from each other.

Hondamatic transmission

5 Follow the instruction in paragraph 1.
6 Unscrew the bellhousing splash guard retaining bolts and remove the guard.
7 Remove the engine to transmission retaining bolts.
8 Remove the starter motor.
9 Rotate the crankshaft and remove the respective drive plate attachment bolts in turn.
10 Separate the engine and transmission units by pulling apart in line directly away from each other.

6 Engine dismantling - general

1 It is best to mount the engine on a dismantling stand, but if this is not available, stand the engine on a strong bench at a comfortable working height. Failing this, it will have to be stripped down on the floor.
2 During the dismantling process, the greatest care should be taken to keep the exposed parts free from dirt. As an aid to achieving this thoroughly clean down the outside of the engine, first removing all traces of oil and congealed dirt.
3 A good grease solvent will make the job much easier, for, after the solvent has been applied and allowed to stand for a time, a vigorous jet of water will wash off the solvent and grease with it. If the dirt is thick and deeply embedded, work the solvent into it with a strong stiff brush.
4 Finally, wipe down the exterior of the engine with a rag and only then, when it is quite clean, should the dismantling process begin. As the engine is stripped, clean each part in a bath of paraffin or petrol.
5 Never immerse parts with oilways in paraffin (eg, crankshaft and camshaft). To clean these parts, wipe down carefully with a petrol dampened rag. Oilways can be cleaned out with wire. If an air-line is available, all parts can be blown dry and the oilways blown through as an added precaution.
6 Re-use of old gaskets is false economy. To avoid the possibility of trouble after the engine has been reassembled **always** use new gaskets throughout.
7 Do not throw away the old gaskets, for sometimes it happens that an immediate replacement cannot be found and the old gasket is then very useful as a template. Hang up the gaskets as they are removed.
8 To strip the engine, it is best to work from the top down. When the stage is reached where the crankshaft must be removed, the engine can be turned on its side and all other work carried out with it in this position.
9 Wherever possible, refit nuts, bolts and washers finger tight from wherever they were removed. This helps to avoid loss and muddle. If they cannot be refitted then arrange them in a fashion that it is clear from whence they came.

7 Engine ancillary components - removal

1 Having removed the engine from the car and separated it from the transmission, clean down the engine and ancillary outer surfaces as described in the previous Section.
2 Unbolt and remove the alternator and drive belt.
3 Unscrew the carburettor securing nuts and remove them with the washers. Lift the carburettor from the manifold studs.
4 Remove the upper manifold heat shield.
5 Remove the coolant pipe from the water pump. Situated beneath the exhaust manifold, it is retained by a single bolt to the cylinder block (photo) and is also interconnected to the by-pass hoses to the thermostat housing. On removal of the bolt and hose, pull the pipe to withdraw it from the water pump housing where it is sealed by an 'O' ring.
6 Remove the exhaust manifold hot air cover (photo).
7 Unscrew the inlet and exhaust manifold retaining nuts and washers from the studs and remove the inlet and exhaust manifolds complete with gasket (photo). Note the respective washer positions.
8 To separate the inlet and exhaust manifolds, unscrew the two upper bolts and one lower bolt.
9 Rotate the crankshaft to the top dead centre (TDC) position. This can be seen by removing the rubber plug from the cylinder block to the rear of the engine mounting on the oil filter side. Align the 'T' mark on the flywheel to the pointer on the rear face of the cylinder block, for manual transmission and on the red line for Hondamatic models (see Fig.
10 Mark the distributor in relation to the rotor arm position and the distributor housing in the head. Unscrew the retaining bolt and remove the distributor.
11 Unscrew the head (cam) cover retaining nuts and remove the cover.
12 Remove the water pump and plate with the rubber timing case seal attached (photo).
13 Unscrew and remove the thermostat cover bolts. Remove the cover and thermostat.
14 Unscrew the thermostat housing retaining bolts and remove the housing.

8 Rocker gear and camshaft (standard engine) - removal

1 *If the engine is still in the car,* remove the distributor (see Chapter 4), drain the cooling system and unbolt the distributor drive housing.
2 Unscrew and remove the two domed nuts and lift the camshaft cover from the cylinder head. Unbolt and remove the timing belt upper cover.
3 Unscrew and remove the bolts which secure the camshaft bearing shaft pedestal assemblies in position and remove the pedestal assemblies complete with rocker shafts and arms.
4 Push off the toothed drivebelt and lift the camshaft complete with sprocket from the cylinder head.
5 The sprocket should be removed from the camshaft using a two or three-legged puller.
6 The rocker shaft can be extracted from the pedestal assemblies after withdrawing the tension pins. Prise the tension pins upwards using a pair of side cutting pliers.
7 Extract the rocker and springs and keep them in correct sequence for refitting in their original locations if they are not being renewed.

9 Rocker gear and camshaft (CVCC engine) - removal

1 The procedure is similar to that described in the preceding Section except that an auxiliary rocker shaft is supported in the pedestals, the rocker arms which are fitted to it operate the valves of the auxiliary chamber assembly.

10 Cylinder head - removal

1 If the engine is still in the car, carry out the following operations with the engine cold to avoid distortion of the cylinder head:
2 Disconnect the battery negative lead.
3 Drain the cooling system.
4 Identify the connecting hoses and then remove the air cleaner.
5 Disconnect the leads from the coolant temperature switch, the fuel cut-off solenoid valve.
6 If air conditioning is fitted, disconnect the lead from the idle cut-off solenoid valve, remove the compressor drivebelt cover and release the drivebelt tension. Unbolt the compressor and secure it to the front upper rail with wire. There is no need to have the system discharged (see Warning note in Section 3). Remove the compressor bracket.
7 Disconnect the fuel lines and throttle cable from the carburettor.
8 Disconnect the remaining hoses and unbolt and remove the carburettor.
9 Remove the distributor cap and move it aside.
10 Disconnect the radiator upper hose from the intake manifold.
11 Disconnect the exhaust downpipe from the manifold and its cylinder head steady bracket, also the cylinder block steady bracket (accessible from below).
12 Disconnect the engine stabiliser bar.
13 Remove the bolt which secures the alternator bracket to the cylinder head and release the alternator adjuster bracket.
14 Disconnect the tachometer cable.
15 Remove the rocker cover and the timing belt upper cover.
16 Release the timing belt tensioner and slip the toothed belt from the camshaft sprocket.
17 Remove the oil pump gear cover and withdraw the oil pump shaft up and out of the cylinder head.
18 Unscrew in sequence (see Fig. 1.8) and in a progressive manner the cylinder head retaining bolts.
19 Lift the head from the cylinder block straight upwards so that the oil pump driveshaft is not distorted.
20 If preferred the cylinder head can be removed after the removal of the rocker shafts and camshaft (see preceding Sections).

11 Cylinder head - dismantling

1 With the cylinder head removed from the engine, remove the

7.5 Remove the coolant pipe retaining bolt

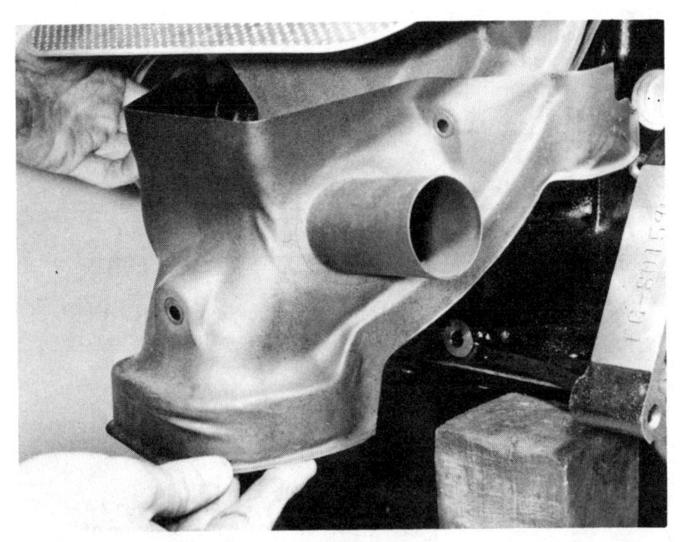
7.6 Remove the exhaust manifold hot air cover

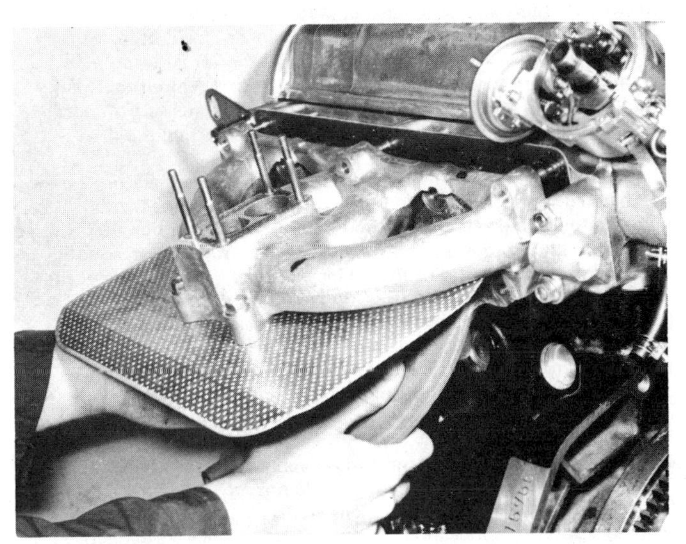
7.7 Remove the inlet and exhaust manifolds

7.12 The water pump showing position of timing cover seal plate

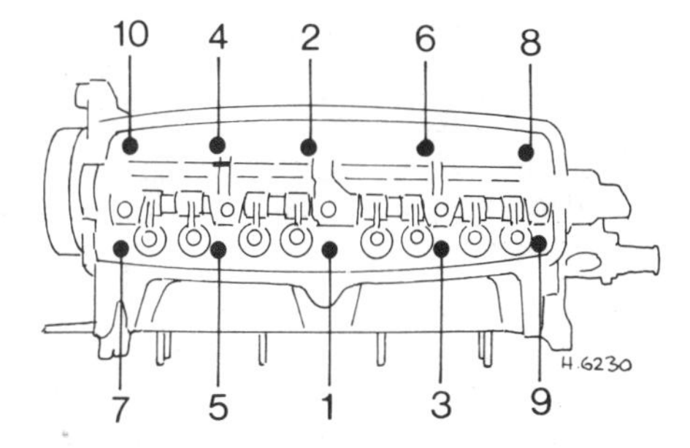

Fig. 1.8. The cylinder head bolt removal (Sec. 10)

rocker gear, camshaft and distributor housing as given in Sections 8 and 9 accordingly.

2 Unscrew the retaining bolts and remove the oil pump drive gear cover (photo). Extract the gear and shaft.

3 On removal it is essential that the valves and their components are left in strict sequence for refitting in their original positions. A tray or box with interval divisions numbered 1 to 8 (and additionally 1 to 4 CVCC engine) is useful for this purpose. The valves should be regarded as 1 to 8 (and 1 to 4 CVCC engine) from the camshaft sprocket end of the cylinder head. The valves, springs and seats differ in size between

11.2 Lift off the oil pump drive gear cover

inlet and exhaust.
4 Using a suitable compressor, compress each valve spring in turn and extract the split cotters. Release the compressor and remove the spring retainer, the outer and inner springs and the spring seat. Withdraw the valve.
5 On CVCC engine, follow the same procedure to dismantle the four auxiliary valves.
6 Remove and discard the valve stem oil seals.

12 Timing belt, tensioner and drive sprocket - removal

Engine in vehicle

1 Jack-up the front left-hand side of the vehicle and remove the wheel.
2 Apply a socket wrench to the crankshaft pulley bolt and turn the crankshaft anticlockwise until the TDC mark on the flywheel (or driveplate) is opposite the crankcase pointer. Now pass a bar or thick screwdriver through one of the cut-outs on the pulley and hold the pulley still by levering against the crankcase while the pulley bolt is unscrewed and removed in an anticlockwise direction.
3 Remove the rocker cover.
4 Remove the alternator drivebelt.
5 Remove the timing belt upper cover and mark the direction of rotation on the belt if being used again.
6 Unbolt and remove the water pump pulley.
7 Unbolt and remove the sealing plate which fits between the water pump and the timing belt lower cover.
8 From the front face of the timing belt lower cover, unscrew the two belt tensioner bolts two or three turns only. Prise out the two rubber sealing rings from behind the bolt heads.
9 Pull off the crankshaft pulley.
10 Remove the timing belt lower cover by unbolting it and pulling it downwards.
11 Disconnect the left-hand engine mounting from the engine bracket and push the outer member as far as possible into the housing on the inner wing (photo). No support for the engine is required.
12 Extract the dished belt-retaining washer from the front of the crankshaft drive sprocket, prise the belt tensioner's pulley upwards to release its tension and then slide the belt from the crankshaft and camshaft sprockets, pressing the belt out through the gap in the engine mounting bracket components. Avoid turning the crankshaft or camshaft sprocket whilst the belt is removed or the valve heads may impinge or jam on the piston crowns.
13 To remove the belt tensioner, unscrew the pivot and adjustment bolts and remove the tensioner and spring noting the spring location.
14 Withdraw the timing belt drive sprocket and dished washers from the crankshaft, noting the respective washer positions.

Engine out of vehicle

15 The procedure is identical to that just described except that the ancillary components such as the alternator and water pump will probably have been completely removed and also the transmission separated from the engine, in which case, the starter ring gear can be jammed with a cold chisel or large screwdriver to prevent the crankshaft rotating while the crankshaft pulley bolt is unscrewed.
16 Installation of the timing belt is a reversal of removal **if the engine is still in the vehicle** except that the camshaft sprocket and flywheel timing marks must not have been moved from their positions set

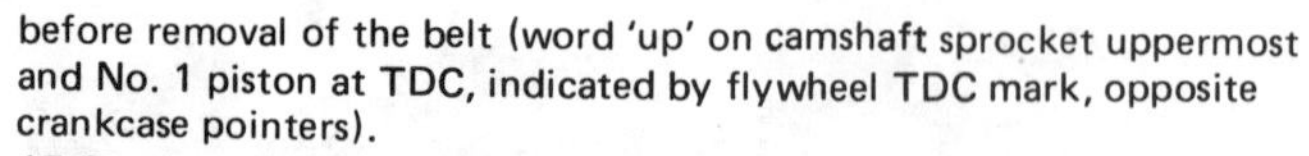

before removal of the belt (word 'up' on camshaft sprocket uppermost and No. 1 piston at TDC, indicated by flywheel TDC mark, opposite crankcase pointers).
17 Tension the belt after installation, as described in Section 40.
18 Installation and reconnection of the timing belt **when the engine is out of the car** is fully described in Sections 38 and 40 of this Chapter.
19 It is strongly recommended that the camshaft timing belt is renewed after 30000 miles (48000 km) with a maximum service life of 50000 miles (80000 km). It will be appreciated that severe damage can occur if a belt breaks when the engine is running and this will mean the renewal of valves and pistons certainly, if nothing worse!
20 An old belt, which is to be used again should be marked with its direction of travel before removing it so that it can be refitted in the same way. A new belt should be fitted so that any wording on it can be read when standing in front of the timing belt cover looking down at the engine.

13 Pistons/connecting rods - removal and dismantling

1 Remove the cylinder head as described in Section 10.
2 Unscrew and remove the sump securing bolts, withdraw the sump and gasket from the crankcase. The rear two sump bolts secure the engine rear plate which can also be removed.
3 Examine the tops of the cylinder bores. If a severe wear ridge is evident then this must be scraped or ground carefully away before the pistons are removed from the top of the cylinder block, otherwise damage may be caused to the piston rings, pistons or gudgeon pins.
4 Unbolt and remove the oil pump assembly from within the crankcase. One bolt is located under the filter screen and the screen must be carefully prised out to gain access to it. Avoid distorting the filter screen.
5 Note that the connecting rod big-ends and their caps are not numbered in respect of their position in the cylinder block. Any numbers found indicate big-end bore tolerances, see Section 19.
Dot punch the rods and caps 1 to 4 at adjacent points starting at the crankshaft pulley end of the engine and note to which side of the engine the punch marks face (photo). Note that this may already have been done if the engine has previously been dismantled.
6 Turn the crankshaft by means of the flywheel until No. 1 piston (nearest crankshaft pulley) is at the lowest point of its travel in its bore. Unscrew and remove the big-end bearing cap nuts and remove the cap.
7 Using the wooden handle of a hammer applied to the end of the connecting rod, drive the piston/rod assembly from the cylinder bore. Take care that the big-end bolt threads do not score the bores.
8 If for any reason the bearing shells are to be used again, identify them in respect of connecting rod and cap using a piece of adhesive tape or a spirit marker.
9 Repeat the foregoing operations on the remaining three pistons/connecting rod assemblies.
10 A press and special adaptors are required to remove and refit the piston to the connecting rod as the gudgeon pin is an interference fit in the rod. It is recommended that this work is left to your Honda dealer. When correctly assembled, the dot on the piston crown should be nearest the oil drilling in the connecting rod (photo).
11 To remove the rings from a piston, slide two or three old feeler

12.11 Left-hand engine mounting pushed into the bracket

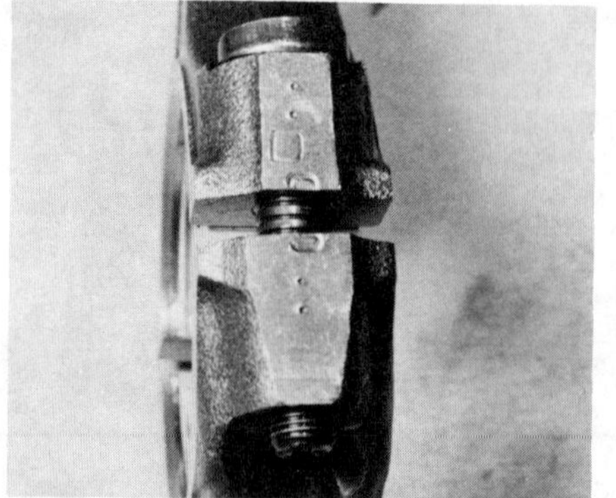

13.5 Dot punch the respective connecting rods and caps numerically starting from the crankshaft pulley end

13.10 Oil hole in connecting rod to dot mark in piston crown

blades behind the top ring and then remove the ring using a twisting motion. Remove the second compression ring and the oil control ring in a similar way. The feeler blades will prevent the lower rings dropping into the higher vacant grooves as they are withdrawn.

14 Clutch, flywheel (or drive plate), crankshaft and main bearings - removal

1 Mark the clutch pressure plate in relation to the flywheel if they are not already marked.
2 Lock the flywheel by jamming the ring gear teeth with a bar or screwdriver and unscrew evenly and progressively the eight pressure plate bolts. Remove the pressure plate and clutch disc from the flywheel.
3 Unbolt and remove the flywheel (or drive plate - auto transmission) from the crankshaft.
4 Note the main bearing cap positions and numbers which are cast on the outer face. If they are not already numbered, dot punch them (1 to 5) from the pulley end of the crankshaft, at adjacent points on each cap and the crankcase.
5 Unbolt and remove the main bearing caps together with the seals. If the bearing shells are to be used again, identify them in respect of their main bearing cap using adhesive tape or a spirit marker.
6 Lift the crankshaft from the crankcase. Remove the rear oil seal.
7 Extract the bearing shells from the crankcase and again place them with their respective main bearing caps if they are to be used again. Note the semi-circular thrust washers located either side of the No. 4 main bearing (numbering from the crankshaft pulley end).

15 Engine lubrication system - description

1 The oil pump is of rotor type mounted within the crankcase and driven by a gear on the upper end of its shaft from the camshaft.
2 Oil from the sump is picked up through the oil pump intake screen and pumped under pressure to the engine bearings. Splash lubrication is used for the cylinder bores, and spray jets at the top of the connecting rods provide additional lubrication for the top of the cylinder bores.
3 A pressure relief valve is incorporated in the oil pump body. With the oil pump and associate components in good condition, there should be good oil pressure as given in the Specifications.
4 A cartridge type full flow oil filter is mounted on the forward facing side of the engine crankcase and is easily accessible for renewal at the specified service intervals.

16 Crankcase ventilation system - maintenance

1 The emission of fumes from the engine crankcase is controlled by a closed type ventilation system.
2 Maintenance consists of occasionally checking the security of the system hoses and at 15000 miles (24000 km) intervals cleaning the fixed orifice of the four-way union using an 0.039 in (1.0 mm) diameter twist drill.
3 Pull the large drain tube from under the air cleaner. Allow any accumulated water or oil to drain out of the tube.
4 Detach the condensation chamber from the air cleaner and tilt it to inspect its interior. Clean out any condensation or deposits from it, and also from the connecting tubes.
5 Check that the gasket which fits between the chamber and the air cleaner is in good condition and then refit the chamber to the air cleaner body and reconnect the drain hose.

17 Engine components - examination and renovation (general)

1 With the engine completely dismantled, every component should be thoroughly cleaned and then examined for wear and renovated, as described in the following Sections.
2 Many of the measurements required will need the use of feeler blades or a micrometer but in many instances wear will be visually evident or the old component can be compared with a new one.

18 Crankshaft and main bearings - examination and renovation

1 Examine the surfaces of the crankpins and journals for scoring. Using a micrometer check that any taper or out of round of the crankpins or journals lies within the limits given in the Specifications. If not, the crankshaft must be renewed, it cannot be reground.
2 The main bearing shells are colour-coded and if the shells are to be renewed, simply change each shell for one of appropriate colour.
3 The method of identifying the main bearing tolerances should be understood. The crankshaft webs carry numbers from 1 to 4. The machined face at the end of the crankcase also carries numbers 1 to 4 but these are represented as lines I-II-III-IIII. By reading off the two sets of numbers from the following table, the correct bearing shells can be selected for any given main bearing journal. **The numbers on the crankshaft webs or crankcase endface do not indicate the position of the main bearing caps.**

Crankshaft main journal numbers	Crankcase main bearing recess numbers			
	I	**II**	**III**	**IIII**
1	*Red*	*Pink*	*Yellow*	*Green*
2	*Pink*	*Yellow*	*Green*	*Brown*
3	*Yellow*	*Green*	*Brown*	*Black*
4 Gr	*Green*	*Brown*	*Black*	*Blue*

4 The main journal diameters are 1.97 in (50.0 mm) and the identification numbers represent the following bearing shell tolerances:

1	*+0.0012 to +0.0009 in (+0.030 to +0.024 mm)*
2	*+0.0009 to +0.0007 in (+0.024 to +0.018 mm)*
3	*+0.0007 to +0.0005 in (+0.018 to +0.012 mm)*
4	*+0.0005 to +0.0002 in (+0.012 to +0.006 mm)*

5 The crankshaft main bearing diameters in the crankcase are 2.13 in (54.0 mm) and the identification numbers represent the following tolerances:

I	*+0.0016 to +0.0018 in (+0.040 to +0.046 mm)*
II	*+0.0018 to +0.0020 in (+0.046 to +0.052 mm)*
III	*+0.0020 to +0.0023 in (+0.052 to +0.058 mm)*
IIII	*+0.0023 to +0.0025 in (+0.058 to +0.064 mm)*

19 Big-end bearings and connecting rods - examination and renovation

1 The big-end bearings are identified individually in the following way. The connecting rods are stamped with a number between 1 and 4 which runs across the rod and cap joint. The crankpins are marked with a letter A, B, C or D. By reading off the two characters from the following table, the correct bearing shells can be selected for any given connecting rod big-end. When renewing bearings, they must be replaced with a bearing of the same colour.

Crankpin identification letters	Connecting rod big-end bearing numbers			
	1	**2**	**3**	**4**
A	*Red*	*Pink*	*Yellow*	*Green*
B	*Pink*	*Yellow*	*Green*	*Brown*
C	*Yellow*	*Green*	*Brown*	*Black*
D	*Green*	*Brown*	*Black*	*Blue*

2 The connecting rod big-end bearing diameters are 1.69 in (43.0 mm) and their identification numbers represent the following tolerances:

1	*0 to +0.0002 in (0 to +0.006 mm)*
2	*+0.0002 to +0.0005 in (+0.006 to +0.012 mm)*
3	*+0.0005 to +0.0007 in (+0.012 to +0.018 mm)*
4	*+0.0007 to +0.0009 in (+0.018 to 0.024 mm)*

3 The crankpin diameters for acceptance of the connecting rod bearing shells are 1.654 in (42.0 mm) and their identification numbers

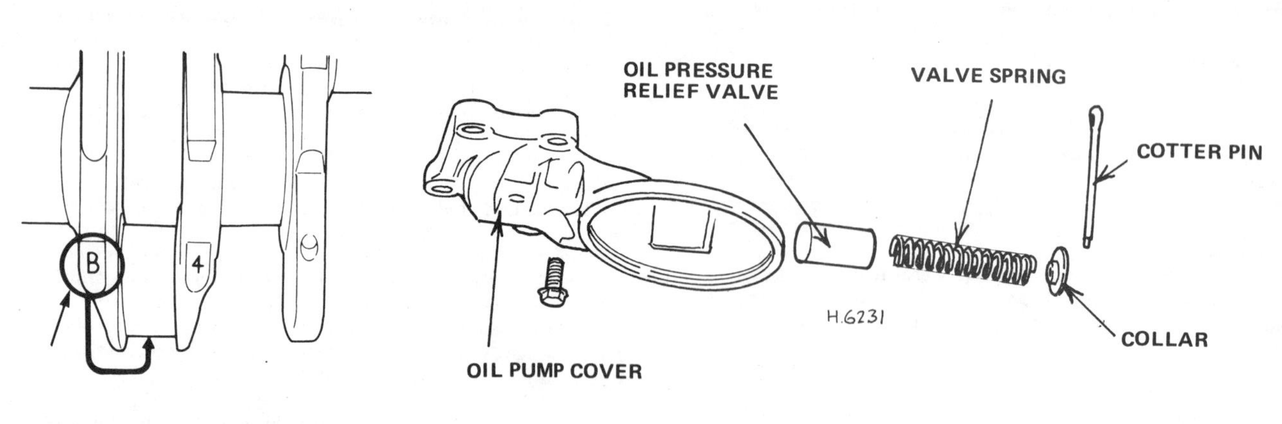

Fig. 1.9. The crankshaft marking position to show the rod journal outside diameter dimensions; (any combination of letters may be used accordingly) (Sec. 19)

Fig. 1.10. The oil relief valve components (Sec. 22)

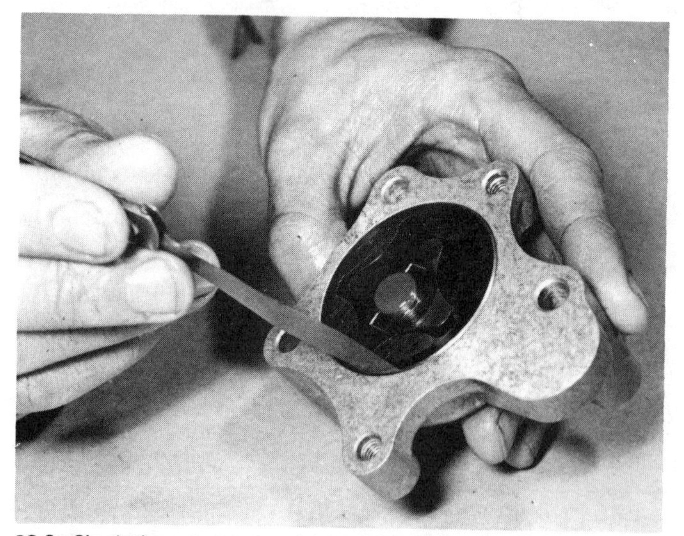

22.3a Check the outer rotor to body clearance

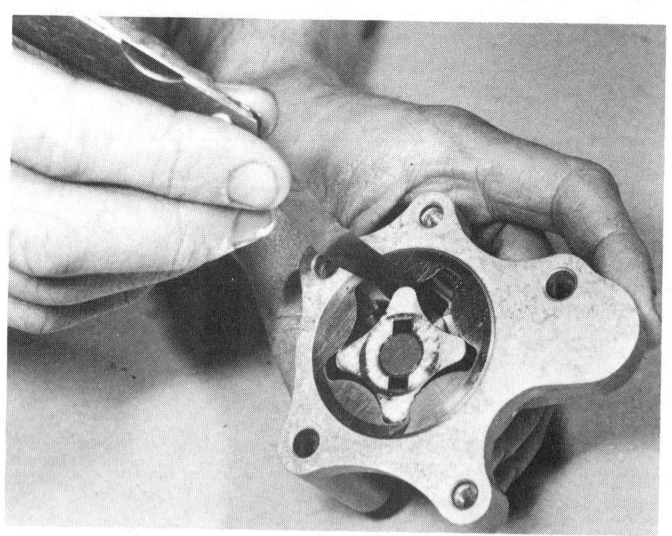

22.3b Check the inner to outer rotor lobe tip clearances

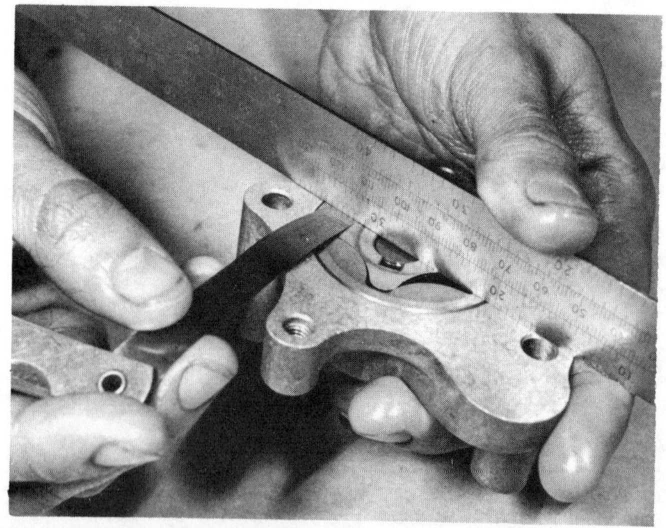

22.3c Check the pump body flange to rotor clearance - although not shown, the gasket should be in position

22.9 Check the drive gear endfloat

represent the following tolerances:

A	*0 to 0.0002 in (0 to 0.006 mm)*
B	*0.0002 to 0.0005 in (−0.006 to −0.012 mm)*
C	*−0.0005 to −0.0007 in (−0.012 to −0.018 mm)*
D	*−0.0007 to −0.0009 in (−0.018 to −0.024 mm)*

4 If the gudgeon pin no longer maintains an interference fit in the connecting rod small end bush, the rod must be renewed. This operation and removal and refitting of the piston are jobs best left to your Honda dealer due to the need for a press and special tools.
5 **The numbers which are marked across the connecting rod and big-end cap joints do not indicate the position of cap or rod in the cylinder block.**
6 Each connecting rod oilway must be kept clear and it is advisable to have each rod checked for alignment by your Honda dealer or local engine reconditioner.

20 Cylinder bores - examination and renovation

1 The cylinder bores must be examined for taper, ovality, scoring and scratches. Start by carefully examining the top of the cylinder bores. If they are at all worn a very slight ridge will be found on the thrust side. This marks the top of the piston ring travel. The owner will have a good indication of the bore wear prior to dismantling the engine, or removing the cylinder head. Excessive oil consumption accompanied by blue smoke from the exhaust is a sure sign of worn cylinder bores and piston rings.
2 Measure the bore diameter just under the ridge with a micrometer and compare it with the diameter at the bottom of the bore, which is not subject to wear. If the difference between the two measurements is more than 0.004 in (0.10 mm), then it will be necessary to fit special piston rings or to have the cylinders rebored and fit oversized pistons and rings. If no micrometer is available, remove the rings from a piston and place the piston in each bore in turn about three-quarters of an inch below the top of the bore. If a 0.010 in (0.25 mm) feeler gauge can be slid between the piston and the cylinder wall on the thrust side of the bore then remedial action must be taken. Oversize pistons are available in +0.010 in (+0.25 mm) gradations.
3 These are accurately machined to just below these measurements so as to provide correct running clearances in bores machined out to the exact oversize dimensions.
4 If the bores are slightly worn but not so badly worn as to justify reboring them, special oil control rings can be fitted to the existing pistons which will restore compression and stop the engine burning oil. Several different types are available and the manufacturer's instructions concerning their fitting must be followed closely.

21 Pistons and piston rings - examination and renovation

1 If the old pistons are to be refitted carefully remove the piston rings and thoroughly clean them. Take particular care to clean out the piston ring grooves. At the same time do not scratch the aluminium. If new rings are to be fitted to the old pistons, then the top ring should be stepped to clear the ridge left above the previous top ring. If a normal but oversize new ring is fitted, it will hit the ridge and break, because the new ring will not have worn in the same way as the old, which will have worn in unison with the ridge.
2 Prior to assembling the rings to the pistons, each ring must be inserted into its respective cylinder bore and the gap measured with a feeler gauge. It is essential that each ring gap is as specified at the beginning of this Chapter. The ring gap must be checked with the ring positioned to within 0.5 to 0.8 in (15 to 20 mm) from the bottom of the cylinder bore. If it is measured at the top of a worn bore and gives a perfect fit, it could easily seize at the bottom. If the ring gap is too small rub down the ends of the ring with a fine file, until the gap, when fitted, is correct. To keep the rings square in the bore for measurement, line each up in turn with an old piston: use the piston to push the ring down. Remove the piston and measure the piston ring gap.
3 When fitting new pistons and rings to a rebored engine the ring gap can be measured at the top of the bore as the bore will now not taper.
4 Piston ring groove clearance will normally be correct with new pistons but even so, check it with a feeler gauge and see that it is as specified.
5 The piston skirt to cylinder bore clearance must also be checked when fitting new pistons. It is essential that the clearance be as stated in the Specifications at the beginning of the Chapter.

22 Oil pump - overhaul

1 Extract the split pin from the end of the pressure relief valve and gently tap the valve components from the pump body.
2 Unbolt the bottom cover/filter assembly from the pump body
3 Clean all components and then check for wear using a feeler blade.

a) *Check the clearance between the outer rotor and the body (photo). The radial clearance must be within 0.004 to 0.008 in (0.1 to 0.2 mm)*
b) *Check the clearance between the lobe tips of the inner and outer rotors (photo). The radial clearance must be within 0.006 in to 0.008 in (0.15 to 0.2 mm)*
c) *Check the clearance between oil pump body flange and the inner and outer rotor surfaces by using a straight edge and feeler blade (photo). The joint gasket should be in position when checking. The axial clearance must be within 0.001 to 0.006 in (0.03 to 0.15 mm).*

4 Check that the relief valve slides freely within its bore.
5 Check that the relief valve spring free length is 2.10 in (53.5 mm).
6 If any of the oil pump components are badly worn, scored or do not comply with the specified tolerances the pump unit must be renewed.
7 When reassembling be sure to use a new gasket and tighten the retaining bolts to the specified torque.
8 The oil pump drive gear backlash should be checked and must be within 0.0016 to 0.004 in (0.04 to 0.1 mm). When checking the backlash, press firmly downwards on the shaft.
9 The drive gear endfloat must also be checked on reassembly. With the drive gear cover bolted to the cylinder head, check the oil pump gear to gear cover clearance which must be within 0.002 to 0.012 in (0.05 to 0.3 mm) (photo).

23 Starter ring gear - examination and renovation

1 If the teeth on the flywheel starter ring gear are badly worn, or if some are missing, then it will be necessary to remove the ring. This is achieved by splitting the old ring using a cold chisel. The greatest care must be taken not to damage the flywheel during this process. Check the availability of spare ring gears before proceeding to remove the gear.
2 To fit a new ring gear, heat it gently and evenly with an oxyacetylene flame until a temperature of approximately 350°C (662°F) is reached. This is indicated by a light metallic blue surface colour. With the ring gear at this temperature fit it to the flywheel with the front of the teeth facing the flywheel register. The ring gear should be either pressed or lightly tapped gently onto its register and left to cool naturally, when the contraction of the metal on cooling will ensure that it is a secure and permanent fit. Great care must be taken not to overheat the ring gear, as if this happens its temper will be lost.
3 Alternatively, your local Honda agent, or local automobile engineering works may have a suitable oven in which the ring can be heated.

24 Camshaft and bearings - examination and renovation

1 Examine the camshaft for signs of wear. If the cams are scored badly, the camshaft will have to be renewed.
2 If the camshaft bearings are worn then the rocker pedestals and the cylinder head will have to be renewed as the bearings are integral with these components.
3 Check the cam lobe height for wear against the dimensions given in Specifications.
4 Place the camshaft in 'V' blocks and, using a dial gauge, rotate the shaft and check the bearing journals for wear. The total indicated run out should not exceed 0.004 in (0.10 mm).
5 If the camshaft is to be renewed then the oil pump drive gear and shaft should be renewed also since it is not good practice to mesh a new gear with a worn one.

25 Rocker assembly - examination and renovation

1 Thoroughly clean out the rocker shaft. As it acts as the oil passages for the valve gear, clean out the oil holes and make sure they are quite clear. Check the shaft for straightness by rolling it on a flat surface, such as a piece of plate glass. The surface of the shaft should be free from any wear ridges caused by the rocker arms. If any wear is present renew the rocker shaft. Wear is likely to have occurred only if the rocker shaft oil holes have been blocked.
2 Check the rocker arms for wear of the rocker bushes, for wear at the rocker arm face which bears on the cam, and for wear of the adjusting ball ended screws. Wear in the rocker arm bush can be checked by gripping the rocker arm tip and holding the rocker arm in place on the shaft, noting if there is any lateral rocker arm play. If any play is present, and the arm is very loose on the shaft, renew the arm.
3 On assembly to the rocker shaft each rocker arm must be refitted in its original position.

26 Timing components - examination and renovation

1 Check the crankshaft and camshaft sprocket for wear in the teeth and if evident, renew as required.
2 Check the belt tensioner, if it rotates noisily or has any tendency to shake due to wear, renew it.
3 The timing belt should be renewed if it is oil stained or the right angular corners of the teeth are deformed. Always renew the belt if it has been in use for 30000 miles (48000 km) or more at the time of major overhaul. Always renew the belt cover sealing strips.

27 Inlet and exhaust valves - examination and renovation

1 Examine the heads of the valves for pitting and burning; especially the heads of the exhaust valves. The valve seating should be examined at the same time. If the pitting on the valves and seats is very light the marks can be removed by grinding the seats and the valves together with coarse and then fine, valve grinding paste. Where bad pitting has occurred to the valve seats it will be necessary to recut them to fit new valves. Valve seats should be recut in three stages, 30°, 60° and 46° . If the valves seats are so worn that they cannot be recut, then it will be necessary to fit new valve seat inserts. These latter two jobs should be entrusted to the local Honda agent or automobile engineering works. In practice it is very seldom that the seats are so badly worn that they require renewal. Normally, it is the valve that is too badly worn for refitting, and the owner can easily purchase a new set of valves and match them to the seats by valve grinding.
2 Valve grinding is carried out as follows: Place the cylinder head upside down on a bench, with a block of wood at each end to give clearance for the valve stems.
3 Smear a trace of coarse carborundum paste on the seat face and apply a suction grinder tool to the valve head. With a semi-rotary action, grind the valve head to its seat, lifting the valve occasionally to redistribute the grinding paste. When a dull matt even surface finish is produced on both the valve seat and the valve, wipe off the paste and repeat the process with fine carborundum paste, lifting and turning the valve to redistribute the paste as before. A light spring placed under the valve head will greatly ease this operation. When a smooth unbroken ring of light grey matt finish is produced, on both valve and the valve seat faces, the grinding operation is complete.

28 Inlet and exhaust valve guides - examination and renovation

1 If side-to-side movement of a valve indicates wear in the guide, the guide will have to be pressed out of the bottom face of the cylinder head and a new one installed.
2 As a special positioning tool must be used when installing the new guide, to give it the correct projection and then the guide must be reamed, it is recommended that this operation is left to your Honda dealer.

29 Valve springs - examination and renovation

1 Inspect the respective valve springs for distortion or signs of wear.
2 Check the free length of each spring against the length quoted in the Specifications.
3 If the springs are under length or the valves and guides are to be renewed then the spring must be renewed also.

30 Auxiliary valves (CVCC engine) - examination and renovation

1 The auxiliary valves can be removed from the cylinder head using a long box spanner and dismantled using a normal valve spring compressor, Special Tool No. 07957-3290001 or as in Fig. 1.13.
2 Note the fitting sequence of the valve components.
3 Always renew the 'O' rings and gaskets.
4 The valve can be ground into its seat in the valve holder if the latter is carefully clamped in the jaws of a vice. If the seat is badly burnt or corroded it can be recut in three stages' 30°, 60°, 45°.

31 Cylinder head - decarbonising and examination

1 This operation can be carried out either with the engine in, or out, of the car. With the cylinder head off carefully remove with a wire brush and blunt scraper all traces of carbon deposits from the combustion spaces and brush down with petrol and scrape the cylinder head surface of any foreign matter with the side of a steel rule or a similar article. Take care not to scratch the surface.
2 Clean the pistons and top of the cylinder bores. If the pistons are still in the cylinder bores then it is essential that great care is taken to ensure that no carbon gets into the cylinder bores as this could scratch the cylinder walls or cause damage to the piston and rings. To ensure that this does not happen first turn the crankshaft so that two of the

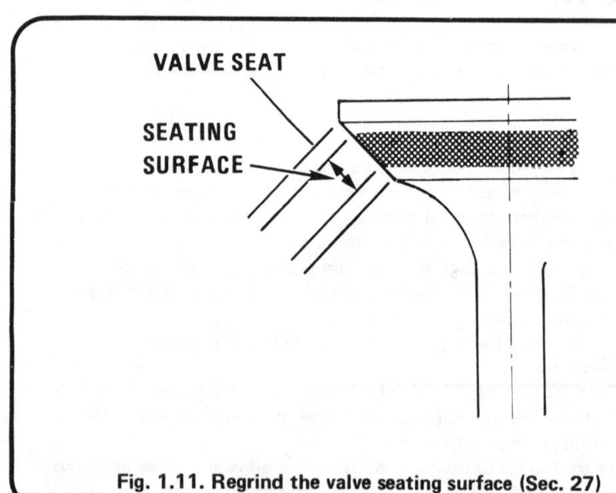

Fig. 1.11. Regrind the valve seating surface (Sec. 27)

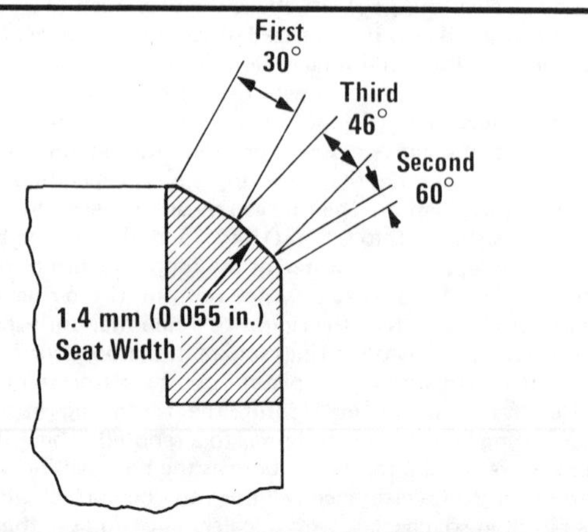

Fig. 1.12. Inlet and exhaust valve seat cutting diagram (Sec. 27)

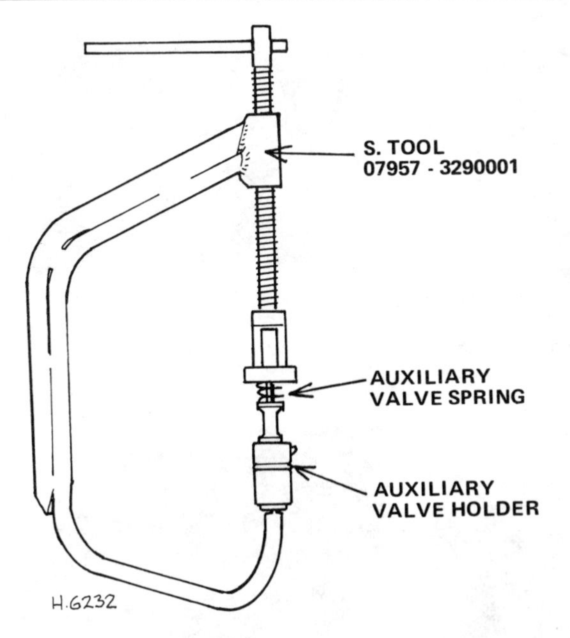

Fig. 1.13. Special tool No. 07957 - 3290001 used for compressing the auxiliary valve spring (Sec. 30)

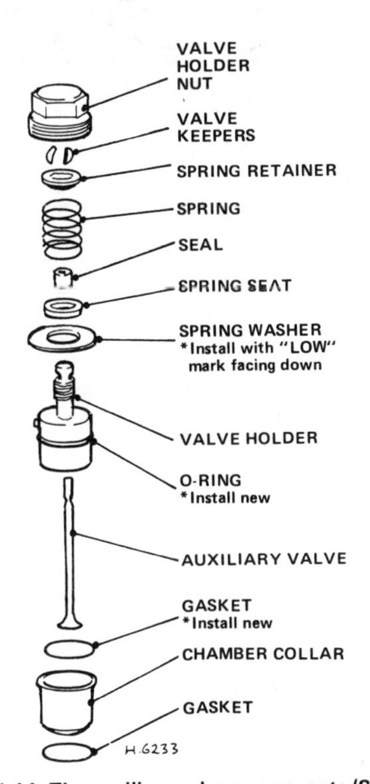

Fig. 1.14. The auxiliary valve components (Sec. 30)

pistons are at the top of the bores. Place clean non-fluffy rag into the other two bores or seal them off with paper and masking tape. The waterways and pushrod holes should always be covered with a small piece of masking tape to prevent particles of carbon entering the cooling system and damaging the water pump or entering the lubrication system and damaging the oil pump or bearings.

3 Press some grease into the gap between the cylinder walls and the two pistons which are being worked upon. With a blunt scraper carefully scrape away the carbon from the piston crowns taking care not to scratch the aluminium surface. Also scrape the carbon ring from the top of the bores.

4 Remove the rags and masking tape and wipe away the rings of grease which will now be mixed with carbon particles.

5 The crankshaft can now be turned to bring the other two pistons to the top of their strokes and the operations previously described can be repeated.

6 Wipe away every trace of carbon and pour a little thin oil round the pistons to lubricate the rings and to help flush out any remaining carbon particles from the piston grooves.

7 Clean out any holes in the cylinder head and examine for cracks. Any studs which have stripped their threads should be removed and new thread inserts installed.

8 Where distortion of the cylinder head is suspected and may have been evident by leaking of 'blown' gaskets, then check the surface using a straight edge or a piece of plate glass and a feeler blade. Check in all directions and if a warpage of 0.002 in (0.05 mm) is found, the cylinder head should be re-surfaced provided its overall thickness is not reduced below 3.55 in (90.3 mm).

32 Oil seals - renewal

1 At the time of major overhaul, always renew all oil seals, 'O' rings and gaskets.

2 Make sure that the seal lips are facing the correct way and any direction of rotation arrows are correctly positioned.

33 Engine reassembly - suggested sequence

1 It is recommended that the following sequence is used during engine reassembly:

Refit:
Crankshaft and main bearings.
Flywheel (or driveplate - automatic transmission).
Piston/connecting rod assemblies.
Oil pump
Sump.
Crankshaft sprocket.
Timing belt tensioner, belt and lower cover.
Cylinder head (reassembled) with or without manifold.
Timing belt (connection and belt tensioning)
Water pump (see Chapter 2).
Valve clearance adjustment.
Oil pump drive gear and shaft.
Water distribution tube.
Water pump pulley, crankshaft pulley.
Inlet and exhaust manifolds (if not previously installed with cylinder head).
Camshaft rocker cover.
Alternator and drivebelt.

2 Make sure that absolute cleanliness is observed and lubricate all metal components and oil seals before reassembly using clean engine oil.

34 Crankshaft and main bearings - refitting

1 If the original bearing shells are being refitted, place them in their original positions in the crankcase.

2 If new shells are being installed, these will have been selected as described in Section 18. Make sure that the backs of the shells are wiped absolutely clean and that the two semi-circular thrust washers are placed either side of the crankcase main bearing web No. 4 (counting from the crankshaft pulley end) and have their grooved sides facing outwards (photo).

3 Install new oil seals to the front and rear of the crankshaft so that the numbers stamped on the seals face outwards and apply a liberal coating of oil to each seal lip. Oil the bearing shells liberally and lower the crankshaft into the crankcase (photos).

4 Fit the main bearing caps (photo) in their correct numbered sequence having installed their original or colour selected shells so that the tabs engage in the cut-out in the caps.

5 Install the main bearing cap bolts and tighten to the specified torque, (photo).

6 Now check the crankshaft endfloat by prising the crankshaft first in one direction and then the other and measuring the endfloat with a dial gauge or feeler blades. Where the endfloat exceeds that specified,

34.2 Fit the main bearing shells and thrust washers in position

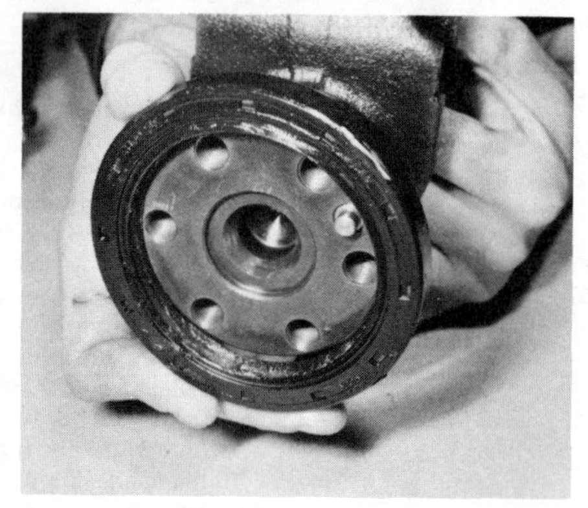
34.3a Locate the oil seals onto the crankshaft ...

34.3b ... and lower into position

34.4 Fit the respective main bearing caps

34.5 Tighten the main bearing cap bolts to the specified torque

35.2 Tighten the flywheel retaining bolts to the specified torque

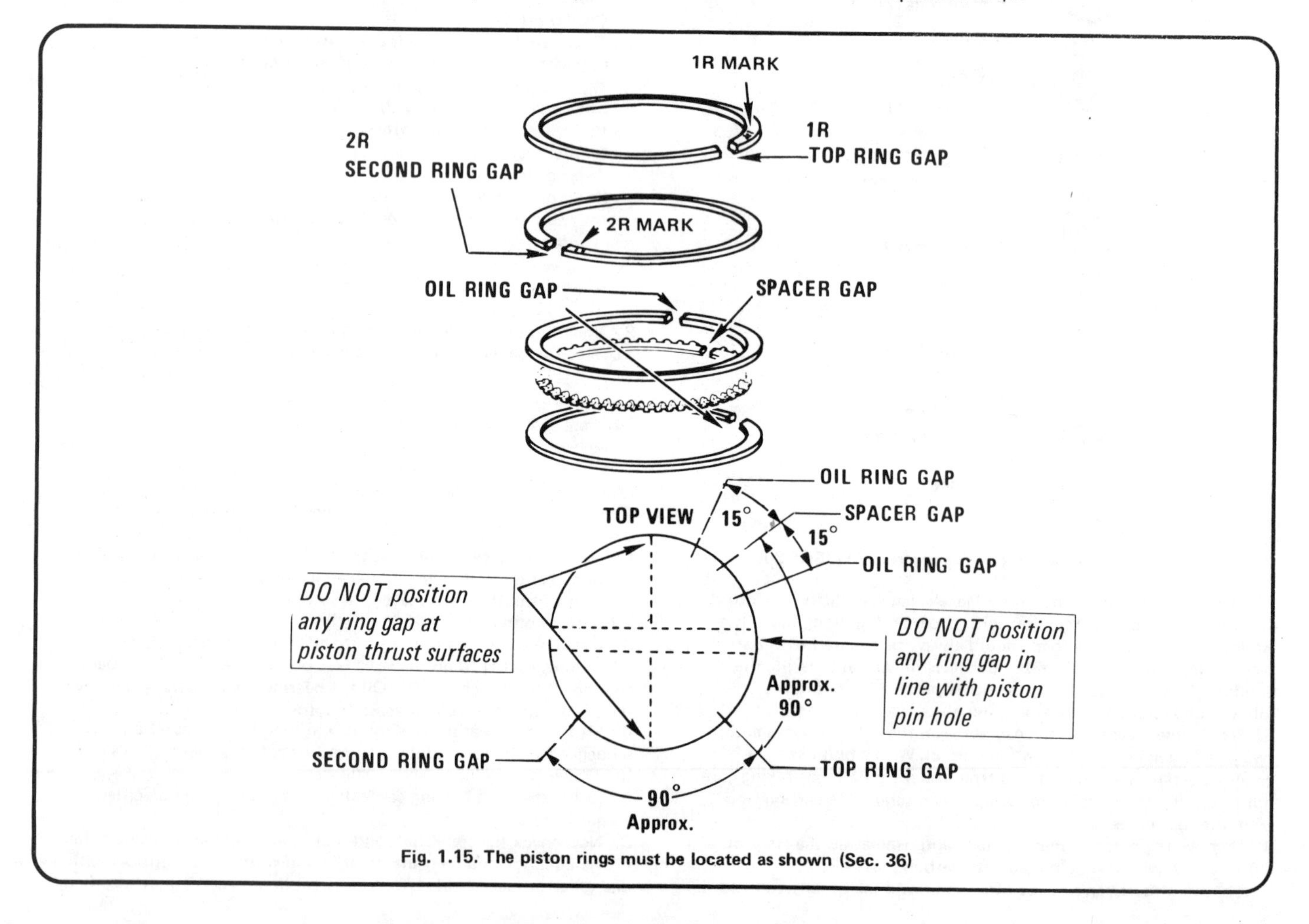

Fig. 1.15. The piston rings must be located as shown (Sec. 36)

renew the thrust washers but if this fails to rectify the situation, the crankshaft will have to be renewed. Where the endfloat is too small, do not reduce the thrust washer thickness by filing or grinding but check that the main bearing caps have been installed in their correct order and have the crankshaft tested for distortion.

7 Check that the crankshaft turns freely. If it does not, the bearing shells or caps may have been mixed up.

35 Flywheel (or driveplate) - refitting

1 Install the flywheel to the crankshaft rear flange noting the alignment marks must be opposite to each other.

2 Screw in and tighten the securing bolts to the specified torque wrench settings in diagonal sequence (photo).

3 Installation of the driveplate is carried out in a similar manner to the flywheel.

36 Pistons/connecting rods - reassembly and installation

1 With the pistons correctly reassembled to the connecting rods (see Section 13) the piston rings should be fitted to the piston grooves.

2 The correct ring gaps should already have been established and the ring sets identified in respect of cylinder bore, as described in Section 21.

3 Using two or three old feeler blades as slides, push the (lower) oil control ring components down the piston and into the groove. Make sure that the oil control ring spacer is correctly engaged at its joint.

4 The second compression ring should now be fitted making sure that the mark '2R' is visible on its top face when looking down on the piston crown.

5 Fit the top compression ring making sure that the mark '1R' is visible on its top face when looking down on the piston crown.

6 Rotate each piston ring in its groove to ensure that it does not bind. When new rings are fitted check the clearances to the ring land using a feeler gauge on the top and second rings. See Specifications for clearance.

7 With all three piston rings fitted, twist them so that their end gaps take up the positions shown in the diagram (Fig. 1.15).

8 Lubricate the piston rings liberally and fit a piston ring compressor to the piston/rod assembly which is to be installed in No. 1 cylinder bore. Lubricate the cylinder bores.

9 Carefully lower the connecting rod into the cylinder making sure that the dot on the piston crown is towards the inlet manifold and that the underside of the piston ring compressor is resting squarely on the top of the cylinder block (photo).

10 Place the wooden handle of a hammer on the piston crown and give the head of the hammer a sharp blow to drive the piston into the block.

11 Draw the connecting rod down until it engages with the crankpin (positioned at its lowest point of travel).

12 Fit the big-end cap complete with bearing shell making sure that it is the right way round (as marked before removal, see Section 13).

13 Insert and tighten the big-end nuts to the specified torque (photo).

14 Repeat the operations on the remaining piston/rod assemblies.

15 When all of the connecting rod bearing caps are tightened to the specified torque, rotate the crankshaft to ensure that it is not binding.

37 Oil pump and sump - refitting

1 Bolt the oil pump into position in the crankcase using the three long bolts and then refit the filter screen (photos).

2 Use jointing compound to stick a new sump gasket in position on the flange of the crankcase. Make sure that the gasket is securely engaged in the grooves of the front and rear main bearing caps and then apply jointing compound to corners of the gasket at the points where it bends up and over the main bearing caps (photo).

3 Offer the sump into position, insert the bolts and tighten in diagonal sequence (Fig. 1.16). Check that the sump drain plug is tight. Leave out the two bolts near the rear of the sump so that the engine endplate can be fitted later.

36.9 Fitting the piston/connecting rod assembly using a ring compressor

36.13 Tighten the connecting rod nuts to the specified torque

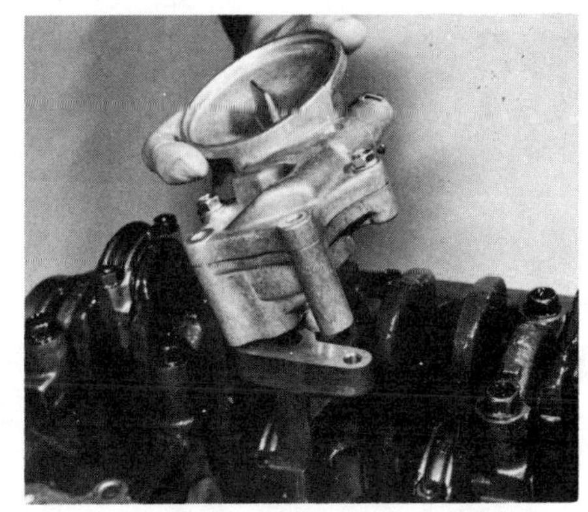

37.1a Refit the oil pump ...

37.1b ... and tighten bolts to the specified torque

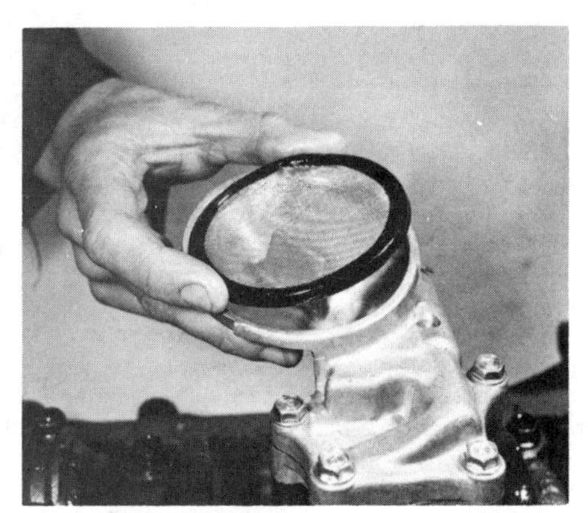

37.1c Relocate the filter screen

37.2 Fit the sump gasket and sump

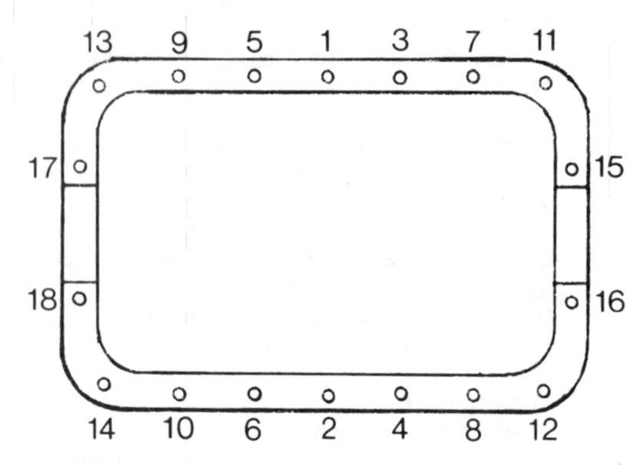

Fig. 1.16. The sump retaining bolt tightening sequence (Sec. 37)

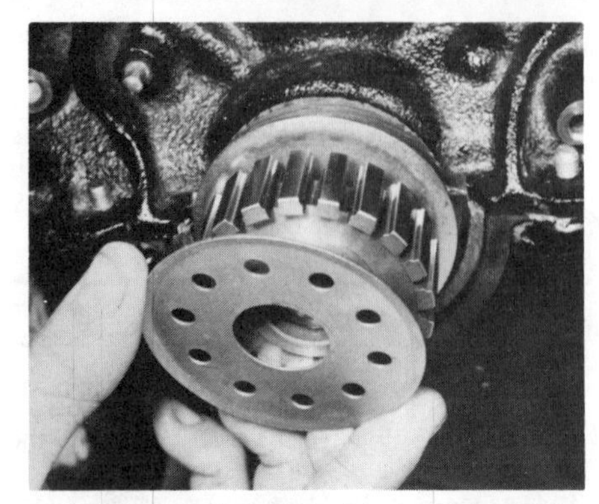

38.2 Refit the timing belt drive sprocket and dished washers

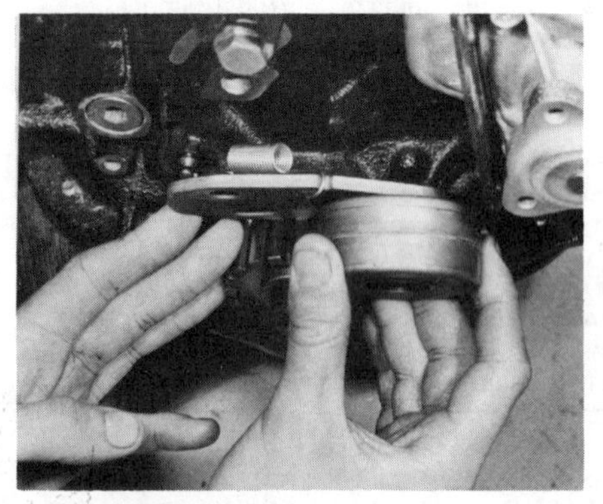

38.3a Locate the spring to the tensioner ...

38.3b ... and refit the tensioner, but do not tighten bolts yet

38.6 Refit the crankshaft pulley

39.2 Insert the valves

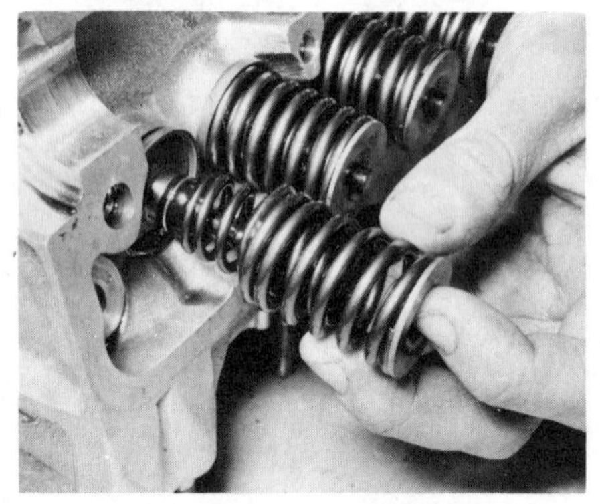

39.4 Relocate the valve springs and cap

39.5 Using compressor to refit the collets

38 Timing components - refitting

1 Locate the timing belt inner retaining disc to the front of the crankshaft with its dished rim facing inwards towards the engine.

2 Fit the timing belt drive sprocket followed by the outer belt retaining disc (with holes) having its dished rim turned facing outwards away from the engine (photo).

3 Locate the spring to the rear of the belt tensioner and hook into the notch in tensioner plate (photo). Locate the other end of the spring to the location pin in the crankcase front face and fit the belt tensioner (photo) retaining in position with the pivot and adjustment bolts. Do not tighten the bolts at this stage.

4 Fit the timing belt on the crankshaft sprocket making sure that its directional mark is correct (belt rotates anticlockwise when engine running). Engage the belt round the tensioner and then pull it upwards and fit the lower cover complete with new rubbber seals. Retain the belt by draping it over the tip of the lower cover until it can be connected to the camshaft sprocket after the cylinder head has been installed.

5 Install the water pump and the flexible sealing plate but do not fit the water pump pulley at this stage.

6 Install the crankshaft pulley and its retaining bolt. Tighten the bolt to the specified torque (photo).

39 Cylinder head - reassembly and installation

1 The cylinder head reassembly is accomplished in three main phases. Firstly, the valves (exhaust and inlet) are assembled into the cylinder head. Then, secondly, the rockers and camshaft/rocker support pedestals are gathered into a subassembly. Finally, the cylinder head block with valves fitted, the camshaft, and the rockers subassembly are brought together to complete the assembly of the cylinder head. The cylinder head can be fitted to the engine block with only the valves fitted. The camshaft and rockers being fitted afterwards. It must be noted that the valve springs and applying seats are not inter-changeable between inlet and exhaust valves. The shorter springs are

for **inlet** valves.

2 To refit the valves into the cylinder head proceed as follows: Rest the cylinder head block on its side and slide the valves into their appropriate positions. If valves are being reused, they should be fitted into the same position from which they were taken. Apply clean engine oil to the stems before inserting the valves (photo).

3 Now place the low spring seat in position around the valve guide, and the inlet valve seals into position on top of the valve guide.

4 Slip the two valve springs in place, followed by the spring's cap (retainer) (photo).

5 The valve spring compressor should be used to compress the spring sufficiently to allow the split collets to be inserted into the cotter groove machined into the valve stem (photo).

6 Remove the valve spring compressor and repeat this procedure until all eight valves have been assembled into the cylinder head.

7 *On CVCC type engines* the chamber collars are located into their respective auxiliary valve apertures in the cylinder head with the round hole facing to the spark plug hole and the oval shaped hole facing downwards to the cylinder head. New gaskets must always be fitted when installing the chamber collar.

8 Assemble the valve into the holder, and fit the new 'O' ring, the

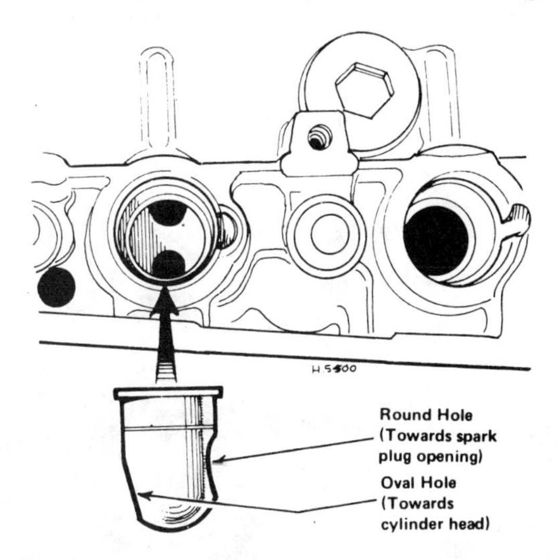

Fig. 1.17. Auxiliary valve (CVCC engine) chamber installation (Sec. 39)

valve spring washer ('LOW' mark to face down), spring seat, seal spring and retainer cap. Compress the spring and locate the valve keepers (split collets).

9 Assemble the auxiliary valves to the cylinder head and screw in the valve holder nuts tightening to the specified torque. To ensure that the chamber collar does not rotate when tightening the holder nut, a suitable rod or if available alignment tool No. 07944-6590000 should be inserted through the spark plug hole to retain the collar in position.

10 If preferred, the cylinder head may be refitted to the cylinder block at this stage and the camshaft and rocker gear installed later. If the engine is installed in the car, it is advisable to fit the inlet and exhaust manifolds and associate parts to the cylinder head prior to refitting to the engine. The following description assumes that the cylinder head will be installed complete.

11 Oil the camshaft bearings on the cylinder head and lower the camshaft into position.

12 Reassemble the main and auxiliary (CVCC engine) rocker shafts making sure that the arms are refitted in their original positions.

13 Unscrew the rocker arm adjuster screws and locknuts to their fullest extent and then install the rocker assembly complete with pedestals to the cylinder head. If the cylinder head has already been fitted to the cylinder block, make sure that No. 1 piston is at TDC before installing the rocker assembly.

14 Insert the pedestal bolts and tighten to the specified torque. Tighten the bolts starting from the two centre bolts and working outwards in the sequence shown in Fig. 1.19.

15 Oil the lips of the camshaft oil seal and drive it into position using a piece of tubing as a drift. Make sure that the oil seal is fitted so that the number stamped on it is visible when it is installed.

16 Fit the timing sprocket to the camshaft making sure that the word 'up' is visible from the front. Keep the word 'up' at the highest point of the sprocket pending installation of the cylinder head, also set No. 1 piston to TDC (top-dead-centre) by turning the crankshaft pulley bolt (photo).

17 Bolt the inlet and exhaust manifolds to the cylinder head using new gaskets.

18 Clean the surfaces of the cylinder head and cylinder block and then position a new gasket on the block (photo).

19 Lower the cylinder head carefully onto the gasket (photo) ensuring that the dowel pins are located correctly, and screw in the cylinder head bolts. Note that the short head bolt is located in the rear hole on the spark plug side (photo).

20 Tighten the cylinder head bolts to the specified torque, progressively and in the sequence shown (photo) (Fig. 1.20).

21 If the cylinder head was removed from the cylinder block while the

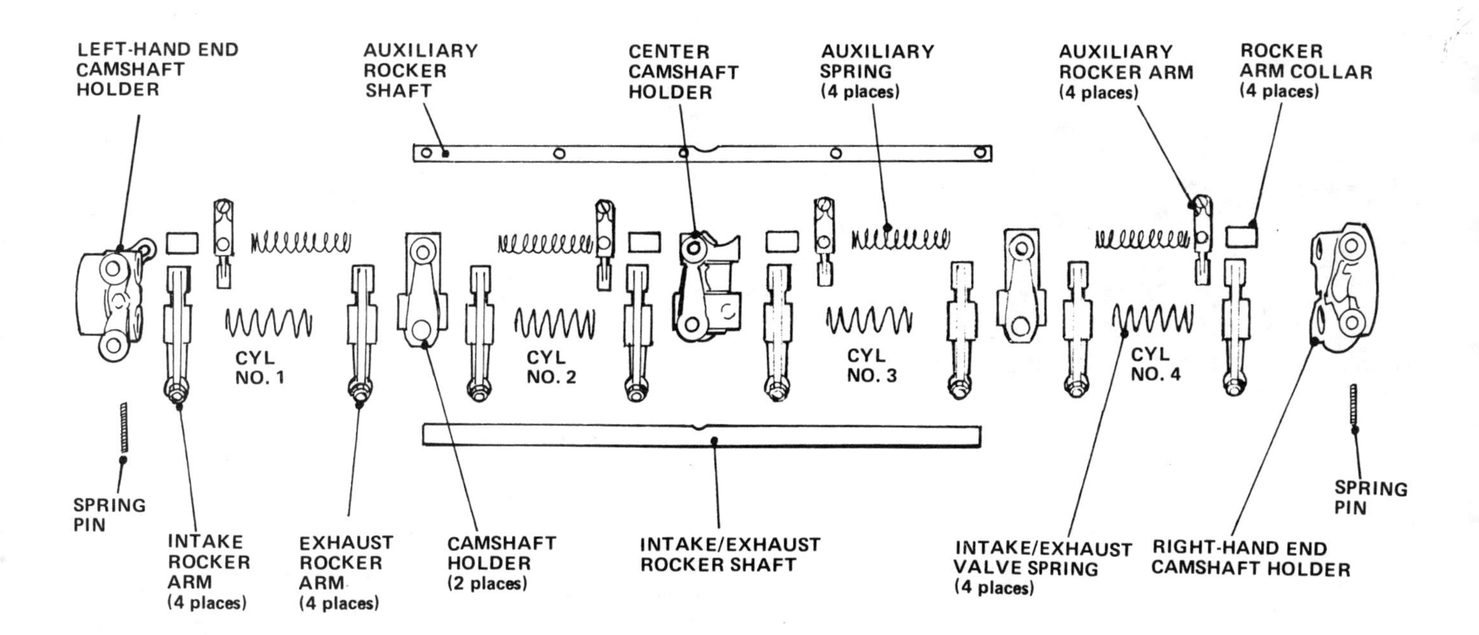

Fig. 1.18. The main and auxiliary rocker shaft assemblies (Sec. 39)

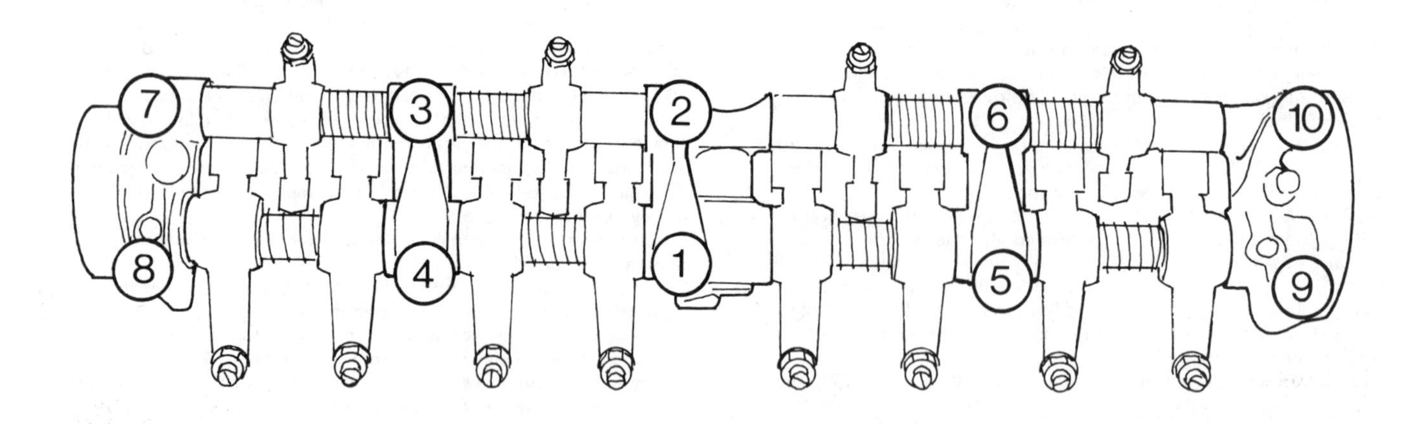

Fig. 1.19. Rocker arm pedestal bolt tightening sequence (Sec. 39)

39.16 Fit the camshaft sprocket with 'UP' mark upwards and facing out

39.18 Fit the cylinder head gasket locating over the dowels

39.19 Fit the cylinder head

39.20 Tighten the head bolts to the specified torques (the short bolt being tightened)

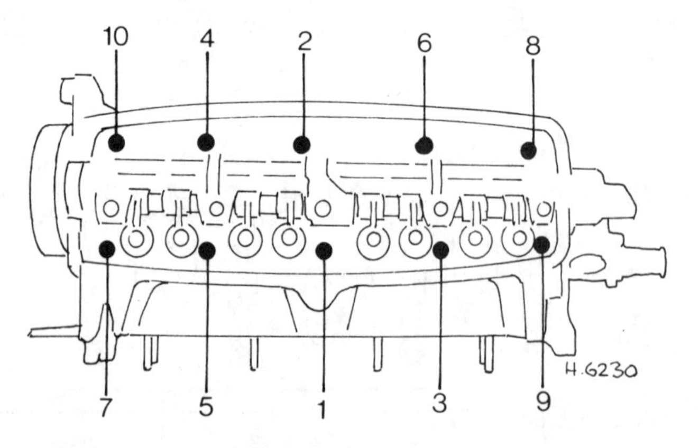

Fig. 1.20. The cylinder head bolt tightening sequence (Sec. 39)

engine was still in the car, reverse the operations described in Section 10, paragraph 1.

22 Install the distributor drive thermostat housing (photo).

23 Refer to Chapter 4 for installation of the distributor.

24 Fit the oil pump driveshaft/gear and fit the cover (photo).

25 The timing belt can now be fitted as described in the next Section.

40 Timing belt - reconnecting and adjusting

1 Set No. 1 piston at TDC. This position can be found by observing the flywheel (or torque converter - auto transmission) marks in relation to the crankcase pointer (Fig. 1.21).

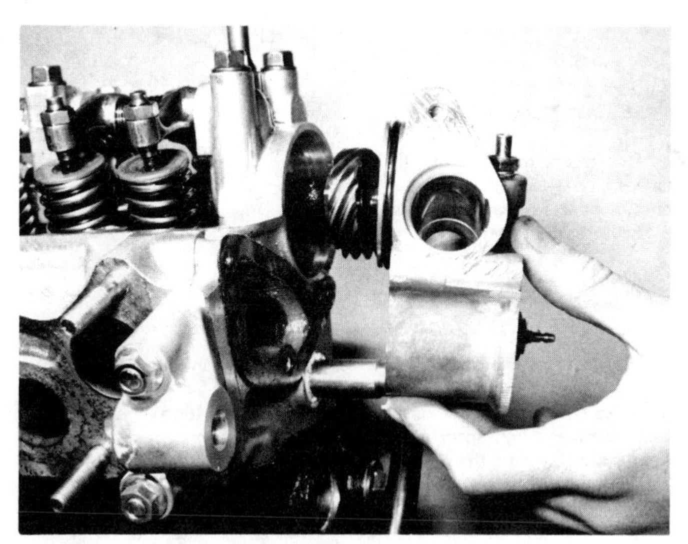
39.22 Fit the distributor drive/thermostat housing

39.24 Fit the oil pump driveshaft/gear

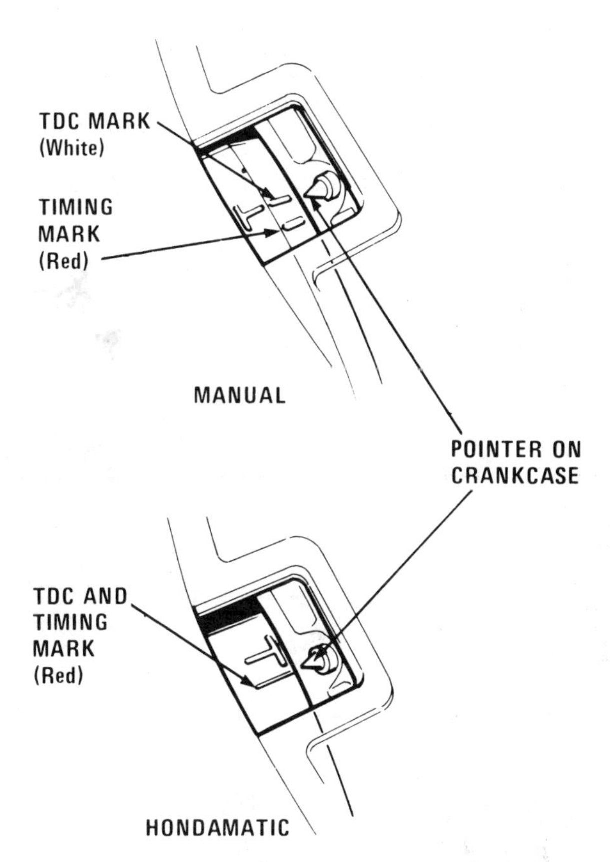

Fig. 1.21. The flywheel to crankcase timing marks (Sec. 40)

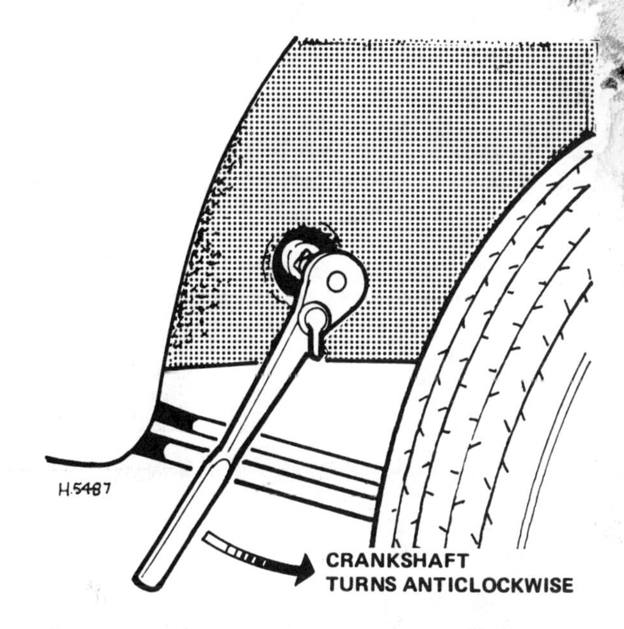

Fig. 1.22. Crankshaft pulley bolt accessible under front wing after removal of rubber bung (Sec. 40)

2 If the engine is in the car, the crankshaft pulley bolt can be turned anticlockwise by applying a socket wrench to it through the hole under the left-hand wing (Fig. 1.22).
3 Make sure that the 'up' mark on the camshaft sprocket is at its uppermost position and that the 'arrow' markings on the front face of the cylinder head align with the marks on the camshaft drive belt sprocket (Fig. 1.23).
4 Ensuring that neither sprocket moves from its set position locate the belt over the camshaft drivebelt sprocket. Check that the belt teeth are meshed correctly with those of the sprocket (photo).
5 Fit the rubber seals over the pivot bolt (photo) and adjustment bolt of the belt tensioner (if not already fitted).
6 Using the crankshaft pulley bolt, turn the pulley through one quarter of a turn in an anticlockwise direction. The belt tensioner bolts having been left loose (see Section 38, paragraph 3) the belt will now be correctly tensioned by the action of the tensioner spring. Tighten both tensioners bolts to a torque of 29 - 33 lb f ft (4.0 - 4.6 kg f m).
7 Fit the upper timing cover (photo) and retain with bolts tightened to the specified torque.
8 Fit the pulley to the water pump and tighten the retaining bolts.

41 Valve clearances - adjusting

1 This operation is the same whether carried out with the engine in or out of the car. When performed as a maintenance task with the engine in the car, the work must only be carried out when the engine is cold.
2 Remove the rocker cover and then turn the crankshaft to set No. 1 piston to TDC. Achieve this by turning the crankshaft pulley bolt in an anticlockwise direction until the flywheel (or torque converter) timing marks are in alignment with the crankcase pointer and then check that the 'UP' mark on the camshaft sprocket is at its uppermost point. Removal of the spark plugs will make turning the crankshaft easier.

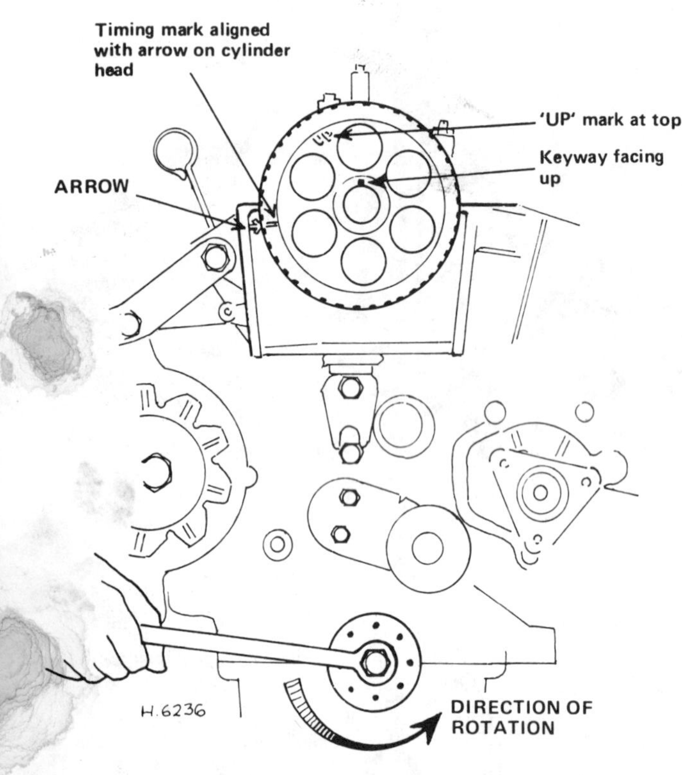

Fig. 1.23. Check the timing alignment marks for TDC (Sec. 40)

3 Numbering from the camshaft sprocket, adjust valves:

1 and 4 (inlets)
2 and 6 (exhausts)
Auxiliary valves (CVCC) 1 and 2

4 Rotate the crankshaft pulley through 360° (one complete turn) in an anticlockwise direction. The 'up' mark on the camshaft sprocket will now be upside down at its lowest point and No. 4 piston at TDC.
5 Still numbering from the camshaft sprocket, adjust valves:

5 and 8 (inlets)
3 and 7 (exhausts)
Auxiliary valves (CVCC) 3 and 4

6 To adjust a valve clearance, release the locknut and unscrew the adjusting screw. Insert the appropriate feeler blade between the end of the valve stem and the rocker arm. Tighten the adjusting screw until the feeler blade is a light interference sliding fit and then tighten the lock-nut without moving the position of the adjusting screw (photo).
7 The correct clearance for all valves is 0.004 to 0.007 in (0.12 to 0.18 mm).
8 With the valve clearances correctly adjusted, fit a new rocker cover gasket, applying jointing compound at the gasket corners and install the rocker cover.

42 Engine ancillary components - refitting

1 Before installing the engine to the car, refit the ancillary components by reversing the removal operations described in Section 7 but observe the following points.
2 Smear the sealing ring of a new oil filter with engine oil and clean the mating flange on the crankcase and then screw the filter into position using hand pressure only.
3 Adjust the drivebelt tension to give a total deflection of ½ inch (13 mm) at the centre of the longest run of the belt.
4 Centralise the clutch driven plate, as described in Chapter 5.

40.4 The drive belt located (cover removed)

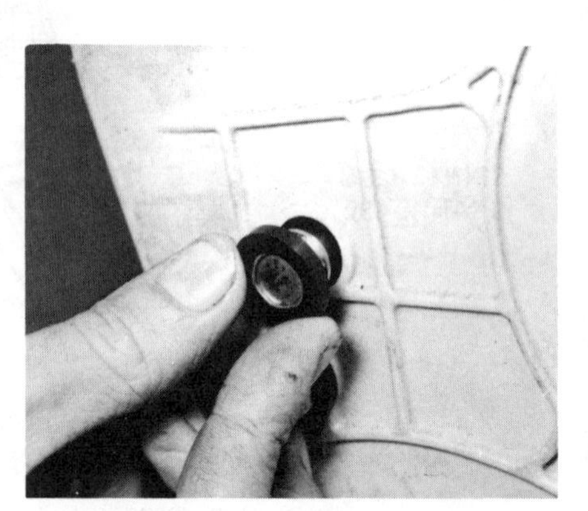

40.5 Fit the rubber seals over the pivot and adjustment bolts

40.7 Fit the upper timing cover

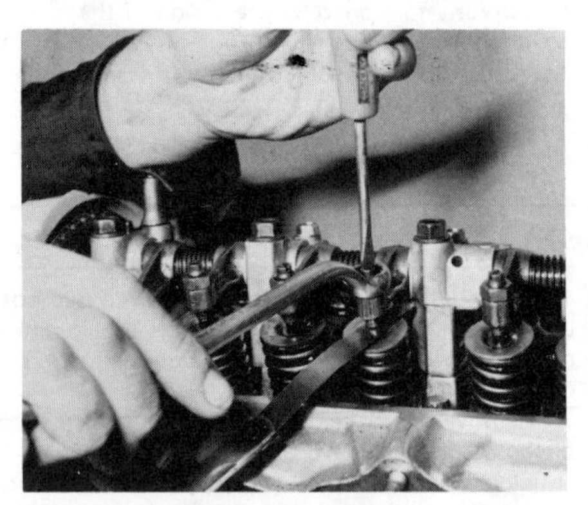

41.6 Valve clearance adjustment

43.1 Refitting the transmission (manual) to the engine

43 Engine to transmission - reconnection

1 Reverse the operations described in Section 5 according to transmission type (photo).
2 With manual gearbox, make sure that its weight does not hang upon the clutch shaft as it passes through the clutch driven plate.

44 Engine/transmission - refitting

1 Reverse the operations described in Section 4 and note the following:
2 When lowering the engine and gearbox into position, ensure that they are kept perfectly level on the sling.
3 When the engine/transmission is in position on the respective mountings remember to locate the earth straps under the respective bolt heads.
4 Refit the driveshafts and front suspension components. Take care not to damage the oil seals to the differential when fitting the driveshafts. Torque all nuts/bolts to the figures specified and always use new split pins where fitted.
5 Reconnect the exhaust downpipe to the manifold and on starting the engine, check for leaks.
6 On vehicles with a manual gearbox, adjust the clutch.
7 On vehicles with automatic transmission, check the speed selector adjustment (Chapter 6).
8 Fill up the engine and transmission with the specified quantity of lubricant (ensure that the drain plugs are in position and secure!).
9 Refill the engine and radiator coolant - see Chapter 2 and check for leaks.
10 Ensure that all electrical connections are correct before reconnecting the battery earth (ground) cable, and adjust the alternator drive belt (see Chapter 10).

45 Engine - initial start-up, after overhaul or major repair

1 Make sure that the battery is fully charged and that all lubricants, coolant and fuel are replenished.
2 Check that no tools or rags have been left within the engine compartment, also that a socket wrench has not been left on the crankshaft pulley bolt under the front wing. Operate the starter key.
3 As soon as the engine fires and runs, keep it going at a fast tickover only (no faster) and bring it up to the normal working temperature.
4 As the engine warms up there will be odd smells and some smoke from parts getting hot and burning off oil deposits. The signs to look for are leaks of water or oil which will be obvious if serious. Check also the exhaust pipe and manifold connections, as these do not always 'find' their exact gas tight position until the warmth and vibration have acted on them, and it is almost certain that they will need tightening further. This should be done, of course, with the engine stopped.
5 When normal running temperature has been reached adjust the engine idling speed as described in Chapter 3.
6 Stop the engine and wait a few minutes to see if any lubricant or coolant is dripping out when the engine is stationary.
7 Road test the car to check that the timing is correct and that the engine is giving the necessary smoothness and power. Do not race the engine - if new bearings and/or pistons have been fitted it should be treated as a new engine and run in at a reduced speed for the first 300 miles (500 km).
8 Check the torque of cylinder head and manifold bolts after 1000 miles (1600 km) with the engine cold, then check the valve clearances.

46 Fault diagnosis - engine

Symptom	Reason/s
Engine fails to turn when starter operated	Flat or defective battery. Loose battery leads. Defective starter solenoid or switch or broken wiring. Engine earth strap disconnected. Defective starter motor.
Engine turns on starter but will not start	Ignition damp or wet. Ignition leads to spark plugs loose. Shorted or disconnected low tension leads. Dirty, incorrectly set, or pitted contact breaker points. Faulty condenser. Defective ignition switch. Ignition leads connected wrong way round. Faulty coil. Contact breaker point spring earthed or broken. No petrol in petrol tank. Vapour lock in fuel line (in hot conditions or at high altitude) Blocked float chamber needle valve. Fuel pump filter blocked. Choked or blocked carburettor jets. Faulty fuel pump.
Engine stalls and will not re-start	Too much choke allowing too rich a mixture to wet plugs. Float damaged or leaking or needle not seating. Float level incorrectly adjusted. Ignition failure - sudden. Ignition failure - misfiring precludes total stoppage. Ignition failure - in severe rain or after traversing water splash. No petrol in petrol tank. Sudden obstruction in carburettor. Water in fuel system.

Symptoms	Reasons
Engine misfires or idles unevenly	Ignition leads loose. Battery leads loose on terminals. Battery earth strap loose on body attachment point. Engine earth lead loose. Low tension leads to coil terminals loose. Low tension lead from coil to distributor loose. Dirty, or incorrectly gapped plugs. Dirty, or incorrectly set, or pitted contact breaker points. Tracking across inside of distributor cover. Ignition too retarded. Faulty coil. Mixture too weak. Air leak in carburettor. Air leak at inlet manifold to cylinder head, or inlet manifold to carburettor.
Lack of power and poor compression	Incorrect valve clearances. Burnt out exhaust valves. Sticking or leaking valves. Weak or broken valve springs. Worn valve guides or stems. Worn pistons and piston rings. Burnt out exhaust valves. Blown cylinder head gasket (accompanied by increase in noise). Worn or scored cylinder bores. Ignition timing wrongly set; too advanced or retarded. Contact breaker points incorrectly gapped. Incorrectly set spark plugs. Carburation too rich or too weak. Dirty contact breaker points. Fuel filters blocked causing poor top end performance through fuel starvation. Distributor automatic balance weights or vacuum advance and retard mechanisms not functioning correctly. Faulty fuel pump giving top end fuel starvation.
Excessive oil consumption	Excessively worn valve stems and valve guides. Worn piston rings. Worn piston and cylinder bores. Excessive piston ring gap allowing oil to bypass. Piston oil return holes choked. Leaking oil filter gasket. Leaking rocker cover gasket. Leaking sump gasket. Loose sump plug.
Unusual noises from engine	Worn valve gear (noisy tapping from rocker box). Worn big-end bearing (regular heavy knocking). Worn main bearings (rumbling and vibration).

Chapter 2 Cooling System

Contents

Specifications

System type ... Thermosyphon with belt driven water pump, radiator and electric cooling fan

Radiator cap pressure ... 11.38 to 14.22 lb/in^2 (0.8 to 1.0 kg/cm^2)

Thermostat

Starts to open ...	178 to 183°F (80 to 84°C)
Fully open ...	203°F (95°C)

Fan thermoswitch operating temperature

Switch opens below ...	188°F (86.5°C)
Switch closes at ...	191° to 197°F (88.5° to 91.5°C)

Coolant capacity ... 1.3 Imp gal (5.7 litre) (1.5 US gal)

Torque wrench settings

	lb f ft	kg f m
Water pump pulley bolts ...	6 to 9	0.8 to 1.2
Thermostat cover bolts ...	7 to 10	1.0 to 1.4
Water pump retaining bolts ...	7 to 10	1.0 to 1.4
Thermostat/distributor housing bolts ...	7 to 10	1.0 to 1.4

1 General description

The engine cooling is by the thermosyphon system assisted by a water pump, which is fitted to the front of the cylinder block, and is driven by a belt from the crankshaft pulley.

A thermostat is fitted and is located at the rear of the engine in a dual thermostat/distributor housing. The thermostat may be removed from the housing without disturbing the distributor. The temperature sender unit is also located in this housing.

The radiator is front mounted and is of the sealed type with an expansion tank. Additional cooling to the radiator is provided by a thermostatically controlled electric fan.

The car interior heater works from coolant supplied from the engine cooling system.

General maintenance of the cooling system consists mainly of regularly checking the coolant level and inspecting the hoses for security and signs of leakage. Periodically the system should be drained and flushed and refilled with a new antifreeze coolant mixture.

2 Cooling system - draining

1 Place the heater control to maximum heat.
2 Remove the radiator cap. If the engine is hot remove the cap very slowly having first covered it with a cloth to prevent escaping steam or coolant, which is under pressure, from causing injury.
3 If the coolant is to be used again, place a container of sufficient capacity (5.7 litres, 1.3 Imp gals, 1.5 US gals) under the radiator drain plug.
4 Unscrew and remove the plug and drain the coolant into the container.
5 Remove the expansion tank and empty the contents into the container.
6 If the system requires flushing, proceed as described in the next Section.
7 If the system is in good condition and does not require flushing, refit the radiator drain plug and refer to Section 4.

3 Cooling system - flushing

1 Drain the cooling system as described in Section 2, then refit the drain tap and cap.
2 Unscrew the thermostat cover bolts and remove the cover and thermostat together.
3 Insert a cold water hose into the thermostat aperture in the cylinder head and reverse flush the cooling system. The heater control must be set to maximum heat during flushing.
4 When the water coming out of the top hose is seen to be clean, remove the radiator cap and drain plug and drain the system.
5 Refit the thermostat, thermostat housing cover with a new gasket, the expansion tank and radiator drain plug.
6 Refill the cooling system as follows.

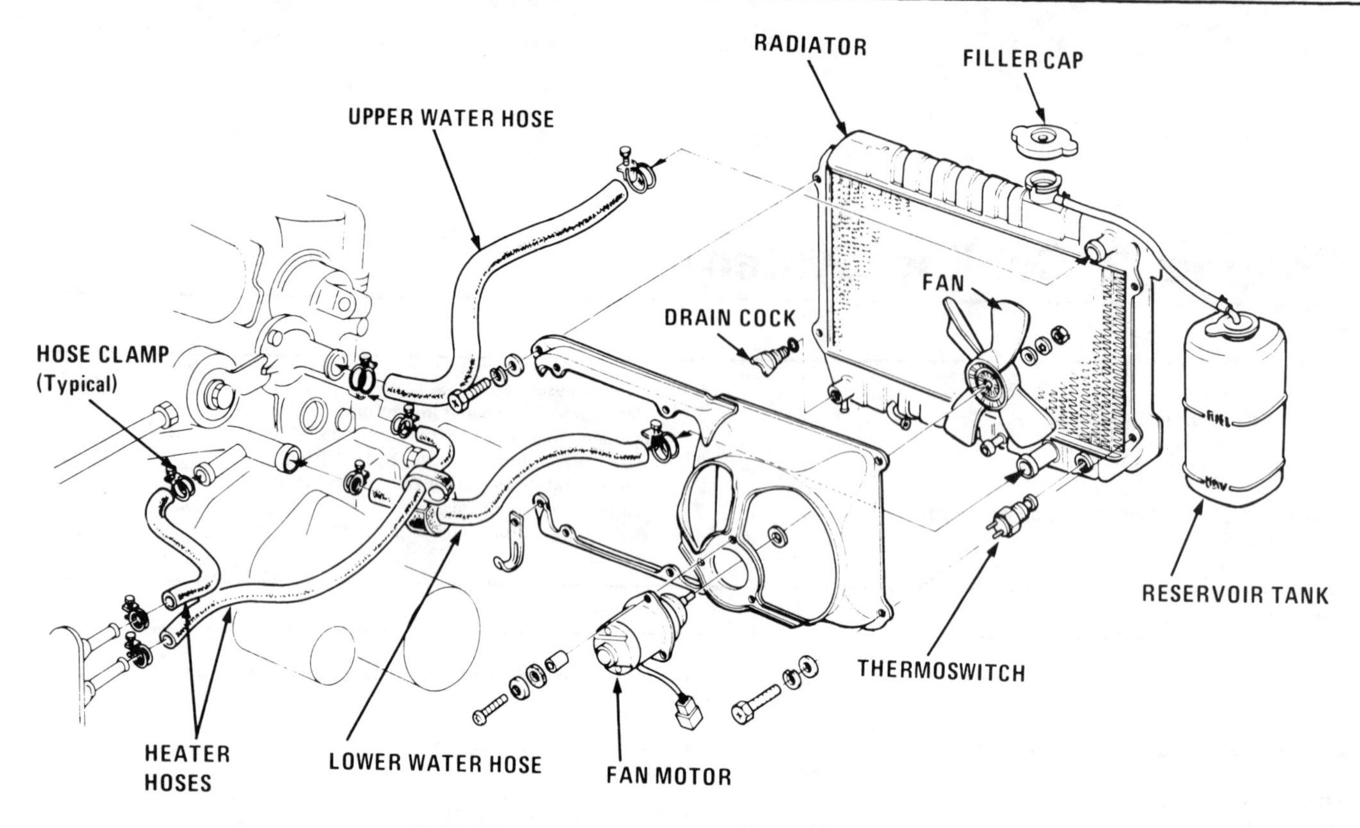

Fig. 2.1. The radiator, cooling fan and coolant hose layout

4 Cooling system - filling

1 Release the bleed screw (located on top of the thermostat housing) and refill the system by pouring coolant slowly through the radiator filler cap, also half fill the expansion tank.
2 When air ceases to escape from the bleed nipple and coolant is seen to emerge, tighten the bleed screw.
3 With the radiator cap still removed, start the engine and run it to normal operating temperature until the electric cooling fan cuts in.
4 Switch off the engine, top-up the radiator to the base of the filler neck and refit the cap.
5 Top-up the expansion tank to the 'FULL' mark.

5 Antifreeze mixture

1 In order to maintain the correct antifreeze and anti-corrosive properties of the coolant it is recommended that an antifreeze product suitable for use with aluminium is used in a proportion of 50% with purified water when refilling the cooling system in temperate zones.
2 In more severe climatic conditions, increase the ratio of antifreeze to water to 60% and 40% respectively, for temperatures between -34° to -62°F, and 70% and 30% for temperatures below -62°F.
3 If topping-up is necessary due to leakage losses, use coolant mixed in similar proportions to the original.
4 Take care when handling anti-freeze. It will damage paintwork if spilled.

6 Radiator/fan unit - removal and refitting

1 Disconnect the battery earth (ground) lead.
2 Drain the coolant as in Section 2.
3 Disconnect the hoses from the radiator at the top and bottom and filler neck (from expansion container).
4 Disconnect the electric fan leads.
5 Through the front of the grille, remove the upper radiator retaining bolts from each side. The lower retaining bolts are removed from below the front bumper.
6 The radiator can now be lifted clear (photo).
7 The electric fan and cowling can be removed from the radiator if desired by unscrewing and removing the four retaining setscrews.
8 Refitting is a reversal of removal.

7 Radiator - cleaning and inspection

1 With the radiator removed from the car, the electric fan unit can be removed and the radiator core exterior can be cleaned by hosing through to remove road dirt, insects, etc.
2 It can also be internally flushed by turning it upside down and hosing through.
3 Blow dry the core with an air line and inspect for signs of damage and/or leak points.
4 Minor leaks can be repaired by soldering or filling with a compound such as Cataloy. It should be mentioned that solder repairs are best completed professionally as it is too easy to damage the surrounding area by excessive heating.
5 The radiator hoses and connections must also be cleaned and inspected for signs of cracks, distortion or perishing. Renew or repair as necessary.
6 Examine the hose clips and renew them if they are rusted or distorted. The drain plugs and washers must be renewed if they are leaking.
7 If a leak is difficult to trace, have the radiator pressure tested by your local Honda dealer. This is best tested with the radiator in the car as it may be that the leak is elsewhere in the cooling system.

8 Radiator fan thermoswitch - testing and renewal

1 The radiator cooling fan motor is actuated by a thermoswitch located in the radiator bottom tank. If the cooling system is overheating due to non-operation of the fan, check the switch in the following way.
2 Run the engine until the coolant temperature is between 191 and 197°F (88.5 and 91.5^{o}C). This temperature range can be checked by inserting a thermometer in the radiator filler neck.
3 If the fan motor does not cut in, switch off the engine and disconnect the black/yellow and blue leads from the thermoswitch and join their ends together.
4 Turn the ignition switch on when the motor should start running.

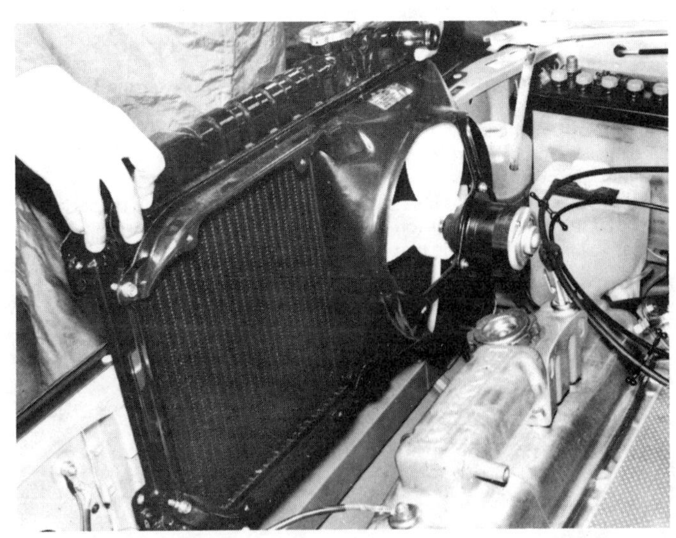
6.6 Carefully lift the radiator clear

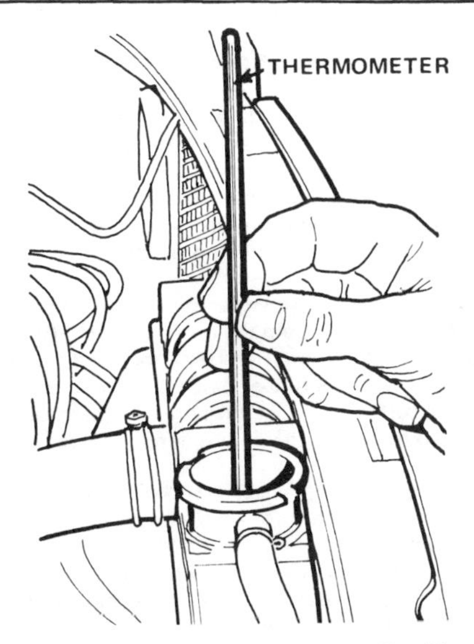

Fig. 2.2. Radiator coolant temperature reading (Sec. 8)

If it does, renew the thermoswitch which must be faulty. To do this, drain the system and unscrew the switch from the radiator bottom tank.

5 If the motor does not operate, check the motor leads and connections and the fuse. If these are in order, remove the motor as described in the following Section.

9 Fan and motor - removal, inspection and refitting

1 Disconnect the leads from the fan motor.

2 Unscrew and remove the four bolts which secure the fan cage and motor to the radiator and then lift the fan/motor assembly from the engine compartment. The fan motor is mounted on the cage with three bolts and bushes. The fan itself is retained on the motor shaft by a single nut.

3 It will be necessary to remove the fan before the motor can be detached. Hold the fan, whilst the motor shaft nut is undone, then jolt the fan off the shaft.

4 If the fan motor shaft bearings are sloppy or the motor does not run, or runs unevenly, the only remedy is to renew the motor.

5 The motor unit has no facility for repair.

6 The fan itself is of moulded nylon and is not repairable.

7 Reassembly of the fan unit follows the reversal of the dismantling procedure.

8 Refit the fan assembly to the radiator and connect the leads.

10 Thermostat - removal, testing and refitting

1 Drain the cooling system as previously described.

2 Unbolt and remove the thermostat cover from the distributor housing at the end of the cylinder head.

3 Extract the thermostat (photo).

4 The thermostat may be tested for correct functioning by suspending it together with a thermometer in a saucepan of cold water. Heat the water and note the temperature at which the thermostat begins to open. This temperature should be between 80 and 84°C (178 - 183°F). Discard the thermostat if it is open too early. Continue heating the water until the thermostat is fully open and note that temperature - 95°C (203°F). Turn off the heat to allow the thermostat to cool down. If the thermostat does not open fully in near boiling water, or close completely when cooled, the unit must be discarded and a new thermostat fitted.

5 Refit the thermostat to the housing and locate the pin in the thermostat outer body in the up position (photo).

6 Fit a new 'O' ring seal in the cover groove, and tighten the cover retaining bolts to the specified torque.

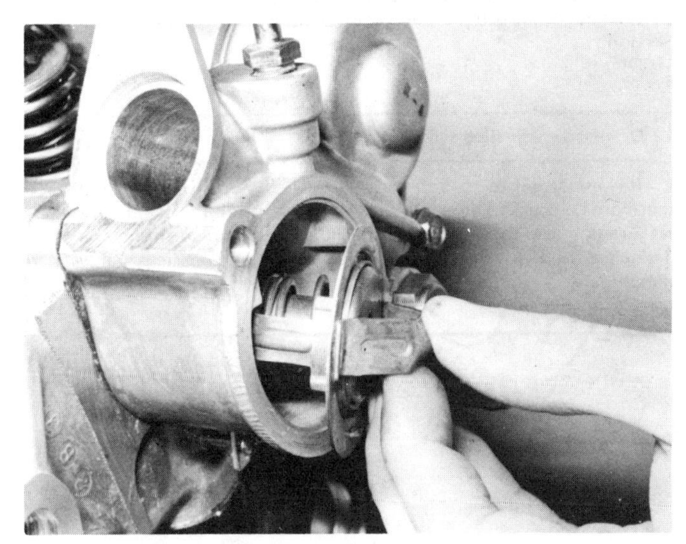
10.3 Extract the thermostat

10.5 Refit the thermostat with the air release pin at the top

11 Water pump - removal and refitting

1 The water pump is mounted on the front face of the cylinder block and is driven by a belt from the crankshaft pulley which also drives the alternator.
2 To remove the water pump, drain the cooling system.
3 Slacken the alternator mounting and adjustment strap bolts, push the alternator in towards the engine and slip the drivebelt from the water pump pulley.
4 Unscrew and remove the water pump securing bolts.
5 Extract the water pump from the cylinder block. Part of the pump body passes between the timing belt cover and engine block. The pump should be removed with the rubber dust seal which sits between the pump and timing belt cover. Once the pump has been removed and it has been found to be faulty, the only action is to discard it and fit a new pump.
6 Before refitting the pump, check that the 'O' ring seal is in good condition and not cracked or broken. Clean the joint faces of the pump and cylinder block.
7 Position the timing belt cover seal on the pump body and offer the pump into position (photo). Once the impeller has entered the pump housing in the cylinder block the pump can be slid into position. Ensure that the timing cover seal is properly seated.
8 Insert the four pump bolts and tighten to the specified torque.
9 Reconnect the drivebelt and adjust it, as described in the next Section.
10 On refilling the cooling system, check the pump for signs of leakage.

12 Drivebelt - adjusting tension

1 It is important to keep the drivebelt correctly adjusted: it should therefore be checked at regular intervals. If the belt is slack, it will slip, wear rapidly and cause water pump and/or alternator malfunction. If the belt is too tight, the alternator and water pump bearings will wear rapidly.
2 The belt tension is correct when there is just ½ in (12.7 mm) of vertical movement at the mid-point position (A, Fig. 2.3) between water pump and alternator pulleys.
3 To adjust the belt tension, slacken the alternator pivot and slot arm bolts, just sufficiently for the unit to be levered away from the engine, with a long screwdriver. Once the new position of the alternator has been obtained for the correct belt tension, the unit's bolts can be tightened.
4 If a new drivebelt has been fitted, the tension should be rechecked after the initial running period and adjustment made to take up any excess slack caused by the belt stretching.

11.7 Refit the water pump - note the 'O' ring seal must be in good condition and seated correctly

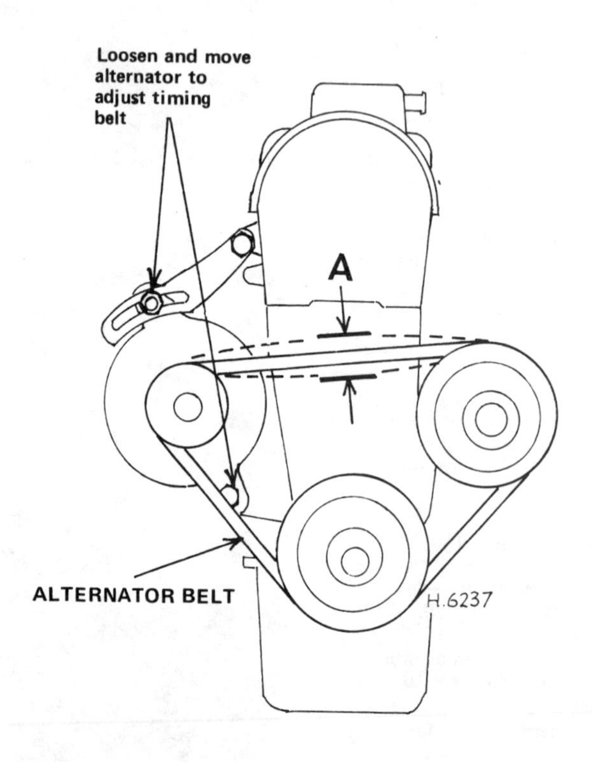

Fig. 2.3. Alternator/water pump drivebelt tension adjustment (Sec. 12)

13 Water temperature gauge and sender unit - testing

1 If the water temperature gauge reads incorrectly according to the known engine condition, first check the gauge.
2 To do this, disconnect the yellow/green lead from the sender unit and earth the end of the lead.
3 Turn the ignition switch 'ON' and observe the needle of the gauge which should move to the maximum 'H' position. If this is not the case, renew the gauge, as described in Chapter 10.
4 If the foregoing test proves satisfactory check the sender unit but an ohmmeter will be required and unless one is already owned, the cheaper alternative may be to substitute a new sender unit.
5 To test the sender unit, disconnect the yellow/green lead from it and having applied the ohmmeter lead to the sender unit terminal, take a reading with the engine cold. Start the engine and take further readings as the engine warms up. The resistances at various temperature levels should approximate those shown in the following table. Use a thermometer inserted in the radiator filler neck to establish the temperature levels.

Temperature	*122°F (50°C)*	*176°F (80°C)*	*212°F (100°C)*
Resistance (ohms)	*154*	*48 - 56*	*26 - 29*

6 If the sender unit fails to meet the resistance test, drain the cooling system and unscrew it from the distributor housing at the end of the cylinder head and renew it.

14 Fault diagnosis - cooling system

Symptom	Reason/s
Overheating	Low coolant level. Slack drivebelt to pump. Thermostat not operating. Fan thermoswitch faulty Radiator pressure cap faulty or of wrong type. Defective water pump. Cylinder head gasket blowing. Radiator core clogged with flies or dirt. Radiator blocked. Binding brakes. Bottom hose or tank frozen.
Engine running too cool	Defective thermostat. Faulty water temperature gauge.
Loss of coolant	Leaking radiator or hoses. Cylinder head gasket leaking. Leaking cylinder block core plugs. Faulty radiator filler cap or wrong type fitted.

Chapter 3 Carburation; fuel, exhaust and emission control systems

For modifications, and information applicable to later models, see Supplement at end of manual

Contents

Specifications

System type ... Downdraft carburettor, electric fuel pump and rear mounted fuel tank

Fuel pump

Delivery pressure	1.85 to 2.56 lb/in^2 (0.13 to 0.18 kg/cm^2)
Displacement at 12V	30 cu in (500 cc/min)

Fuel tank capacity ... 11 Imp gals (13.2 US gals) (50 litres)

Idle speed

	Without CVCC	With CVCC
Manual gearbox	700 to 800 rpm	650 to 750 rpm
Hondamatic (in 2nd gear)	630 to 730 rpm	600 to 700 rpm
Fuel octane rating	2 star	

Exhaust gas CO content ... 0 to 0.4%

Torque wrench settings

	lb f ft	kg f m
Manifold to cylinder head nuts	14 - 17	2.0 - 2.4
Hot air cover bolt	7 - 10	1.0 - 1.4
Inlet to exhaust manifold bolt	14 - 17	2.0 - 2.4
Carburettor flange nuts	13 - 16	1.8 - 2.2
Fuel pump cover bolts	5 - 9	0.7 - 1.2
Fuel pump retaining bolts	5 - 9	0.7 - 1.2
Fuel tank strap nuts	7 - 9	0.9 - 1.2
Fuel tank drain plug	29 - 51	4.0 - 7.0

1 General description and maintenance

The fuel system comprises a rear mounted fuel tank, an electrically-operated fuel pump and a carburettor which is of different type according to whether the engine is a standard or CVCC version.

A number of emission control devices can be installed to make up a very comprehensive emission control system but the complexity of the system depends upon the market for which the vehicle is intended as not all operating territorial regulations require the complete system to be installed.

Maintenance

Regular maintenance of the fuel supply and exhaust system is essential for economy, reliability and to comply with local emission control regulations. Regular checks should be made to ensure that there are no leakages in the fuel supply lines and components and from the carburettor. The carburettor must be correctly adjusted and its linkages occasionally lubricated and free to operate without binding. Finally, the exhaust system must be in good condition and its location attachments secure.

2 Air cleaner - removal, servicing and refitting

1 Prior to entering the carburettor, the air is filtered through a dry paper element. The filter element must be removed at the regular specified service intervals of 12,000 miles (20,000 km), or less under extreme conditions, and renewed.

2 It is advisable to remove the element periodically between renewals

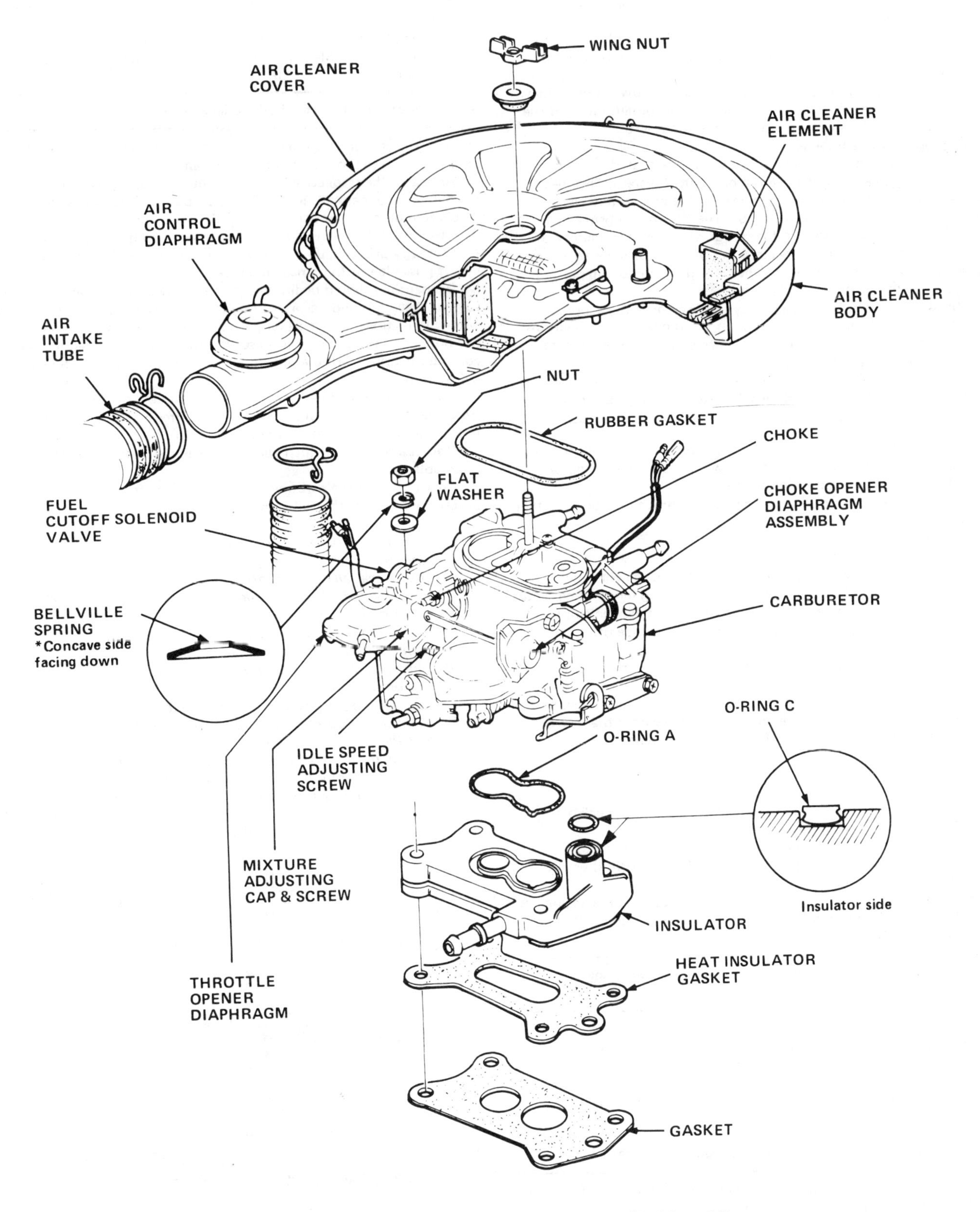

Fig. 3.1. The carburettor and associated components (CVCC model)

and to tap off the dust. A clogged and dirty filter can be solely responsible for bad starting, lower than usual fuel economy and a drop in engine power.
3 To remove the filter element, unscrew the single wing nut on top of the cleaner cover. Unclip the three cover retaining clips and lift the cover clear (photo).
4 Extract the element. If it is to be used again, tap it lightly to remove dust and dirt accumulation. DO NOT wash it, brush it or blow clean with compressed air.
5 When reassembling the unit, ensure that the top cover sealing rings are correctly located. Take care not to damage the bimetal strip of the thermal trip device located within the cleaner unit, as this is part of the emission control equipment.

The air cleaner box inlet has an inlet vacuum actuated flap mechanism fitted, again as part of the emission control system. This mechanism works with the thermal trip to ensure that moderately warm air is always supplied to the carburettor. The flap mechanism acts to allow warm air to be drawn into the carburettor from the vicinity of the exhaust manifold. The warm air in the carburettor helps to ensure proper dispersion of the petrol/air emulsion in the air stream passing through the carburettor.
6 If the air cleaner is to be completely removed note the support bracket attached to the rocker cover and the various hose connections. On reassembly, ensure that all hose and wire connections are secure. Renew any worn or perished hoses.

3 Keihin carburettor (standard models) - slow running adjustment

1 The carburettors are fitted with limiter caps to the adjuster screws. These should not be broken off unless new parts are to be fitted or satisfactory adjustment cannot be achieved.
2 Run the engine to normal operating temperature and make sure that the ignition timing and dwell angles are correct.

CO meter method

3 If such a meter is available, connect it in accordance with the manufacturers' instructions. Have the electric cooling fan running (actuacted by the coolant temperature having risen) and the headlamps ON. On Canadian models only, the cooling fan should be off and the headlamps ON.
4 Adjust the throttle speedscrew until the engine is running at the specified idle speed.
5 Now adjust the mixture control screw until the CO level is according to the specification. If this cannot be achieved within the travel of the screw cap limit stops, break off the cap, but fit a new one on completion.

Idle drop method

6 Run the engine to normal operating temperature and break off the limiter cap from the adjusting screw.
7 Turn the throttle speed screw and the fuel mixture screw to achieve the smoothest idle at 830 rpm (manual transmission) or 700 rpm (Hondamatic in 2nd gear).
8 Now turn the mixture adjusting screw clockwise until the engine speed drops to 750 rpm (manual) or 680 rpm (Hondamatic in 2nd gear). Fit a new limiter cap.

4 Keihin carburettor (standard models) - float level checking and adjustment

1 A special gauge is required to measure the fuel level in the float chamber but where the level is thought to be too low (fuel starvation, flat spot on acceleration, etc) or too high indicated by an excessively rich mixture which cannot be adjusted, or leakage from the carburettor, then the float needle valve seat adjustment screw can be turned fractionally to correct.

5 Keihin carburettor (standard models) - removal and refitting

1 Disconnect the air cleaner vacuum tubes and remove the air cleaner unit from the carburettor - see Section 2.
2 From the carburettor, disconnect the accelerator and choke cables, (photo) also the fuel supply and vacuum pipes (photo).
3 Unscrew and remove the carburettor to manifold retaining nuts and carefully lift the carburettor from the manifold. Unless a replacement carburettor gasket kit has previously been obtained, take care not to damage the gaskets during removal and any subsequent dismantling procedures (photo).
4 To remove the insulator, disconnect the brake servo vacuum tube from it. When refitting the insulator, use two new gaskets and a new 'O' ring.
5 Refitting the carburettor is a direct reversal of removal but the throttle and choke cable adjustments will have to be checked as described in Sections 9 and 10.

6 Keihin carburettor (standard models) - overhaul

1 With the carburettor removed from the inlet manifold, clean the external surfaces thoroughly to free dirt and oil.
2 Access to the respective jets within the main body is obtained by removing the upper carburettor body. To do this first disconnect the diaphragm pump operating arm from the control rod (photo).
3 Unscrew and remove the upper body section retaining screws.
4 Carefully prise the upper body section from the main body taking care if possible not to damage the gasket.
5 Dismantling should be limited to the removal of jets and adjusting screws. Clean jets and passages using compressed air, never probe them with wire or their precise calibration will be ruined. Before removing jets note carefully their location so that they can be refitted in their correct position. Mark the position of the auxiliary idle mixture screw before removing it.
6 It is not recommended that the valve plates or spindles are removed from the throttle body but if wear has occurred in these components, it is probably time to install a new carburettor.
7 Obtain a repair kit which will contain all the necessary gaskets and renewable items.
8 Reassembly of the carburettor is the reversal of the dismantling procedure but note the following points:

a) Do not interchange the primary and secondary emulsion tubes which are externally similar.
b) Ensure that all components are absolutely clean before assembly and where possible always use new gaskets and cotter pins (photo).
c) The piston dust cover must be placed on the choke chamber first with the cover lip in the chamber.
d) Tighten all bolts/screws securely and evenly.
e) On completion ensure that the respective linkages operate smoothly without binding (photo).
f) When the carburettor is completely reassembled, check that the idle mixture screw has been returned to its original position. If it was not marked before removal, screw it in gently until it seats and then unscrew it approximately 2 turns. Adjust finally as described in Section 3.

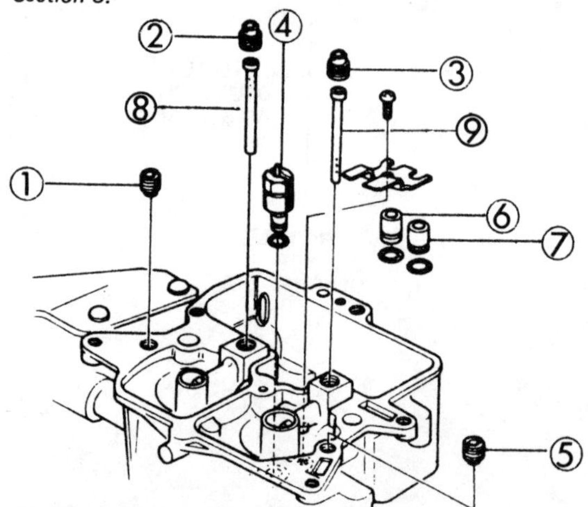

Fig. 3.2. The jets and locations - standard model (Sec. 6)

1 Primary slow air jet
2 Primary air jet
3 Secondary air jet
4 Power jet
5 Secondary slow air jet
6 Primary main jet
7 Secondary main jet
8 Primary emulsion tube
9 Secondary emulsion tube

2.3 The air filter element

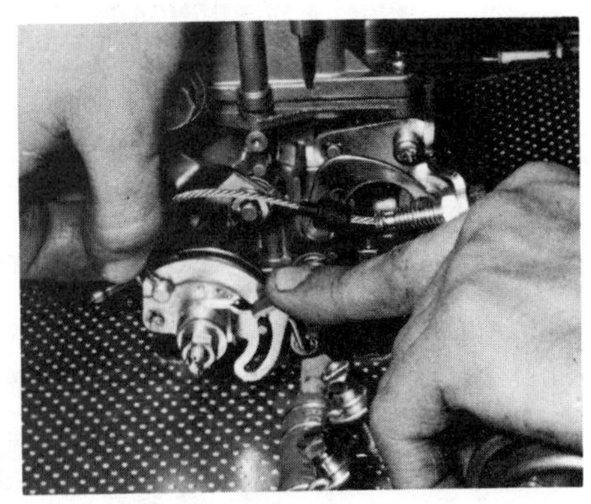

5.2a Disconnect the accelerator cable

5.2b Disconnect the fuel supply and vacuum tubes

5.3 The carburettor upper body (air horn) retaining screws 'A', the diaphragm pump operating arm and rod 'B', and the solenoid 'C'

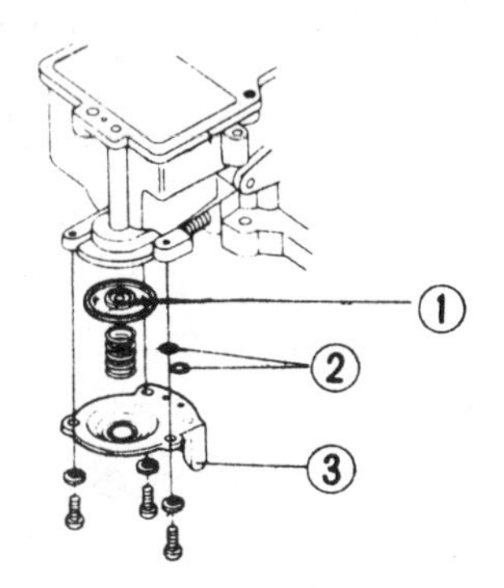

Fig. 3.3. The diaphragm pump components (Sec. 6)
1 Diaphragm
2 O-rings
3 Cover

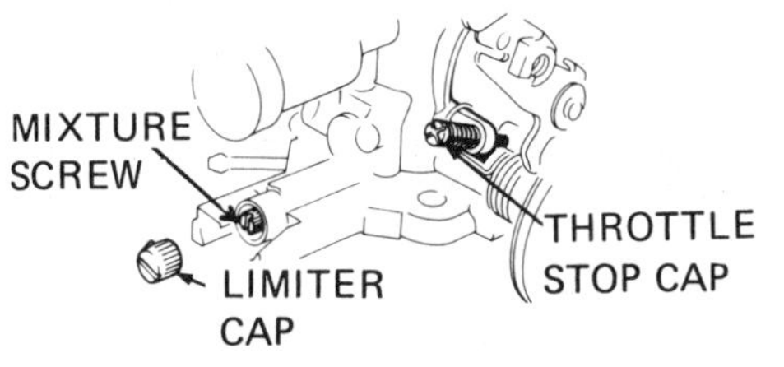

Fig. 3.4. The idle mixture screw and limiter cap position (Sec.6)

6.2 Disconnect the diaphragm pump operating arm

6.8b Always fit a new seal (A) (carburettor inverted)

6.8e Overhauled carburettor ready for refitting. Check that the linkages operate freely

7 Keihin carburettor (CVCC models) - removal and refitting

1 Remove the air cleaner unit from the carburettor as described in Section 2.
2 Disconnect the throttle and choke linkages from the carburettor.
3 Disconnect the fuel hoses and evaporation hoses from the carburettor.
4 Disconnect the vacuum pipe and the respective solenoid valve connections.
5 Unscrew and remove the carburettor flange mounting nuts and carefully lift the carburettor from the manifold.
6 Installation is the reversal of removal but be sure to fit new gaskets to the flanges each side of the insulator and deflector plate. Fit new 'O' ring seals into the location grooves in the insulator.

8 Keihin carburettor (CVCC models) - overhaul and adjustment

1 With the carburettor removed from the engine manifold, clean the external surfaces free from dirt and oil.
2 If a complete overhaul is being undertaken, remove the external components which include the throttle controller diaphragm assembly, the secondary dashpot diaphragm assembly, the primary/main solenoid valve and the vapour (idle) cut-off solenoid valve used in conjunction with the fuel evaporative system.
3 Disconnect the accelerator pump lever from the shaft.
4 Disconnect the choke opener diaphragm assembly.
5 Dismantling the upper body should be limited to the removal of jets and adjusting screws. Clean jets and passages using compressed air, never probe them with wire or their precise calibration will be

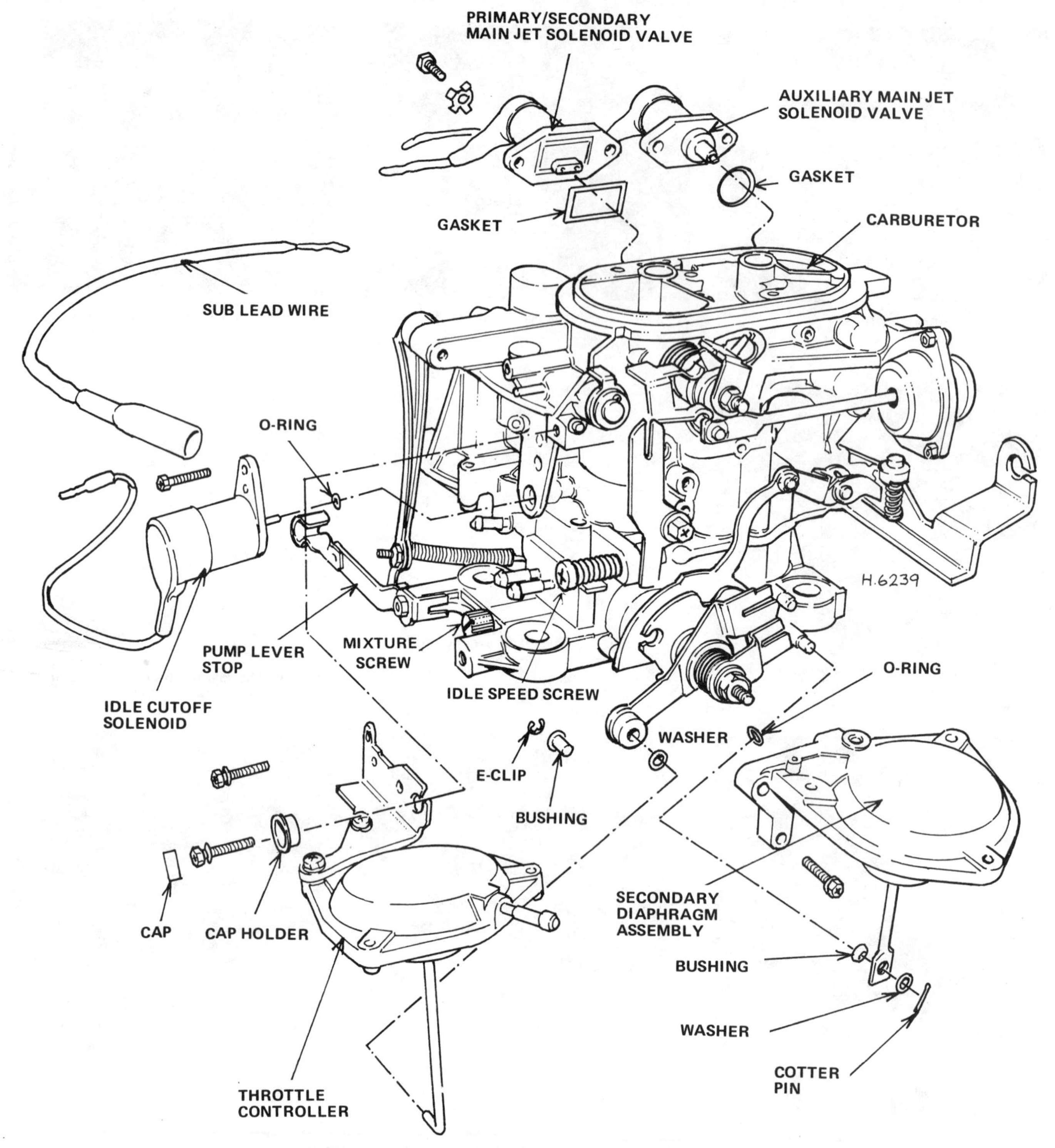

Fig. 3.5. The principal carburettor components (CVCC models) (Sec. 8)

ruined. Before removing jets note carefully their location so that they can be refitted in their correct position. Mark the position of the auxiliary idle mixture screw before removing it.

6 It is not recommended that the valve plates or spindles are removed from the throttle body but if wear has occurred in these components, it is probably time to install a new carburettor.

7 Obtain a repair kit which will contain all the necessary gaskets and renewable items.

8 When the carburettor is completely reassembled, check that the auxiliary idle mixture screw has been returned to its original position. If it was not marked before removal, screw it in gently until it seats and then unscrew it 1¾ turns.

Auxiliary throttle linkage adjustment

9 To adjust the auxiliary throttle linkage, unscrew the throttle speed screw, then remove the cap from the adjustment screw and locknut of the (LAMBDA) auxiliary throttle assembly.

10 Release the locknut and tighten the linkage adjustment screw until the primary throttle valve plate just opens. Now loosen the screw until the valve plate just closes and then unscrew the screw a further 2¼ turns.

11 Tighten the adjustment screw locknut without disturbing the setting of the screw. The throttle stop screw will require setting after the carburettor has been refitted to the car.

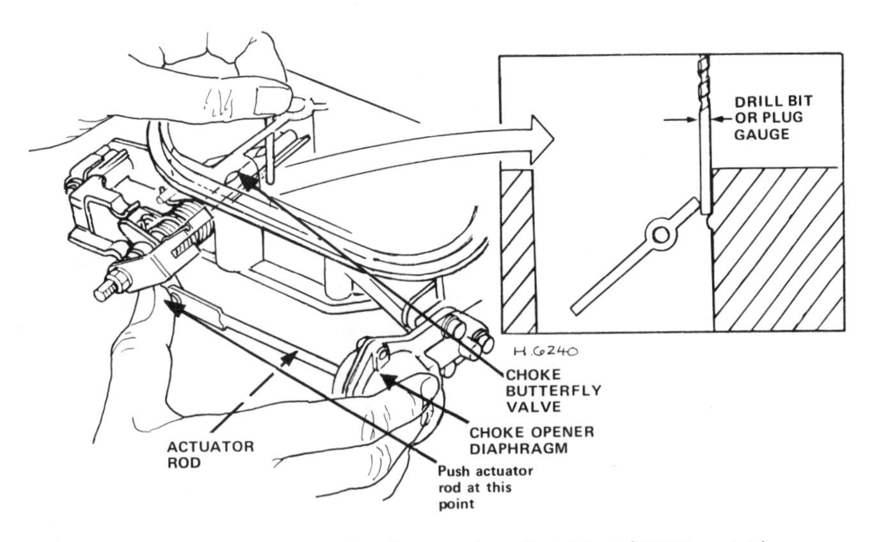

Fig. 3.6. Checking valve plate opening - first detent (CVCC models) (Sec. 8)

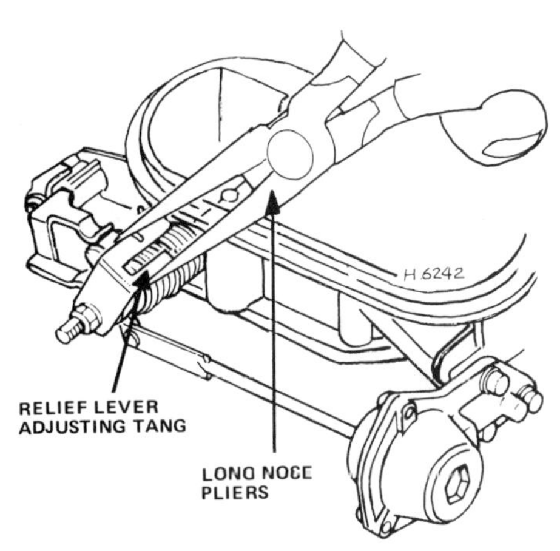

Fig. 3.7. Bend relief lever to adjust choke valve plate opening (CVCC models) (Sec. 8)

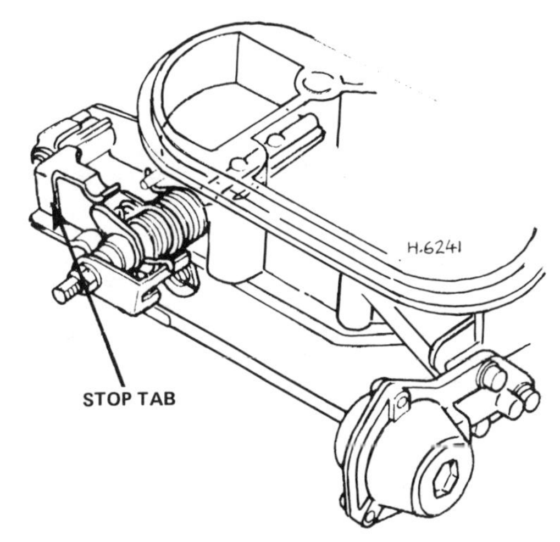

Fig. 3.8. Checking the choke valve opening - second detent (CVCC models) (Sec. 8)

Choke and fast idle setting

12 Remove the air filter unit.

13 Set the choke knob in the first detent position.

14 Refer to Fig. 3.6, and, pressing the choke actuator rod towards the diaphragm, check the clearance between the venturi opening and the butterfly valve as in Fig. 3.6. A 3/16 in drill shank or equivalent plug gauge is ideal for this purpose.

15 If adjustment is required to set the correct clearance, bend the tang of the relief lever, using a suitable pair of pliers as in Fig. 3.7. and recheck the clearance.

16 Pull the choke knob out to the second detent position and press the choke actuator rod towards the diaphragm. Check the clearance between the venturi and butterfly valve using a 7/64 in drill or plug gauge. If the clearance is incorrect, bend the stop tab accordingly, (Fig. 3.8), and recheck the clearance.

Fast idle adjustment and choke opener diaphragm testing

17 These operations can only be carried out when the carburettor has been refitted to the engine.

18 Start the engine and run it to normal operating temperature. Pull the choke knob out to its second detent position when the fast idle speed should be between 2500 and 3500 rev/min. If the fast idle speed is too high, pinch the slotted part of the fast idle adjusting link together; if the fast idle speed is too low, insert a screwdriver in the slot of the link and widen the slot slightly.

19 To check that the choke opener diaphragm is operating correctly, remove the air cleaner and pull the choke knob to its second detent position.

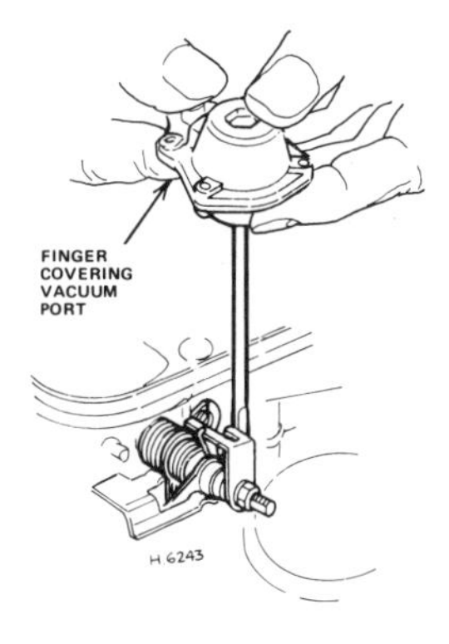

Fig. 3.9. Checking the butterfly valve operation (CVCC models) (Sec. 8)

20 Operating the starter, observe that the choke butterfly valve plate fluctuates.

21 If the retaining screws are removed from the choke opener diaphragm, the unit can be swung upwards and the actuator rod fully depressed and released. The rod should be able to move quite freely and not show any signs of binding. With the actuator rod in the depressed position, cover the vacuum port with the finger and release the rod. The rod should remain in the retracted position under the

MODEL	Trans. Type	XXX R.P.M.	YYY R.P.M.
KL	Manual Transmission	850	800
	Hondamatic (in gear)	720	680
HA	Manual Transmission	920 970 at sea level	800
	Hondamatic (in gear)	760 780 at sea level	680
KA	Manual Transmission	850	800
	Hondamatic (in gear)	710	680

Fig. 3.10. The idle speed chart (CVCC models) (Sec. 8)

effect of vacuum for at least five seconds. If this is not the case, the choke opener diaphragm must be renewed.
22 Inspect the vacuum port of the carburettor to ensure that it is clear and that the 'O' ring seal is in good condition.

Idle speed adjustment

23 This operation can only be carried out with the carburettor refitted to the engine.
24 Start the engine and run until the normal operating temperature is reached (when the cooling fan commences operation).
25 Adjustment should be made with the headlights on.
26 Detach the mixture screw limiter cap and turn the mixture adjustment screw and the idle adjustment screw to obtain a smooth idle speed shown in column XXX in Fig. 3.10 according to model.
27 Now turn the mixture adjustment screw in a clockwise direction to weaken the mixture until the idle speed is as given in column YYY according to model. For reference to models see Section 16.
28 When the correct idle speed is obtained stop the engine and turn off the lights.
29 If difficulty is experienced in adjusting the idle speed, check the throttle cable for correct adjustment.
30 Fit a new limiter cap.

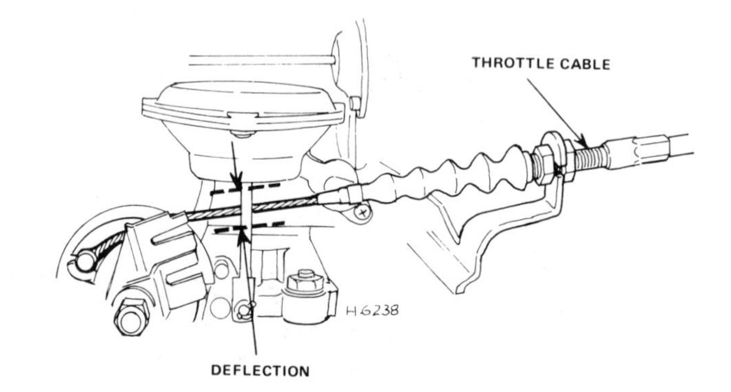

Fig. 3.11. The throttle cable deflection check point (CVCC models) (Sec. 9)

9 Throttle cable - inspection, adjustment, removal and refitting

Inspection and adjustment

1 Periodic inspection of the throttle cable is necessary to ensure that it is not binding or sticking and that the cable adjustment is correct. First remove the air filter unit.
2 Inspect the cable free play at the carburettor throttle linkage. The cable should have a deflection tolerance of 0.16 to 0.40 in (4 - 10 mm).
3 To adjust the cable, loosen the locknut and turn the adjusting nut to take up any free play. Now loosen the adjustment nut sufficiently to provide the cable with the specified tolerance. Retighten the locknut whilst retaining the adjustment nut in the position set.
4 On adjustment, get an assistant to press down the throttle from within the car, and check that the cable and throttle linkage are fully operational. If necessary readjust the cable to suit, but ensure that when the cable is released the throttle is fully closed.

Removal and installation

5 Remove the air cleaner unit.
6 Open the throttle cable by hand and disconnect the cable nipple from the quadrant when there is sufficient slack in the cable.
7 Unscrew the cable adjustment nut and locknut and detach the cable from the carburettor.
8 Unclip the cable from the retainer on the cam cover and disconnect the adjoining choke cable from the interconnecting clip.
9 Disconnect the throttle cable from the throttle pedal linkage and remove from the car, withdrawing from the engine compartment side.
10 Installation is the reverse of removal but readjust the free play at the carburettor and check that the throttle is fully operational as described in paragraphs 2 to 4 above.

10 Choke cable - inspection and adjustment

1 To check the choke cable for adjustment, first ensure that the choke control knob is fully closed.
2 Remove the air cleaner unit.
3 Observe through the top of the carburettor and ensure that the choke butterfly valve is fully open (Fig. 3.13).
4 Get an assistant to pull the choke knob out to the second detent position, at which stage the valve should just shut.
5 With the choke knob fully out, the butterfly valve should stay in the same position. In the fully out position additional spring tension is applied to the butterfly valve for cold starts.
6 Check that the choke indicator lamp is operating correctly by pressing and pulling the choke cable knob through its full travel.
7 If it is found that the choke butterfly valve does not fully open when the choke knob is in the off position, the adjustment locknut must be loosened and the adjustment nut turned so that the butterfly valve is freed from the stop tab. Reverse the direction of the adjusting nut so that the valve just touches the stop tab and tighten the locknut whilst retaining the adjustment nut in the set position (Fig. 3.14).
8 Check that the butterfly valve can close correctly and ensure that the movement is smooth.

11 Fuel pump cut-off relay - description, removal and refitting

1 The fuel pump cut-off relay unit is located under the dash panel and energizes the fuel pump to provide fuel to the carburettor.
2 When the ignition is initially switched on, the cut-off relay is not actuated. When the ignition switch is turned to the start position, the

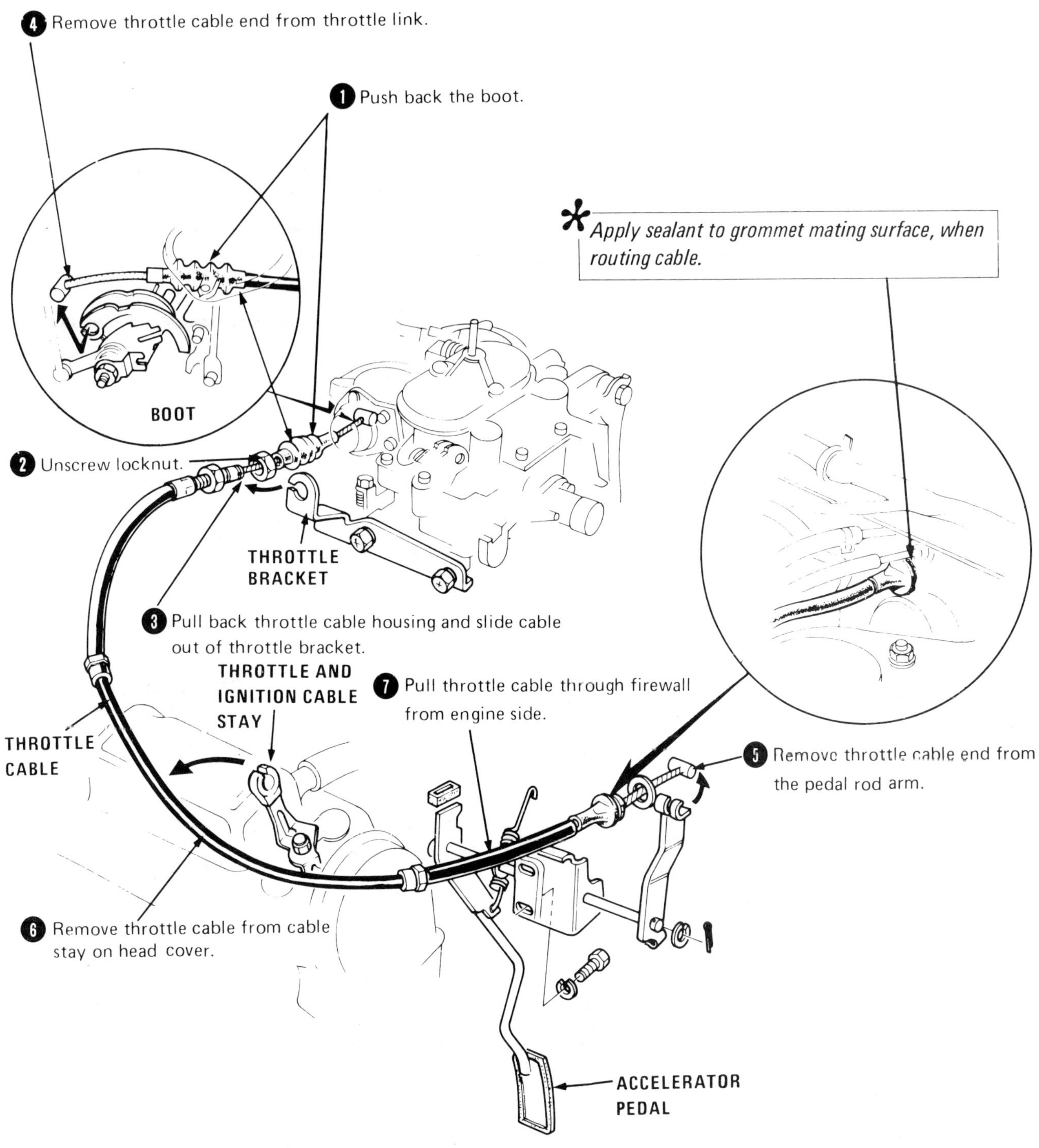
4 Remove throttle cable end from throttle link.
1 Push back the boot.
* Apply sealant to grommet mating surface, when routing cable.
BOOT
2 Unscrew locknut.
THROTTLE BRACKET
3 Pull back throttle cable housing and slide cable out of throttle bracket.
THROTTLE AND IGNITION CABLE STAY
7 Pull throttle cable through firewall from engine side.
5 Remove throttle cable end from the pedal rod arm.
THROTTLE CABLE
6 Remove throttle cable from cable stay on head cover.
ACCELERATOR PEDAL

Fig. 3.12. The throttle cable and components (Sec. 9)

relay unit is energized and switches on the fuel pump, and this continues to operate when the ignition switch returns to the 'ON' position with the engine running. The relay unit is interconnected with the oil pressure switch, which when the engine is running, opens and continues to energize the relay unit when the ignition switch is returned from the 'START' position to the 'ON' position (Fig. 11.15).

3 When the ignition is switched off the oil pressure switch closes and de-energizes the relay unit.

4 In the event of the fuel pump not working, it must first be ascertained that the fuse, and relay unit are in working order. Also check the engine oil level and oil pressure switch and the respective interconnecting wires.

5 If the relay unit is defective, it cannot be repaired and must be renewed. Remove as follows.

6 Pull the respective connecting wires from the switch noting their respective locations.

7 Unscrew the cut-off relay unit retaining screw and remove the unit.

8 Installation is the reverse of removal but ensure that the wires are reconnected in their original positions as in Fig. 3.16.

12 Fuel pump - removal and refitting

1 The fuel pump is located adjacent to the fuel tank at the rear of the vehicle, on the left-hand side. Access to the pump for checking or removal/installation is from underneath, and the vehicle should there-

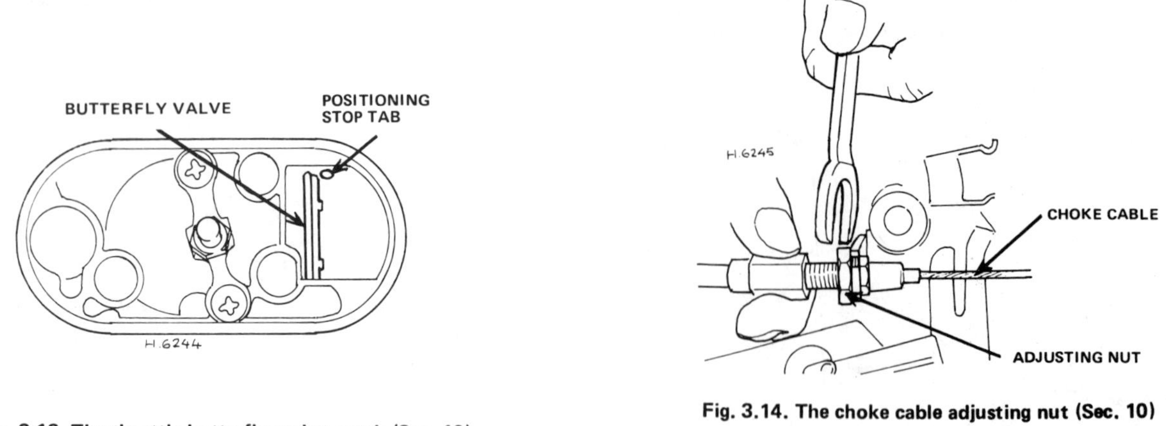

Fig. 3.13. The throttle butterfly and stop tab (Sec. 10)

Fig. 3.14. The choke cable adjusting nut (Sec. 10)

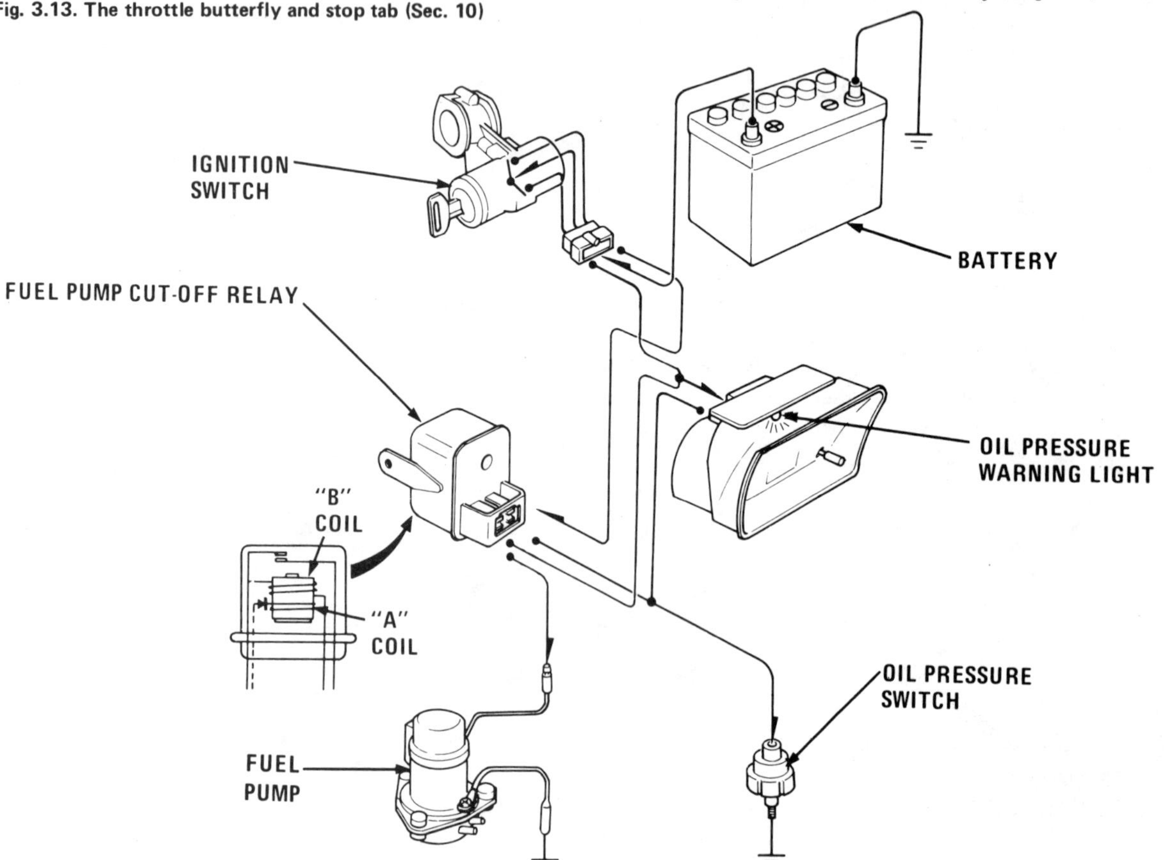

Fig. 3.15. The fuel pump and relay circuit (Sec. 11)

fore be positioned over an inspection pit, placed on ramps or jacked up at the rear and axle stands securely located for additional support.
2 Unscrew the four retaining bolts and remove the fuel pump cover (photo).
3 Disconnect the fuel pipes from the pump unit and fuel filter.
4 Unscrew the retaining bolts and remove the pump unit from the cover, and detach the fuel filter.
5 Disconnect the fuel pump wires at the snap connectors and remove the pump.
6 The fuel pump is not repairable and if defective must be replaced with a new or reconditioned unit.
7 Installation is the reverse of removal. Renew the connecting hoses and clips if necessary.

13 Fuel filter - removal and renewal

1 The fuel filter is located next to the fuel pump adjacent to the fuel tank at the rear of the vehicle.
2 Follow paragraphs 1 and 2 in the preceding Section.
3 Unclip the filter unit from the cover and disconnect the hose from the fuel tank and the hose to the pump unit. Remove the filter.
4 Replacement is a direct reversal of removal but if the connecting hoses or clips are defective they must also be renewed.

14 Fuel tank - removal and refitting

1 Disconnect the earth (ground) cable from the battery.
2 Position the vehicle over an inspection pit, on ramps or jack it up at the rear and support it securely with axle/chassis stands. Engage reverse gear (or Park - Hondamatic).
3 Unscrew the fuel tank drain bolt and drain any fuel remaining in the tank into a suitable clean container. Place a cap or cover over container and store in a safe place away from heat or naked flame.
4 Disconnect the fuel gauge sender unit wires from the snap connector.
5 Disconnect the fuel pump unit and remove it as described in

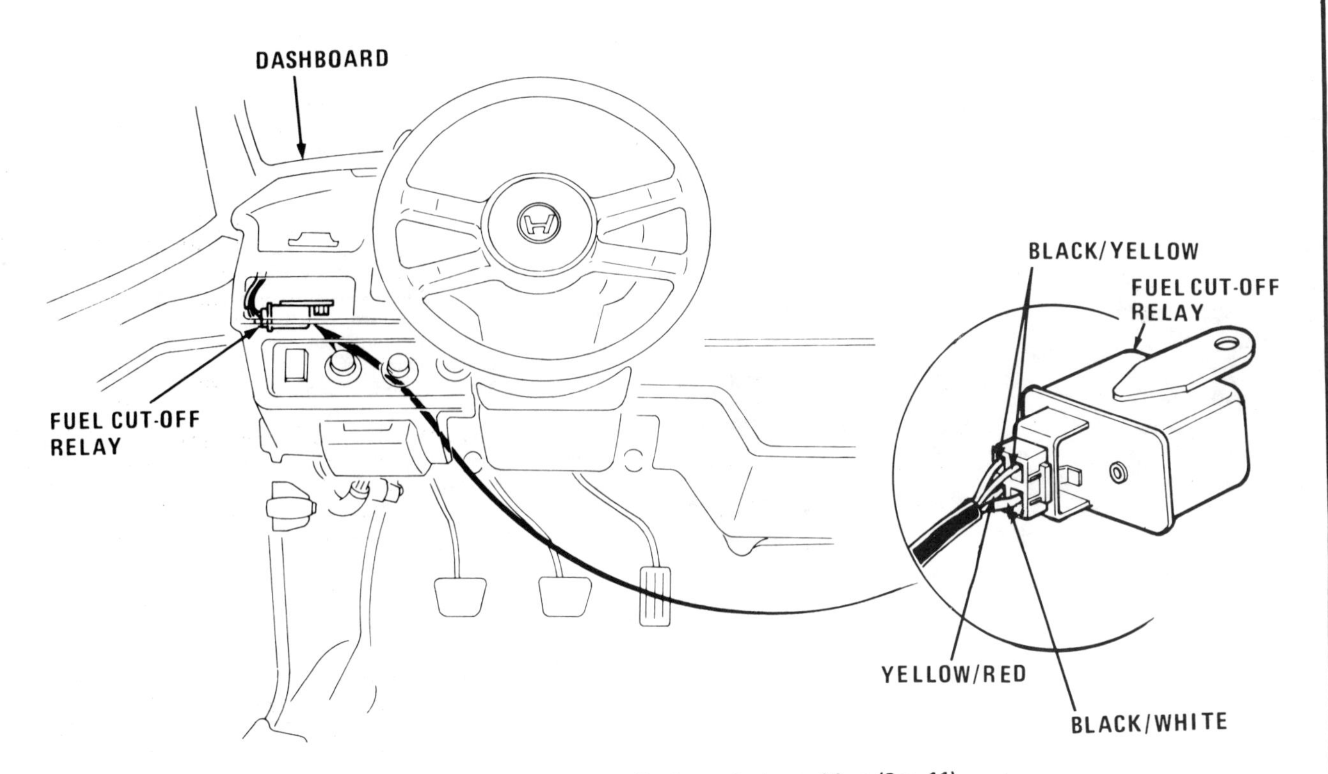

Fig. 3.16. The fuel pump cut-off relay and wire positions (Sec. 11)

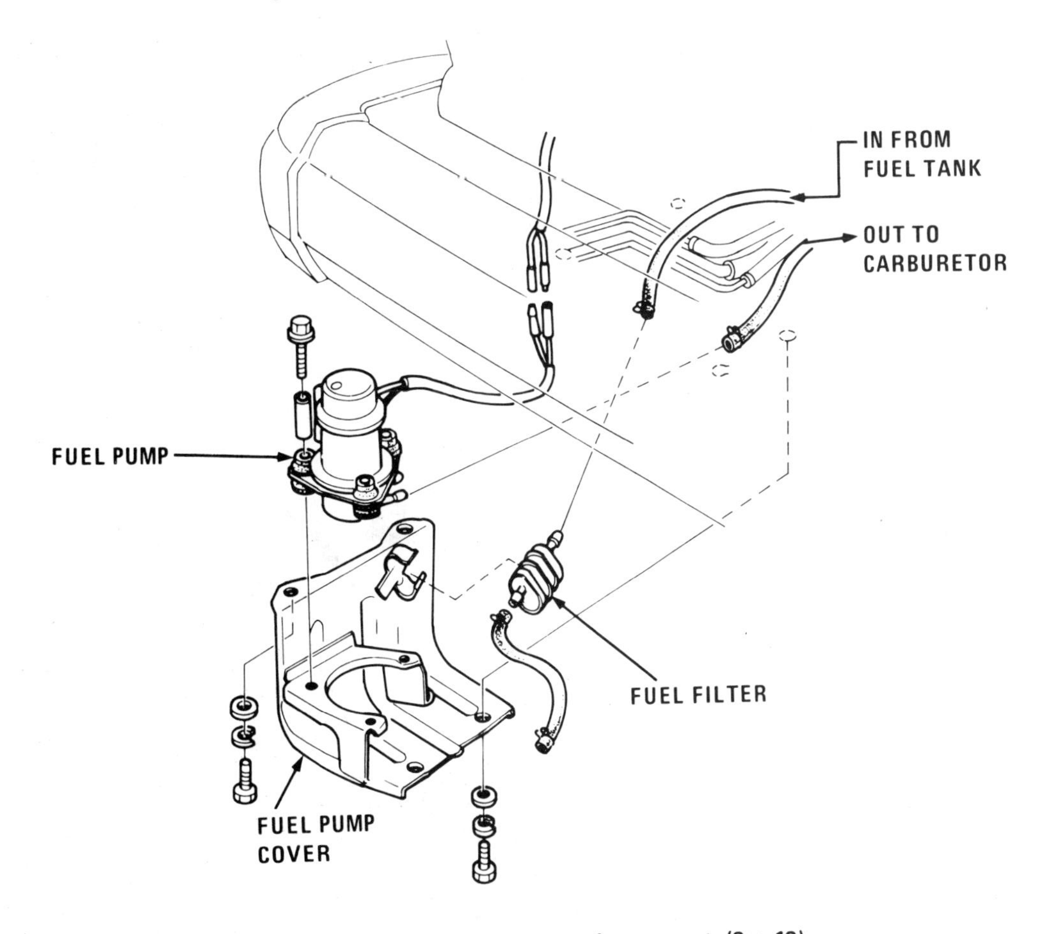

Fig. 3.17. The fuel pump and components (Sec. 12)

12.2 Remove the fuel pump

Section 12.

6 Disconnect the vapour hoses from the fuel tank, together with the filler neck hose and filler neck ventilation hose.

7 Supporting the tank from underneath, unscrew the tank retaining straps securing nuts. Carefully lower the tank unit and remove from the vehicle, guiding it clear of the handbrake (parkbrake) cable.

8 If the fuel tank contains a quantity of sediment, it should be swilled out with several changes of clean fuel. Prior to swilling, the sender unit must be removed from the tank as described in the following Section as it is easily damaged.

9 If the tank is leaking, a temporary repair can be made with a proprietary product, but any permanent cure can only be effected by a professional repair or renewing the tank. On no account should any attempt be made to solder or weld the tank as even experts will not do this until the tank has been steamed out for several hours to remove all traces of vapour.

10 Installation of the sender unit and tank is a direct reversal of the removal sequence but always renew any defective connecting hoses or clips. It is also advisable to renew the fuel filter during assembly.

15 Fuel gauge and sender unit - testing, removal and refitting

1 If the reading of the fuel gauge does not correspond to the known quantity of fuel in the tank, make sure that the ignition switch is off and then disconnect the yellow/white and the black electrical leads which are located on the right-hand side of the fuel tank and which run to the tank sender unit. Join the leads together and switch on the ignition when the fuel gauge should read 'FULL'.

2 If the gauge does not indicate 'FULL' check all connections and the circuit fuse. If these are in order, the gauge is faulty and must be renewed (Chapter 10). During the foregoing test do not leave the ignition switch on for periods of more than 15 seconds.

3 If the gauge proves satisfactory, the fault must lie in the sender unit. This can be checked by connecting the probes of an ohmmeter between the yellow/white and black leads which come from the terminals on the sender unit. The resistance measured for a known quantity of fuel in the tank should be as follows:

Tank half-full	*25.5 to 39.5 ohms*
Tank full	*2 to 8 ohms*

4 Where these readings are not obtainable, the sender unit must be renewed. To do this, remove the fuel tank, as described in the preceding Section, and using a suitable flat bar engaged in the cut-outs of the unit, twist and release it. Withdraw the unit carefully from the tank to avoid damaging the float mechanism.

5 Refitting is a reversal of removal but use a new sealing gasket.

16 Engine emission control - description

1 The emission control system is basically divided into three parts. The exhaust emission control system is designed to reduce the harmful gases given off by the exhaust system; the crankcase vapour emission control ensures that any blow-by vapour within the crankcase is redirected to the combustion chambers via the carburettor and inlet manifold and is burnt off; and the evaporative emission control system dispenses with fuel vapour given off by the fuel storage and supply systems of the car.

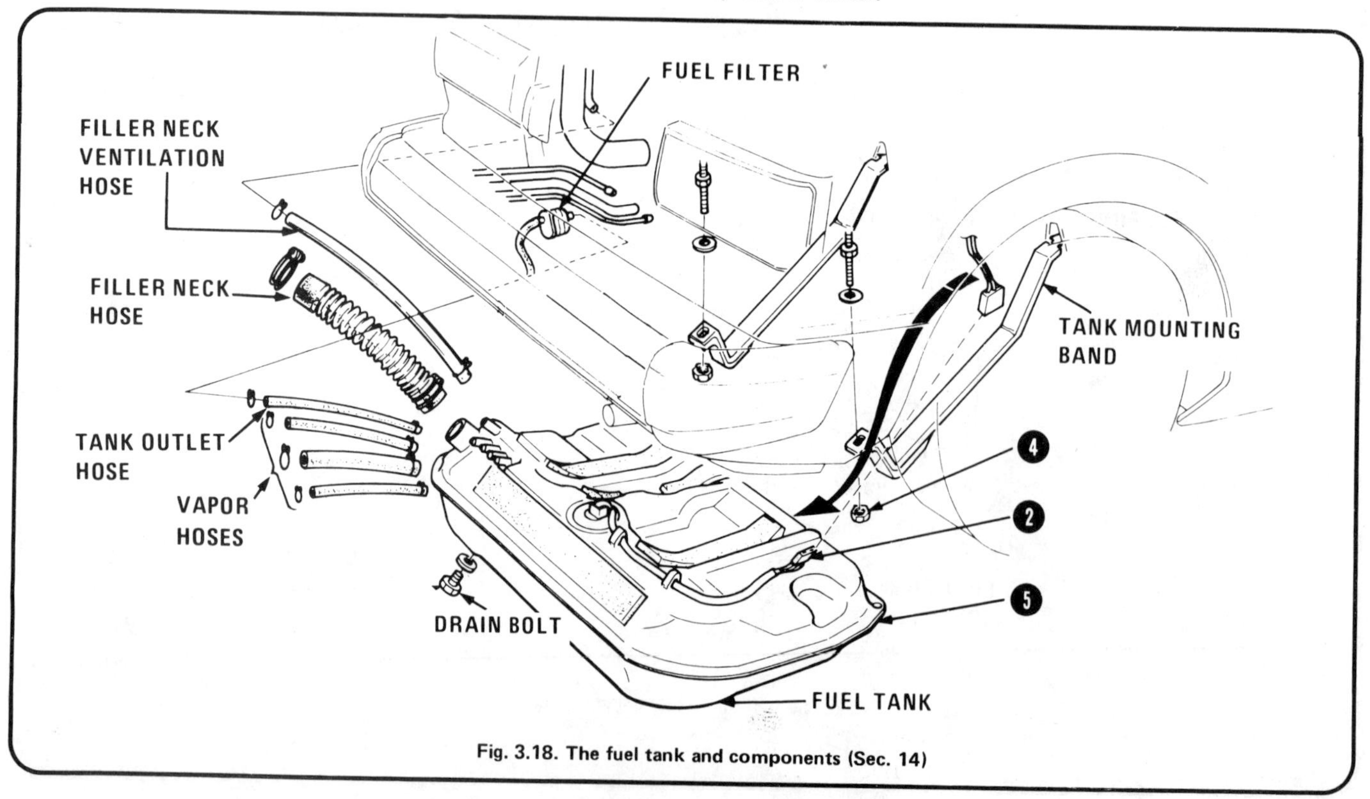

Fig. 3.18. The fuel tank and components (Sec. 14)

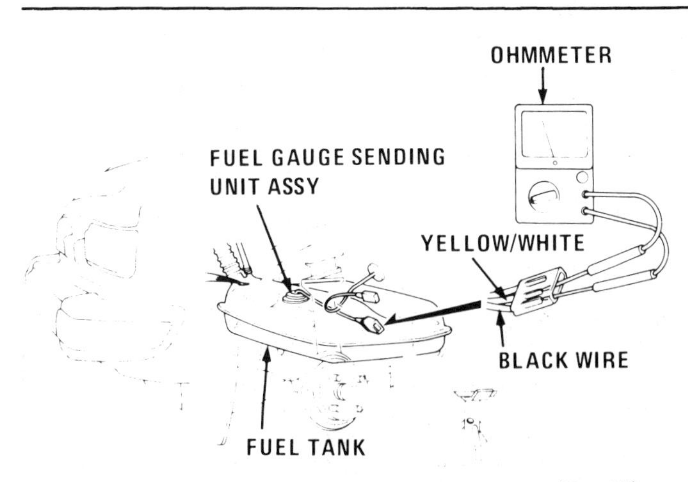

Fig. 3.19. Check the sender unit using an ohmmeter (Sec. 15)

2 The type of emission control system fitted is dependant on the country and area to which the vehicle is supplied.

3 For USA models the system types are divided into three main categories according to area and these are recognized as follows:

High altitude (HA)	-	*engine serial no. group type EFI - 2900001 on.*
California (KL)	-	*engine serial no. group type EFI - 2000001 on.*
USA except California (KA)	-	*engine serial no. group type EFI - 2500001 on.*

4 Honda engines having exhaust emission control systems are unique in that they are fitted with a CVCC type engine. The CVCC (Compound Vortex Controlled Combustion) engine has a special cylinder head in which there are two combustion chambers per cylinder. The main chamber is supplied with a very weak mixture whilst the auxiliary chamber receives a rich mixture, and contains the spark plug. When the rich mixture in the auxiliary(small) chamber is ignited, the flame produced passes to the main chamber and the weak mixture therein is in turn ignited. The principle advantage of this system is that the engine is able to operate on a relatively weak fuel/air mixture thus reducing the harmful exhaust emissions, and it also disposes of the many auxiliary components normally fitted to achieve this on vehicles of other manufacture.

5 In addition to the CVCC engine, there are four exhaust emission control sub-systems fitted according to model and operating territory and these may comprise one or more of the following:

1) Start Control.
2) Air Intake Control.
3) Ignition Timing Control.
4) Throttle Control.

6 In order that the emission control system can operate efficiently, it is most important that the engine and its associate components (ignition, carburation, valve settings, etc) are in good condition, and correctly set and adjusted.

7 The various emission control equipment hose and wiring connections must be regularly inspected as must the exhaust system. Any leaks or defects must be repaired at the earliest opportunity.

8 Testing the emission control equipment requires specialist knowledge and equipment, and should therefore be entrusted to your local Honda dealer.

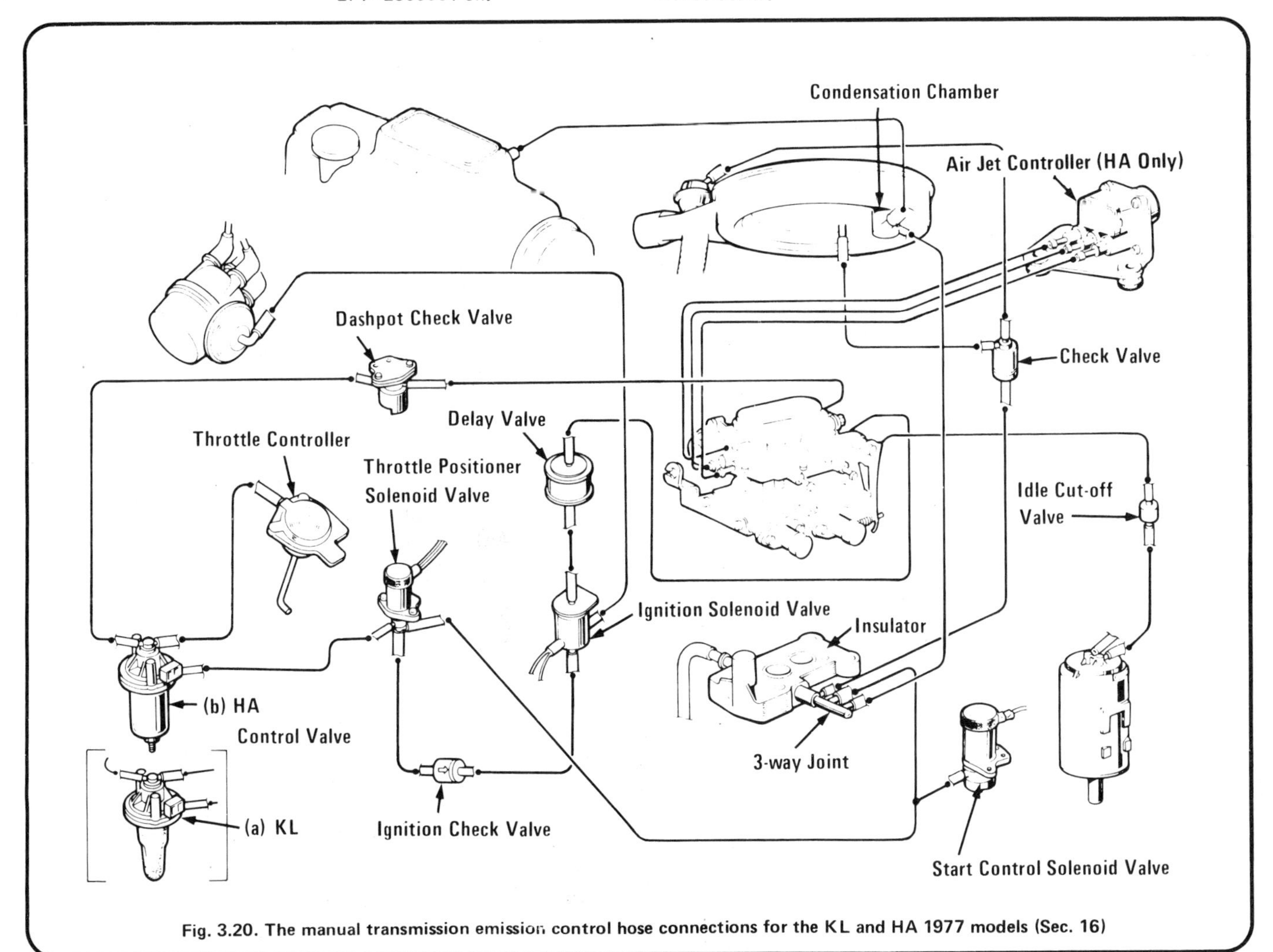

Fig. 3.20. The manual transmission emission control hose connections for the KL and HA 1977 models (Sec. 16)

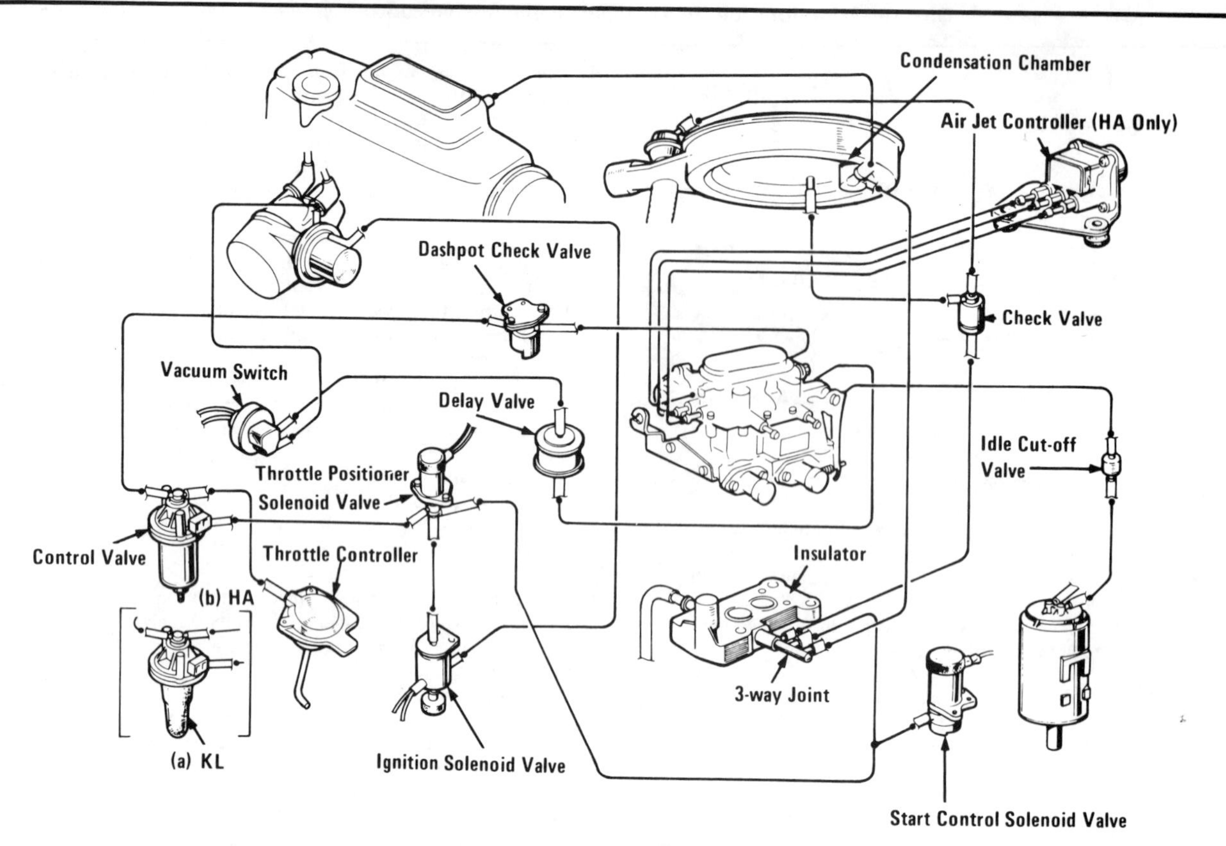

Fig. 3.21. The Hondamatic transmission emission control hose connections for the KL and HA 1977 models (Sec. 16)

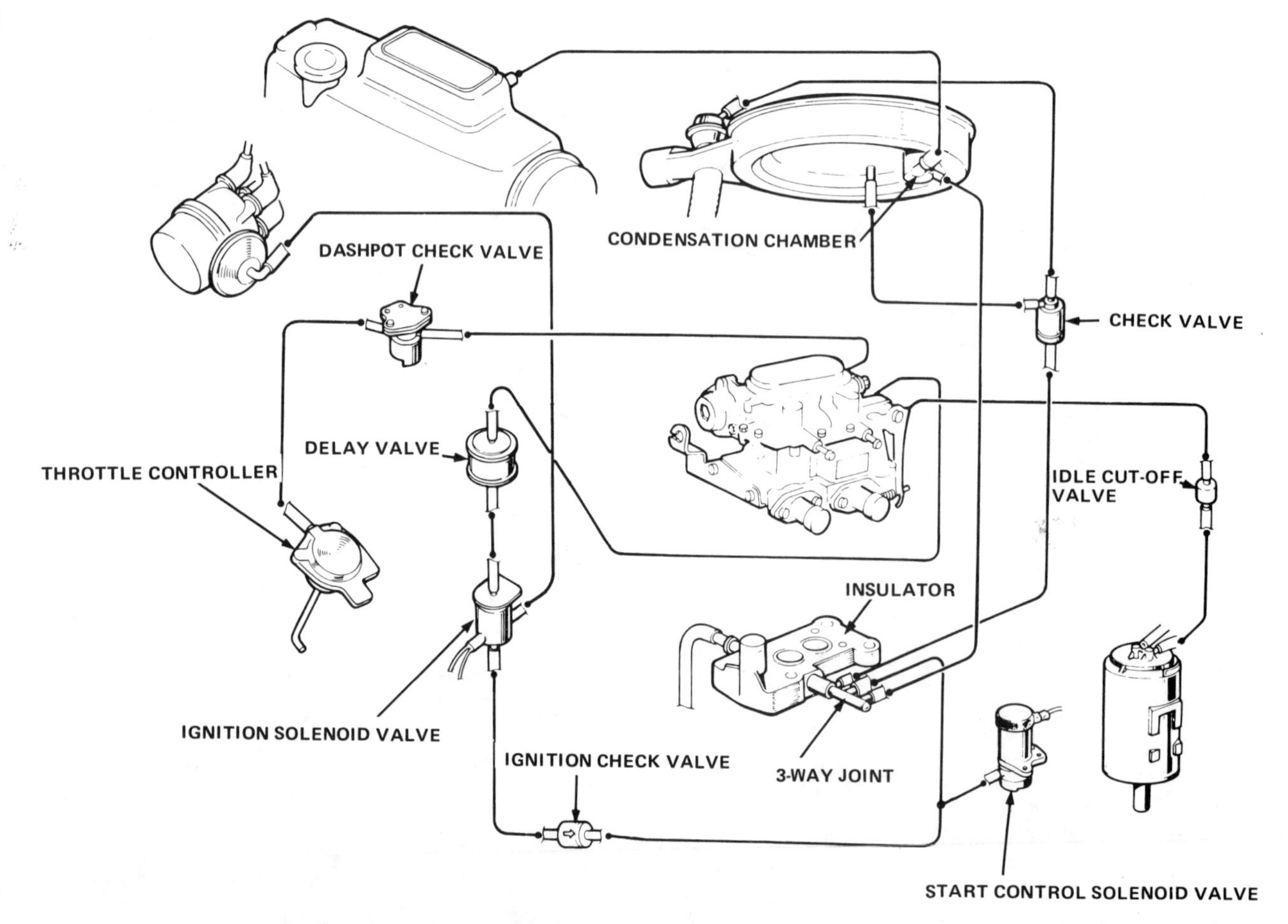

Fig. 3.22. The emission control hose connections for the 1977 KA models (Sec. 16)

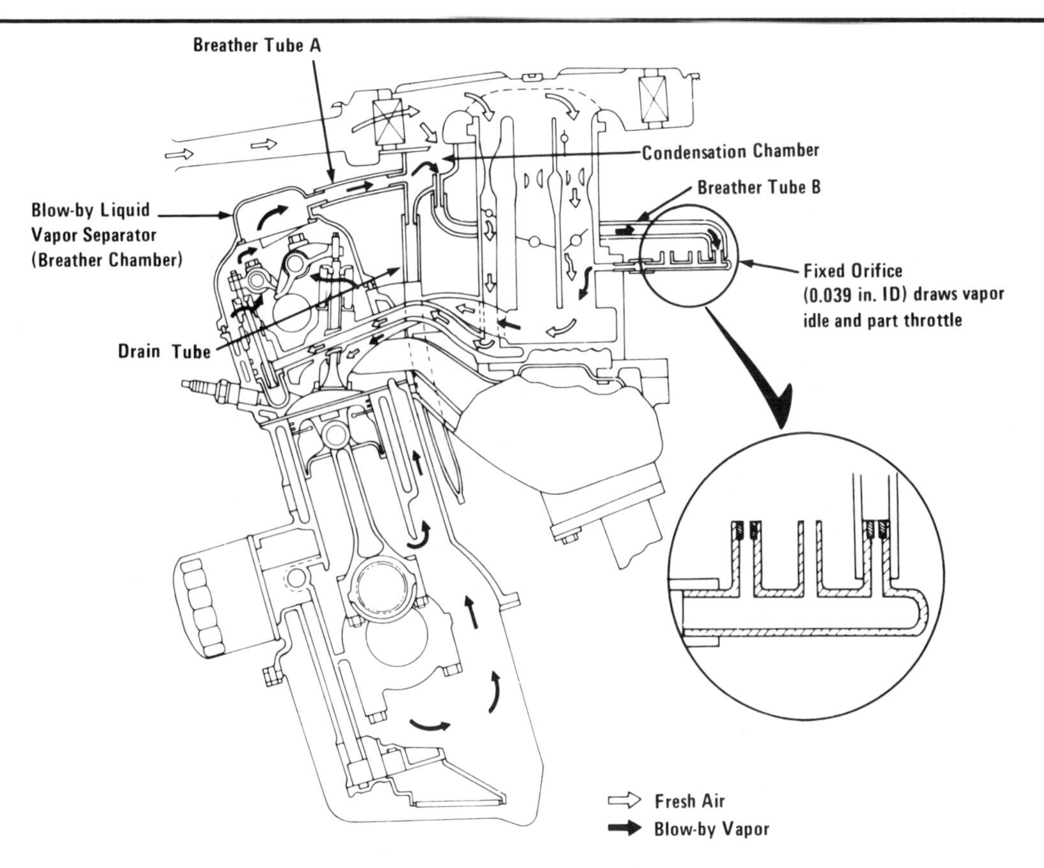

Fig. 3.23. The crankcase emission control system (1976 models) (Sec. 16)

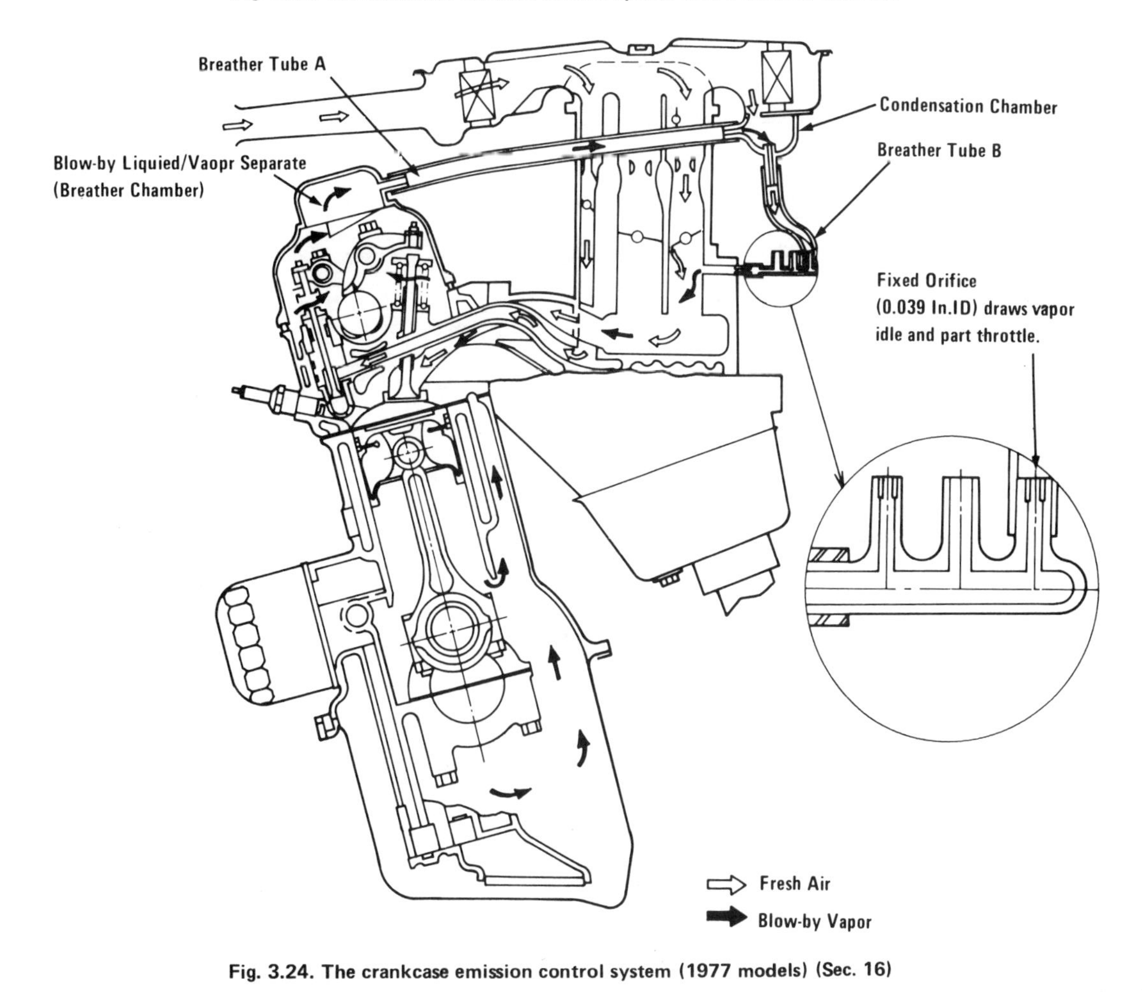

Fig. 3.24. The crankcase emission control system (1977 models) (Sec. 16)

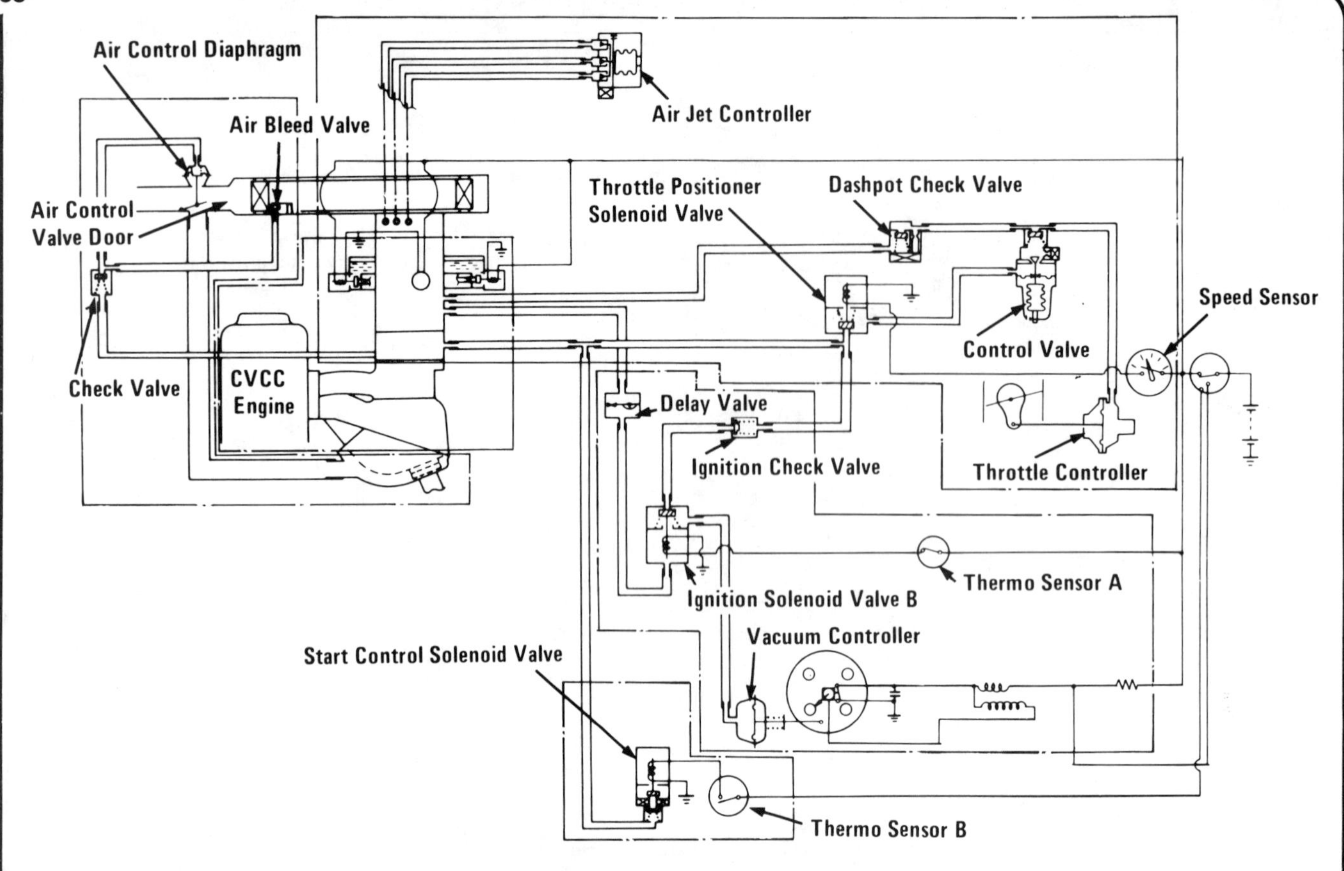

Fig. 3.25. The exhaust emission control system for the 1977 manual transmission models KL and HA (Sec. 16)

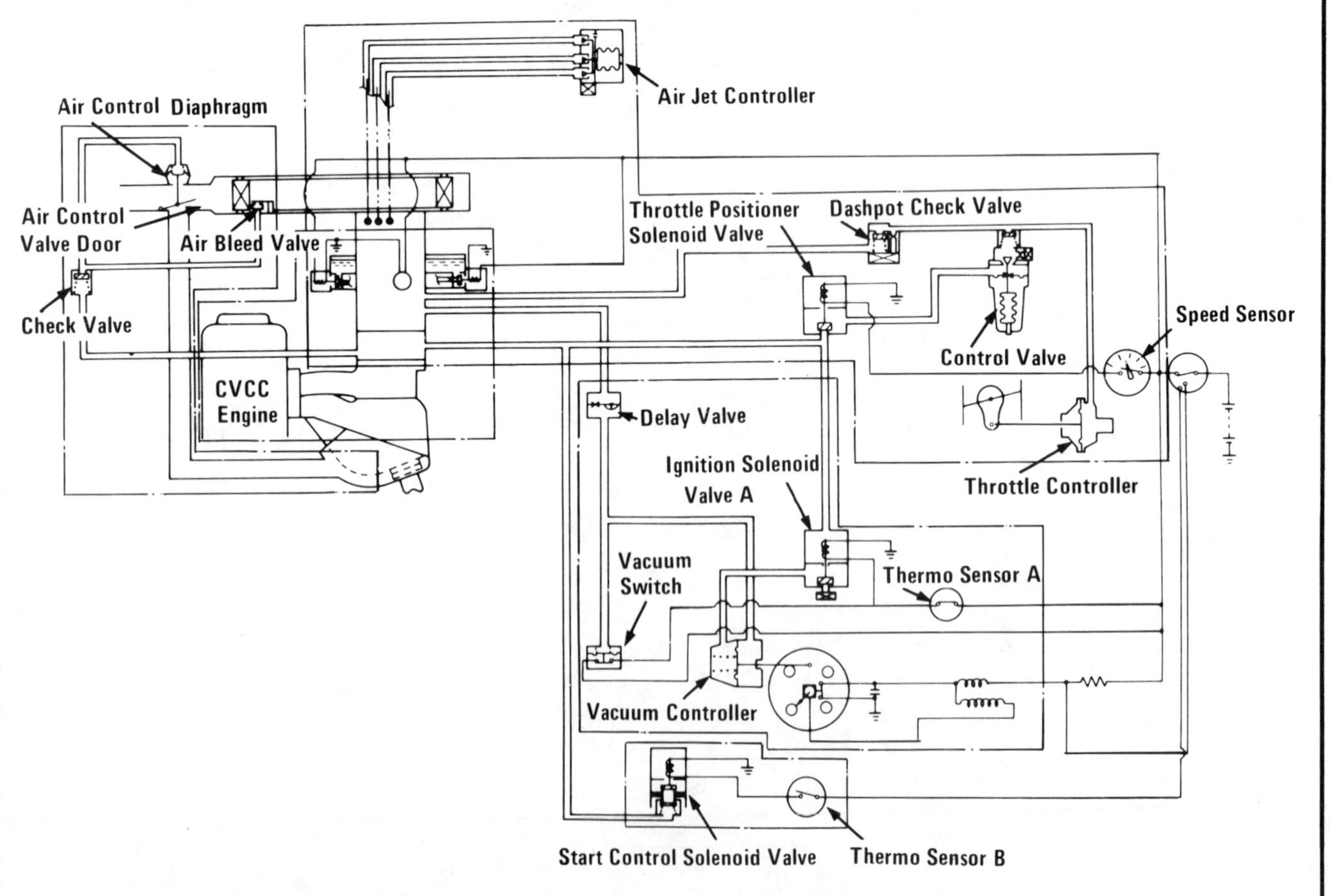

Fig. 3.26. The exhaust emission control system for the 1977 Hondamatic transmission models KL and HA (Sec. 16)

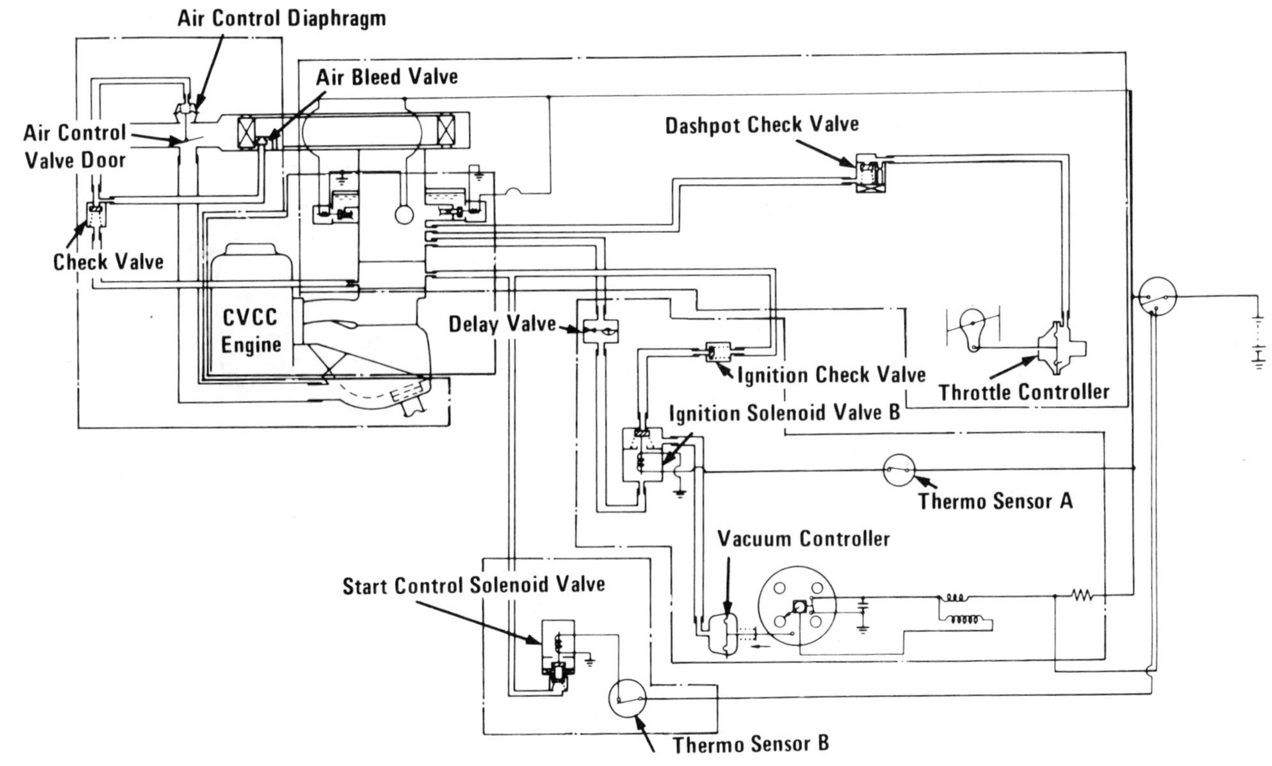

Fig. 3.27. The exhaust emission control system for the 1977 KA models (Sec. 16)

17 Start control - description, maintenance and testing

1 The purpose of the start control system is to admit fresh air to the inlet manifold when starting a hot engine (above 122°F/50°C). The fresh air dilutes any residual fuel vapour present in the inlet manifold and so prevents over-rich exhaust emissions on starting. The system only operates when the ignition key is turned to 'START' (Fig. 3.28).
2 Maintenance consists of periodically checking the security of the system connecting hoses and electrical leads. The solenoid valve can only be tested using a vacuum pump and this will have to be carried out by your Honda dealer.
3 Every 15,000 miles (24,000 km) renew the air filter located in the base of the solenoid valve.

18 Air intake control - description and testing

1 This part of the emission control system concerns the maintenance of specified air intake temperature and volume by a combination of a vacuum actuated and thermostatically controlled flap valve within the air cleaner casing (Fig. 3.29).
2 Maintenance of the air cleaner element is described in Section 2.
3 To test the operation of the device, remove the air cleaner cover and extract the filter element. Operate the starter for about five seconds (low tension lead to distributor disconnected) and observe that the air control valve flap within the air cleaner rises as the engine is cranked and remains fully open, after cranking ceases, for at least three seconds.
4 If it does not, clear the four-way union using an 0.020 in (0.5 mm) diameter twist drill and then check the operation of the non-return valve, the air bleed valve and the vacuum diaphragm.

19 Ignition timing control - description

1 This is the vacuum control of the distributor contact breaker. It is in addition to the centrifugal advance mechanism and is more sophisticated than the normal vacuum advance/retard vacuum diaphragm usually found on engines without emission control systems.
2 *On vehicles with manual gearbox and Hondamatic KA models,* when the coolant temperature is below 149°F (65°C) and the engine idling or running at higher speeds, the thermosensor 'A' (Fig. 3.30) energizes the ignition solenoid valve to allow manifold vacuum to be applied to the distributor advance diaphragm capsule. A non-return valve is incorporated to retain some vacuum conditions when manifold vacuum is very low such as at wide throttle openings.
3 When the coolant temperature rises above 149°F (65°C), and the engine is running at speeds above idling, the thermosensor de-energises the ignition solenoid valve and allows vacuum to be applied to the distributor advance diaphragm capsule through the delay valve. The vacuum pressure applied is in proportion to the particular throttle and engine load conditions.
4 *On vehicles with automatic transmission (models KL and HA),* when the coolant temperature is above 149°F (65°C), and the engine is at idling speed, the thermosensor 'A' (Fig. 3.31) de-energises the ignition solenoid valve to allow manifold vacuum to be applied to the retard side of the vacuum diaphragm capsule on the distributor. This condition applies for a short pre-determined period, however, as vacuum bleeding through the delay valve trips the vacuum switch to destroy the vacuum retard.
5 When the coolant temperature is below 149°F (65°C) no additional vacuum retard is applied at engine idling speed.
6 At engine speeds above idling, the distributor timing is advanced or retarded according to engine load and to the characteristics of the delay valve.
7 The foregoing systems are designed to ensure that ignition timing is adjusted at all times to give optimum economy and performance with the minimum emission of exhaust pollution.
8 Refer to Chapter 4, for details of distributor maintenance and overhaul. The other components of the ignition timing control system cannot be tested or adjusted without special equipment but periodically check the security and condition of all connecting hoses and electrical leads.

20 Throttle control - description

1 Two interrelated systems are used to control excessive emissions of exhaust gas hydrocarbons during periods of deceleration or when shifting gears and the throttle will be closed (Figs. 3.32, 3.33 and 3.34).
2 The first system (fitted to KL and HA models), is essentially a throttle positioner in which a speed sensor in the speedometer head

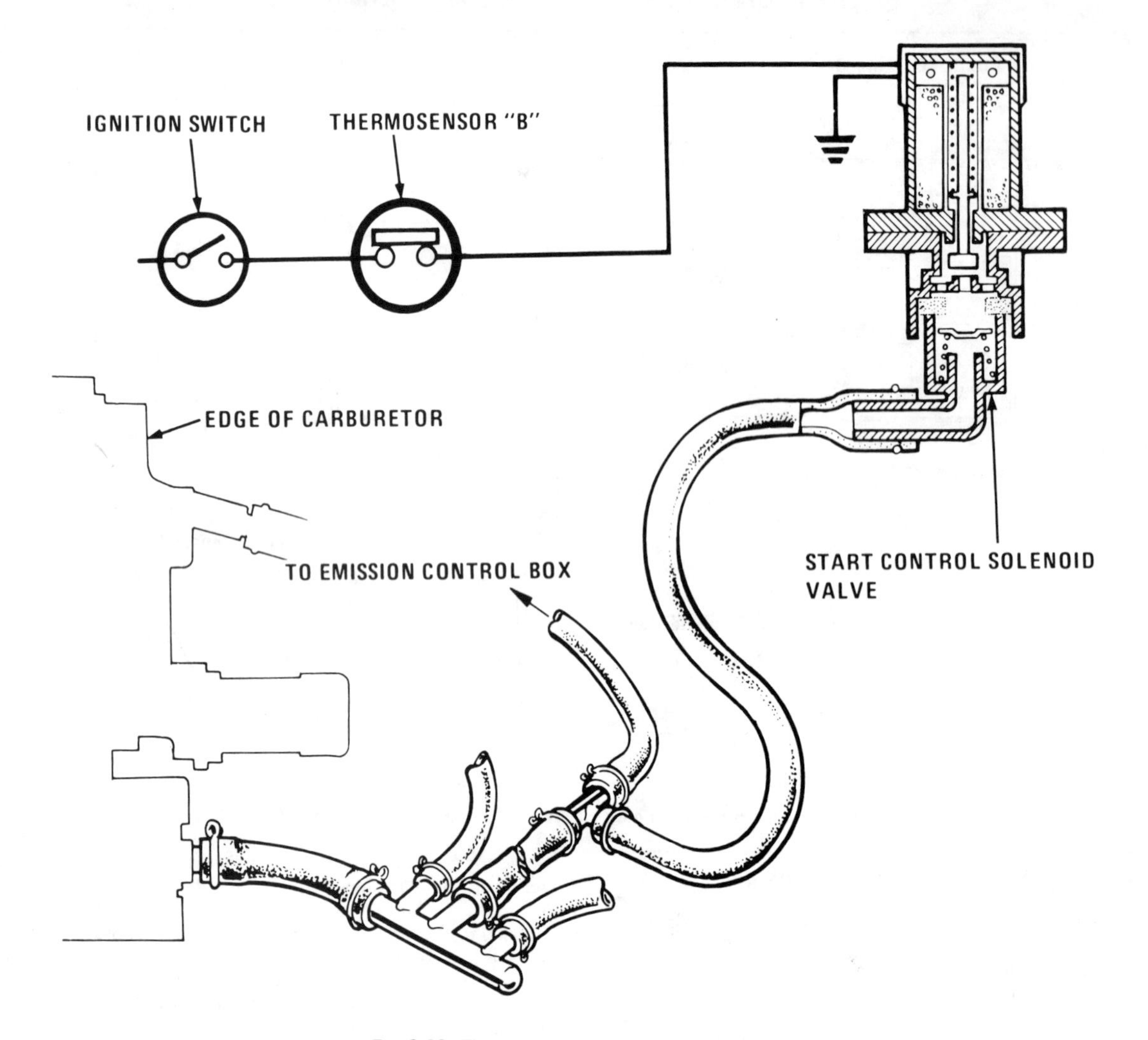

Fig. 3.28. The start control system (Sec. 17)

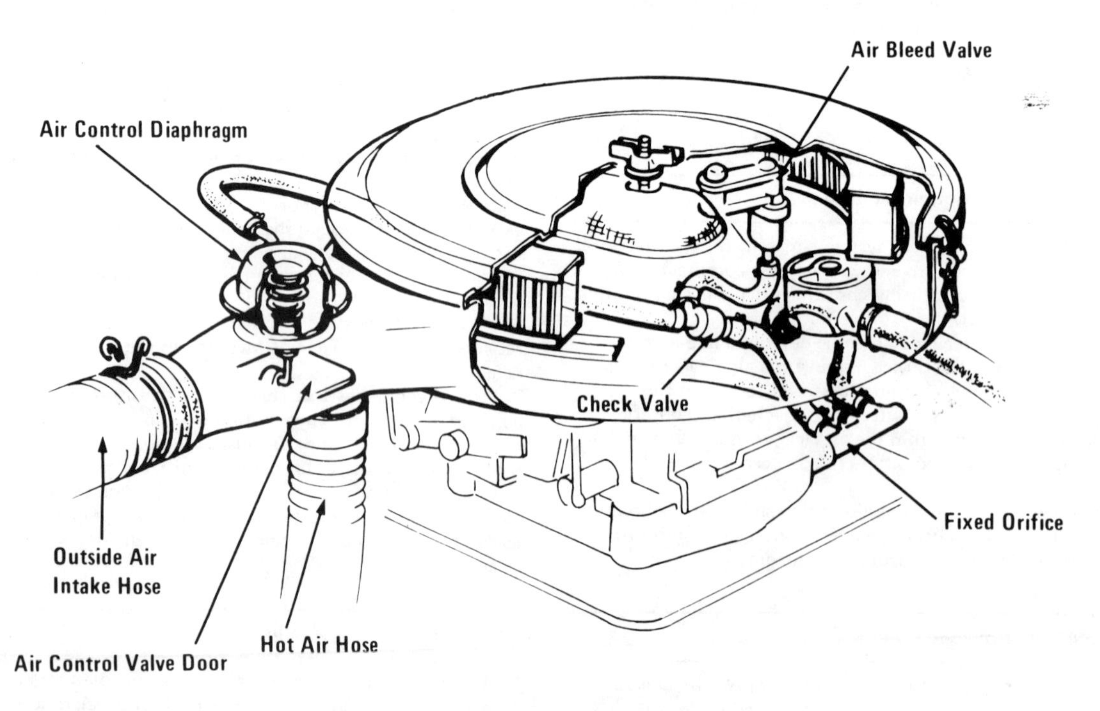

Fig. 3.29. The air intake control system (Sec. 18)

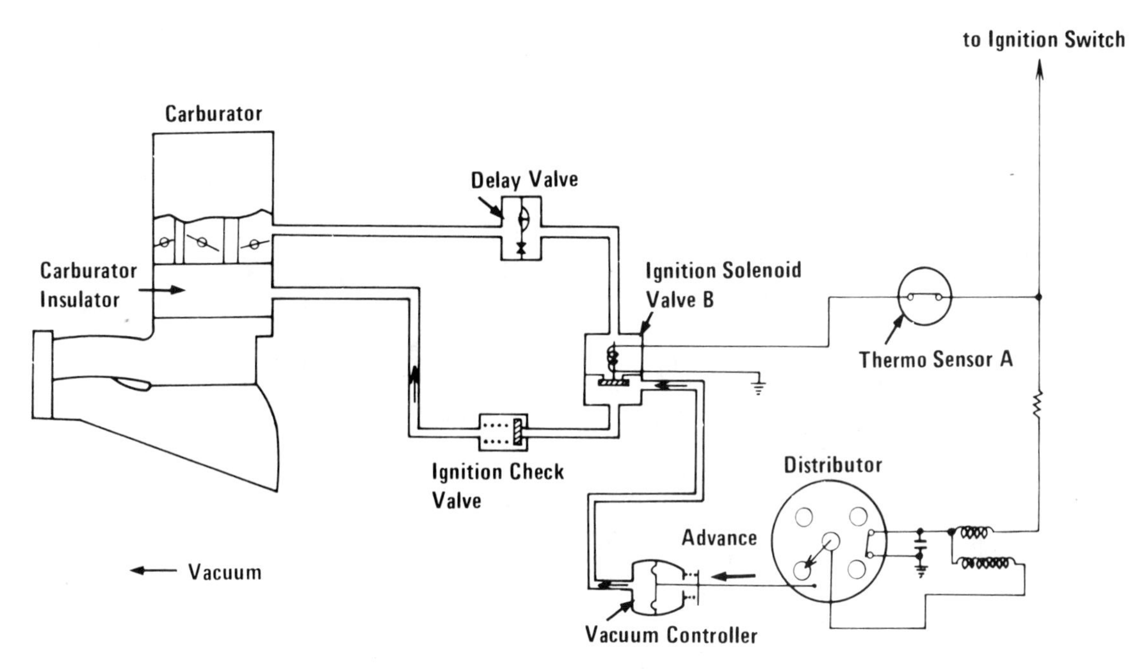

Fig. 3.30. Ignition timing control layout for the manual and KA Hondamatic transmission models (Sec. 19)

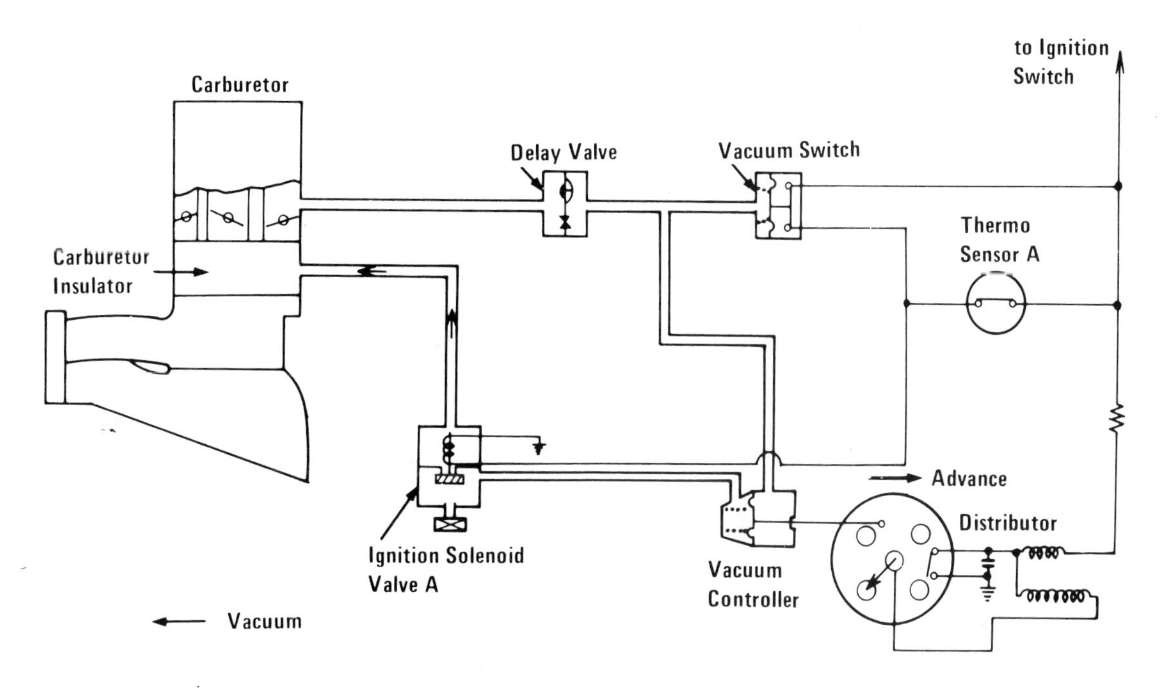

Fig. 3.31. Ignition timing control diagram for the Hondamatic transmission models KL and HA (Sec. 19)

signals (at roadspeeds above approximately 20 mph (32 kph) a solenoid valve which opens and applies vacuum to the throttle control valve. When this vacuum pressure exceeds a preset value during deceleration, the throttle control valve opens and in turn the throttle controller diaphragm opens the throttle in the carburettor a fixed amount to improve combustion.

3 When the vehicle speed drops to 10 mph (16 kph) or the vacuum pressure drops below the preset value of the throttle control valve this valve closes and the residual vacuum in the system is destroyed by the entry of air at atmospheric pressure through the valve orifice.

4 The second system (all models) incorporates a dashpot to restrict the closing speed of the throttle. The dashpot solenoid valve actuated by the manifold vacuum displaces air from the rear of the throttle controller diaphragm and so prevents the throttle plate closing too quickly.

5 During the period of throttle closure, the flow of air is restricted by the dashpot solenoid valve orifice and flows to both the carburettor and the throttle controller diaphragm. When the throttle valve plate finally closes, and blocks the carburettor vacuum port then air flows only to the throttle controller diaphragm.

6 Any malfunction in the system may be due to loose hoses or electrical connections. Testing of individual components cannot be carried out without special equipment.

21 Charcoal canister - maintenance and testing

1 Incorporated into the evaporative emission control circuit, the charcoal canister must be inspected every 15,000 miles (24,000 km) and renewed every 30,000 miles (48,000 km).

2 In addition a regular check should be made to ensure that the hose connections are secure and that the interconnecting hoses are in good

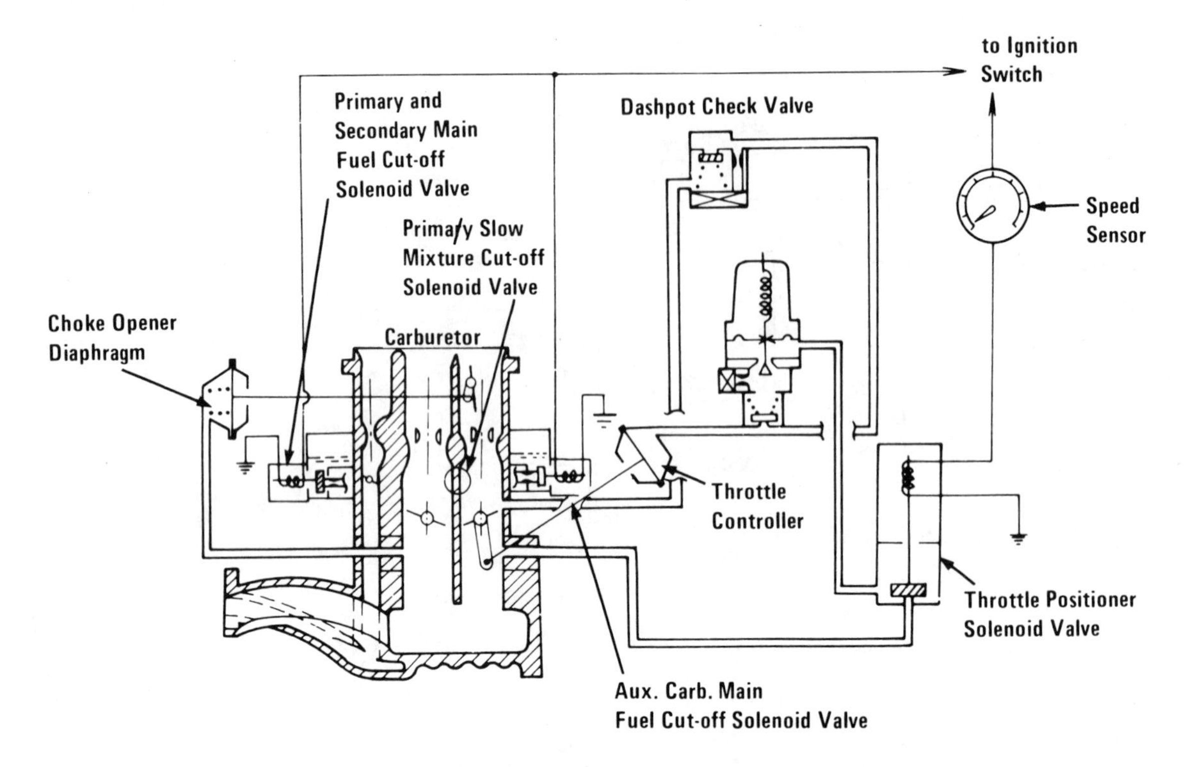

Fig. 3.32. The KL model throttle controller system (Sec. 20)

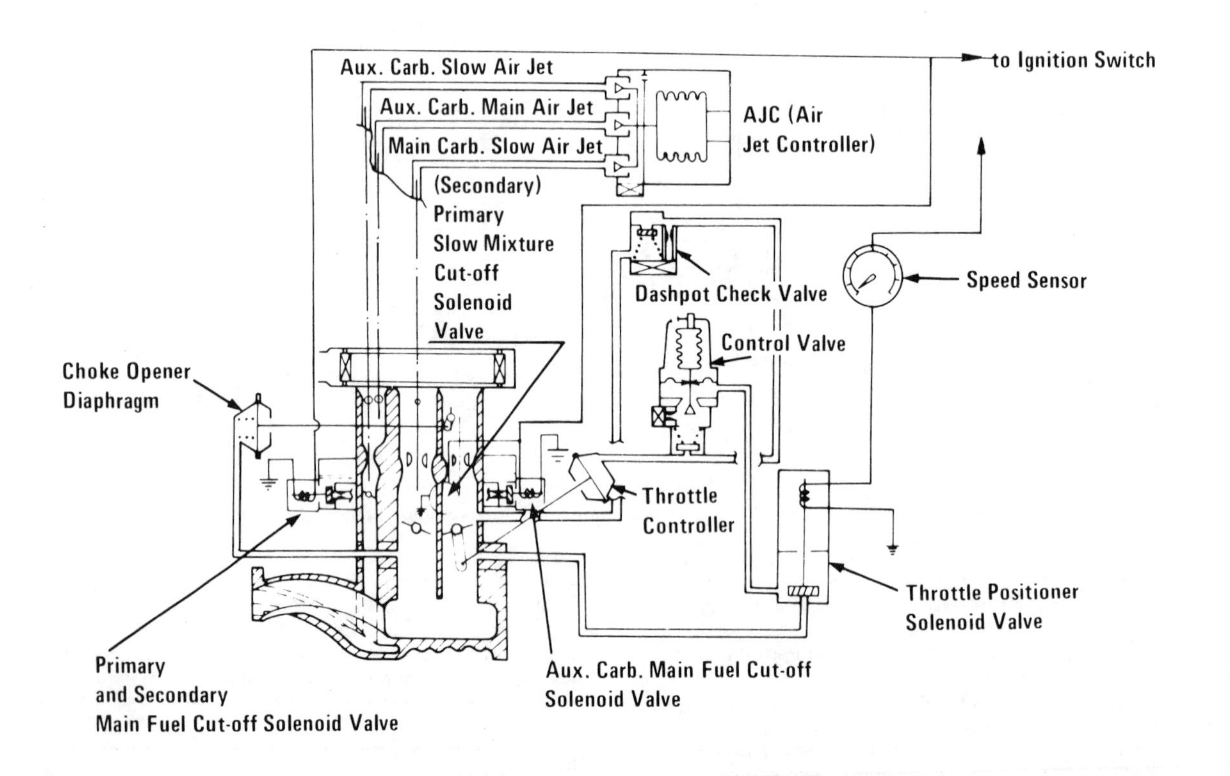

Fig. 3.33. The HA model throttle controller system (Sec. 20)

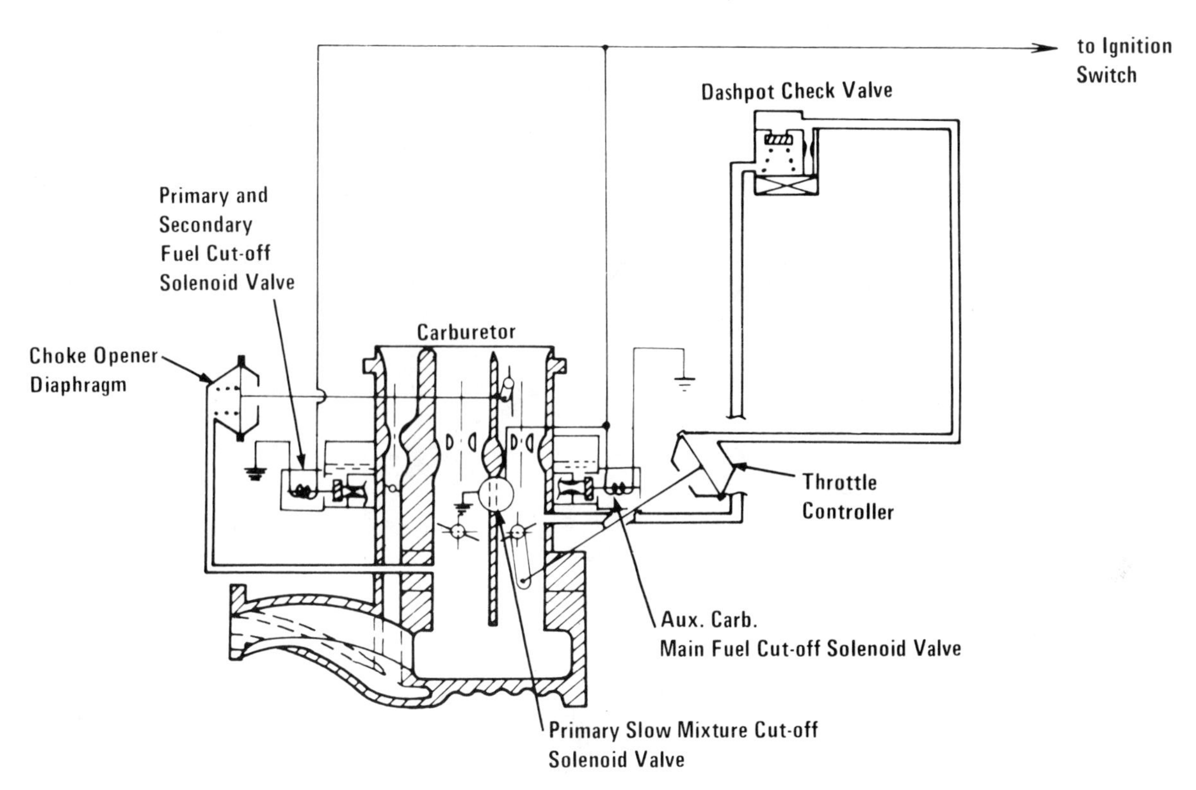

Fig. 3.34. The KA model throttle controller system (Sec. 20)

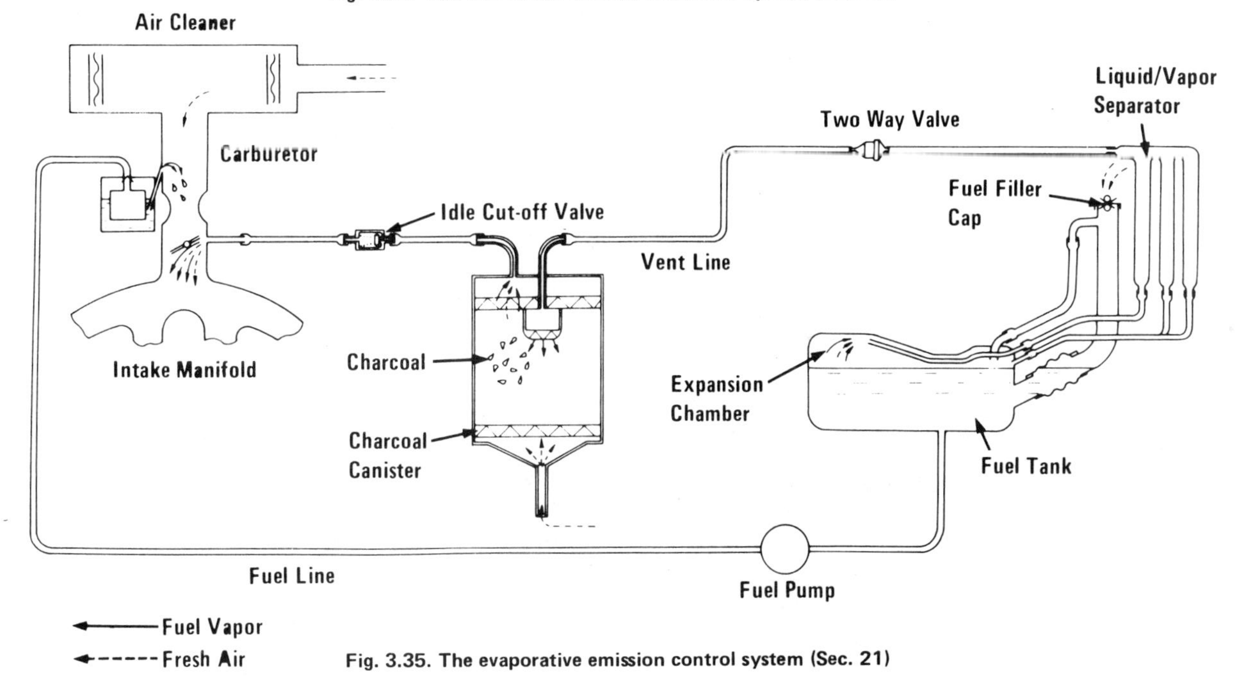

Fig. 3.35. The evaporative emission control system (Sec. 21)

condition.

3 If the canister operation is suspect, test as follows:

a) Remove the charcoal canister from the inner wing panel, but do not disconnect the upper connection hoses. Take care not to damage the canister when handling.

b) Disconnect the intake tube hose and place a finger over the end of the canister inlet ube as in Fig. 3.35.

c) Run the engine at idle and increase the speed to 2,500 rpm. If the canister is functioning correctly, air will be drawn into the canister via the inlet tube and suction should be felt. If there is no suction then the canister must be renewed.

22 Manifolds and exhaust system - removal and refitting

Exhaust system

1 The exhaust system is of three section type and includes a single silencer (Fig. 3.36).

2 The exhaust pipe, silencer and manifolds must be inspected at regular intervals to ensure that they are securely located and do not leak or show signs of severe rust.

3 Any leaks must be repaired at the earliest opportunity as apart from the noise factor, the poisonous fumes given off can enter the car with

FUEL TANK
HEAT SHIELD
MUFFLER
HEAT SHIELD
"B"
HEAT SHIELD
"A"
FRONT
HEAT SHIELD
EXHAUST PIPE "A"
EXHAUST PIPE "B"
SPECIAL NUT
* Inspect for damage

Fig. 3.36. The exhaust system components (Sec. 22)

NOTE: 1978 models have 3 stud flange at manifold downpipe

22.4 The exhaust downpipe to manifold connections

22.9 Remove the upper heat shield

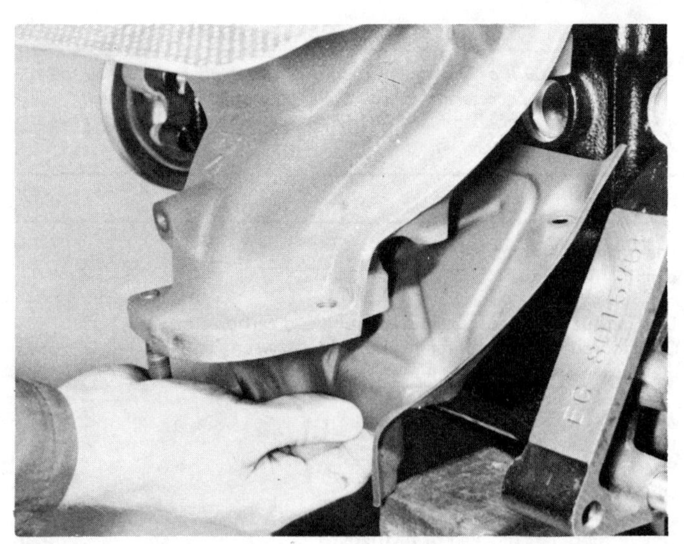
22.11 Remove the hot air cover

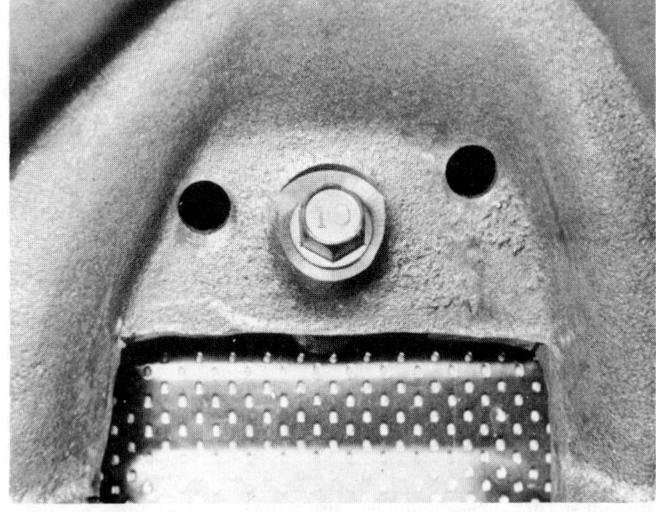
22.13 The exhaust to inlet manifold lower retaining bolt position

disastrous results for both driver and passengers.

4 The exhaust pipe system can be removed as a unit by disconnecting from the exhaust manifold and support bracket and from the central and rear flexible location supports (photo).

5 Alternatively, any individual pipe section may be removed by disconnecting at the respective flange.

6 Installation of the system is a reversal of removal but do not fully tighten the retaining nuts/bolts until the complete system is located and clear of bodywork and surrounding fittings.

Inlet/exhaust manifolds

7 The inlet and exhaust manifolds are removed as a pair and then separated. Remove as follows:

8 Remove the air cleaner and carburettor - see appropriate Sections.

9 Remove the upper heat shield (photo) and gasket.

10 Disconnect the exhaust pipe from the manifold and support bracket.

11 Remove the hot air cover (photo).

12 Unscrew the respective manifold to cylinder head retaining nuts and washers and remove the inlet and exhaust manifolds.

13 To separate the inlet and exhaust manifolds, unscrew the two upper and one lower (photo) retaining bolts.

14 Installation is the reversal of removal but be sure to fit new gaskets and tighten the retaining nuts/bolts to the specified torques. Check the system on completion for exhaust leaks and the fuel line to carburettor for fuel leaks.

See overleaf for 'Fault diagnosis - fuel system and carburation' and 'Fault diagnosis - emission control system'

23 Fault diagnosis - fuel system and carburation

Unsatisfactory engine performance and excessive fuel consumption are not necessarily the fault of the fuel system or carburettor. In fact they more commonly occur as a result of ignition and timing faults. Before acting on the following it is necessary to check the ignition system first. Even though a fault may lie in the fuel system it will be difficult to trace unless the ignition is correct. The faults below, therefore, assume that this has been attended to first (where appropriate).

Symptom	Reason/s
Smell of petrol when engine is stopped	Leaking fuel lines or unions. Leaking fuel tank.
Smell of petrol when engine is idling	Leaking fuel line unions between pump and carburettor. Overflow of fuel from float chamber due to wrong level setting, ineffective needle valve or punctured float.
Excessive fuel consumption for reasons not covered by leaks or float chamber faults	Worn jets. Incorrect jets. Sticking mechanism on choke. Dirty air filter.
Difficult starting, uneven running, lack of power, cutting out	One or more jets blocked or restricted. Float chamber fuel level too low or needle valve sticking. Fuel pump not delivering sufficient fuel.
Engine run-on (dieseling)	Primary slow mixture cut-off solenoid valve faulty. Primary and secondary main cut-off solenoid valves faulty
Engine will not start	Auxiliary main solenoid cut-off valve faulty.

Fault diagnosis - emission control system

Symptom	Reason/s
Air cleaner deflector flap fails to operate correctly	Faulty air bleed valve. Faulty diaphragm in vacuum capsule. Clogged non-return valve.
Throttle closure too fast or too slow	Leaks in system hoses. Faulty dashpot solenoid valve. Faulty throttle control valve. Faulty throttle positioner solenoid valve. Faulty speed sensor. Blown fuse in system.

Chapter 4 Ignition system

For modifications, and information applicable to later models, see Supplement at end of manual

Contents

Specifications

System type	12V battery, coil and distributor
Firing order	1 - 3 - 4 - 2 (No 1 nearest to timing belt)
Distributor	
Rotor rotation direction	Counterclockwise
Contact breaker points gap	0.018 to 0.022 in (0.45 to 0.55 mm)
Dwell angle	52 ± 3°
Point spring pressure	17.6 to 22.9 oz (500 to 650 g)
Spark plug type	
Standard	NGK B-6ES or NGK BR6EB ND W-20ES or Denso W20ESR-L
High speed	NGK B-7ES or NGK BR6ES ND W-22ES or Denso W20ESR
Spark plug gap	0.028 to 0.032 in (0.70 to 0.80 mm)
Ignition coil	
Specific voltage	6V - without resistor 12V - with resistor
Ballast resistance	1.6 ohms $\pm$ 10% at $70^{o}F$ ($21^{o}C$)
Primary coil resistance	1.35 to 1.65 ohms at $70^{o}F$ ($21^{o}C$)
Secondary coil resistance	8000 to 12000 ohms at $70^{o}F$ ($21^{o}C$)
Ignition timing (at idle)	
Manual transmission	
Standard	6° BTDC $\pm 2^{o}$
CVCC engine models	2° BTDC
Hondamatic transmission	
Standard	6° BTDC $\pm 2^{o}$
CVCC engine models	0° TDC
Swedish models	2° BTDC $\pm 2^{o}$

1 General description

The ignition system is of 12 volt battery, coil and distributor type, the distributor being driven by a gear from the camshaft.

In order that the internal combustion engine with coil ignition can operate properly, the spark which ignites the air/fuel charge in the combustion chamber must be delivered at precisely the correct moment. This correct moment is that which will allow time for the charge to burn sufficiently to create the highest pressure and temperature possible in the combustion chamber as the piston passes top-dead-centre and commences its power stroke. The distributor and ignition coil are the main devices which ensure that the spark plug ignites the charge as required.

Very high voltages are required to be generated in the ignition system in order to produce the spark across the plug gap which ignites the fuel/air charge. The device in which these high voltages - several thousand volts - are generated, is the coil. The coil contains two sets of windings - the primary and the secondary windings. A current at 12 volts is fed through the primary windings via the contact breaker mechanism in the distributor. It is precisely when the flow is interrupted by the contact breaker that the huge voltage is momentarily induced in the secondary windings and that voltage is conveyed via HT leads and the rotor arm in the distributor cap to the appropriate spark plug.

It follows therefore that the contact breakers must part the instant a spark is required and the rotor arm must be aligned to the appropriate stud in the distributor cap which is 'connected' to the spark plug which 'needs' the spark. The distributor shaft revolves at half crankshaft speed, and there are four lobes on the distributor cam and four studs in the distributor cap, to cater for the four sparks the engine requires each two revolutions of the crankshaft.

On this Honda the timing of the ignition is set by three means:

i) Static timing
ii) Mechanical centrifugal advance
iii) Inlet manifold vacuum advance/retard (automatic)

The static timing is that nominal setting which accounts for the time for combustion at the idling speed of the engine. It is necessary therefore when carrying out ignition or carburation adjustments using a stroboscope to ensure that the engine is turning at the speed appropriate to that test or adjustment.

The centrifugal advance mechanism ensures that the spark arrives in the cylinder in that interval of time for combustion which corresponds to a greater angle of crankshaft movement when the engine is turning quickly than when it turns slowly. The mechanism comprises two weights on an arm on the distributor shaft. As the shaft speed increases the weights move outwards against their restraining spring. The contact breaker cam is attached to the weights so that as they move out, it is rotated relative to the distributor shaft, and therefore the contact breaker will open earlier relative to the distributor shaft and crankshaft as required.

The vacuum advance/retard system functions to alter ignition timing to cater for mixture strength. The time for combustion of the fuel/air mixture will vary slightly with mixture strength. The richer the mixture, the longer time it takes to burn. The system comprises a diaphragm device actuated by inlet manifold and carburettor throat pressure, attached to the distributor. The diaphragm is connected to the contact breaker plate to rotate it relative to the cam, to obtain the required variation of ignition timing.

The diaphragm units vary according to whether the vehicle is equipped with a manual gearbox or automatic transmission.

Reference must also be made to Chapter 3, Section 19 for ignition timing control on CVCC engines having full emission control system fitted.

2 Contact breaker points - adjustment

1 Remove the distributor cap by prising back the two spring clips holding the cap to the distributor body.
2 Clean the inside and outside of the cap with a dry cloth. It is unlikely that the four studs will be badly burned or corroded, but if they are, the complete cap should be renewed. If only small deposits are on the studs, these may be scraped away with a small screwdriver.
3 Push in the carbon brush, located in the centre of the cap, several times to ensure that it moves freely; the brush should protrude at least one-quarter of an inch. Also check the distributor cap for signs of cracks. Renew the cap if cracks are visible.
4 Gently prise open the contact breaker points to examine the condition of the contact faces. If they are rough, pitted or dirty, it will be necessary to remove them for resurfacing, or for new points to be fitted (see next Section).
5 Lift the rotor arm off the cam, and clean with a dry cloth. Scrape away any small deposits with a screwdriver. It will be noticed that the rotor arm cannot be refitted in the wrong position, because of an asymmetric joint between rotor and cam.
6 If the condition of the points is satisfactory, turn the crankshaft until the points are fully open with the heel of the breaker arm on the high point of the distributor shaft cam. To turn the crankshaft, either apply a socket wrench to the crankshaft pulley bolt accessible under the left-hand front wing or jack-up a front roadwheel, select top gear and rotate the roadwheel in the forward direction of travel. This latter method applies of course only to vehicles with a manual gearbox. Remember that the crankshaft and the rotor arm turn in an anticlockwise direction.
7 Now insert a feeler gauge between the contact breaker points and adjust the gap to between 0.018 and 0.022 in (0.45 and 0.55 mm) by releasing the two contact breaker securing screws and turning the eccentric adjusting screw (photo).
8 When the gap is correct, tighten the securing screws.
9 It is recommended that for more precise setting, the dwell angle is now checked and any further adjustment to the points gap carried out to bring the dwell angle to within the specified range of 49 to 55°.
10 The dwell angle is the number of degrees through which the distributor cam turns between the moment of closure and the moment of opening of the contact breaker points. This can only be checked

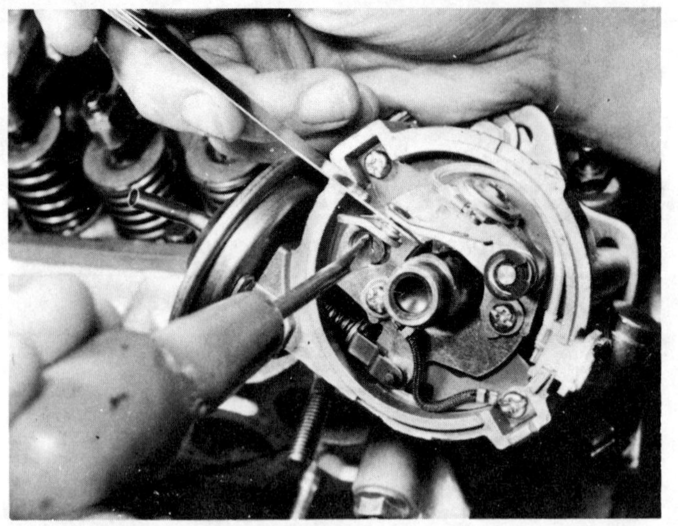

2.7 Adjusting the contact breaker points

using a dwell meter. If the angle is too large, increase the points gap; if too small, reduce the gap.
11 Refit the rotor arm, the distributor cap and clips.

3 Contact breaker points - removal and refitting

1 If the contact breaker points are burnt, pitted or badly worn, they must be either renewed or refaced accordingly.
2 To remove the contact breaker points, unscrew and remove the two retaining screws and lift away the plate earthing wire.
3 Loosen, but do not remove, the condenser lead terminal screw and detach the lead from the contact breaker spring.
4 Lift away the contact breaker set.
5 To reface the points, rub the faces on a fine carborundum stone or on fine emery paper. It is important that the faces are rubbed flat and parallel to each other so that there will be complete face to face contact when the points are closed. One of the points will be pitted and the other will have deposits on it.
6 It is necessary to completely remove the built up deposits but not necessary to rub the pitted points to the stage where all the pitting has disappeared, though obviously if this is done it will prolong the time before the refacing task needs to be repeated.
7 Refitting the contact breaker points follows the reversal of the removal sequence. It will be necessary to adjust the gap, as detailed in the previous Section.

4 Condenser (capacitor) - testing, removal and refitting

1 The purpose of the condenser (sometimes known as a capacitor), is to ensure that when the contact breaker points open there is no sparking across them which would waste voltage and cause wear.
2 The condenser is fitted in parallel with the contact breaker points. If it develops a short circuit, it will cause ignition failure as the points will be prevented from interrupting the low tension circuit.
3 If the engine becomes very difficult to start or begins to misfire after several miles running, and the breaker points show signs of excessive burning, then the condition of the condenser must be suspect. A further test can be made by separating the points by hand with the ignition switched on. If this is accompanied by a flash it is indicative that the condenser has failed.
4 Without special test equipment the only sure way to diagnose condenser trouble is to replace a suspected unit with a new one and note if there is any improvement. Severe erosion of the points can be due to poor earth connections at the battery, distributor or engine earth strap.
5 To remove the condenser on Hondamatic models from the distributor, first remove the distributor cap.
6 Detach the condenser cable from the terminal block and remove

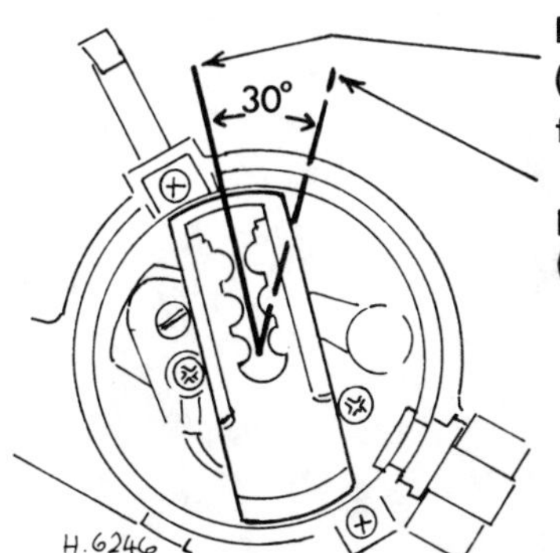

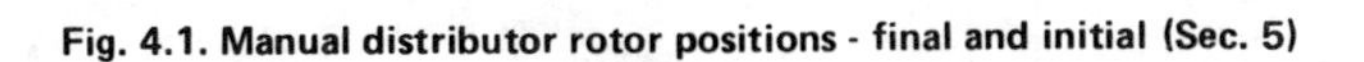
Fig. 4.1. Manual distributor rotor positions - final and initial (Sec. 5)

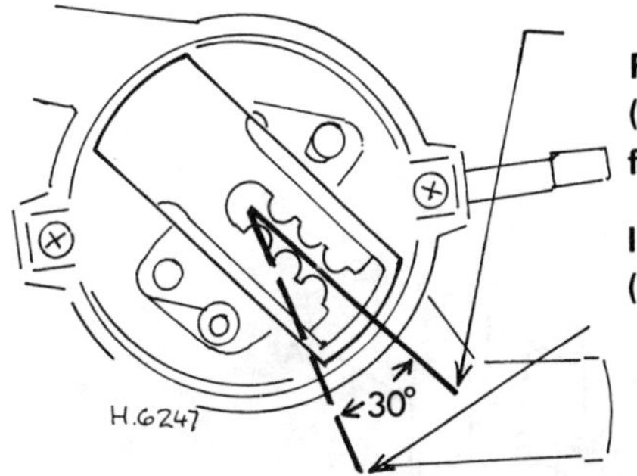

Fig. 4.2. Hondamatic distributor rotor positions - final and initial (Sec. 5)

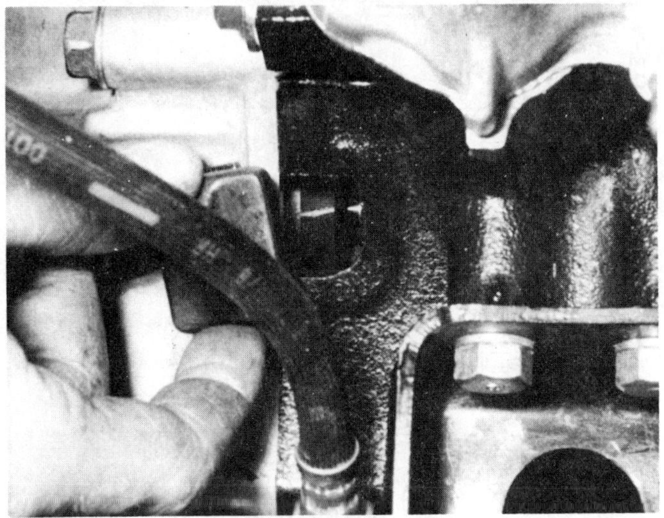
5.3 Remove the plug to check the timing position

5.5 Remove the distributor (manual transmission)

the condenser fixing to the body. Lift away the condenser.

7 Refitting of the condenser is the reversal of removal. On manual models the condenser is located on the outside of the distributor. Removal is otherwise the same.

5 Distributor - removal and refitting

1 Unclip and lift clear the distributor cap and HT leads.

2 Disconnect the low tension lead at distributor (from the coil) and the vacuum advance/retard connection.

3 Rotate the crankshaft to the TDC position. To turn the crankshaft refer to paragraph 6 in Section 2. Refer to Figs. 4.1 and 4.2. accordingly to check that the rotor arm is in the correct position with No. 1 piston at TDC on firing stroke. This is further checked by removing the rubber grommet from the rear of the cylinder block just above the clutch slave cylinder and aligning the mark on the flywheel or driveplate (white for manual transmission - red for Hondamatic) with the pointer on the rear face of the cylinder block (photo).

4 Index mark the distributor body with respect to the fixing plate and distributor/thermostat housing. This simplifies refitting the distributor ensuring correct engagement.

5 Unscrew and remove the bolt securing the distributor clamp plate to the housing and then withdraw the distributor (photo).

6 Refitting is the reversal of removal. When reinserting the distributor align the body to housing marks and initially position the rotor 30° offset to the final position to allow for rotor shaft movement when meshing the gears. Ensure that the 'O' ring is in position prior to installation (Fig. 4.3).

7 Before tightening the clamp plate bolt check and adjust if required the ignition timing as described in Section 7.

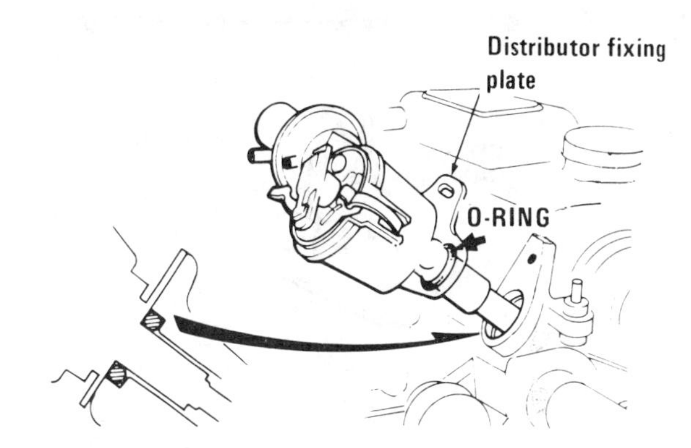

Fig. 4.3. 'O' ring position (Sec. 5)

6 Distributor - overhaul

1 The operational life of the distributor is normally long but when wear is evident in the working components it may prove more economical to renew the distributor complete. If it is decided to overhaul the original distributor, ensure that the necessary spare parts are available first.

2 When obtaining spare parts, be sure to quote the engine serial number as the distributor type varies according to model and year.

3 Having removed the distributor from the engine withdraw the rotor and contact breaker points.

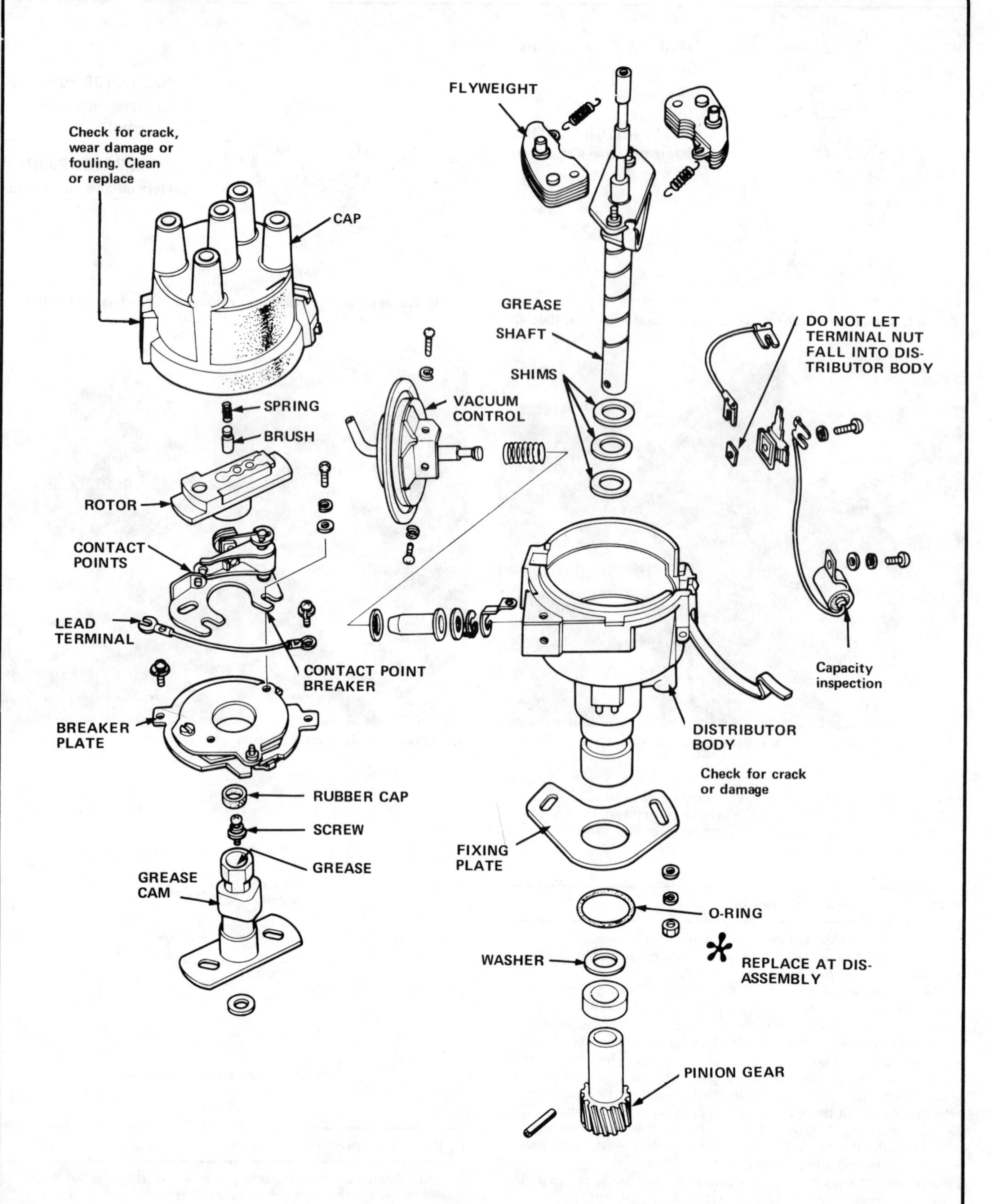

Fig. 4.4. Distributor components - manual transmission models (Sec. 6)

4 Disconnect the vacuum control unit by detaching the advance retard link rod to the breaker support plate, and unscrewing the diaphragm unit retaining screws. Lift the link rod clear, rotate the contact support plate and withdraw the advance/retard unit.
5 Unscrew and remove the contact plate retaining screws. Lift the support plate clear to gain access to the centrifugal advance mechanism.
6 Remove the rubber cap from the top of the distributor cam, and undo and remove the screw which has been exposed. Once the screw is removed the cam can be lifted off the distributor shaft and centrifugal advance mechanism.
7 Turning the distributor on its side drive out the pin which retains the driven gear to the distributor shaft. Remove the gear.
8 Once the driven gear has been removed, pull the distributor shaft upwards out of the distributor case, so that the weights and springs of the centrifugal advance mechanism can be removed. Be careful to recover the washers and seals on the distributor shaft. Note their position ready for reassembly.
9 Examine all components for wear and renew as necessary.
10 Reassembly is a straightforward reversal of the dismantling sequence, but there are a few points to be watched:
11 Lubricate the balance weights and other parts of the centrifugal advance mechanism, and the main distributor shaft with clean engine grade oil during assembly. Do not oil excessively, but ensure adequate lubrication.
12 Check the movement of the centrifugal advance mechanism throughout the whole advance/retard range; ensure that there is no binding and that movement is smooth.
13 Check that the contact breaker support plate turns smoothly on its mounting plate and ensure that there is no radial movement on the centre bearing.
14 Make certain that the vacuum advance/retard mechanism functions smoothly, without any jerks or binding, by sucking the vacuum pipe.
15 If the springs and flyweights have been removed from the shaft, ensure on reassembly that they are correctly located. When fitting the cam, fit it so that the short slot is located over the flyweights with the heavier spring. When the cam is located on the flyweight the flat surface must face the circular hook (Fig. 4.5).
16 Finally, when the distributor is fully assembled on the engine, check the contact breaker gap.

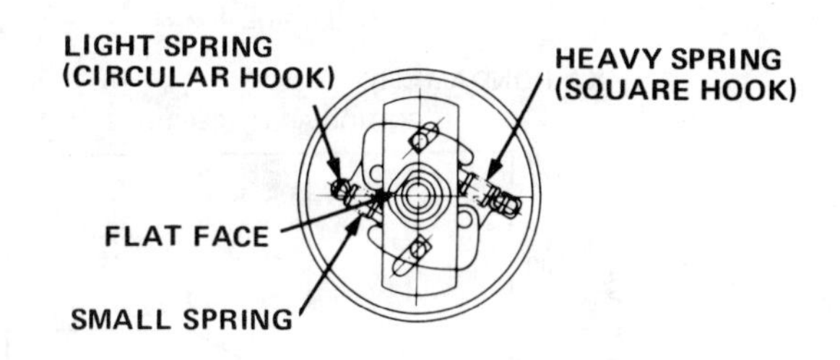

Fig. 4.5. Spring positions (Sec. 6)

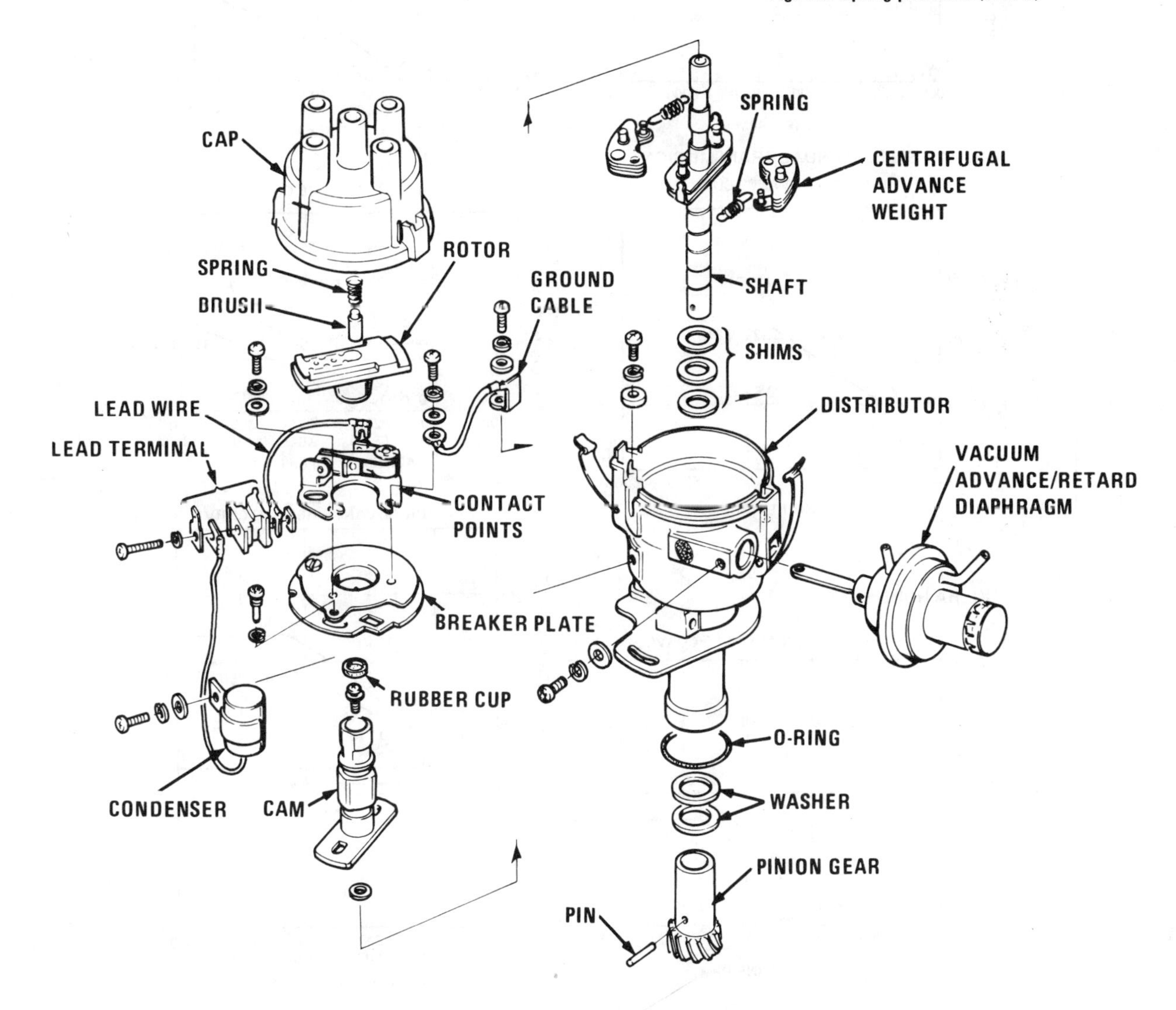

Fig. 4.6. Distributor components - Hondamatic (KL and HA) models (Sec. 6)

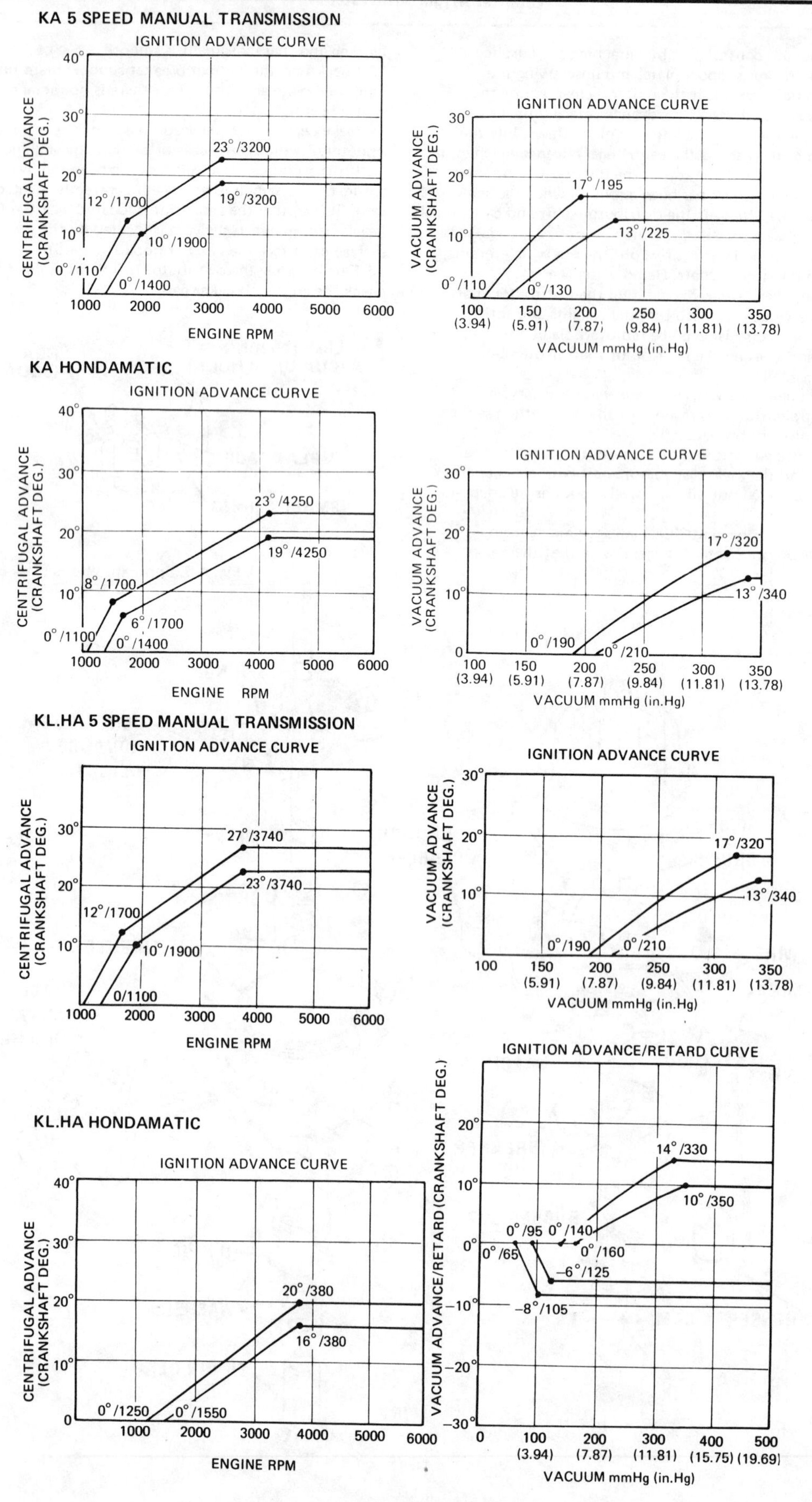

Fig. 4.7. Ignition advance curves

7 Ignition timing (with test lamp)

1 Turn the crankshaft in an anticlockwise direction by one of the methods described in Section 2, until No. 1 piston is just coming up to TDC on its compression stroke. This can be judged if No. 1 spark plug (one nearest crankshaft pulley) is removed and the finger placed over the plug hole. The cylinder compression will be felt being generated as the piston rises up the bore. Continue to rotate the crankshaft very slowly until the appropriate advance mark on the flywheel or drive-plate is opposite the pointer on the crankcase.
2 The timing marks are shown in Figs. 4.8 and 4.9. The manual transmission model timing differs from the Hondamatic transmission models - refer to the Specifications.
3 Now connect a test lamp between the low tension terminal of the distributor and a good earth and switch on the ignition.
4 Release the distributor clamp plate bolt and turn the distributor until the test lamp just lights up or goes out if the distributor is moved fractionally either way.
5 Tighten the distributor clamp plate bolt and remove the test lamp and switch off the ignition.

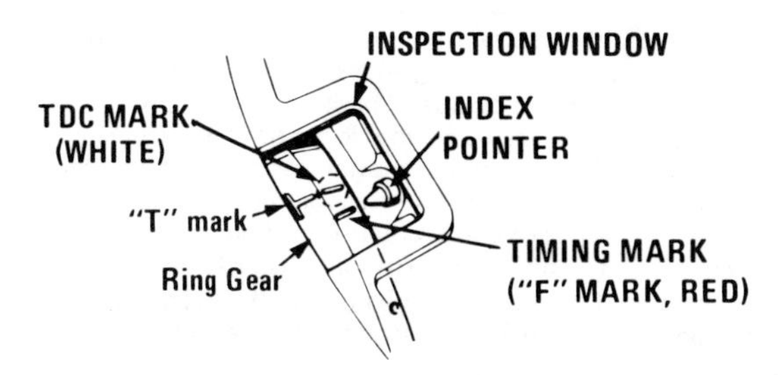

Fig. 4.8. Manual transmission model timing mark (Sec. 7)

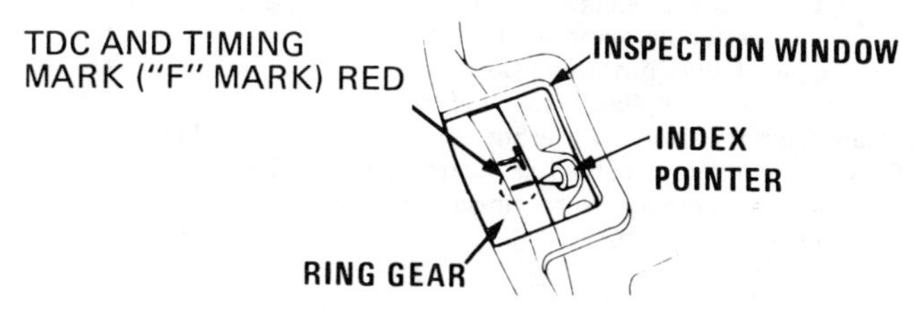

Fig. 4.9. Hondamatic transmission model timing mark (Sec. 7)

8 Ignition timing (with stroboscope)

1 Disconnect the vacuum pipes from the distributor diaphragm capsule and plug the pipes.
2 Connect the stroboscope in accordance with the manufacturer's instructions, this usually being between No. 1 spark plug terminal and the end of No. 1 high tension lead.
3 Start the engine and let it idle at specified idling speed at operating temperature.

Manual transmission (standard) - 750 ± 50 rpm
Manual transmission (CVCC models) - 800 ± 50 rpm
Hondamatic transmission (standard) - 680 ± 50 rpm
Hondamatic transmission (CVCC models) - 680 ± 50 rpm

4 Point the stroboscope at the timing pointer on the crankcase. If the timing is correct, the BTDC mark on the flywheel or driveplate will be in perfect alignment with the pointer on the crankcase. If it is not, release the bolt on the distributor clamp plate and turn the distributor body one way or the other until the marks are in alignment and then retighten the bolt.
5 A secondary purpose of the stroboscope is to check that the centrifugal mechanism is working correctly. If the engine is revved up momentarily, the flywheel mark should be seen to move away from the pointer and then return to its position of alignment as the engine idling speed is resumed.

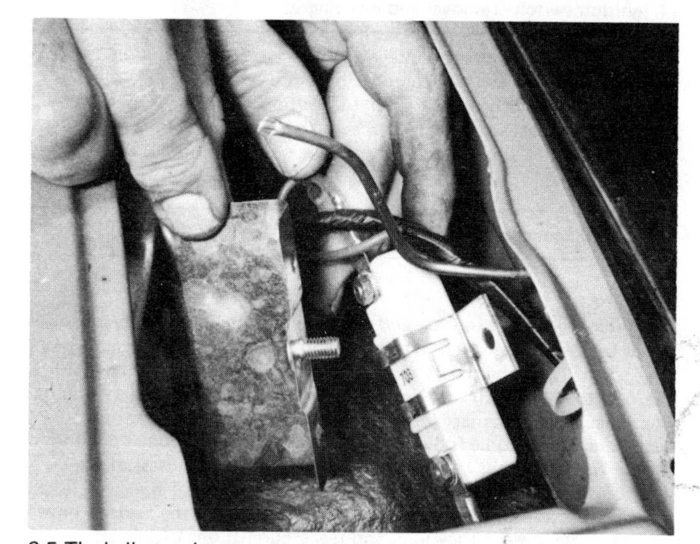

9.5 The ballast resistor

9 The coil - description and maintenance

1 Maintenance of the coil is minimal and involves periodically wiping its surfaces clean and dry and ensuring that the lead connections are good. High voltages generated by the coil can easily short to earth over its surface and prevent spark plugs from receiving the electrical pulses. Water repellant sprays are now available to prevent dampness causing this type of coil malfunction.
2 Damp and dirty HT leads and distributor cap can also cause ignition system failure.
3 Testing the coil performance requires specialized equipment and should therefore be entrusted to your Honda or local auto electrical dealer.
4 The coil is easily removed and refitted. It is retained by two screws and of course the HT and low tension leads will also have to be detached.
5 In order to maintain ignition circuit voltage where the starter motor is operated a ballast resistor is fitted and is used in conjunction with the coil.

An ohmmeter is required to test the resistor which should show a resistance of 1.6 ohms ± 10% at an ambient temperature of 70°F. Access to the ballast resistor is gained by removing the airscoop at the base of the windscreen, and the resistor is located directly behind the ignition coil (photo).

10 Spark plugs and HT leads

1 Correct operation of the spark plugs is vital for optimum performance and efficiency of the engine.
2 At intervals of 5000 miles (8000 km) remove, clean and regap the spark plugs. At intervals of 15000 miles (24000 km) renew the spark plugs.
3 If the insulator nose of the spark plug is clean and white, with no deposits, this is indicative of a weak mixture, or too hot a plug. (A hot plug transfers heat away from the electrode slowly - a cold plug transfers heat away quickly).
4 The plugs fitted as standard are one of those as specified at the beginning of this Chapter. If the top and insulator nose is covered with hard black-looking deposits, then this is indicative that the mixture is too rich. However, plugs removed from CVCC engines may have more carbon build up than normal. This is due to the plug igniting the rich mixture in the auxiliary pre combustion chamber and is quite normal for this engine type. Should the plug be black and oily, then it is likely that the engine is fairly worn, as well as the mixture being too rich.
5 If the insulator nose is covered with light tan, to greyish brown, deposits, then the mixture is correct and it is likely that the engine is in good condition.
6 If there are any traces of long brown tapering stains on the outside

of the white portion of the plug, then the plug will have to be renewed, as this shows that there is a faulty joint between the plug body and the insulator, and compression is being allowed to leak away.
7 Plugs should be cleaned by a sand blasting machine, which will free them from carbon more than cleaning by hand. The machine will also test the condition of the plugs under compression. Any plug that fails to spark at the recommended pressure should be renewed.
8 The spark plug gap is of considerable importance as, if it is too large, or too small, the size of the spark and its efficiency will be seriously impaired. For the best results the spark plug gap should be set in accordance with the Specifications at the beginning of this Chapter.
9 To set it, measure the gap with a feeler gauge, and then bend open, or close, the outer plug electrode until the correct gap is achieved. The centre electrode should never be bent as this may crack the insulation and cause plug failure if nothing worse.
10 When refitting the plugs, remember to use new washers, and refit the leads from the distributor in the correct firing order, which is 1, 3, 4, 2 (No. 1 cylinder being the one nearest the crankshaft pulley).
11 The plug leads require no routine attention other than being kept clean and wiped over regularly.

11 Ignition switch - removal and refitting

1 The ignition switch is an integral part of the steering column lock and the complete assembly can only be removed after drilling out the shear bolts as described in Chapter 11, Section 11.
2 The switch leads can be disconnected by disconnecting the multi-pin plug which is located at the side of the steering column.

12 Fault diagnosis - ignition system

Engine fails to start

1 If the engine fails to start and the car was running normally when it was last used, first check there is fuel in the tank. If the engine turns over normally on the starter motor and the battery is evidently well charged, then the fault may be in either the high or low tension circuits. First check the secondary high tension (HT) circuit. **Note:** If the battery is known to be fully charged; the ignition light comes on, and the starter motor fails to turn the engine **check the tightness of the leads on the battery terminals** and also the secureness of the earth lead to its **connection to the body.** It is quite common for the leads to have worked loose, even if they look and feel secure. If one of the battery terminal posts gets very hot when trying to work the starter motor this is a sure indication of a faulty connection to that terminal .
2 One of the commonest reasons for bad starting is wet or damp spark plug leads and distributor. Remove the distributor cap. If condensation is visible internally, dry the cap with a rag and also wipe over the leads. Refit the cap.
3 If the engine still fails to start, check that current is reaching the plugs, by disconnecting each plug lead in turn at the spark plug end, and hold the end of the cable about 3/16th inch (5.0 mm) away from the cylinder block. Spin the engine on the starter motor.
4 Sparking between the end of the cable and the block should be fairly strong with a regular blue spark. (Hold the lead with rubber to avoid electric shocks). If current is reaching the plugs, then remove them and clean and regap them. The engine should now start.
5 If there is no spark at the plug leads take off the secondary high tension (HT) lead from the centre of the distributor cap and hold it to the block as before. Spin the engine on the starter once more. A rapid succession of blue sparks between the end of the lead and the block indicate that the coil is in order and that the distributor cap is cracked, the rotor arm faulty, or the carbon brush in the top of the distributor cap is not making good contact with the rotor arm. Possibly the points are in bad condition. Clean and reset them as described in this Chapter.
6 If there are no sparks from the end of tne lead from the coil, check the connections at the coil end of the lead. If it is in order start checking the low tension (primary) circuit.
7 Use a 12v voltmeter or a 12v bulb and two lengths of wire. With the ignition switch on and the points open test between the low tension wire to the coil (it is marked +) and ground. No reading indicates a break in the supply from the ignition switch. Check the connections at the switch to see if any are loose. Refit them and the engine should run. A reading shows a faulty coil or condenser, or broken lead between the coil and the distributor.
8 Take the condenser wire off the points assembly and with the points open, test between the moving point and ground. If there now is a reading, then the fault is in the condenser. Fit a new one and the fault is cleared.
9 With no reading from the moving point to earth take a reading between earth and the CB or – terminal of the coil. A reading here shows a broken wire which will need to be replaced between the coil and distributor. No reading confirms that the coil has failed and must be replaced, after which the engine will run once more. Remember to refit the condenser wire to the points assembly. For these tests it is sufficient to separate the points with a piece of dry paper while testing with the points open.

Engine misfires

10 If the engine misfires regularly, run it at a fast idling speed. Pull off each of the plug caps in turn and listen to the note of the engine. Hold the plug cap in a dry cloth or with a rubber glove as additional protection against a shock from the HT supply.
11 No difference in engine running will be noticed when the lead from the defective circuit is removed. Removing the lead from one of the good cylinders will accentuate the misfire.
12 Remove the plug lead from the end of the defective plug and hold it about 3/16th inch (4.8 mm) away from the block. Restart the engine. If the sparking is fairly strong and regular the fault must lie in the spark plug.
13 The plug may be loose, the insulation may be cracked, or the points may have burnt away giving too wide a gap for the spark to jump. Worse still, one of the points may have broken off. Either renew the plug, or clean it, reset the gap, and then test it.
14 If there is no spark at the end of the plug lead, or if it is weak and intermittent, check the ignition lead from the distributor to the plug. If the insulation is cracked or perished, renew the lead. Check the connections at the distributor cap.
15 If there is still no spark, examine the distributor cap carefully for tracking. This can be recognised by a very thin black line running between two or more electrodes, or between an electrode and some other part of the distributor. These lines are paths which now conduct electricity across the cap thus letting it run to earth. The only answer is a new distributor cap.
16 Apart from the ignition timing being incorrect, other causes of misfiring have already been dealt with under the section dealing with the failure of the engine to start. To recap - these are that:

a) The coil may be faulty giving an intermittent misfire;
b) There may be damaged wire or loose connection in the low tension circuit;
c) The condenser may be short circuiting;
d) There may be a mechanical fault in the distributor (broken driving spindle or contact breaker spring).

17 If the ignition timing is too far retarded, it should be noted that the engine will tend to overheat, and there will be a quite noticeable drop in power. If the engine is overheating and the power is down, and the ignition timing is correct, then the carburettor should be checked, as it is likely that this is where the fault lies.

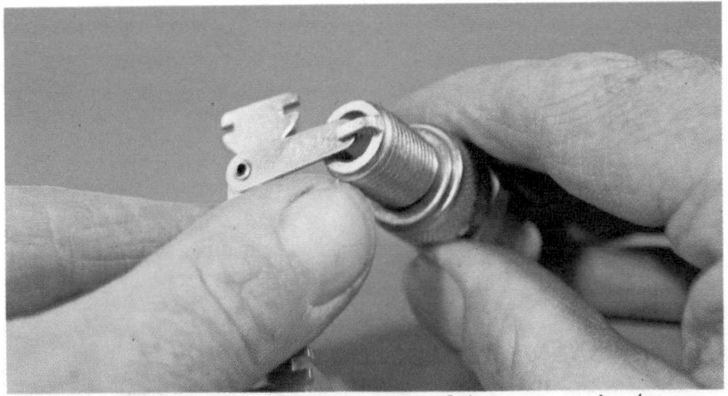

Measuring plug gap. A feeler gauge of the correct size (see ignition system specifications) should have a slight 'drag' when slid between the electrodes. Adjust gap if necessary

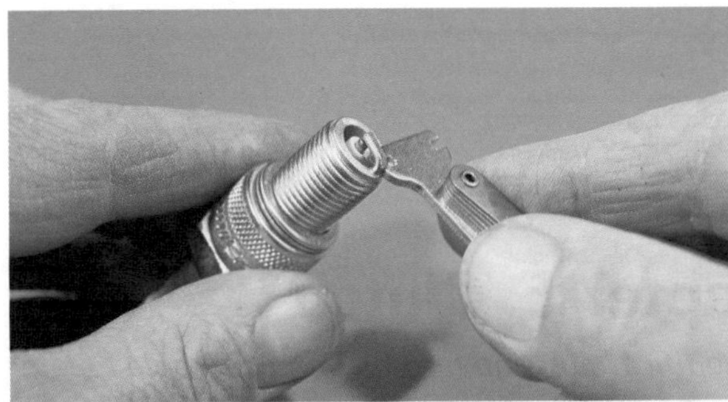

Adjusting plug gap. The plug gap is adjusted by bending the earth electrode inwards, or outwards, as necessary until the correct clearance is obtained. Note the use of the correct tool

Normal. Grey-brown deposits, lightly coated core nose. Gap increasing by around 0.001 in (0.025 mm) per 1000 miles (1600 km). Plugs ideally suited to engine, and engine in good condition

Carbon fouling. Dry, black, sooty deposits. Will cause weak spark and eventually misfire. Fault: over-rich fuel mixture. Check: carburettor mixture settings, float level and jet sizes; choke operation and cleanliness of air filter. Plugs can be re-used after cleaning

Oil fouling. Wet, oily deposits. Will cause weak spark and eventually misfire. Fault: worn bores/piston rings or valve guides; sometimes occurs (temporarily) during running-in period. Plugs can be re-used after thorough cleaning

Overheating. Electrodes have glazed appearance, core nose very white – few deposits. Fault: plug overheating. Check: plug value, ignition timing, fuel octane rating (too low) and fuel mixture (too weak). Discard plugs and cure fault immediately

Electrode damage. Electrodes burned away; core nose has burned, glazed appearance. Fault: pre-ignition. Check: as for 'Overheating' but may be more severe. Discard plugs and remedy fault before piston or valve damage occurs

Split core nose (may appear initially as a crack). Damage is self-evident, but cracks will only show after cleaning. Fault: pre-ignition or wrong gap-setting technique. Check: ignition timing, cooling system, fuel octane rating (too low) and fuel mixture (too weak). Discard plugs, rectify fault immediately

Chapter 5 Clutch

For modifications, and information applicable to later models, see Supplement at end of manual

Contents

Specifications

Type ... Single dry plate, diaphragm spring, hydraulically operated

Pressure plate

Transverse warpage ...	0.001 to 0.005 in (0.03 to 0.15 mm)

Friction disc

Thickness: new ...	0.326 to 0.354 in (8.3 to 9.0 mm)
Wear limit ...	0.232 to 0.259 in (5.9 to 6.6 mm)
Spline radial play wear limit ...	0.019 in (0.5 mm)
Surface run out limit ...	0.039 in (1.0 mm)
Minimum rivet depth ...	0.007 in (0.2 mm)

Master cylinder

Bore inside diameter ...	0.624 to 0.626 in (15.87 to 15.91 mm)
Piston outside diameter ...	0.622 to 0.623 in (15.81 to 15.83 mm)
Maximum piston to bore clearance ...	0.0059 in (0.15 mm)

Slave cylinder

Bore inside diameter ...	0.750 to 0.752 in (19.05 to 19.10 mm)
Piston outside diameter ...	0.747 to 0.749 in (18.99 to 19.03 mm)
Maximum piston to bore clearance ...	0.015 in (0.15 mm)

Clutch pedal

Stroke (A) ...	5.94 in (150 mm)
Play (C) ...	0.04 to 0.12 in (1.0 to 3.0 mm)
Height (B) ...	7.24 in (184 mm)

Clutch release holder

Inside diameter - new ...	1.141 to 1.142 in (29.0 to 29.03 mm)
Inside diameter wear limit ...	1.144 in (29.06 mm)
Holder to guide cover clearance - new ...	0.0158 to 0.0039 in (0.04 to 0.10 mm)
Holder to guide cover clearance wear limit ...	0.0079 in (0.2 mm)
Release fork free play ...	0.08 to 0.10 in (2 to 2.6 mm)

Flywheel run out limit ... 0.0016 in (0.04 mm)

Torque wrench settings	**lbf ft**	**kgf m**
Master cylinder pushrod locknut ...	21.7 to 28.9	3.0 to 4.0
Master cylinder retaining nuts ...	5 to 9	0.7 to 1.2
Pressure plate retaining bolts ...	7 to 10	1.0 to 1.4
Master cylinder hydraulic hose retaining bolt ...	22 to 29	3.0 to 4.0
Slave cylinder hydraulic hose retaining nut ...	11 to 18	1.5 to 2.5
Slave cylinder retaining bolts ...	14 to 18	1.9 to 2.5
Slave cylinder pushrod locknut ...	7 to 12	1.0 to 1.6
Flywheel retaining bolts ...	34 to 38	4.7 to 5.3
Transmission housing to engine bolts ...	22	3.0

1 General description

The clutch unit fitted to all manual transmission models is a single dry disc (driven plate) type. The unit comprises the clutch cover and pressure plate assembly, the clutch disc and the release mechanism.

The clutch release mechanism is actuated hydraulically by means of a slave cylinder mounted on the transmission housing and a master cylinder mounted in front of the clutch pedal on the engine compartment side of the firewall.

The clutch engagement is controlled by a one-way valve within the master cylinder and this regulates the return flow of the fluid when pressure on the clutch pedal is released.

2 Clutch adjustment

Release fork

1 Loosen the pushrod locknut.

2 Retain the pushrod end nut in position and, using a screwdriver, turn the pushrod accordingly to increase or decrease the free play of the release fork. The specified free play requirement is 0.08 to 0.1 in (2.0 to 2.6 mm).

3 Initially take up any free play and then slacken off the pushrod by 1.75 to 2 turns which give the free play required. Retain the pushrod in the set position and tighten the locknut. Apply some grease (Molybdenum Disulphide) between the locknut and the release fork.

Clutch pedal adjustment

4 Loosen the pedal stopper bolt locknut.

5 Turn the pedal stopper bolt accordingly to obtain the correct pedal height of 7.24 in (184 mm). Retighten the locknut whilst retaining the bolt in the set position (Fig. 5.2).

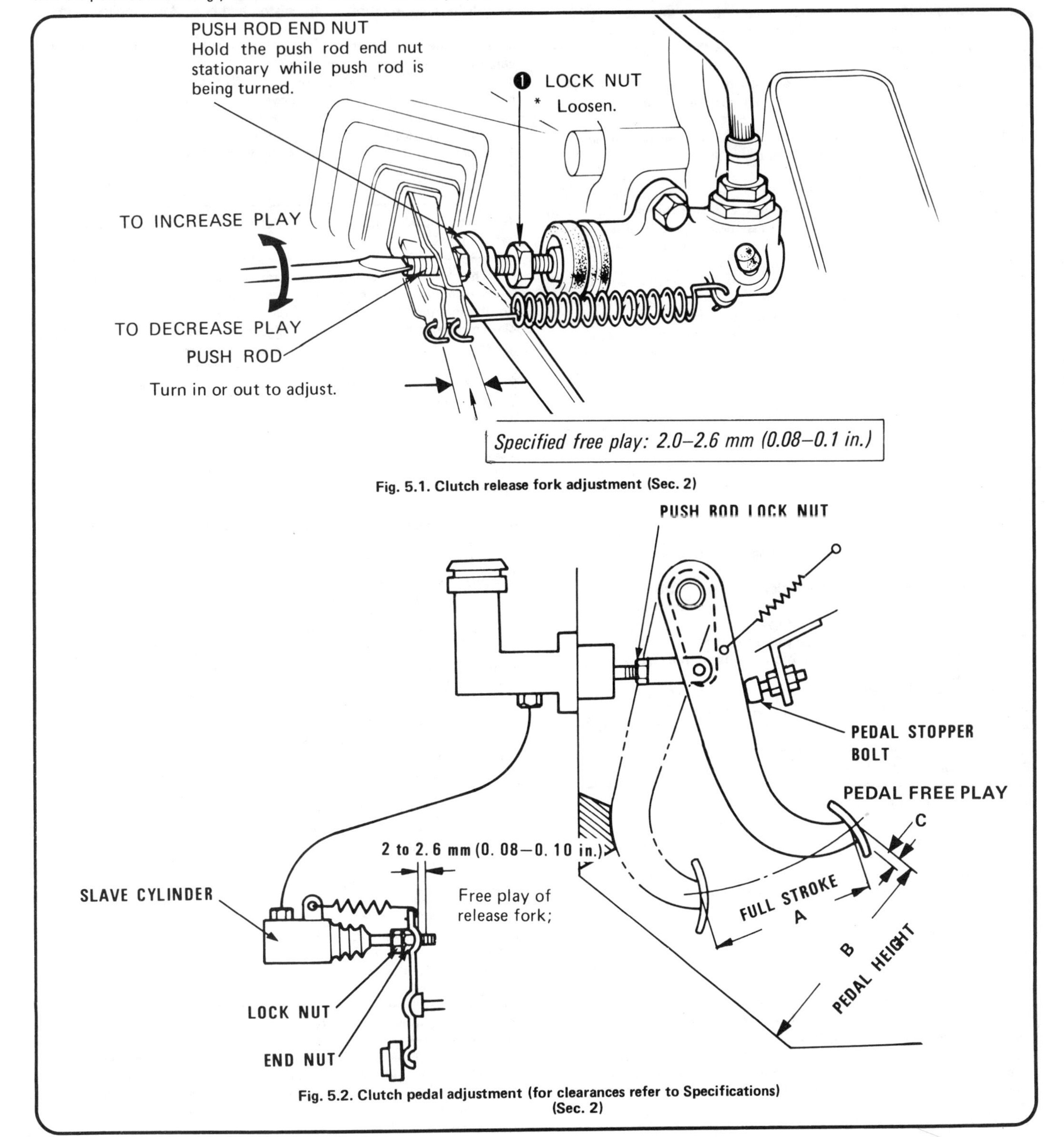

Fig. 5.1. Clutch release fork adjustment (Sec. 2)

Fig. 5.2. Clutch pedal adjustment (for clearances refer to Specifications) (Sec. 2)

6 Loosen the locknut on the master cylinder pushrod and rotate the rod accordingly to obtain the specified pedal play between the pushrod and master cylinder piston, which is 0.04 to 0.12 in (1 to 3 mm). Retighten the locknut whilst retaining the rod in the set position.

3 Clutch hydraulic system - bleeding

1 In the event of failure of any of the seals in the hydraulic system, or where part of the system has been disconnected, air will enter and need to be bled off as with the braking system.
2 To prepare for the operation, a clean jar, a short length of flexible tubing, a new supply of the recommended fluid and the services of an assistant will be required. Ensure that the master cylinder reservoir is topped-up to the full mark, and put about 1 in (25 mm) of fluid in the jar.
3 Remove the cap from the slave cylinder bleed valve and install the flexible tube to the valve. Put the other end of the tube into the fluid in the jar.
4 With the assistant inside the vehicle, slacken the bleed valve and then get the assistant to depress the clutch pedal fully and hold it down. Tighten the bleed valve.
5 The pedal can now be released, the bleed valve loosened again and the procedure repeated until no more air is expelled for each depression of the pedal. During the operation it is essential that the reservoir level is repeatedly topped-up to prevent air from entering, and that the end of the tube is kept submerged in the fluid.
6 Remove the tube on completion and install the bleed valve cap. Discard all the old fluid; it is false economy to try to use it again since it will probably be contaminated with moisture and dirt.
7 Finally check the operation of the clutch during a test drive. If necessary, adjust as described in Section 2.

4 Clutch master cylinder - removal and refitting

1 The utmost care must be taken when working on the clutch hydraulic circuit and components, in order that they are kept perfectly clean. Try not to spill any hydraulic fluid as it is harmful to the paintwork.
2 Disconnect the hydraulic fluid line at the master cylinder outlet fitting.
3 Unscrew the master cylinder retaining nuts and washers (note the plain washer on the right side only).
4 Withdraw the split pin from the clevis pin, and extract the pin.
5 Carefully withdraw the cylinder from the engine compartment rear bulkhead complete with pushrod and yoke.
6 On reassembly, insert the pedal pushrod into the master cylinder piston as the cylinder is relocated into position on the engine compartment rear bulkhead.
7 Fit and tighten the cylinder retaining nuts and washers. Reconnect the hydraulic fluid line to the outlet fitting, and bleed the hydraulic circuit as described in Section 3. Readjust the linkage if required.

5 Clutch master cylinder - dismantling and reassembly

1 The clutch master cylinder is rarely in need of attention other than a periodical topping up of the fluid. When it is to be overhauled, all rubber parts **must** be renewed, it is therefore preferable to obtain the new components prior to dismantling.
2 With the master cylinder removed from the car (see previous Section), clean off the exterior using a lint-free cloth and drain off the brake fluid. Discard the old brake fluid. Do not attempt to clean the master cylinder or its components with petrol (gasoline), paraffin (kerosene) or cleaning solvents. It is generally sufficient to use new brake fluid for cleaning purposes but isopropyl alcohol or methylated spirit are also suitable.
3 Detach the rubber dust boot from the pushrod end of the cylinder.
4 Carefully remove the snap-ring from the internal bore groove using suitable snap-ring pliers and withdraw the pushrod and stopper.
5 Extract the piston, piston cap, return spring and retainer and the valve unit. If available, apply compressed air to the hydraulic fluid line connection aperture in the cylinder body but take care not to damage the piston on removal.
6 Carefully remove and dismantle the components of the one-way valve making a note of the respective component positions and locations.
7 Clean all the component parts as in paragraph 2, but discard the rubber cups. Examine the bore of the cylinder for wear, scoring or roughness; check the piston to bore clearance against the specified clearance, and renew any defective components. Clean all passageways with compressed air.
8 When reassembling the respective parts, smear them with new hydraulic fluid.
9 Fit the valve seal to the valve stem, then locate the valve spring and guide followed by the return spring and retainer.
10 Fit the rubber cup to the piston.
11 Fit the valve assembly to the piston and bend down the locating tab.
12 Insert the valve and piston assembly into the cylinder bore taking care not to distort the rubber cup.
13 Refit the pushrod and stopper and refit the snap-ring into its groove. Relocate the rubber boot over the end of the cylinder.
14 Fill the reservoir with new hydraulic fluid and operate the piston rod until fluid is ejected from the outlet.
15 Wipe any spilt fluid from the cylinder and refit it to the car.
16 Bleed the hydraulic system.

6 Clutch slave cylinder - removal, dismantling, reassembly and refitting

1 The clutch slave cylinder does not normally require attention. When dismantled all rubber components **must** be renewed and it is advisable to obtain a repair kit prior to dismantling (Fig. 5.4).
2 To remove the slave cylinder, disconnect the hydraulic fluid supply pipe from the cylinder and plug the end to prevent fluid spillage.
3 Unhook the return spring from the release fork lever.
4 Unscrew the bolts retaining the cylinder to the transmission housing; remove the slave cylinder.
5 Clean the exterior of the cylinder using a lint free cloth. Do not clean it with petrol (gasoline), paraffin (kerosene), or any type of cleaning solvent. Use new hydraulic fluid to clean the cylinder and components or as an alternative, isopropyl alcohol or methylated spirits are suitable.
6 Detach the dust boot from the cylinder and withdraw the pushrod.
7 Extract the piston by tapping the pushrod end of the cylinder on a hard wooden surface or alternatively, if available, apply compressed air to the inlet connection.
8 Unscrew and remove the air bleed screw.
9 Unscrew the inlet pipe union plug and remove the metal gasket valve plate and set spring.
10 Clean the respective components as described in paragraph 5, and inspect for signs of wear or damage. If the surfaces of the cylinder bore and/or piston are scored or marked badly then they must be renewed. Discard the old rubber piston cup and dust boot and lubricate the new ones with hydraulic fluid prior to assembly. Check the springs are not broken or distorted and renew as required. Clean the passageways out thoroughly using compressed air.
11 When reassembling immerse the respective components in new hydraulic fluid.
12 Assemble the cup to the piston and then fit the piston and cup with the cup leading. Refit the dust boot.
13 Refit the set spring valve plate and union plug with a new metal gasket. Refit the air bleed screw.
14 Carefully install the pushrod.
15 Reconnect the hydraulic fluid pipe to the slave cylinder and locate the pushrod into the release fork lever. Then insert the retaining bolts with washers (photo) and tighten to the specified torque.
16 Relocate the return spring.
17 Top up the master cylinder fluid level and bleed the system as described in Section 3. Readjust the release fork as in Section 2.

7 Clutch - removal and refitting

1 If the clutch unit is to be removed for inspection and overhaul, access to it is gained by either removing the engine and transmission units complete and then separating them (see Chapter 1) or by removing the transmission only leaving the engine in position (see Chapter 6).

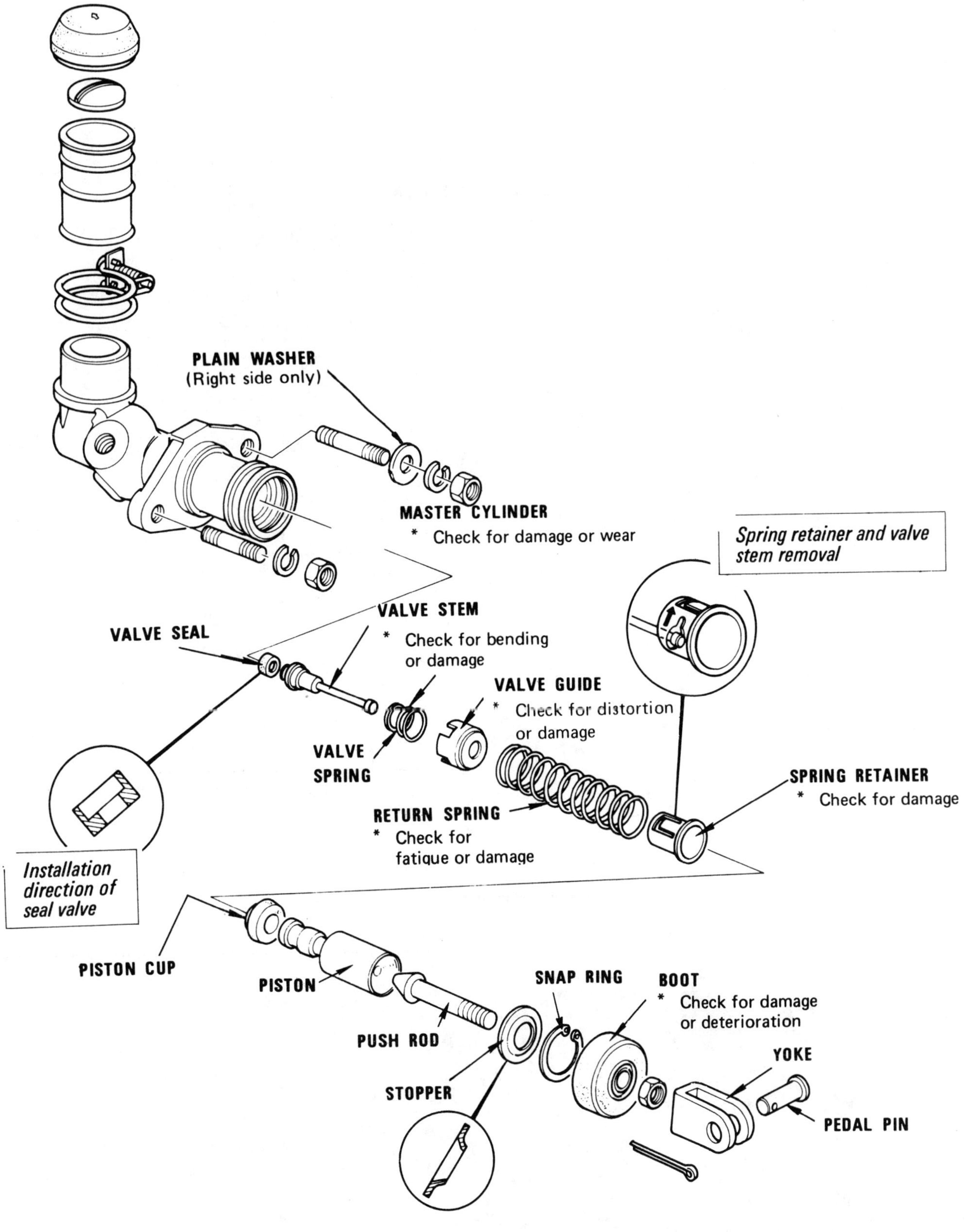

PLAIN WASHER
(Right side only)

MASTER CYLINDER
* Check for damage or wear

Spring retainer and valve stem removal

VALVE STEM
* Check for bending or damage

VALVE SEAL

VALVE GUIDE
* Check for distortion or damage

VALVE SPRING

SPRING RETAINER
* Check for damage

RETURN SPRING
* Check for fatique or damage

Installation direction of seal valve

PISTON CUP

PISTON

SNAP RING

BOOT
* Check for damage or deterioration

PUSH ROD

YOKE

STOPPER

PEDAL PIN

Fig. 5.3. The master cylinder components (Sec. 5)

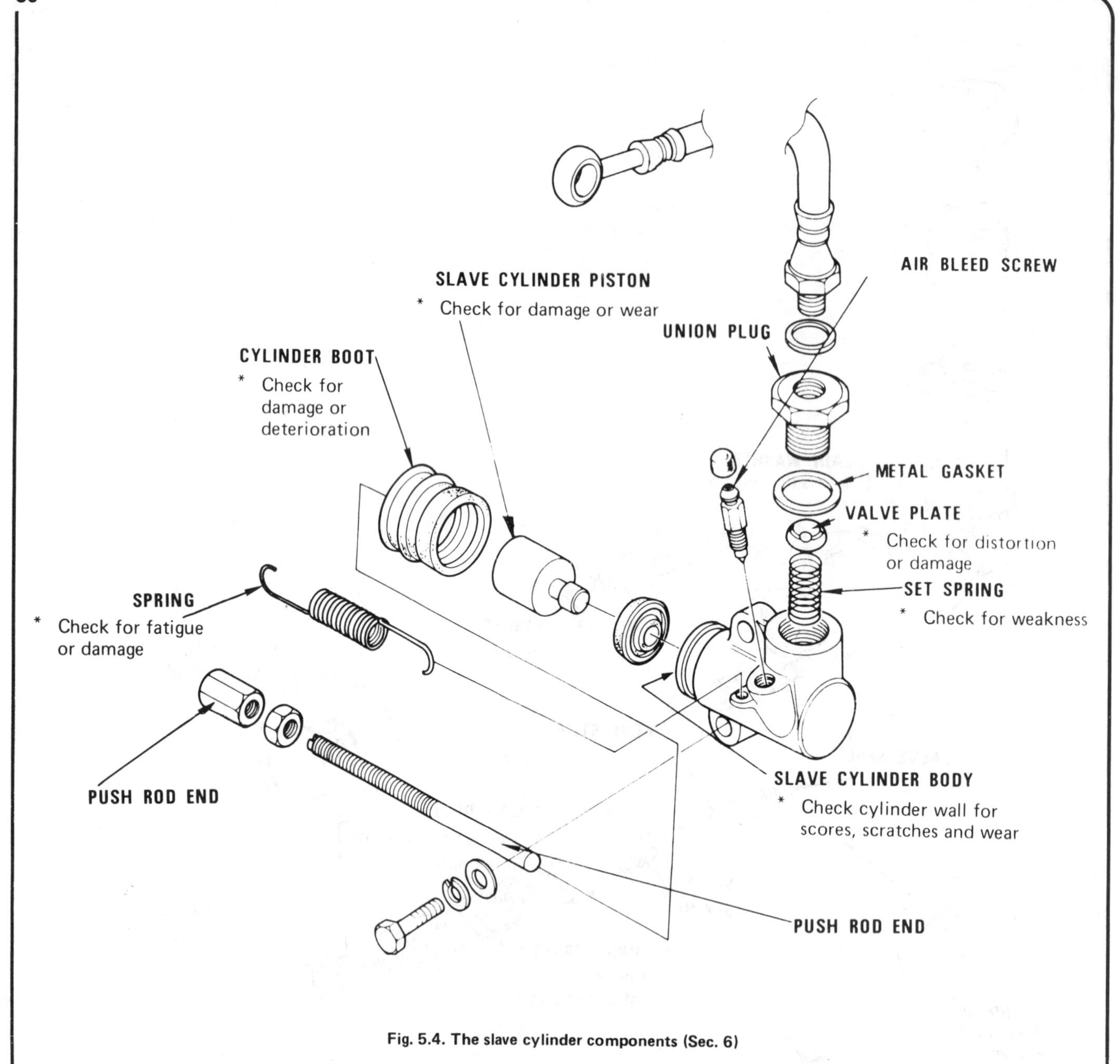

Fig. 5.4. The slave cylinder components (Sec. 6)

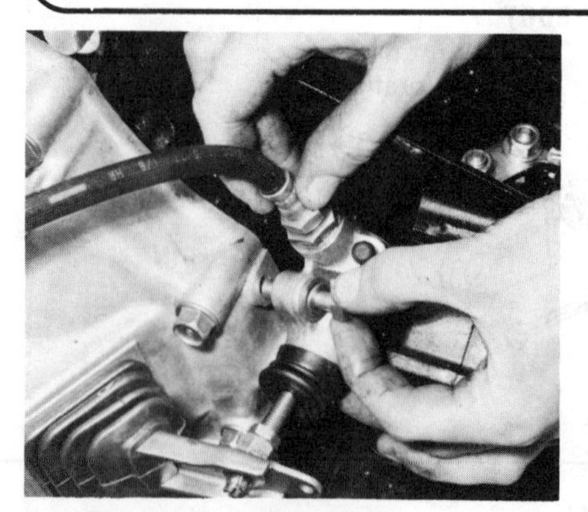

6.15 Refit the slave cylinder bolts

7.6 Refit the pressure plate and friction disc

7.8 Centralize the friction disc using an old input shaft

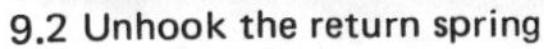
9.2 Unhook the return spring

9.4 The release fork retaining clip

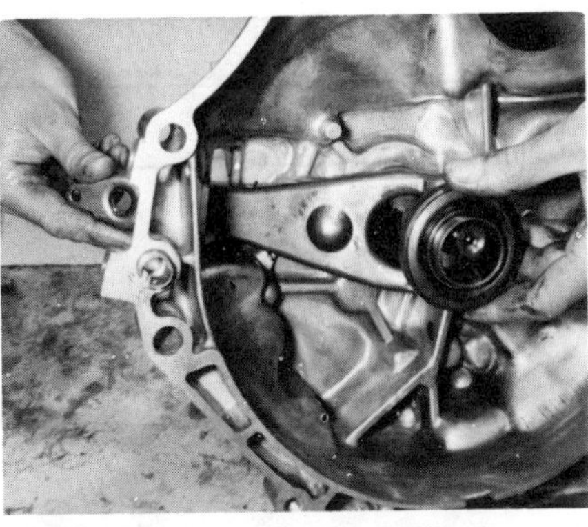
9.5 Remove the fork and bearing from inside the housing

2 The clutch unit can then be unbolted and detached from the flywheel. When unscrewing the pressure plate retaining bolts, undo them a turn at a time in a diagonal sequence until the spring tension of the diaphragm is released. To prevent the flywheel turning when undoing the pressure plate bolts, the starter ring gear can be locked by using a screwdriver located between the teeth of the gear and levered against a bolt inserted through a vacant bell housing bolt hole.
3 With the bolts removed, lift the pressure plate clear together with the driven plate from the flywheel.
4 Prior to refitting, ensure that the friction surfaces of the pressure plate and the flywheel are clean and free of oil or grease.
5 Position the friction disc against the flywheel with the projecting side offset away from the engine.
6 Position the pressure plate to the flywheel (photo) with the locating pin in the flywheel face and alignment marks on the flywheel and pressure plate in line.
7 Insert the pressure plate retaining bolts and tighten them finger tight.
8 The friction disc must now be aligned so that when refitting the transmission to the engine, the gearbox input shaft will locate easily with the splines of the friction disc and engage with the pilot bearing in the flywheel. To centralize the disc, use a clutch aligning tool such as an old input shaft (photo) or a suitable piece of dowel rod which can pass through the friction disc splines and locate in the pilot bearing.
9 When the centralising tool is a sliding fit, tighten the pressure plate bolts in a diametrically opposite sequence a turn at a time to the specified torque, then withdraw the alignment tool.
10 Reconnect the transmission to the engine and check the clutch adjustment.

8 Clutch - inspection and renovation

1 To inspect or renovate the clutch unit it is necessary to remove it from the clutch housing (see the previous Section).
2 With the clutch unit removed from the flywheel, the various components can be cleaned ready for inspection.
3 Inspect the diaphragm spring and clutch pressure plate for signs of wear and damage. If the release bearing groove on the diaphragm spring fingers is worn beyond 0.0012 in (0.03 mm) the pressure plate unit must be renewed.
4 Inspect the pressure plate surface for wear, cracks or signs of excessive heat. Place a straight edge across the adjacent surface area of the pressure plate and measure the inward taper using a feeler gauge. The maximum allowable wear is 0.006 in (0.15 mm). Any minor scratches or score marks may be removed using grade 500 or 600 emery paper. If the scratches or score marks are severe the pressure plate must be renewed.
5 If the friction disc is worn beyond the permissible limit, warped, or is contaminated with oil, it must be renewed. If the friction disc lining is loose or the rivets are within 0.008 in (0.2 mm) of the lining surface the disc must be renewed.
6 Check the flywheel face. If it is scored or badly worn, it must be refaced. This is a job for an engineering workshop. The maximum allowable flywheel run out is 0.0016 in (0.04 mm). Where a flywheel face is unmarked but glazed it may be lightly refaced using grade 500 or 600 emery paper. Reface using circular movements.
7 If, when dismantled, the clutch is soaked with oil, the rear crankshaft oilseal and/or gearbox input shaft oilseal must be checked and renewed as required, prior to reassembling the respective units. The clutch disc must also be renewed.

9 Clutch release mechanism - removal and refitting

1 To inspect and/or overhaul the clutch release lever and bearing, remove the transmission as described in Chapter 6.
2 To disconnect the release fork, unhook the return spring to the slave cylinder (photo), pull the fork from the slave cylinder and withdraw the pushrod.
3 Detach the dust boot from the bellhousing aperture.
4 Compress and detach the set clip from the fork channel (photo).
5 Slide and remove the release fork from inside the housing together with the release bearing and holder (photo).
6 Clean and inspect the respective components. Do not wash or immerse the release bearing in petrol or a solvent.
7 To remove the bearing from the holder, detach the set clip and support the holder. Drive the bearing from the holder using a suitable sized tubular drift. Refitting the bearing is a reversal of this procedure but ensure that the radiused side is opposite to the holder.
8 Renew any worn or damaged parts as necessary.
9 Refitting is a reversal of the removal procedure but to ease assembly, fit the set clip in the bearing holder and locate the holder in the fork. Fit the set clip into position in the fork channel and assemble the fork and bearing unit together. Apply pressure to the domed section of the fork to snap the set clip over the release fork bolt head.
10 Refit the rubber boot and check the release fork action before reassembling the gearbox to the engine.

See overleaf for 'Fault diagnosis - clutch'.

10 Fault diagnosis - clutch

Symptom	Reason/s
Judder when taking up drive	Loose engine/transmission mountings or worn flexible mountings Badly worn friction surfaces or friction plate contaminated with oil deposits Worn splines in the friction plate hub or on the transmission input shaft, or damaged plate Worn or loose input shaft
Clutch drag (or failure to disengage) so that gears cannot be meshed	Clutch clearance too great Clutch friction disc sticking because of rust on splines (usually apparent after standing idle for some length of time) Damaged or misaligned pressure plate assembly
Clutch slip - (increases in engine speed does not result in increase in car speed - especially on hills)	Clutch clearance too small resulting in partially disengaged clutch at all times Clutch friction surfaces worn out (beyond further adjustment). Clutch surfaces oil soaked

Chapter 6 Manual gearbox

For modifications, and information applicable to later models, see Supplement at end of manual

Contents

Specifications

Type	Five forward and one reverse. Synchromesh on all forward gears
Ratios	
1st	3.181 to 1
2nd	1.823 to 1
3rd	1.181 to 1
4th	0.846 to 1
5th	0.714 to 1
Reverse	2.916 to 1
Final drive	4.266 to 1
Oil capacity	4.5 Imp pints (2.5 litres/2.6 US quarts)
Synchroniser ring to gear clearance	
Standard	0.039 in (1.0 mm)
Wear limit	0.020 in (0.5 mm)
Shift fork to synchroniser sleeve clearance	
Standard	0.017 to 0.025 in (0.45 to 0.65 mm)
Wear limit	0.039 in (1.0 mm)
1st/2nd, 3rd/4th and reverse shift fork end width	
Standard	0.252 to 0.255 in (6.4 to 6.5 mm)
Wear limit	0.236 in (6.0 mm)
5th gear shift fork end width	
Standard	0.212 to 0.216 in (5.4 to 5.5 mm)
Wear limit	0.196 in (5.0 mm)
1st gear to thrust washer clearance	
Standard	0.001 to 0.003 in (0.03 to 0.08 mm)
Wear limit	0.007 in (0.18 mm)
2nd gear to spacer plate	
Standard	0.002 to 0.004 in (0.05 to 0.12 mm)
Wear limit	0.007 in (0.18 mm)
3rd gear to spacer plate clearance	
Standard	0.002 to 0.004 in (0.05 to 0.12 mm)
Wear limit	0.007 in (0.18 mm)
4th gear to thrust washer clearance	
Standard	0.001 to 0.003 in (0.03 to 0.08 mm)
Wear limit	0.007 in (0.18 mm)
5th gear to thrust plate clearance	
Standard	0.002 to 0.016 in (0.05 - 0.40 mm)

Torque wrench settings

	lb f ft	kg f m
Gear selector mechanism bolts	7 - 10	1 - 1.4
Countershaft locknut	50 - 72	7 - 10
Reverse shift fork special nut	14 - 19	2 - 2.8
Shift fork bolts	7 - 10	1 - 1.4
Transmission housing bolts	16 - 22	2.3 - 3.1
Drain plug bolt	25 - 32	3.5 - 4.5
Detent screw	14 - 17	2 - 2.4
Transmission cover bolts	7 - 10	1 - 1.4
Right side cover bolts	7 - 10	1 - 1.4
Oil level plug	10	1.4

1 General description

The gearbox and final drive are integral units mounted transversely to the rear side of the engine. The manual gearbox has five forward and one reverse gear. All forward gears are fitted with synchromesh.

The transmission housing is of aluminium alloy construction and has a detachable clutch housing and rear cover. The rear cover encloses the fifth gear and the reverse/fifth shift shaft and reverse shift fork.

Drive from the engine is transmitted in the clutch, through the gear train and differential unit to the driveshafts and roadwheels.

Gear selection is by a centrally floor mounted gearshift lever which is connected to the gearbox by a shift rod.

Maintenance consists of checking the oil level at the specified intervals. Remove the combined filler/level plug. If oil does not dribble out, add some through the hole until it does. Refit the plug.

It is important that the gearbox oil is drained and renewed at the specified intervals with the correct grade of oil.

Periodically check the security of all nuts and bolts on the transmission assembly.

2 Gearbox - removal and refitting

1 Disconnect the lead from the battery negative terminal.
2 Disconnect the earthing strap from the transmission casing.
3 Place the gearshift lever in the neutral position.
4 Disconnect the battery positive lead from the starter motor.
5 Disconnect the lead from the starter solenoid.
6 Disconnect the lead from the water temperature sender unit.
7 Where fitted, detach the temperature sensor leads (emission control system).
8 Disconnect the reversing lamp lead from the switch.
9 Drain the gearbox oil into a suitable container.
10 Jack up the front of the car under the bodyframe and remove the two front roadwheels.
11 Support the transmission by placing a jack (preferably trolley type) under it.
12 Remove the speedometer drive pinion securing bolt and pull the pinion/cable assembly from the transmission. Take care not to drop the pinion or drive pin into the transmission interior.
13 Unbolt and remove the centre subframe member.
14 Remove the buffer bracket from the front of the clutch bellhousing.
15 Remove the lower torsion rod from the transmission.
16 Disconnect the gearshift linkage (photo) at the transmission by driving out the connecting pin.
17 Disconnect the stabiliser bars from both front suspension radius rods and bodyframe.
18 Disconnect both trackrod-end balljoints from their steering arms.
19 Disconnect and withdraw both inner driveshafts from the transmission housing.
20 Remove the semi-circular cover plate from the bottom half of the clutch bellhousing.
21 Remove the respective retaining bolts from the starter motor and withdraw it from its location.
22 Unclip the clutch lever return spring and unscrew the slave cylinder retaining bolts. Lift the slave cylinder clear and place it out of the way (with the hydraulic line still attached).
23 Unscrew and remove the remaining engine/transmission retaining bolts.
24 Check that all of the transmission securing bolts and fittings have been disconnected. Support the transmission and pull it in a straight line from the engine initially to clear the two dowel pins and input shaft from the flywheel pilot bearing and clutch. Then withdraw the transmission unit from the car.
25 Refitting is a direct reversal of the removal procedure, but on completion ensure that the drain plug has been refitted and tightened. Refill the transmission with the correct grade and quantity of oil. Tighten all retaining nuts and bolts to their specified torque wrench settings. After initially running the car check the transmission for signs of oil leakage.

1 The transmission oil drain plug

2.16 Disconnect the gearshift rod linkage

3 Gearbox - dismantling into major assemblies

1 With the transmission removed from the car, clean the external surfaces with paraffin (kerosene) or a water soluble solvent.
2 Remove the clutch release fork and thrust bearing.
3 Unbolt and remove the right side cover plate from the transmission cover.
4 Extract the circlip from the groove in the end of the mainshaft. Extract the split collars and thrust washer.
5 Unbolt and withdraw the transmission cover and peel away the gasket. The ball bearing will come away with the cover.
6 Extract the distance collar from the mainshaft.
7 Engage reverse gear by pushing on the gearshift rod and twisting it in a clockwise direction.
8 Drive out the tension pin which secures the 5th gear shift fork to its selector rod.
9 Remove the 5th gear shift fork, synchroniser sleeve and synchroniser hub as an assembly.
10 Remove the 5th gear synchroniser ring, spring and then the 5th gear itself.
11 Withdraw the needle bearing and thrust washer.
12 Lift off the housing spacer and gasket.
13 Unscrew and remove the three detent threaded plugs and extract the springs and balls.
14 Extract the circlip from the groove of the mainshaft bearing and unscrew the eleven bolts which secure the transmission casing to the clutch housing.
15 Tap the transmission casing with a plastic faced hammer and drive it from the clutch housing. Peel off the flange gasket.
16 Remove reverse idler shaft and gear.
17 Remove the nut and special washer and then remove the reverse shift fork from the gear selector mechanism.
18 Flatten the tabs of the lockplates and then unscrew and remove the lock bolts from the three shift forks.
19 Extract the 5th/reverse selector rod.
20 Remove the 5th/reverse selector dog.
21 Withdraw the 1st/2nd gear selector rod.
22 Remove the 3rd/4th selector rod and fork as an assembly.
23 Move the 1st/2nd synchroniser into 2nd gear position, and then extract the 1st/2nd shift fork.
24 Measure the endfloat of the gears before removing the mainshaft or countershaft assemblies, see Fig. 6.1, 6.2, 6.3 and 6.4.
25 Using feeler blades measure the clearance between the 1st gear thrust washer and the 1st gear shoulder.
26 Measure between the spacer plate and 2nd gear.
27 Measure between the spacer plate and the shoulder on 3rd gear.
28 Measure between 4th gear and the 4th gear thrust washer.
29 The clearance on all these checks should be between 0.0012 and 0.0032 in (0.03 and 0.08 mm) with a wear limit of 0.0071 in (0.18 mm). If the clearances are found to exceed those specified, the countershaft will have to be dismantled and the spacer collars or thrust washers changed (see Section 4).
30 Lock the gears in the transmission and using a thin drift relieve the staking on the countershaft locknut and then unscrew the nut.
31 Withdraw the countershaft and mainshaft assemblies together (with their gears meshed) from the clutch bellhousing.
32 The gear selector mechanism can be removed after withdrawing the securing bolts. The final drive is left in the transmission casing — for removal see Chapter 8.

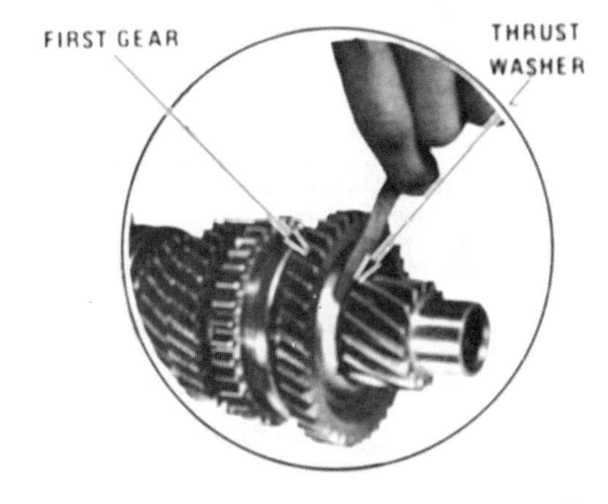

Fig. 6.1. Check the 1st gear to thrust washer clearance (Sec. 3)

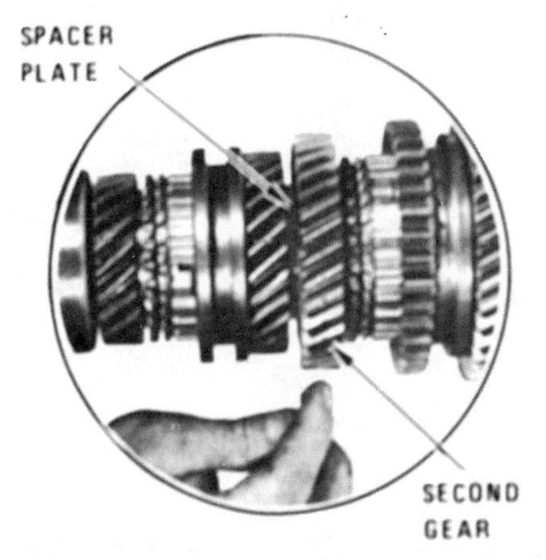

Fig. 6.2. Check the 2nd gear to spacer plate clearance (Sec. 3)

Fig. 6.3. Check the 3rd gear to spacer plate clearance (Sec. 3)

Fig. 6.4. Check the 4th gear to thrust washer clearance (Sec. 3)

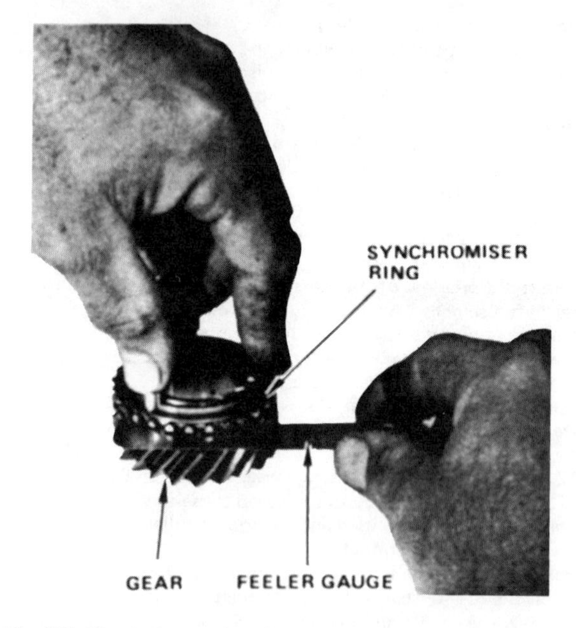

Fig. 6.5. Check the synchroniser ring to gear clearance (Sec. 4)

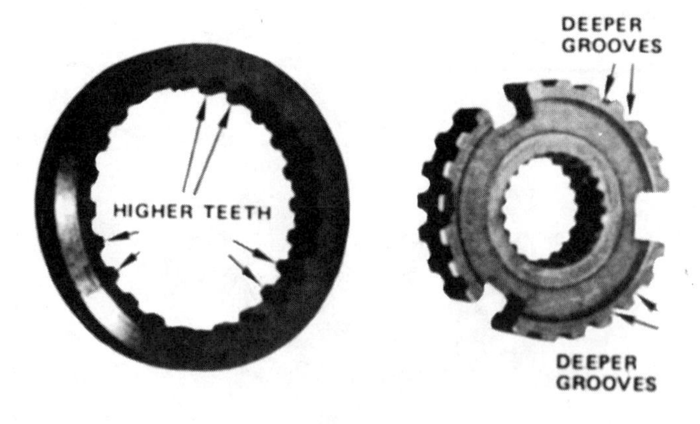

Fig. 6.6. The synchroniser hub and sleeve showing the mating teeth and grooves (Sec. 4)

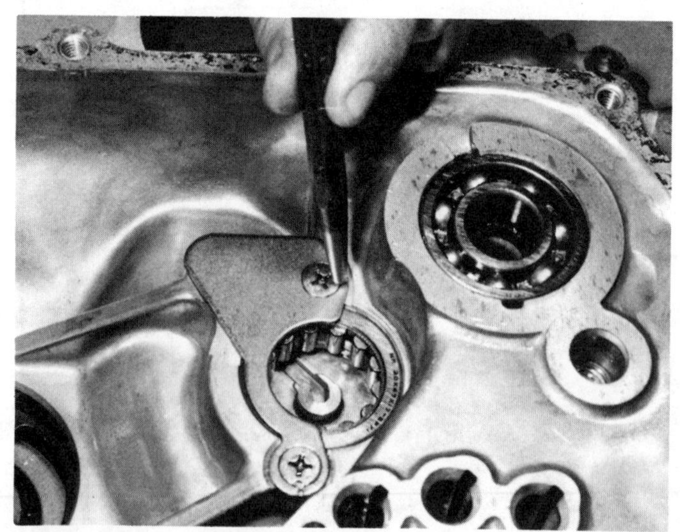

4.10 The bearing retaining plate and set screws, which are staked to secure

4 Gearbox - inspection and overhaul of assemblies

1 Inspect the gear teeth for wear and damage, also the shafts for scoring or grooves. Renew any worn components.
2 If the checks for gear endfloat (see preceding Section paragraphs 24 to 29 indicate the need to dismantle the countershaft, make sure that each component is kept in strict order for refitting in its original position and the correct way round. Mark the spacer collars and thrust washers accordingly for reassembly. A press will be required to remove some of the spacers and a micrometer will be needed to measure the thickness of new spacers and collars required to correct excessive gear endfloat.
3 Pay particular attention to the synchroniser units. If a history of noisy gearchanging has been recorded, renew the affected synchroniser assembly. Check the teeth of the synchroniser ring and if they are rounded off, renew the ring. The clearance between the ring and the gear when the ring is pressed onto the gear cone should not be less than 0.020 in (0.5 mm) otherwise renew the ring or in extreme cases, the ring and gearwheel.
4 When reassembling the synchroniser ring to the gearwheel, install the spring onto the ring and then fit the ring to the cone, twist the ring until it stops.
5 The synchroniser hub will only fit into its sleeve in one position as the higher teeth of the sleeve must engage with the deeper grooves of the hub.
6 Before refitting a synchroniser sleeve, make sure that the shift fork groove has not worn excessively. The clearance between the fork and the groove should not exceed 0.039 in (1.0 mm) The 1st/2nd, 3rd/4th and reverse shift fork thickness wear limit is 0.236 in (6.0 mm). The 5th gear shift fork thickness wear limit is 0.196 in (5.0 mm).
7 When installing the ball race to the end of the countershaft assembly, make sure that the sealed side is towards the 4th thrust washer.

Install the special spring washer next to the bearing so that the convex side of the washer is towards the nut.

When reassembly of the countershaft gear train is complete, screw on a new nut but only tighten it with the fingers at this stage.
8 Any wear in the gear teeth on the mainshaft or in the mainshaft splines can only be corrected by renewal of the mainshaft complete as the component cannot be dismantled. The thrust plate to 5th gear shoulder clearance must be checked. The standard clearance is 0.002 to 0.016 in (0.05 to 0.40 mm). Renew the thrust plate and/or 5th gear if necessary.
9 Dismantling of the gear selector mechanism can be carried out after extracting the two countersunk screws from the holder plate. An impact driver will be required for this. Stake the screw heads on reassembly.
10 The bearings and oil seals in the casing can be renewed if they are removed using a piece of tubing, as a drift. The countershaft bearing in the clutch housing is retained by a plate. To remove the plate extract the countersunk screws with an impact screwdriver and re-stake them on refitting (photo).
11 If the transmission housing, clutch housing or differential side bearings are to be renewed, the side clearance of the differential must be checked on assembly as described in Chapter 8.

5 Gearbox - reassembly

Countershaft assembly

1 Slide the selected 1st gear thrust washer down the countershaft and locate flush to the pinion gear. Lubricate and slide the needle roller bearing into position together with the sleeve and first gear (photo).
2 Assemble and fit the 1st/2nd synchroniser hub unit to the shaft (photo). Note when fitting the hub and sleeves that there are three sets of high teeth at 120° intervals that must be matched when the hub and sleeve are meshed together as in Fig. 6.6.
3 Slide 2nd gear into position (photo).
4 Slide the spacer plate into position down the shaft, and pressing it against 2nd gear, check the clearances between:

a) The spacer and the 2nd gear shoulder.
b) The 1st gear thrust washer and the 1st gear shoulder.

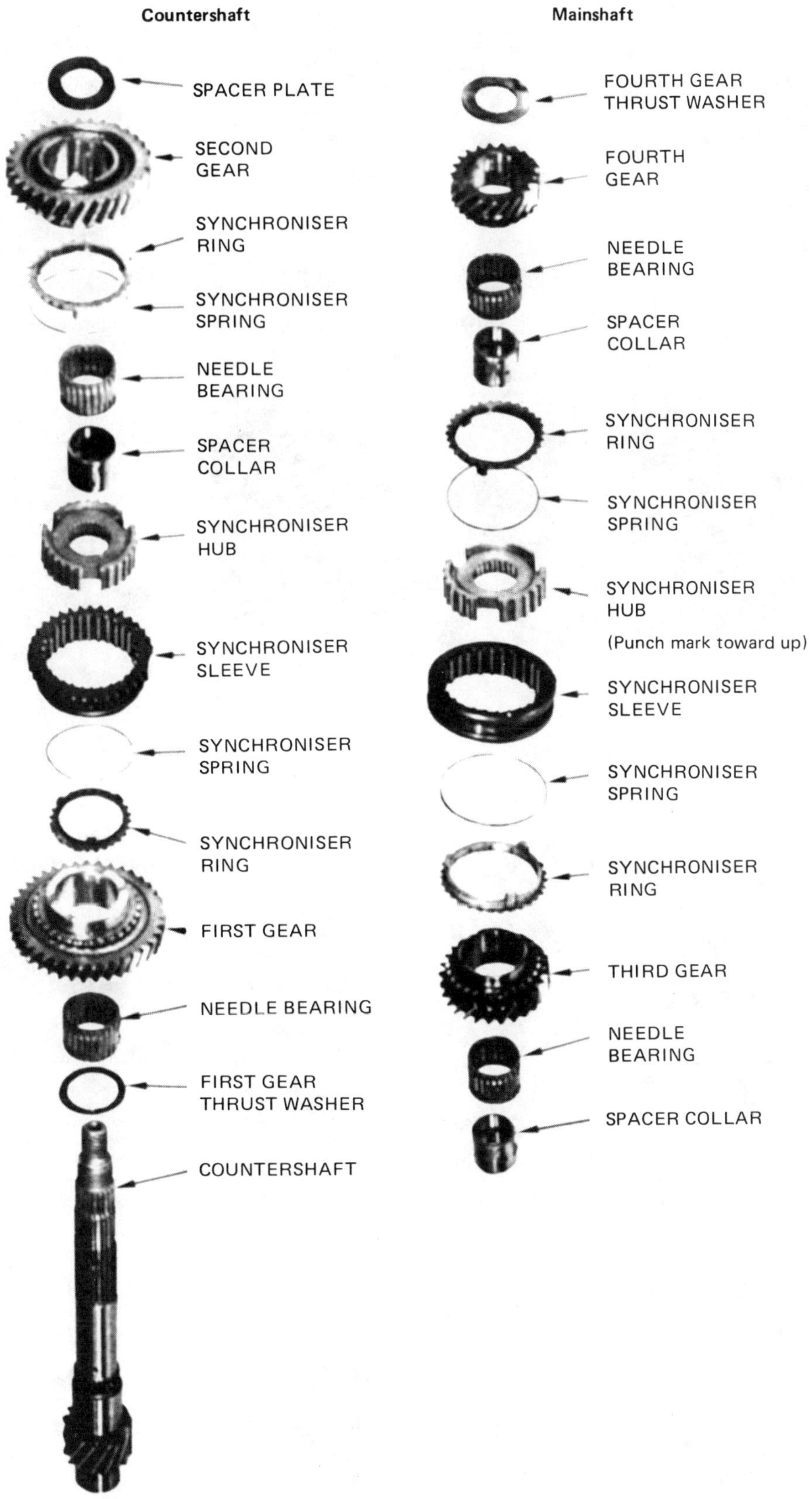

Countershaft

SPACER PLATE

SECOND GEAR

SYNCHRONISER RING

SYNCHRONISER SPRING

NEEDLE BEARING

SPACER COLLAR

SYNCHRONISER HUB

SYNCHRONISER SLEEVE

SYNCHRONISER SPRING

SYNCHRONISER RING

FIRST GEAR

NEEDLE BEARING

FIRST GEAR THRUST WASHER

COUNTERSHAFT

Mainshaft

FOURTH GEAR THRUST WASHER

FOURTH GEAR

NEEDLE BEARING

SPACER COLLAR

SYNCHRONISER RING

SYNCHRONISER SPRING

SYNCHRONISER HUB

(Punch mark toward up)

SYNCHRONISER SLEEVE

SYNCHRONISER SPRING

SYNCHRONISER RING

THIRD GEAR

NEEDLE BEARING

SPACER COLLAR

Fig. 6.7. The gear assemblies (Sec. 5)

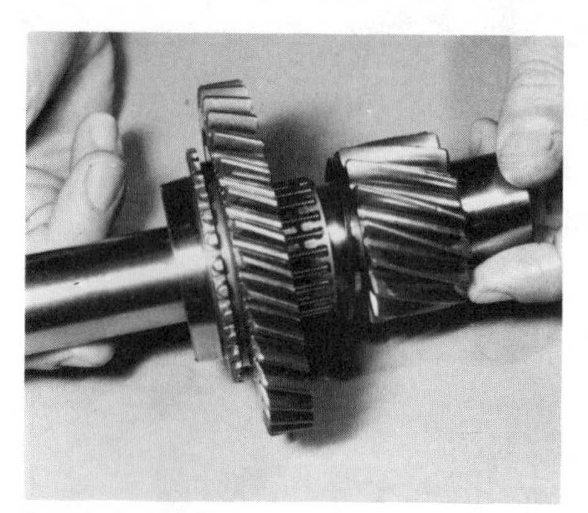

5.1 Fit the thrust washer, 1st gear and roller bearing with sleeve

5.2 Fit the 1st/2nd synchroniser hub unit...

5.3 ... followed by 2nd gear

5.5 Fit 3rd gear with needle bearing and spacer collar

5.6 Slide the synchroniser sleeve into position

5.7a Fit 4th gear with spacer and bearing ...

5.7b ... then slide the thrust washer into position

5.8 Check the washer to 4th gear clearance

5.9 The assembled countershaft less 5th gear

5.11 Install the differential unit into the clutch housing

5.12 The gear selector mechanism
A Shoulder bolts. B Standard bolts

5.13 Install the countershaft and mainshaft

The clearances must be within the specified limits. If necessary, change the thickness of the 1st gear thrust washer, the spacer collar or both.

5 Fit the spacer collar, needle bearing and 3rd gear (photo).

6 Locate the synchroniser ring and spring onto 3rd gear and slide the synchroniser sleeve and hub unit into position (photo).

7 Fit 4th gear together with the spacer collar, and needle bearing (photo). Fit the thrust washer (photo).

8 Press down on the thrust washer and check:

a) The washer to 4th gear shoulder clearance (photo).
b) The spacer plate to 3rd gear shoulder clearance.

The clearances must be within the specified limits. If necessary the fourth gear thrust washer and/or the spacer collar must be changed to suit.

9 Press the ball bearing into position with sealed side towards the 4th gear thrust washer (photo).

10 Install the 5th gear onto the shaft against the bearing. The gear must be offset away from the bearing. Fit the special spring washer with the concave side to the gear, and locate, but do not tighten, the locknut.

Countershaft, mainshaft, selectors and transmission housing assembly

11 Install the differential unit into the clutch housing (photo).

12 Install the gear selector mechanism, tightening the shoulder bolts, 'A' first and then the standard ones 'B' to the torque wrench setting specified (photo).

13 Mesh the gears of the countershaft and mainshaft together, and install the two assemblies simultaneously to the clutch bellhousing (photo).

14 Move 1st/2nd synchroniser sleeve to 2nd gear engaged position.

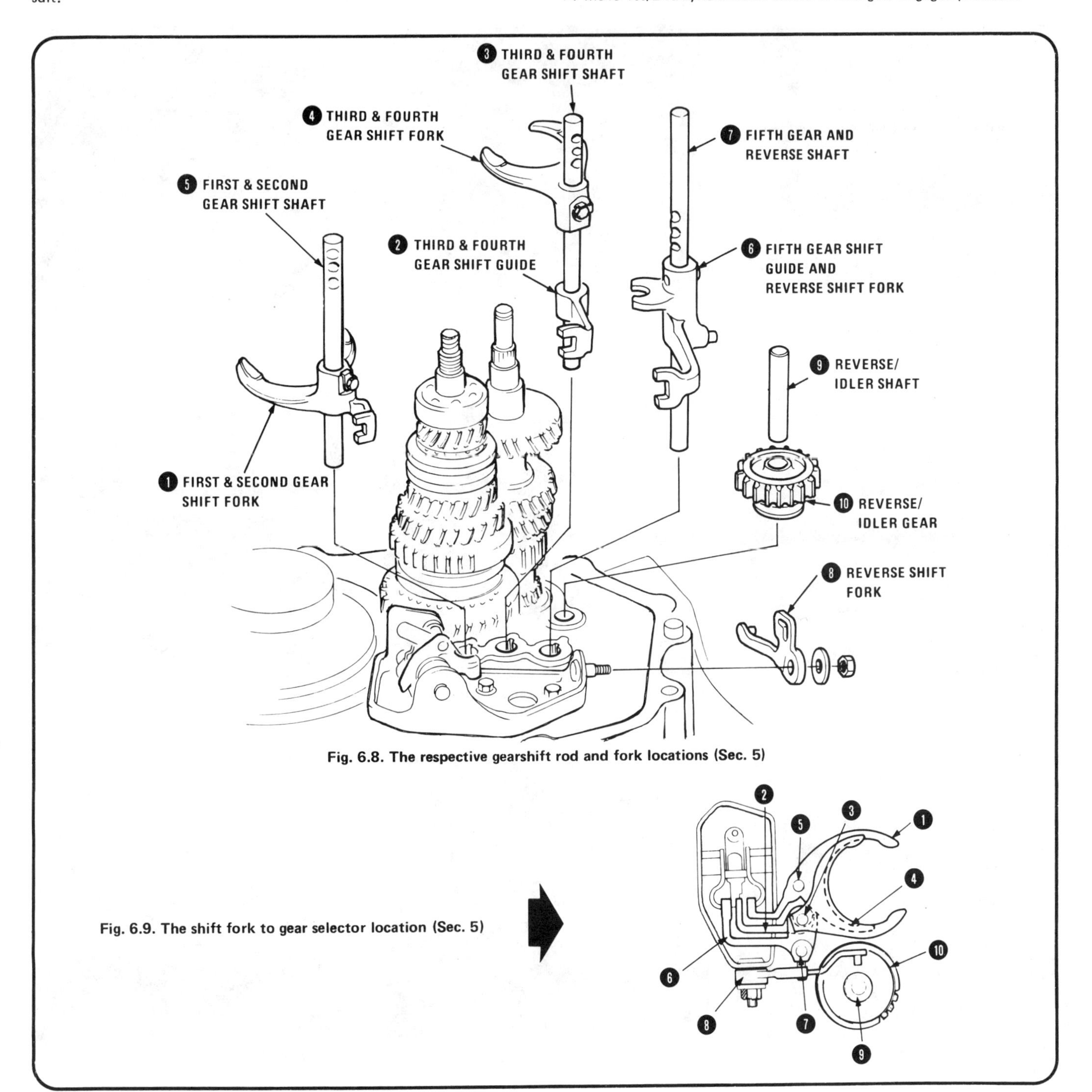

Fig. 6.8. The respective gearshift rod and fork locations (Sec. 5)

Fig. 6.9. The shift fork to gear selector location (Sec. 5)

5.19 Install 5th/reverse selector rod

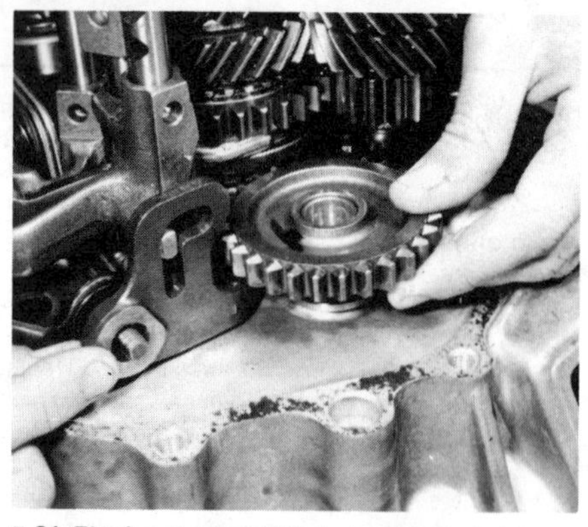

5.21 Fit the reverse shift fork and reverse idler gear

5.22 The shift fork lock bolts and lock-plates with tabs bent over

5.24a Carefully fit the transmission casing to the clutch housing

5.24b Peen the nut to lock in position

5.27 Install the snap rings

5.28 Fit the housing spacer

5.29 Fit the thrust washer and roller bearing

5.30 Install 5th gear

5.31 Fit the synchroniser with sleeve and reverse shift fork

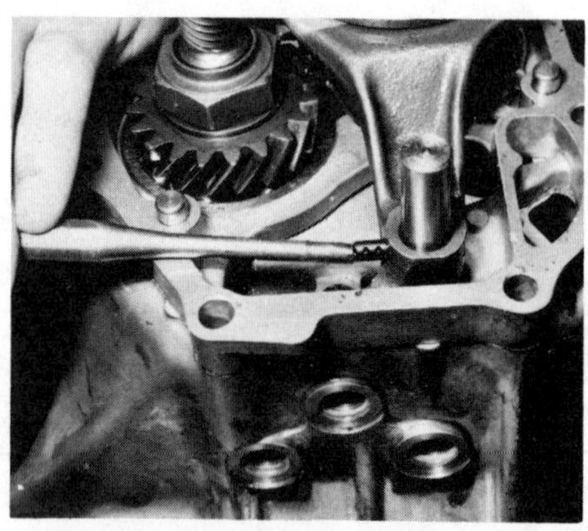

5.32 Drift the spring pin into position

5.33 Fit the distance collar

15 Install 1st/2nd shift fork. A twisting motion will be required to engage the fork with the groove of the synchroniser sleeve.
16 Fit the selector dog to the 3rd/4th selector rod and drive in a new tension pin.
17 Fit 3rd/4th shift fork to the selector rod but do not screw in the fork locking bolt. Install the 3rd/4th fork rod assembly engaging the selector dog with the gearshift mechanism.
18 Install 1st/2nd gear selector rod.
19 Install 5th and reverse selector dog and then insert 5th/reverse selector rod (photo).
20 Install reverse shift fork and tighten the special securing nut to between 15 to 20 lb f ft (2.0 to 2.8 kg f m).
21 Fit reverse idler gear (photo) and reverse idler shaft. Check that this idler gear rotates freely,
22 Fit the respective shift fork lockbolts using new backplates with the exception of 3rd gear shift fork lockbolt/plate. Tighten the shift fork lockbolts to the specified torque 7 to 10 lb f ft (1.0 to 1.4 kg f m) and bend the tabs of the lockplates over to secure (photo).
23 Lift the reverse idler gear on the shaft and engage it. Retain in this position temporarily with a suitable tubular spacer and engage 3rd gear by moving the shift fork.
24 Lower the transmission housing temporarily into position and check that the gears are locked in position. Install 5th gear (with its boss facing the bearing) and the special spring washer. Fit the locknut and tighten to the specified torque of 50 to 72 lb f ft (7 to 10 kg f m). Loosen the nut and retighten to the same torque then lock in position by peening over with a punch (photos).
25 Remove the transmission housing and remove the temporary tubular spacer retaining it in position. Locate the 3rd gear shift fork lock bolt and lock plate and tighten to the specified torque and bend over the lock plate tab to secure.
26 Locate a new gasket on the mating flange of the clutch housing and check that the two positioning dowels are correctly installed. Fit the transmission casing and tighten the securing bolts to the specified torque wrench setting.
27 Fit the snap-rings to the ballbearing outer race on the countershaft and mainshafts (photo) with the large chamfer downwards.
28 Fit the housing spacer and gaskets (photo).
29 Engage reverse gear and fit the thrust washer, and needle roller bearing (photo).
30 Install 5th gear (photo).
31 Install the 5th gear synchroniser hub, sleeve and reverse shift fork (photo). The dot mark on the hub faces the gears.
32 Align the shift fork and shaft pin hole and drift the spring pin into position (photo).
33 Slide the distance collar into position against the synchroniser hub with its tapered face to the top (photo).
34 Install the transmission cover and gasket ensuring that the dowel pins are correctly located (photo). Install but do not tighten the cover retaining bolts.
35 Fit the snap-ring to the outer ball bearing race groove and install the bearing.
36 Locate the two split collars into the mainshaft groove with their rounded faces downwards, and install the thrust washer in position over them (photo). Retain the collar with the snap-ring (photo).
37 Install the 'O' rings in position in the right side cover and refit the oil barrier plate. Fit the right side cover to the gearbox (photo) and retain with the two long and two short bolts. One of the long bolts retains the reverse (back up) light wire clip (photo). Tighten the bolts to the specified torque.
38 Install the speedometer drive gear into the transmission cover (photo) with the retaining belt recess in line with the bolt hole. Fit the bolt and tighten to the specified torque.
39 Install the three detent balls and springs into the retaining screws and fit them into their respective locations in the transmission housing (photo). Tighten the screws to the specified torque of 14 to 17 lb f ft (2 to 2.4 kg f m).
40 If removed, refit the clutch release fork bolt and install the clutch release mechanism as described in Chapter 5.

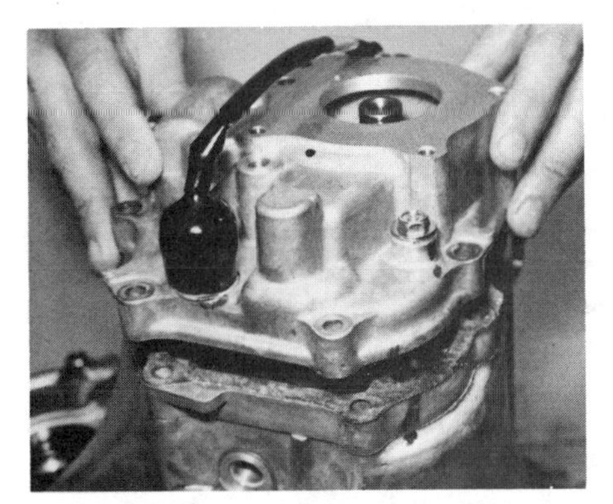

5.34 Install the transmission cover and gasket

5.36a Fit the split collars and thrust washer

5.36b Install the circlip

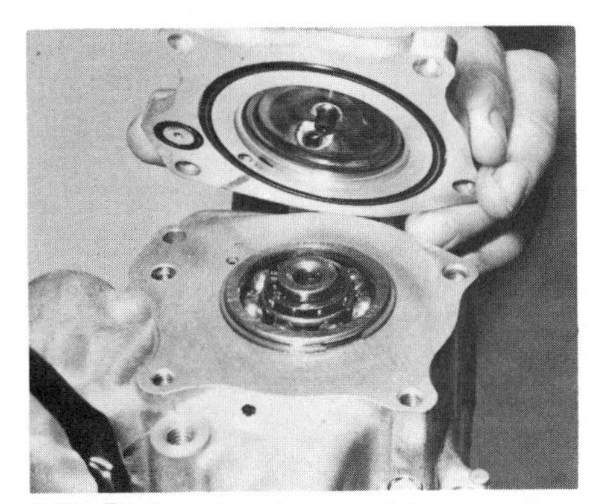

5.37a Fit the right side cover plate

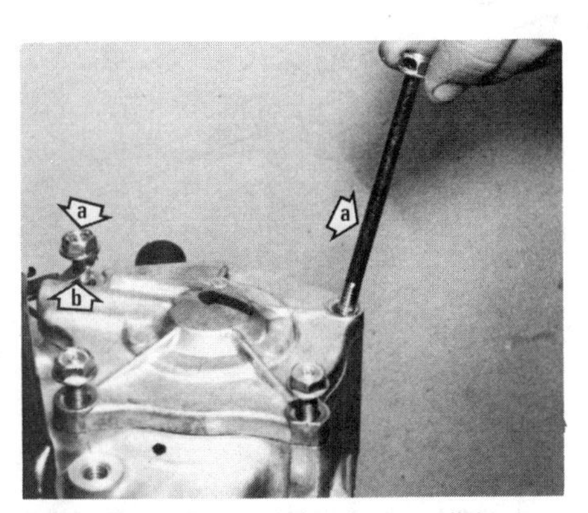

5.37b The long bolts 'A' and reverse light wire clip 'B'

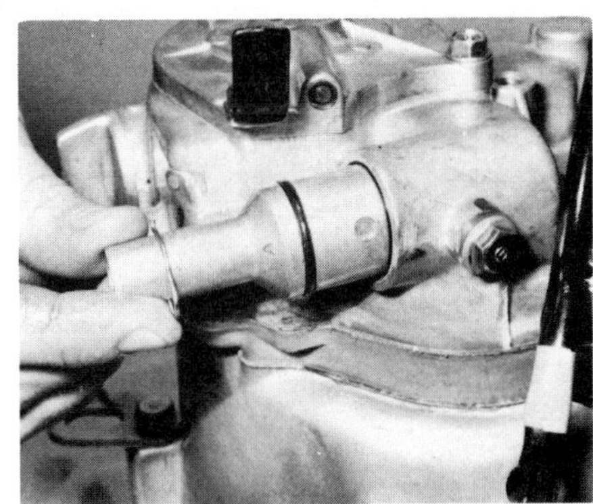

5.38 Fit the speedometer drive gear

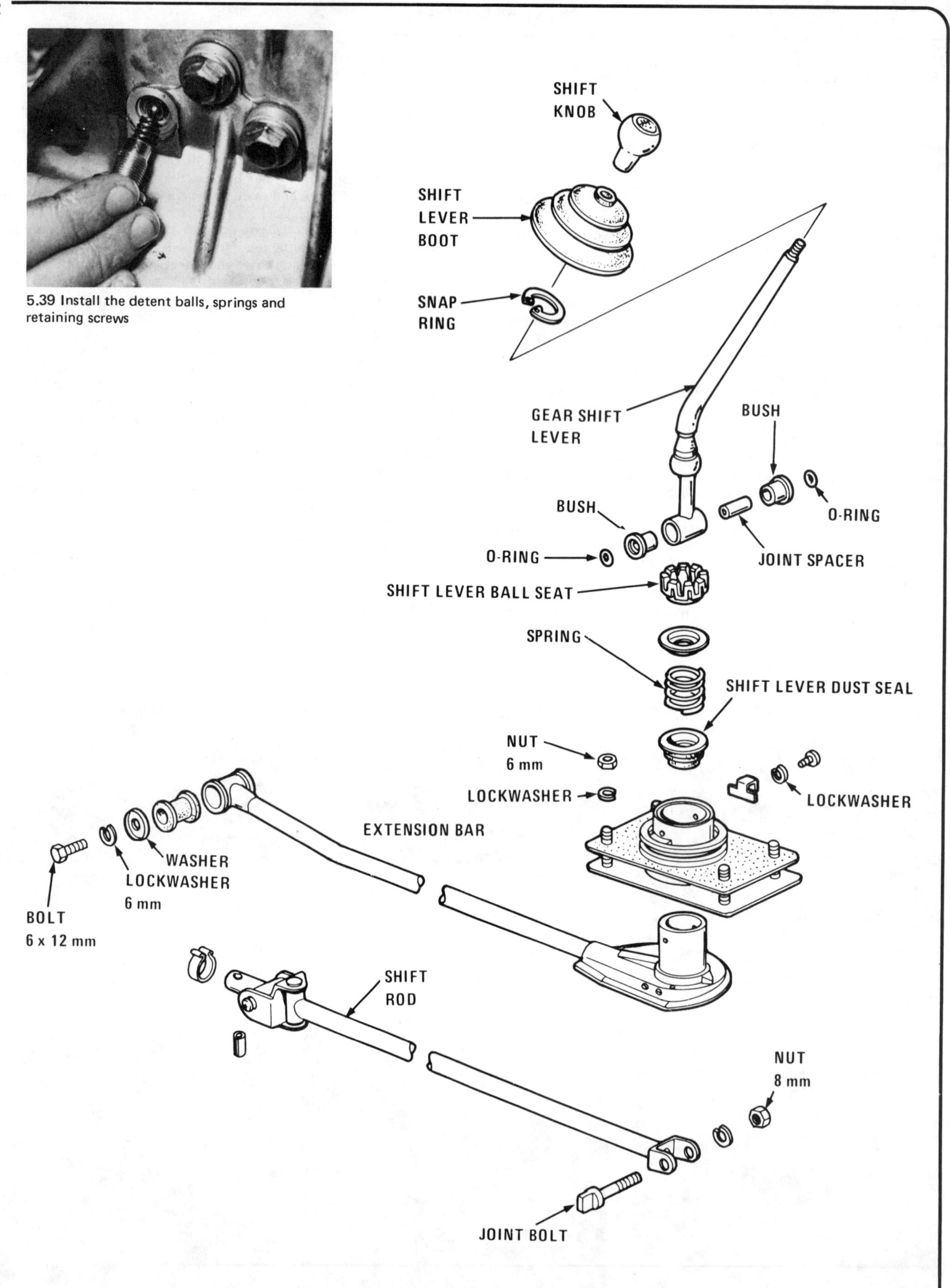

5.39 Install the detent balls, springs and retaining screws

Fig. 6.10. The gear lever to shift rod mechanism (Sec. 6)

6 Gearshift - control linkage

1 The gearshift control linkage is of a very simple design and few problems can therefore be expected from it. Any faults and/or wear occurring in the linkage can only be rectified by renewal of the component concerned.
2 The most likely points of wear are at the shift lever ball seat, the bushes at the base of the lever or the shift rod or extension bar.
3 The various components of the shift linkage can be seen in the accompanying illustration (Fig. 6.10) and from this it will be seen that any dismantling or reassembly work on the linkage is comparatively easy.

7 Fault diagnosis - manual gearbox

Symptom	Reason/s
Ineffective synchromesh	Worn baulk rings or synchro hubs.
Jumps out of one or more gears (on drive or over-run)	Weak detent springs or worn selector forks or worn gears.
Noisy, rough, whining and vibration	Worn bearing and/or thrust washers (initially) resulting in extended wear generally due to play and backlash.
Noisy and difficult engagement of gears	Clutch fault (see Chapter 5).

Note: *It is sometimes difficult to decide whether it is worthwhile removing and dismantling the gearbox for a fault which may be nothing more than a minor irritant. Gearboxes which howl, or where the synchromesh can be 'beaten' by a quick gearchange, may continue to perform for a long time in this state. A worn gearbox usually needs a complete rebuild to eliminate noise because the various gears, if re-aligned on new bearings will continue to howl when different wearing surfaces are presented to each other.*

The decision to overhaul therefore, must be considered with regard to time and money available, relative to the degree of noise or malfunction that the driver has to suffer.

Chapter 7 Hondamatic transmission

For modifications, and information applicable to later models, see Supplement at end of manual

Contents

Specifications

Transmission type ... Semi-automatic with torque converter, two forward and one reverse gear

Primary gear ratio ... 1 : 1 (direct)

Gear ratios

1st	1.565 : 1
2nd	0.903 : 1
Reverse	2.045 : 1
Final drive ratio	4.117 : 1

Oil capacity ... 3.7 Imp. qt (4.4 US qt, 4.2 litres)

Low drive clutch end plate to top clutch disc clearance

Wear limit ... 0.020 to 0.032 in (0.5 to 0.8 mm)

Pump driven gear to valve body thrust surface clearance

Standard	0.001 to 0.002 in (0.03 to 0.06 mm)
Wear limit	0.003 in (0.08 mm)

Stall speed ... 2,200 to 2,600 rpm

Oil pressure test pressure

Standard	95 - 115 lb/in^2 (6.6 to 8.0 kg/cm^2)
Minimum	70 lb/in^2 (5.0 kg/cm^2)

Torque wrench settings	lb f ft	kg fm
Drive plate bolts	7 to 10	1.0 to 1.4
Centre beam bolts	14 to 18	1.9 to 2.5
Stopper bracket bolts	14 to 18	1.9 to 2.5
Engine mounting bolt	25 to 31	3.5 to 4.3
Transmission/engine bolts	29 to 36	4 to 5
Starter motor/transmission bolts	29 to 36	4 to 5
Speedometer drive gear bolt	7 to 10	1.0 to 1.4
Outer cover bolts	7 to 10	1.0 to 1.4
Fluid hose joint bolt	22 to 29	3.0 to 4.0
Bearing retainer bolts	7 to 10	1 to 1.4
Low clutch locknut	32 to 40	4.5 to 5.5
Low gear countershaft locknut	58 to 72	8 to 10
Shift fork bolt	7 to 10	1 to 1.4
Sealing ring guide bolt	7 to 10	1 to 1.4
Valve body bolts	7 to 10	1 to 1.4
Oil pump strainer bolts	7 to 10	1 to 1.4
Link arm bolt	7 to 10	1 to 1.4
Torque converter to drive plate bolts	7 to 10	1 to 1.4
Transmission housing bolts 8 m x 1.25 x 50 mm	17 to 22	2.3 to 3.1
Transmission housing bolt 6 m x 1.0 x 45 mm	7 to 10	1 to 1.4

1 Hondamatic transmission - general description and maintenance

The main components of the semi-automatic transmission are the torque converter and a special gearbox enclosing two forward speeds and one reverse gear.

The torque converter is housed in an enlarged bellhousing between the engine and gearbox, and its appearance is that of a large, almost hemispherical, container with a ring gear for the starter motor attached to the face nearest the engine. The container encloses the torque converter system of vanes, and is kept full of oil under pressure by a pump mounted in the gearbox casing.

The transmission functions as follows: The engine delivers power to the torque converter which balances the speed and torque from the engine to the speed and torque 'required' by the gearbox. The converter has the characteristic that if the input speed from the engine is greater than the output speed to the gearbox, the output torque will be between 1 and 2 times greater than the input torque; depending on the difference of input and output speeds.

This torque characteristic is derived from the way the drive/impeller vanes in the converter are coupled to the output/turbine vanes. The impeller vanes are shaped so that as they rotate, the oil in the impeller is flung radially outwards to the top tip of the vanes and forwards in the direction of the vanes rotation. The oil, on leaving the impeller, impinges onto the output turbine which is driven by the oil in the direction of rotation of the impeller. If the impeller is rotating faster than the turbine - typically when the engine is working to accelerate the car - the oil flung onto the turbine by the impeller creates a greater torque on the turbine than that exerted by the engine on the impeller. The stator in the converter serves to correct the direction of flow of oil from the turbine back to the impeller and improves the efficiency of the converter.

The power output from the converter is transmitted to the final drive via the two speed gearbox. The gears are changed manually; number 1 serves up to a speed of 50 mph (80 kph) and number 2 is the cruising gear. Multiplate wet clutches attached to each gear train connect the selected train to the gearbox mainshaft and final drive via the fixed gears on the countershaft.

The Hondamatic is therefore a semi-automatic system, because the driver must still select the appropriate gear for the particular road conditions at the time. The torque converter adds a degree of flexibility to the gear selected, and does not take the need for thought, regarding choice of gear, from the driver.

Maintenance

At the intervals specified in 'Routine Maintenance', check the fluid level. To do this, run the car for a minimum of 5 miles (8 km) until the fluid is at normal operating temperature and then position the car on level ground and switch off the engine.

Unscrew and remove the dipstick, wipe it clean and re-insert it but do not screw it in. Withdraw the dipstick for the second time and read off the fluid level.

Top-up as necessary and install the dipstick, screwing it in finger-tight only.

With a new vehicle, the transmission fluid should be drained after the first 15000 miles (24000 km) and thereafter every 30000 miles (48000 km).

2 Hondamatic transmission - removal and refitting

1 The Hondamatic transmission can be removed independently of the engine leaving the latter in position in the car but obviously if any major work is required to the engine at the same time, it will be easier to remove the engine/transmission and then separate them, as described in Chapter 1.

2 To remove the transmission on its own, first disconnect the negative lead from the battery terminal and then disconnect the earth strap from the transmission casing.

3 Place the speed selector lever in 'N'.

4 Disconnect the positive lead from the starter motor.

5 Disconnect the black/white lead from the starter solenoid.

6 Disconnect the lead from the water temperature sender unit.

7 On vehicles equipped with full emission control, disconnect the leads from the upper and lower temperature sensors.

8 Disconnect the transmission oil cooler hoses and plug them to prevent leakage.

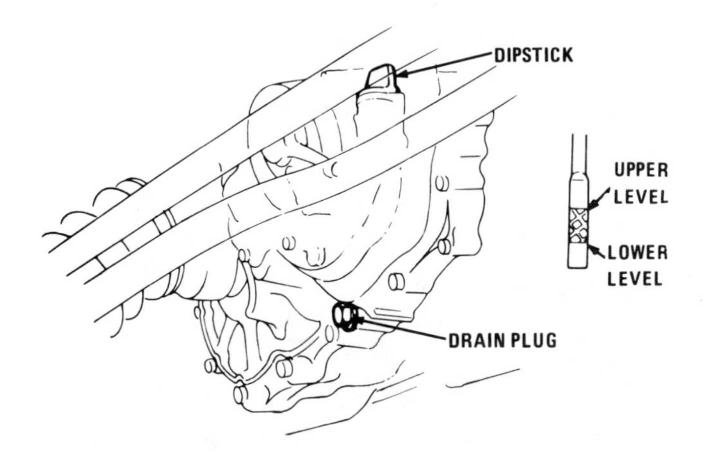

Fig. 7.1 Hondamatic dipstick/filler hole and drain plug (Sec. 1)

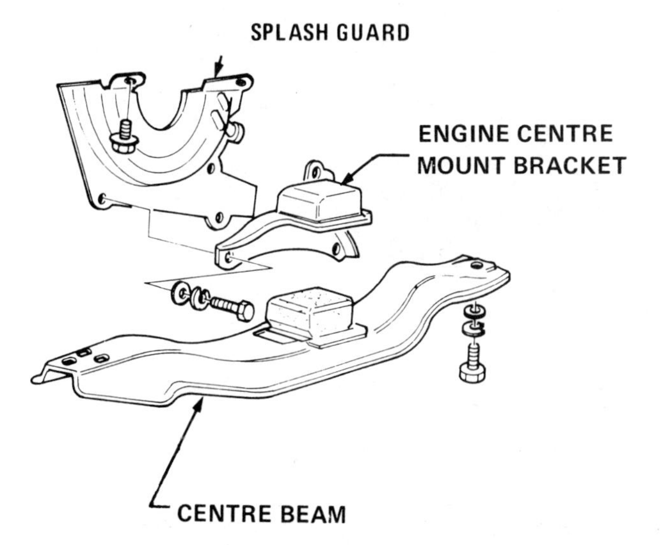

Fig. 7.2. Remove the centre beam, splash guard and mounting bracket (Sec. 2)

9 Drain the transmission fluid into a suitable container.

10 Raise the vehicle at the front and place axle stands securely under the bodyframe side members at the rear of the front wheel arches.

11 Remove the front roadwheels.

12 Position a jack (preferably trolley type) under the transmission.

13 Unscrew the speedometer retaining bolt and carefully withdraw the speedometer drive.

14 Unbolt and remove the centre beam.

15 Unscrew the engine centre mount bracket and splash guard retaining bolts and remove the two components.

16 Extract the control cable retaining clip and pin, unscrew the outer cable attachment bolt and disconnect the control cable.

17 Remove the driveshafts from the transmission as detailed in Chapter 8.

18 Unscrew and remove the eight drive plate attachment bolts (Fig. 7.3). These are accessible through the aperture normally covered by the splash guard. The crankshaft will have to be rotated to enable each bolt in turn to be unscrewed. A socket wrench can be fitted over the crankshaft pulley nut through the hole provided in the left-hand front wing inner panel. Turn the crankshaft in an anticlockwise direction accordingly.

19 It is vital that the driveplate securing bolts are correctly identified before unscrewing them. Only unscrew those bolts which are **not** located in cut-outs in the drive plate. Do **not** unscrew the ring gear/torque converter retaining bolts.

20 Disconnect the exhaust downpipe from the manifold.

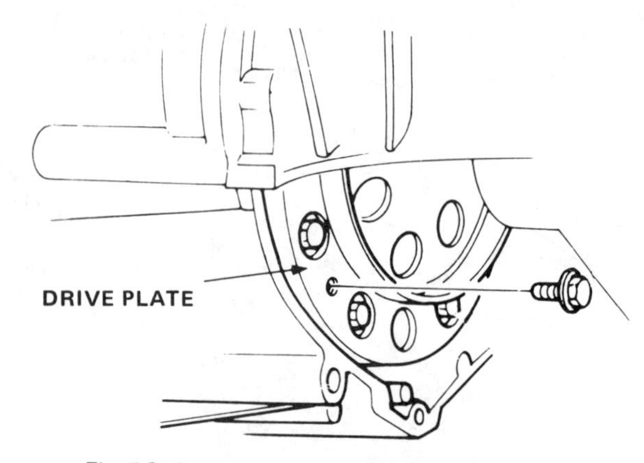

Fig. 7.3 Remove the drive plate bolts (Sec. 2)

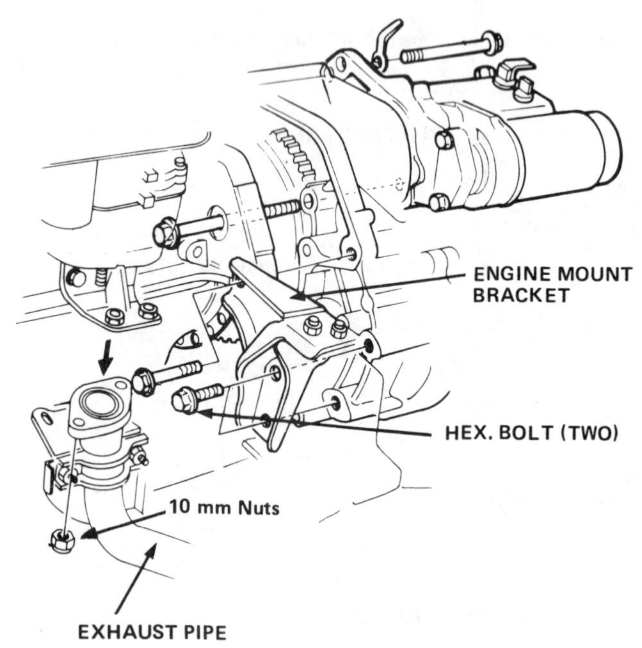

Fig. 7.4 The downpipe and mounting bracket (Sec. 2)

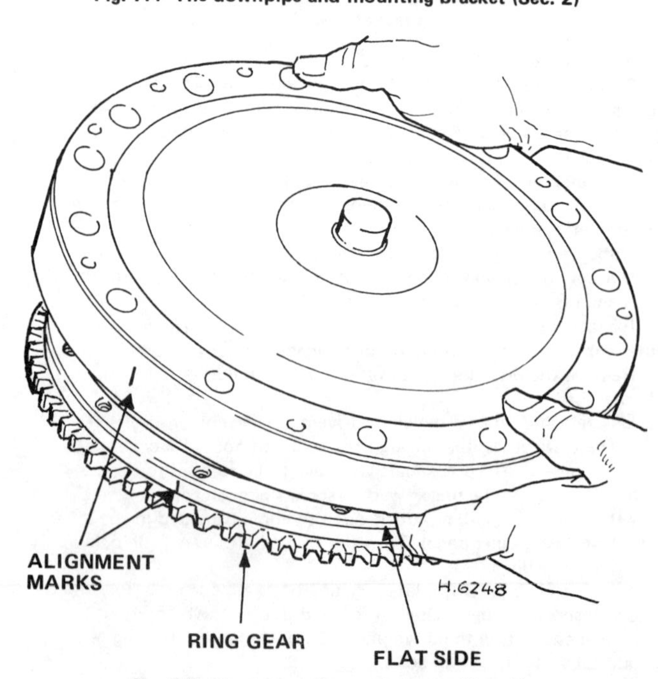

Fig. 7.5. Check the alignment marks (Sec. 3)

21 Unscrew the engine mounting bracket retaining bolts and remove the bracket (between the exhaust manifold and starter motor).
22 Unscrew and remove the starter motor retaining bolts and withdraw the starter motor.
23 Remove the remaining torque converter housing to engine securing bolts.
24 Pull the transmission from the engine in a straight line in order to clear the positioning dowel pins.
25 Lower the jack and withdraw the transmission taking care to retain the torque converter fully within its housing.
26 Refitting is a reversal of removal, then refill the transmission with the correct grade and quantity of fluid.

3 Hondamatic transmission - dismantling into major assemblies

1 Overhaul of the transmission will normally only be required after a fault has been diagnosed: Refer to Section 8.
2 Withdraw the torque converter from the torque housing.
3 Inspect the outer edges of the torque converter pump and the cover to ensure that the respective location marks are in alignment. If no

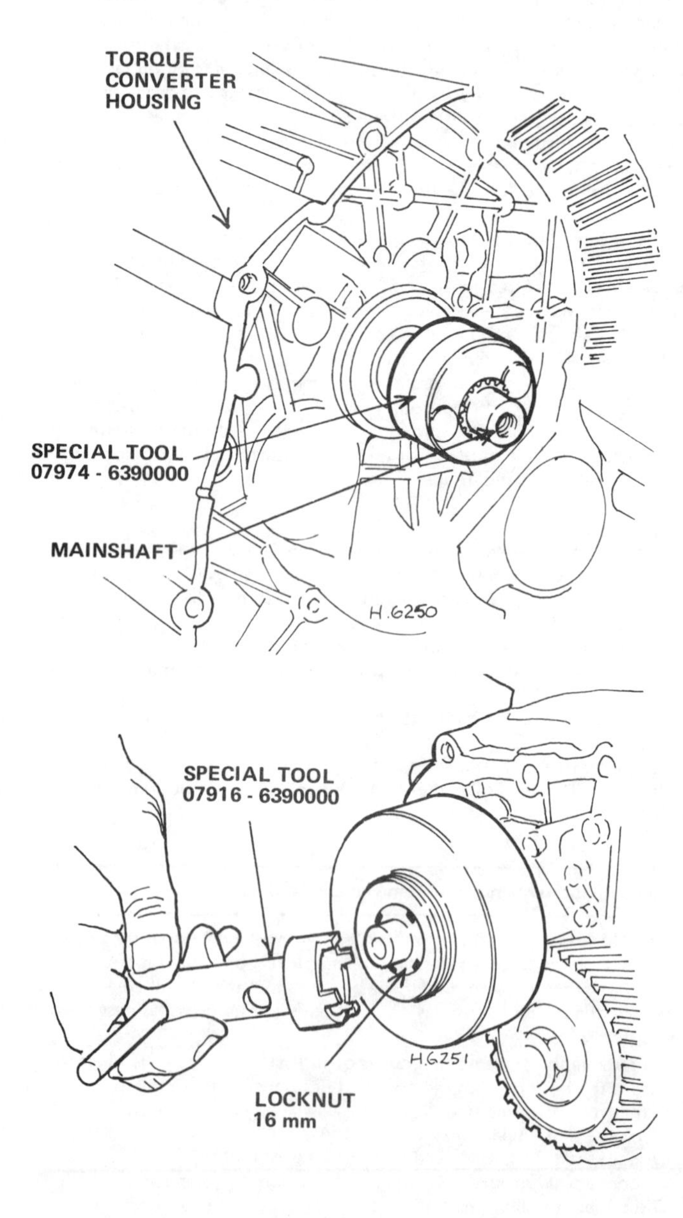

Fig. 7.6 The two special tools required to lock the mainshaft in position while removing the mainshaft nut (Sec. 3)

marks are visible scribe some to ensure refitment in their original positions (Fig. 7.5).

4 Unbolt the cover and separate the internal components, noting carefully their sequence and orientation.

5 Unscrew and remove the fluid dipstick, unscrew the end cover bolts and tap off the end cover using a soft-faced mallet.

6 Move the speed selector arm to the 'park' position.

7 Two special tools will now be required. One (07974 - 6390000) to hold the splined end of the mainshaft still while the mainshaft locknut is unscrewed with the other tool (07916 - 6390000).

8 Remove the low clutch, low gear, needle bearing and spacer as an assembly then extract the thrust washer.

9 Relieve the staking on the countershaft nut and then unscrew and remove it and lift off low gear.

10 Remove the bearing retainer (two bolts) and then extract the three screws using an impact driver.

11 Extract the bolts from the reverse idler shaft retainer.

12 Unbolt and tap the transmission housing from the torque converter housing (Fig. 7.10).

13 From the exposed geartrain, lift off counter reverse gear and then

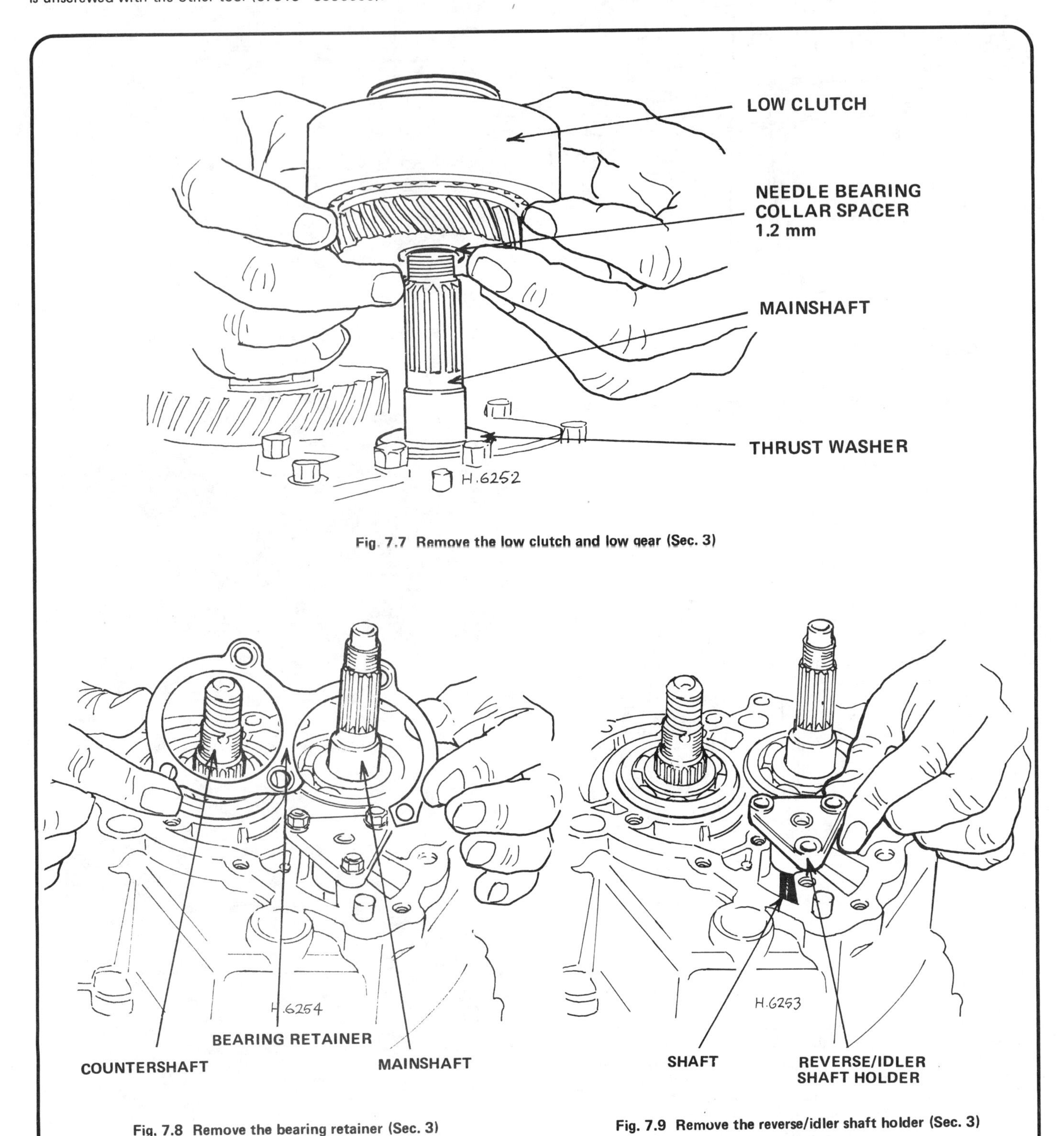

Fig. 7.7 Remove the low clutch and low gear (Sec. 3)

Fig. 7.8 Remove the bearing retainer (Sec. 3)

Fig. 7.9 Remove the reverse/idler shaft holder (Sec. 3)

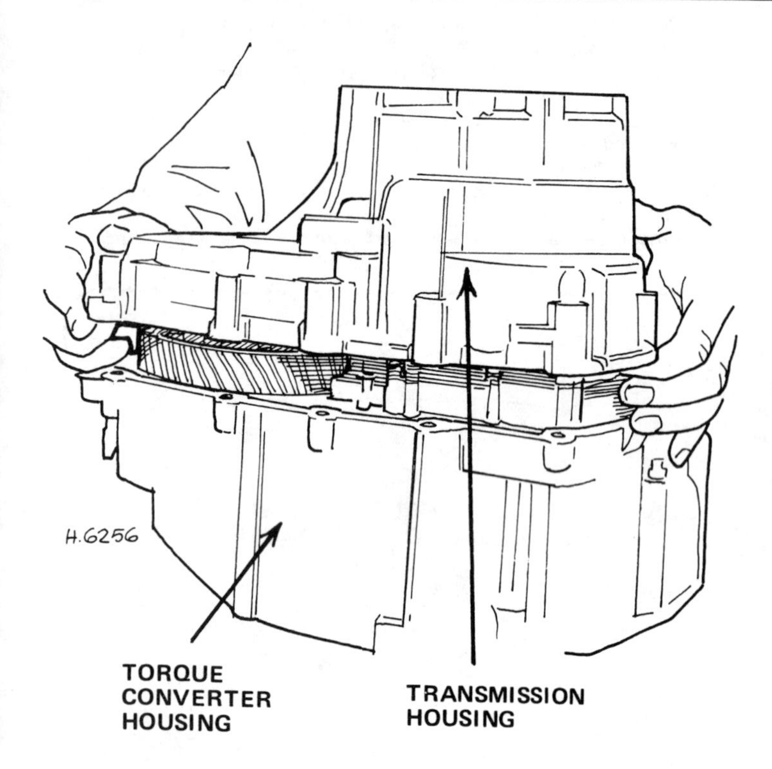

Fig. 7.10 Lift the transmission housing from the torque converter housing (Sec. 3)

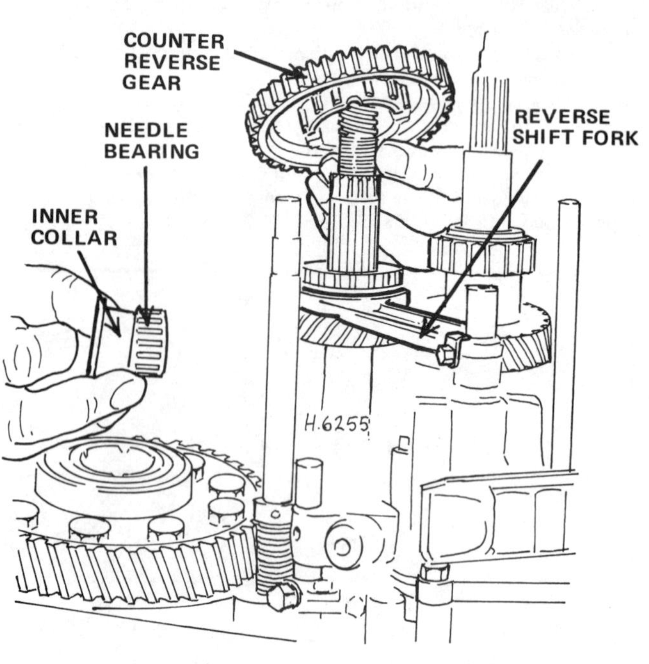

Fig. 7.11 Lift off counter reverse gear (Sec. 3)

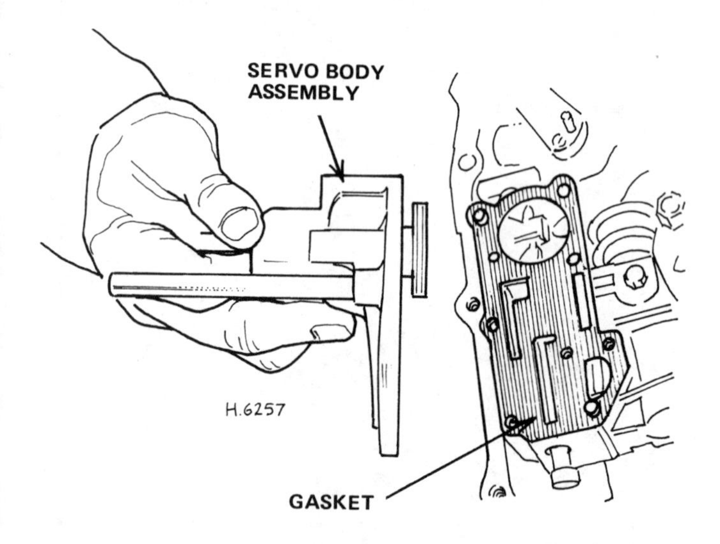

Fig. 7.12 Remove the servo body unit (Sec. 3)

Fig. 7.13 Remove the sealing ring guide (Sec. 3)

Fig. 7.14 Remove the stator torque converter shaft (Sec. 3)

the reverse shift fork/selector gear as an assembly, having first withdrawn the fork lockbolt.

14 Select 'neutral' and then lift the mainshaft and countershaft geartrains away simultaneously with their gears meshed together.

15 Unbolt and remove the oil pump strainer and servo body and then withdraw the sealing ring guide.

16 Remove the stop pin and then tap the stator torque converter shaft out from the transmission housing side of the torque converter housing.

17 Remove the valve body, pump gears and separator plate taking care not to drop the check valve and spring. Remove the lockpin, valve pin and spacers from the manual valve. Before removing the pump driven

Fig. 7.15 Remove the valve body (Sec. 3)

gear, mark it so that it will be refitted with the same face against the housing.
18 Remove the speed selector arm and parking panel mechanism after bending down the lockplate tabs and extracting the bolt and tension pin.

4 Major assemblies - inspection and overhaul

Mainshaft

1 The mainshaft can be completely dismantled after extracting the snap-rings. Check the bearings for wear, the teeth of the gears and the splines of the shaft for wear or deformation. If the shaft is scored it must be renewed together with any other faulty components.
2 Commence reassembly by installing the oil sealing ring, the two snap-rings and the needle bearing then the 'D' drive clutch (refer to paragraph 5, this Section, for complete dismantling) and the (drive) clutch thrust washer and thrust needle bearing. Follow with the collar, needle bearings and drive gear. Rotate the drive gear until the splines engage fully with the clutch discs. Install the thrust washers noting that the thicker one must be fitted with the shouldered side against the drive gear (Figs. 7.17 and 7.18).

Countershaft

3 Inspect the countershaft components for wear and damage and renew as necessary (Fig. 7.20).
4 Reassemble by fitting the needle bearing, the snap-ring, the reverse drive gear and reverse hub, the latter having its recessed side towards the snap-ring (Fig. 7.19).

Low/drive clutch

5 To dismantle the clutch, extract the snap-ring and lift away the end plate, discs and plates (Fig. 7.22).
6 The clutch return coil spring must now be compressed with a suitable compressor (a long bolt with distance pieces will serve for this) so that the snap-ring, retainer and spring can be removed.
7 Place the clutch drum onto a soft surface and eject the clutch piston by applying air from a tyre pump at one oil hole while blocking the other with the finger.
8 Clean all components and renew any which are worn or damaged.
9 Apply clean transmission fluid to all parts and then commence reassembly by installing two oil seal rings to the clutch drum. Space the ring gaps 180° apart.
10 Install a new 'O' ring to the clutch piston and then fit the cushion spring as shown (Fig. 7.21).
11 Fit a new 'O' ring to the clutch drum hub.
12 Press the piston into the clutch drum squarely using firm finger pressure.
13 Refit the clutch spring and retainer, compress the spring and fit the snap-ring.
14 Refit the clutch plates and discs alternately having liberally applied transmission fluid to them. Make sure that the clutch endplate has its flat side against the clutch disc. Install the large securing snap-ring.

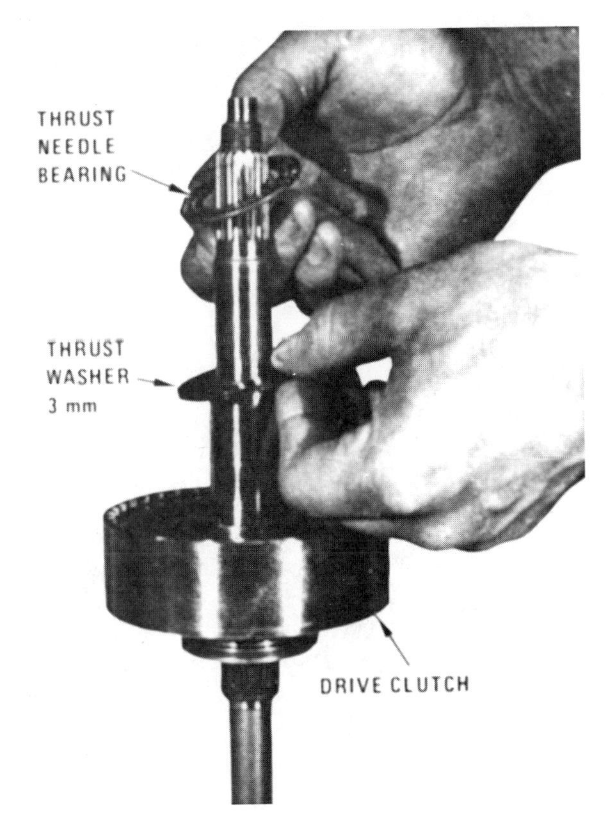

Fig. 7.16 Fit the thrust washer and bearing (Sec. 4)

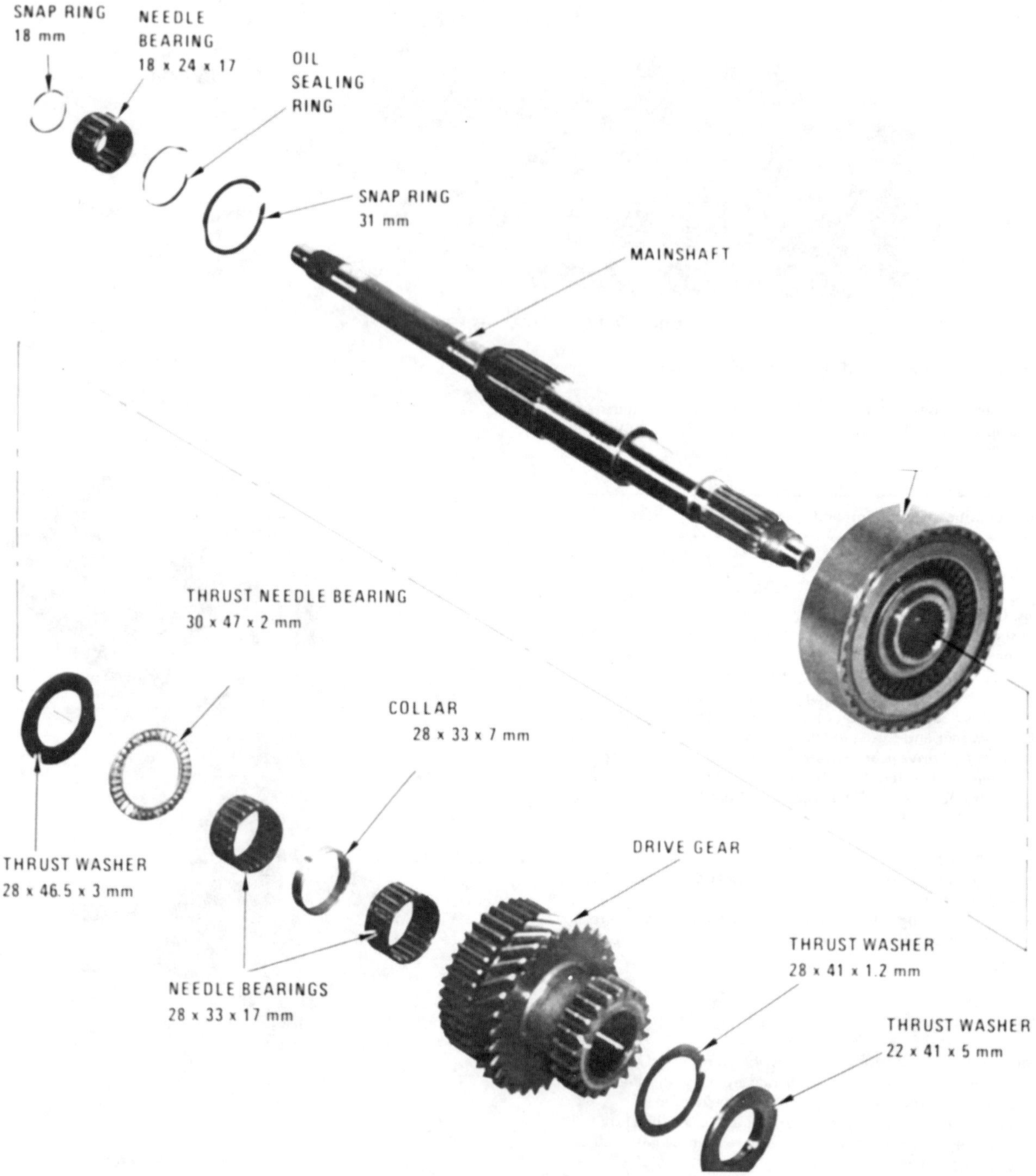

Fig. 7.17 The mainshaft components (Sec. 4)

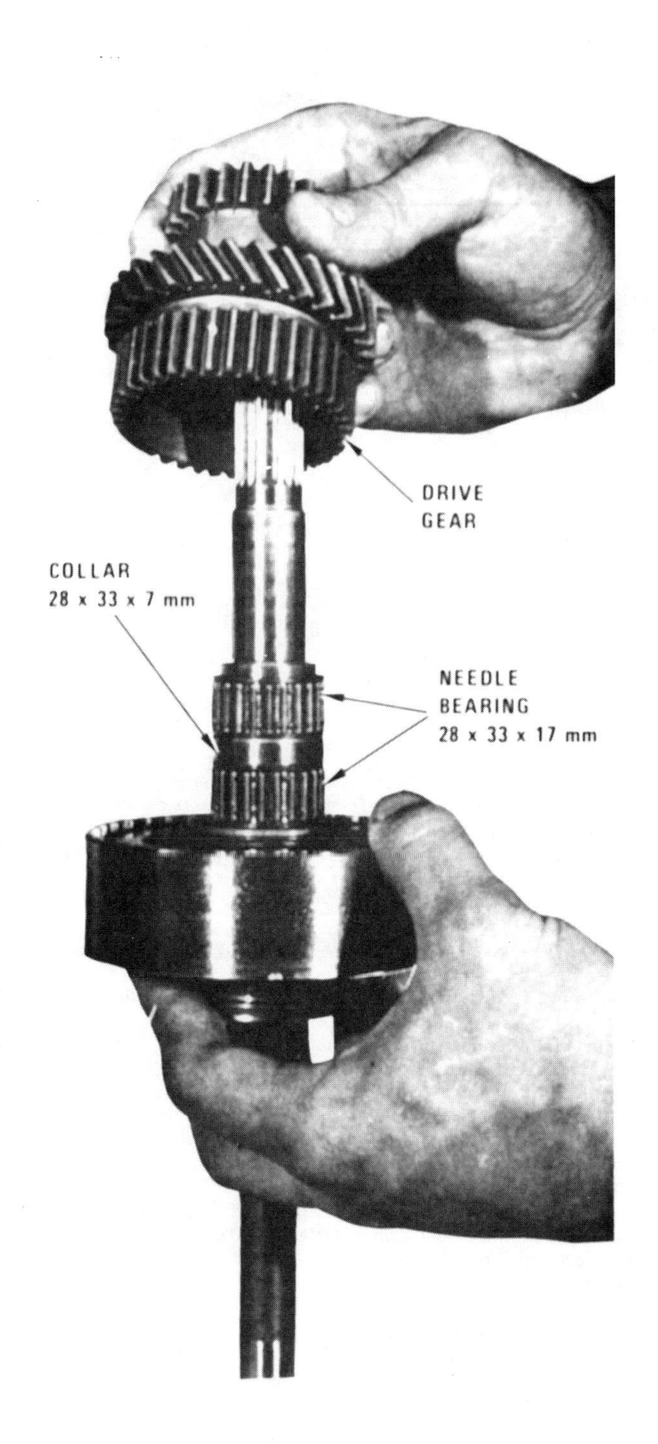

Fig. 7.18 Fit the drive gear (Sec. 4)

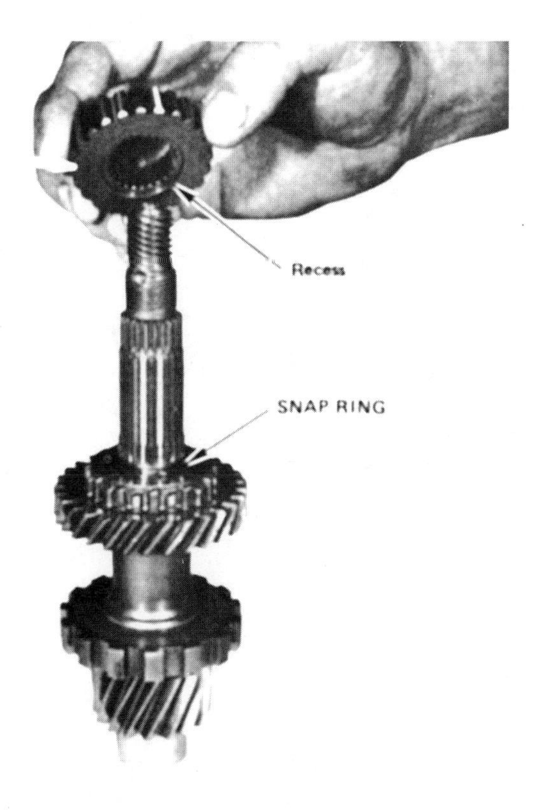

Fig. 7.19 Fit reverse hub gear - recessed side to snap ring (Sec. 4)

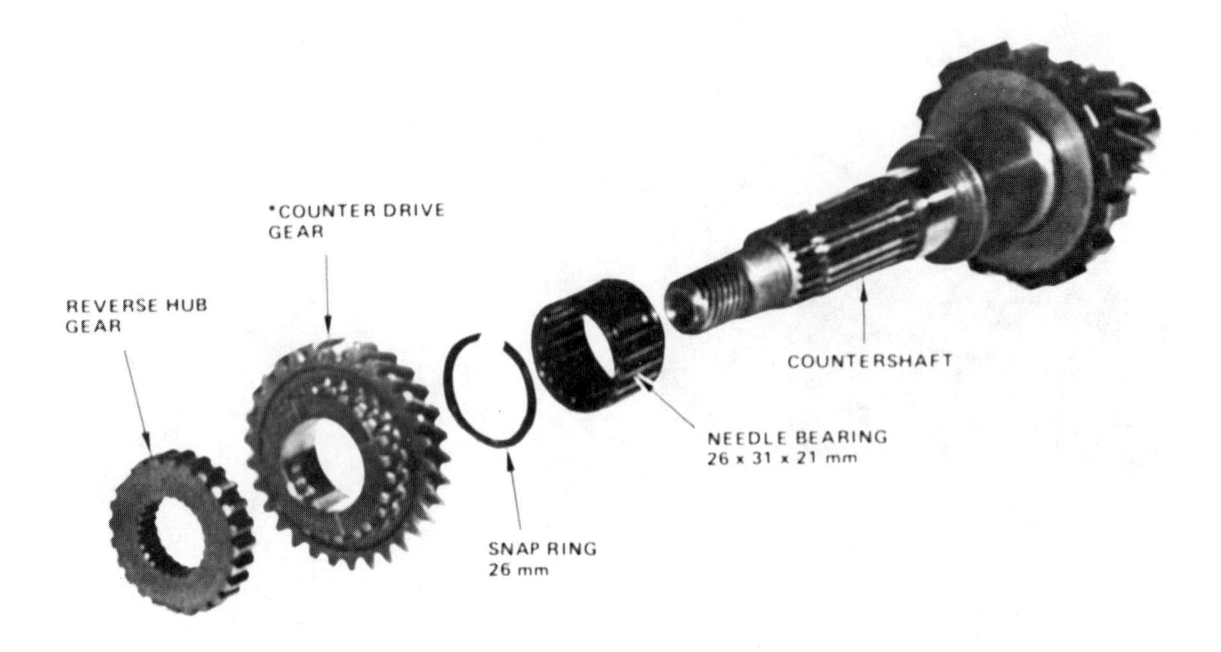

Fig. 7.20. The countershaft components (Sec. 4)

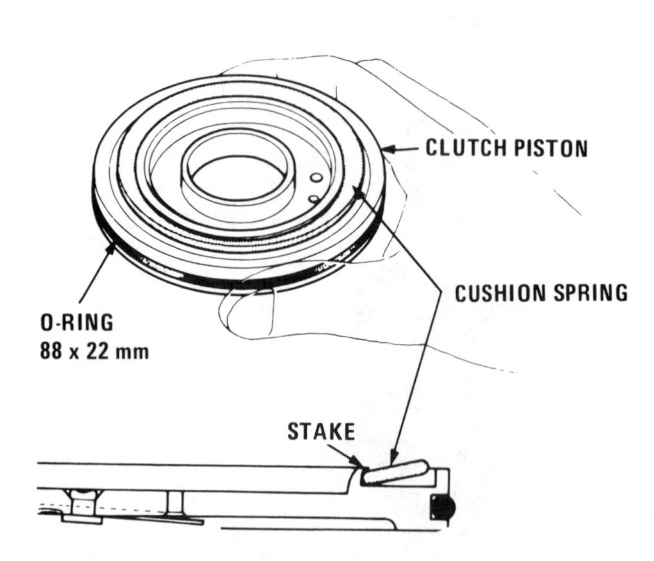

Fig. 7.21 Fit the 'O' ring and piston and cushion spring (Sec. 4)

15 Using a feeler blade, measure the clearance between the last clutch disc and the endplate. This should be between 0.020 and 0.032 in (0.5 and 0.8 mm). If the clearance is incorrect, change the endplate for one of a different thickness, there are six alternative thicknesses available. The clutch can be checked for engagement by applying air pressure to an oilway in the drum hub. On removal of the air pressure the clutch should release.

Servo body

16 Clean and inspect the components of the servo body and blow out the passages with air from a tyre pump (Fig. 7.23).

17 Renew the 'O' ring seal on the servo valve. Renew the valve and body if there is any sign of scoring. The servo valve and body are stamp marked as a set (Figs. 7.24 and 7.25), either 'A', 'B' or 'C'. The standard valve to body clearance is 0.00010 to 0.00014 in (0.025 to 0.036 mm) and the maximum wear limit is 0.0002 in (0.050 mm)

Valve body

18 Dismantle, clean and inspect all components for wear or scoring. Renew as necessary (Fig. 7.26).
19 Commence reassembly by installing the pressure regulator valve and inner and outer valve springs.
20 Install the retainer spring, spring seat and retainer. Align the hole in the retainer and tighten bolt to a torque of 7 to 10 lb f ft (1.0 to 1.4 kg fm).
21 Install manual valve, detent rollers and spring.
22 Install the pump gears and measure the clearance between the drive gear and the valve body using a feeler gauge. This should be between 0.002 and 0.004 in (0.03 and 0.09 mm) (Fig. 7.27).
23 Using a straight-edge and a feeler gauge, check the drive gear endfloat. This should be between 0.001 and 0.002 in (0.03 and 0.06 mm). Any deviation from these clearances will necessitate renewal of the components (Fig. 7.28).

Housing bearings and oil seals

24 The oil seals in the torque converter and transmission housing should be renewed as a matter of routine at the time of major overhaul.
25 The bearings, if worn, can be renewed by driving them out and pressing the new ones in, using a piece of tubing as a drift. Always apply force to the bearing outer track which seats in the casing. The following points must also be observed. The differential must be removed before the countershaft bearing can be removed (refer to Chapter 8). If the differential side bearings or the transmission or torque converter housings are renewed then the differential side clearance must be measured and if necessary, adjusted as described in Chapter 8. The reverse idler shaft and its bearings are removed from the outside of the transmission housing while the reverse idler gear is withdrawn into the interior. The sealing ring screws which are located in the end cover should be removed using an impact driver and restaked when they are refitted.

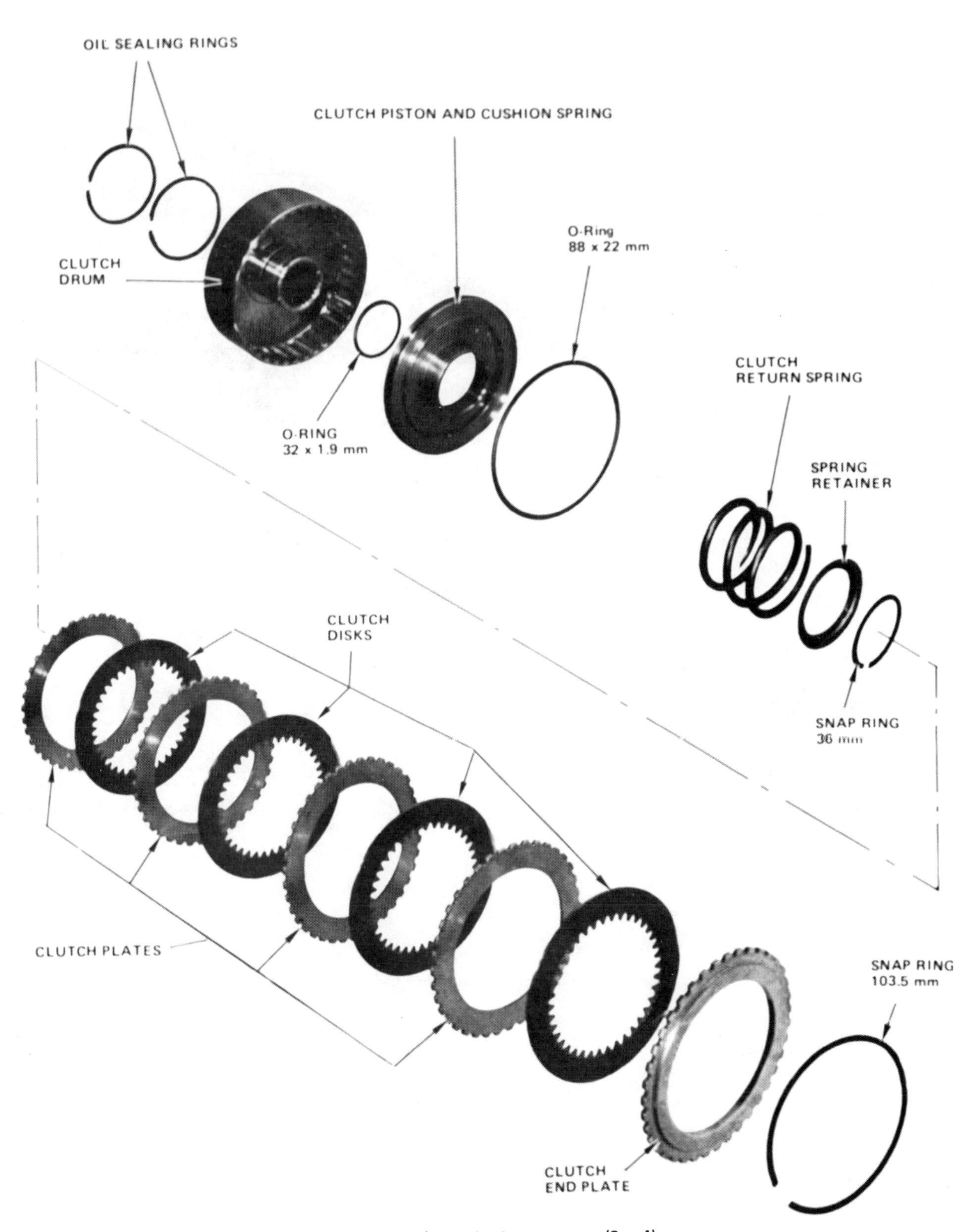

Fig. 7.22 Low/drive clutch components (Sec. 4)

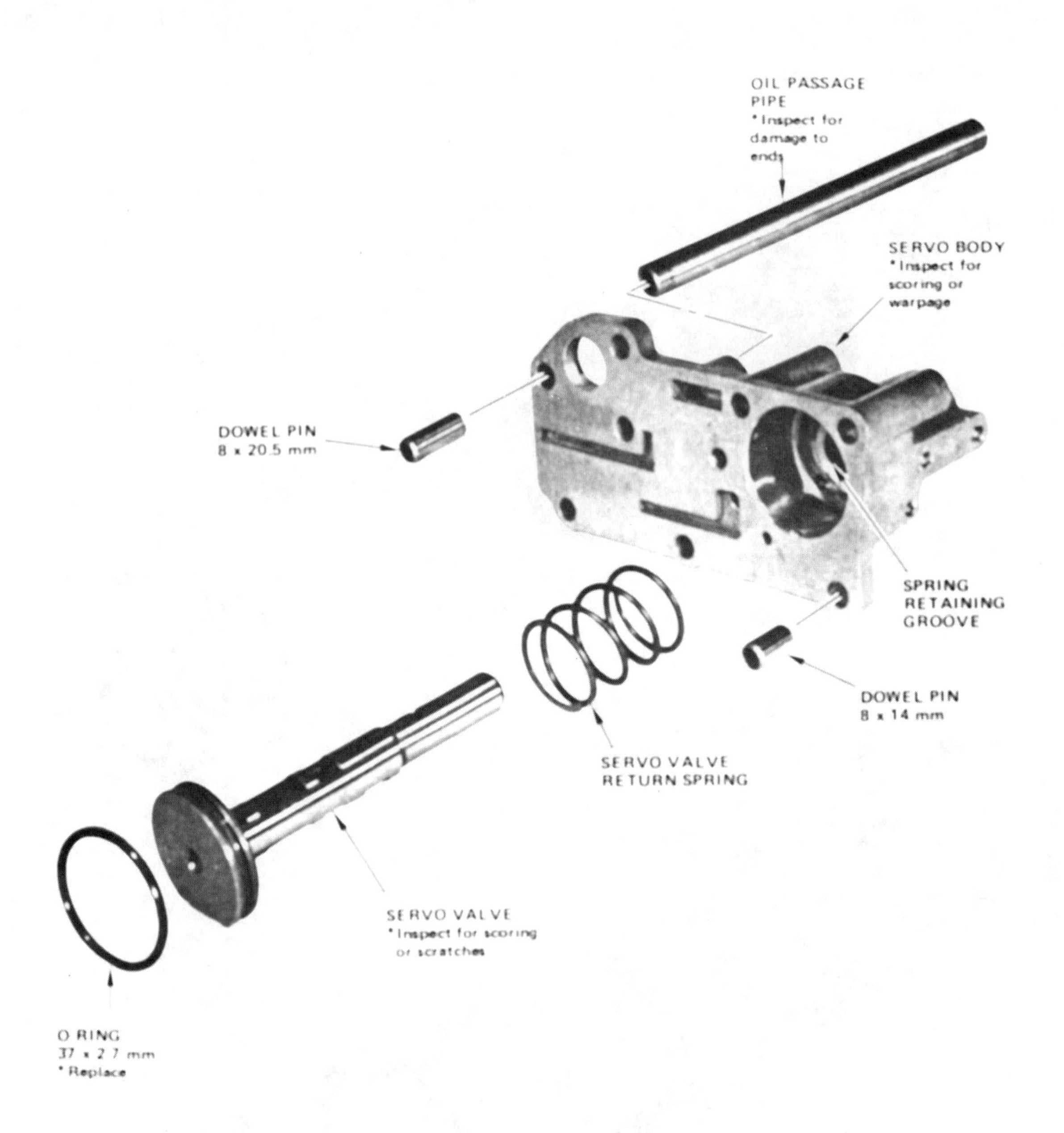

Fig. 7.23 The servo components (Sec. 4)

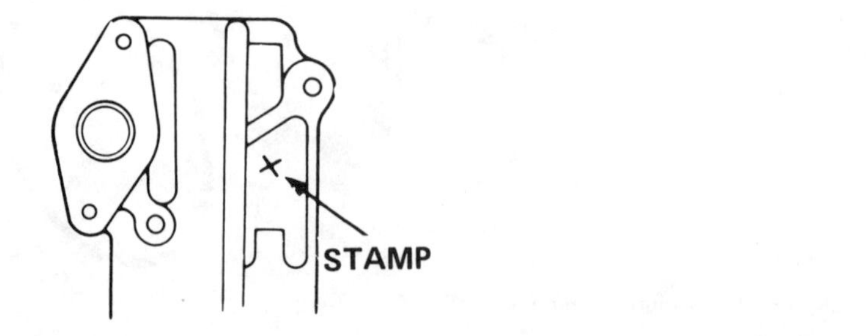

Fig. 7.24 Servo body stamp mark position (Sec. 4)

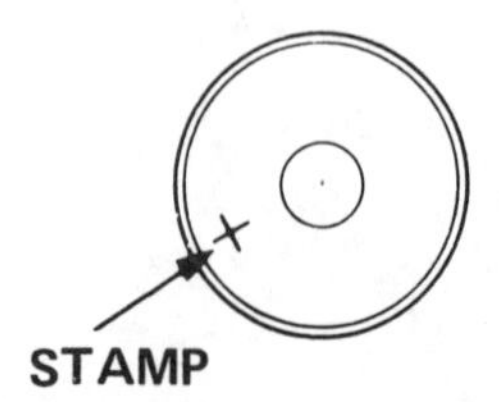

Fig. 7.25 Servo valve stamp mark position (Sec. 4)

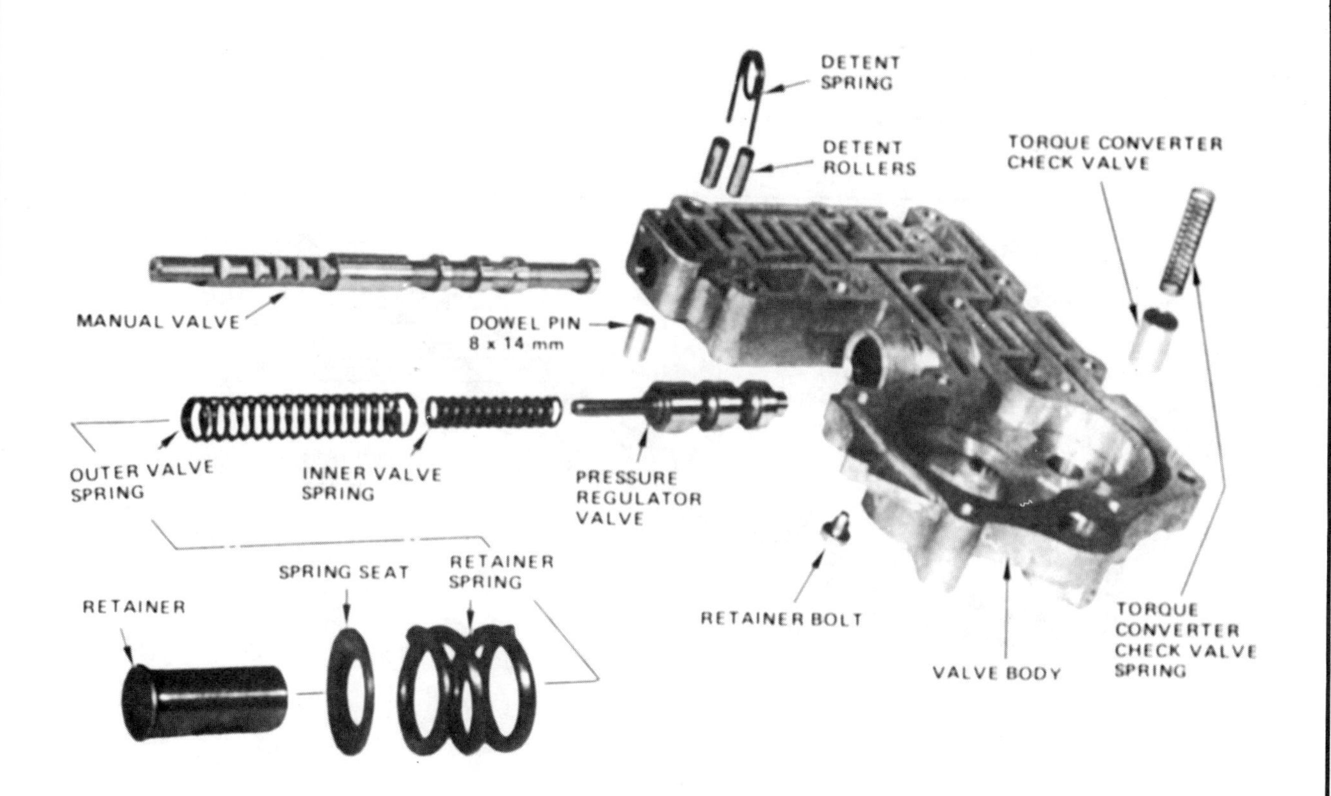

Fig. 7.26 The valve body components (Sec. 4)

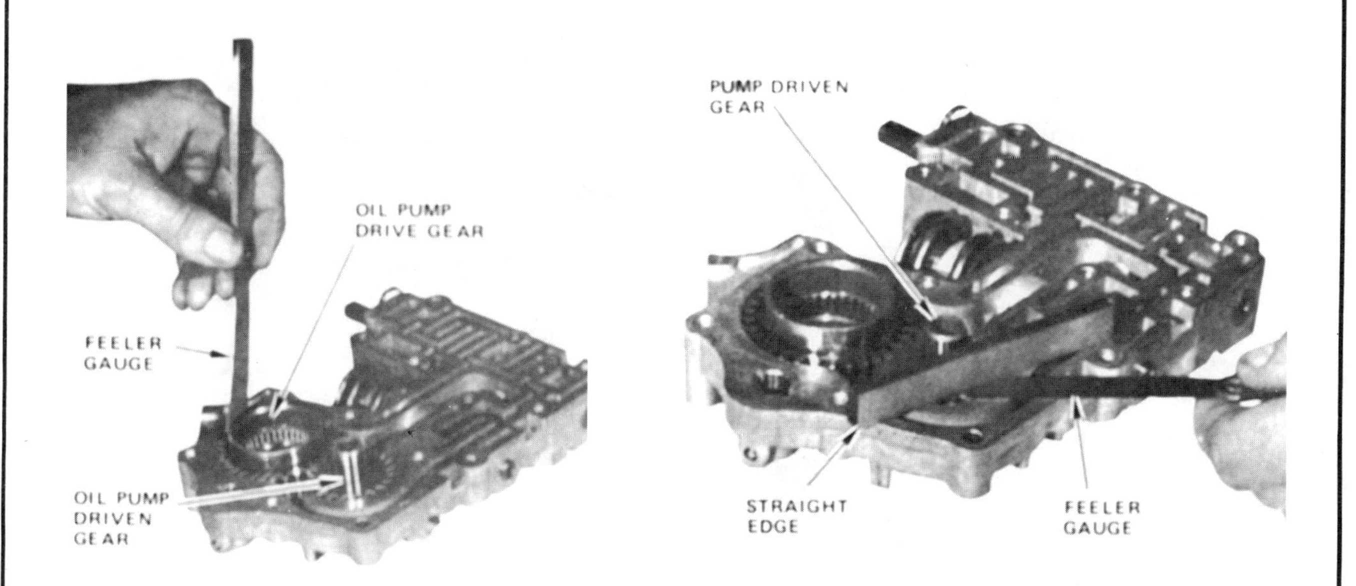

Fig. 7.28 Measure the end thrust clearance (Sec. 4)

Fig. 7.27 Check the oil pump drive gear clearance (Sec. 4)

5 Hondamatic transmission - reassembly

1 Assemble the parking pawl mechanism and speed shift lever and install in the torque converter housing.
2 Install the speed selector linkarm, tighten the lockbolt to 7 to 10 lb f ft (1.0 to 1.4 kg fm) and bend up the tab of the lockplate.
3 Install the separator plate, dowel pin, pump gears and shaft.
4 Fit the torque converter check valve and spring in the valve body and then install the valve body to the torque converter housing, tightening the securing bolts to 7 to 10 lb f ft (1.0 to 1.4 kg fm).
5 Attach the speed shift lever to the manual valve using the pin with a spacer in each side and finally securing it with the lockpin.
6 Insert the stator torque converter shaft.

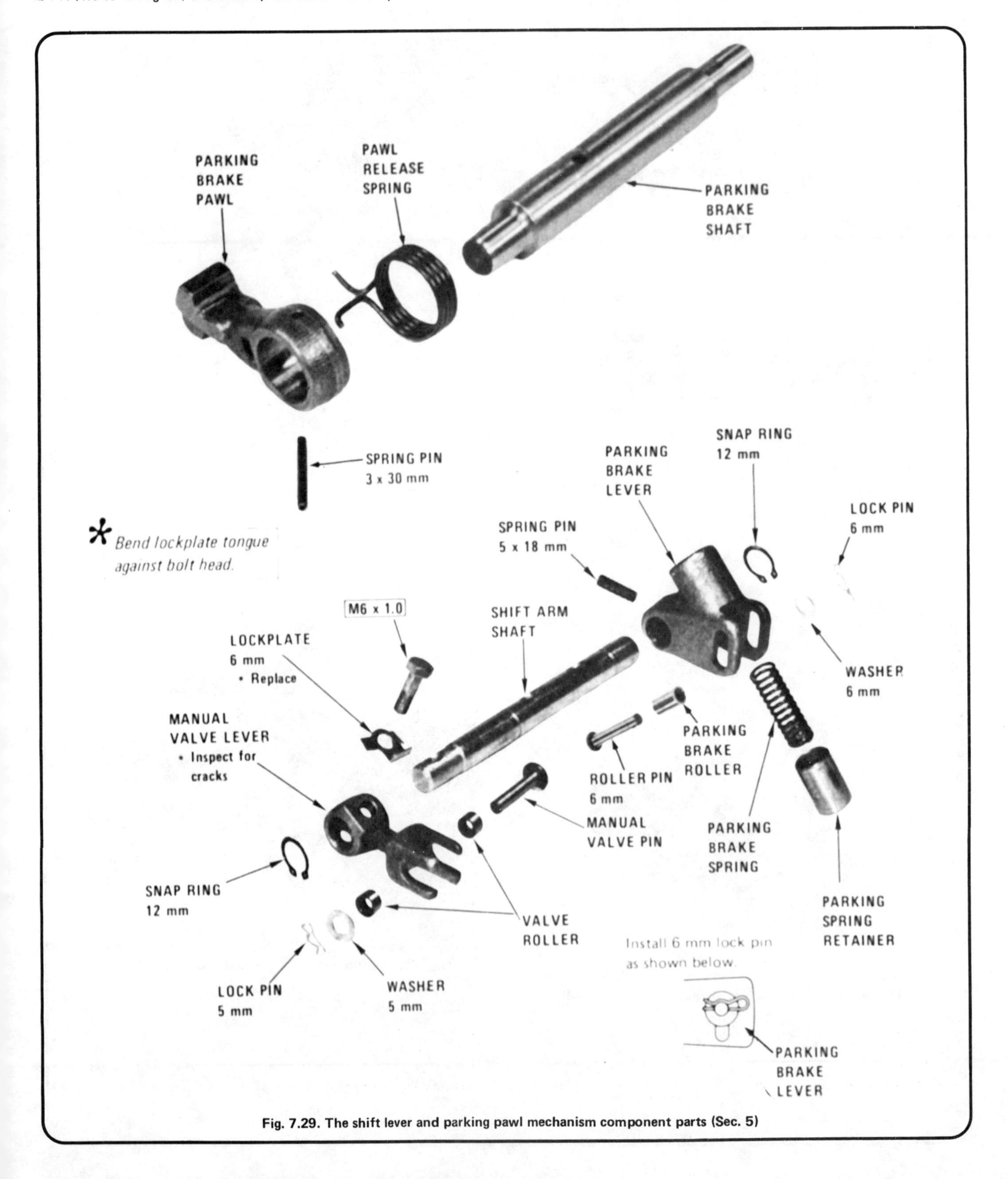

Fig. 7.29. The shift lever and parking pawl mechanism component parts (Sec. 5)

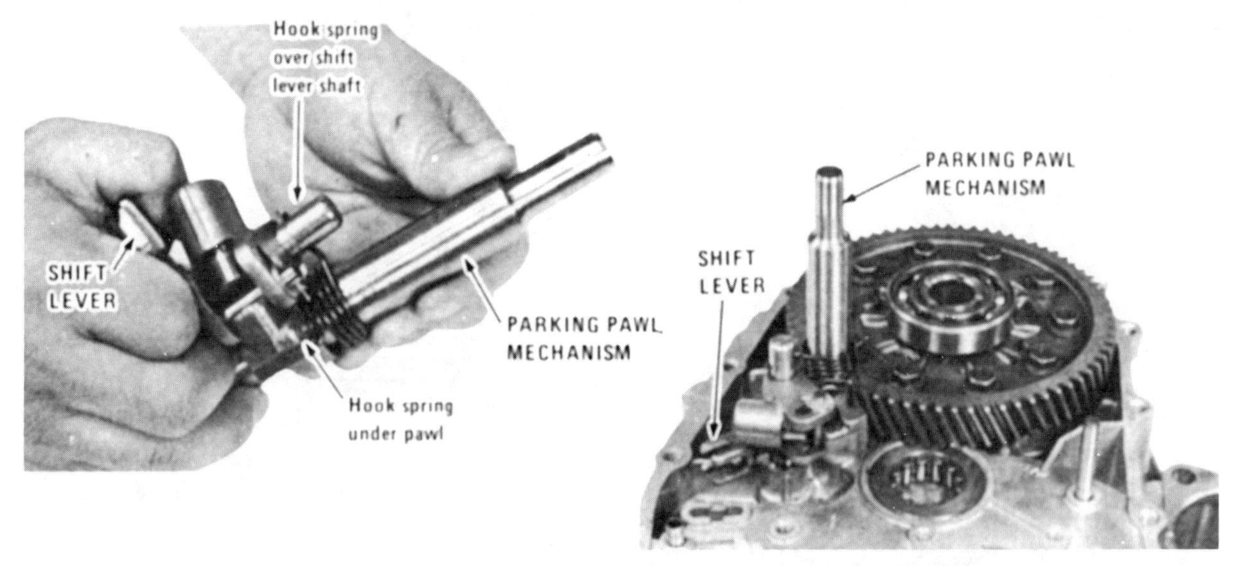

Fig. 7.30 Reassembly of the parking pawl and shift lever (Sec. 5)

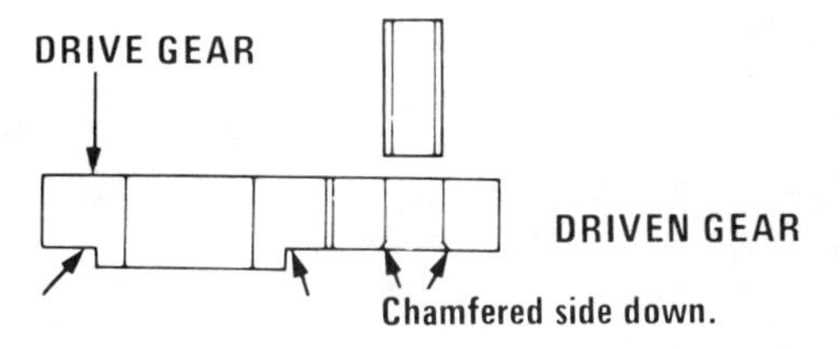

Fig. 7.31 Install the driven gear with the chamfered face downwards (Sec. 5)

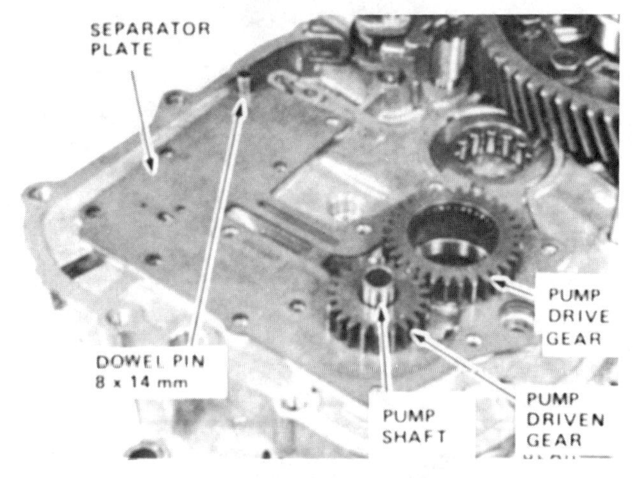

Fig. 7.32 Fit the separator plate with gears, shaft and dowel pin (Sec. 5)

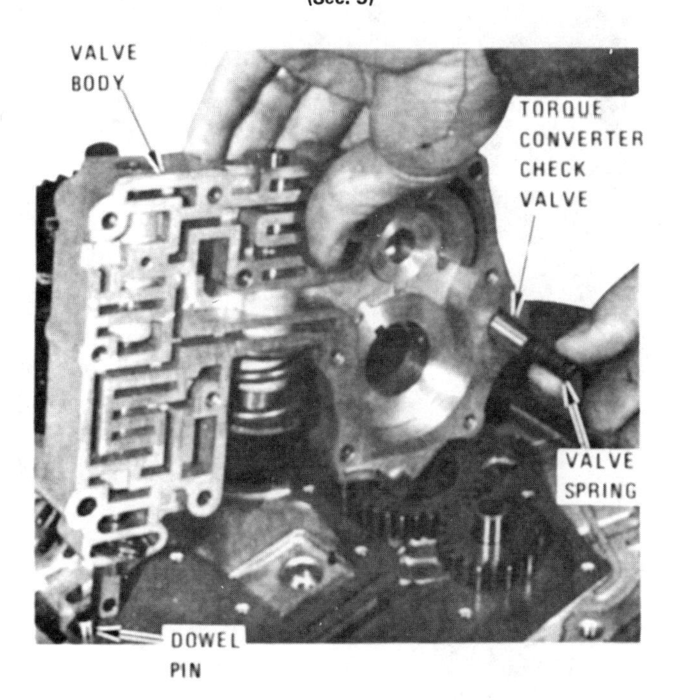

Fig. 7.33 Installing the valve body (Sec. 5)

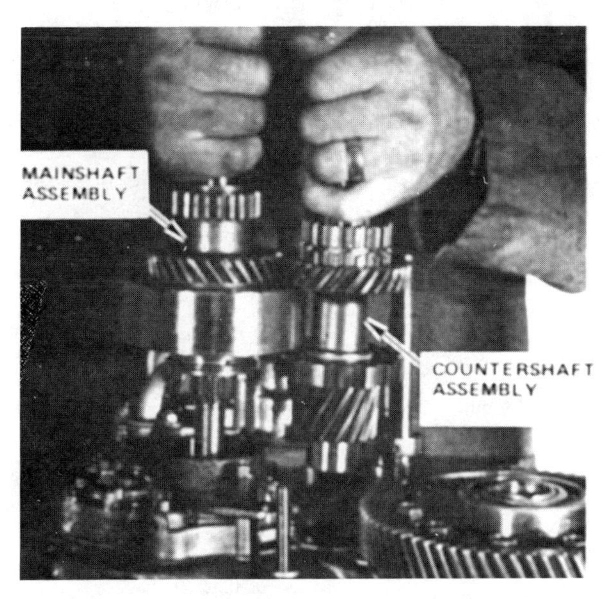

Fig. 7.34 Fit the mainshaft and countershaft assemblies (Sec. 5)

7 Install the sealing ring guide and stop pin, tightening the guide bolts to 7 to 10 lbf ft (1.0 to 1.4 kgf m).

8 Install the servo body gasket, dowel pins and body itself. Tighten the body securing bolts to 7 to 10 lbf ft (1.0 to 1.4 kgf m). Make sure that the different length bolts are correctly positioned.

9 Install the oil pump strainer using a new 'O' ring seal.

10 Mesh the mainshaft and countershaft gears together, and then install

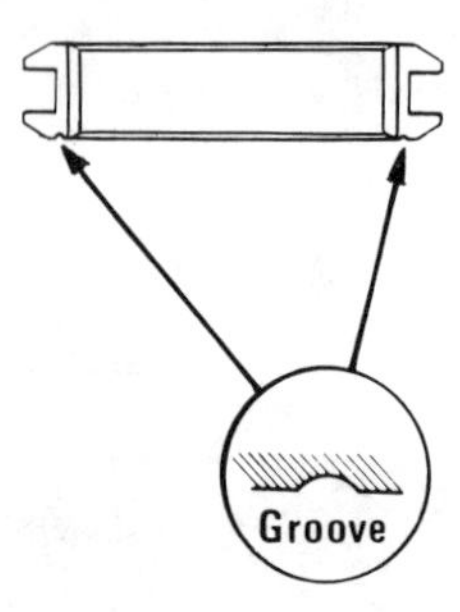

Install reverse selector gear with grooved face side down.

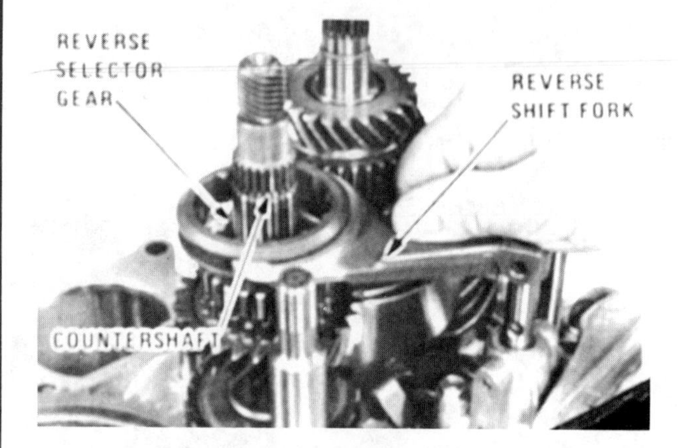

Fig. 7.35 Install reverse selector gear to the shift fork and countershaft (Sec. 5)

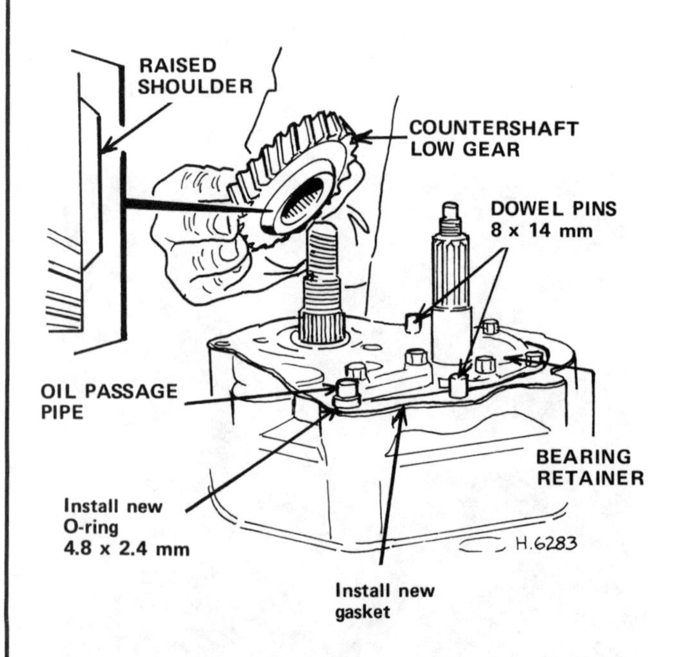

Fig. 7.37 Fit the countershaft low gear with the raised shoulder downwards (Sec. 5)

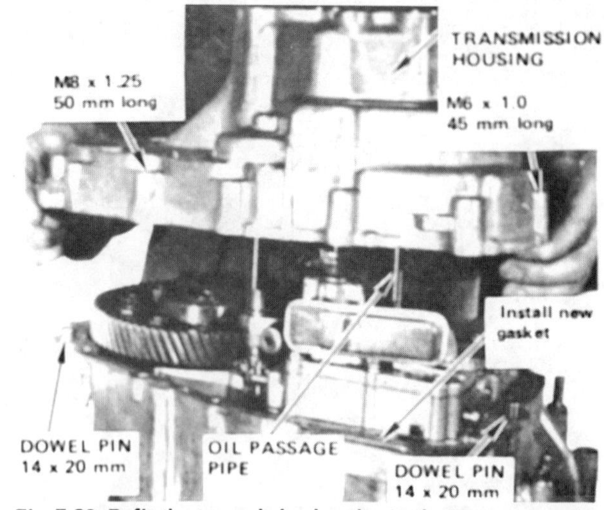

Fig. 7.36 Refit the transmission housing to the torque converter housing (Sec. 5)

Fig. 7.38 Install the needle bearing (Sec. 5)

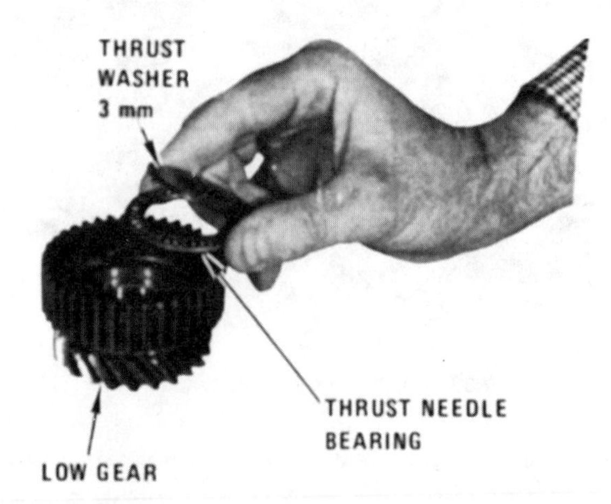

Fig. 7.39 Install the thrust needle bearing and plain washer to the low gear recess (Sec. 5)

both assemblies simultaneously.
11 Assemble the reverse selector gear to the shift fork (with the grooved side facing downwards) and install the assembly to the countershaft. Tighten the lockbolt to 7 to 10 lb f ft (1.0 to 1.4 kg fm) and bend up the tab of a new lockplate.
12 Install the counter reverse gear, needle bearing and the inner collar into the countershaft.
13 Locate a new gasket and then install the transmission housing to the torque converter housing taking care not to bend the oil pipe. Install the connecting bolts, tightening the smaller ones to 7 to 10 lb f ft (1.0 to 1.4 kg fm); the larger ones to 17 to 22 lb f ft (2.3 to 3.1 kg fm).
14 Install the bearing retainer to the transmission housing. Tighten the bolts to 9 lb f ft (1.3 kg fm) and stake the countermesh screw heads.
15 Bolt on the reverse idler shaft retainer, tighten the bolts to 7 to 10 lb f ft (1.0 to 1.4 kg fm).
16 Fit the countershaft low gear so that the raised shoulder on the gear is towards the bearing retainer.
17 Install a new gasket and a new 'O' ring on the oil pipe and check that the locating dowels are in position.
18 Select 'park' and use the special tool to hold the mainshaft still. Screw on a new countershaft nut and tighten it to 58 to 72 lb f ft (8 to 10 kg fm), then stake the rim of the nut into the slot in the countershaft.
19 To the mainshaft install the thrust washer, spacer, inner collar and needle bearing.
20 Fit the thrust needle bearing and plain thrust washer into the recess in low gear.
21 Insert low gear into low clutch, rotating the gear until complete engagement is secured. Install the clutch and gear as an assembly to the mainshaft.
22 Using the special tools, fit the lockwasher and screw the locknut onto the mainshaft with the recessed face inwards. Tighten to 32 to 40 lb f ft (4.5 to 5.5 kg fm), and bend up tabs of lockwasher.
23 Fit the end cover and dipstick to the transmission housing.
24 Install the torque converter into the torque converter housing. If the torque converter was dismantled, install the snap-ring and the stator side plate. Install the ring and cam in the stator followed by the rollers and springs.
25 Fit the second stator side plate and snap-ring and then insert the torque converter shaft into the stator from the pump side and check the operation of the one-way clutch, which must only rotate counter-clockwise.
26 Insert the thrust washer into the torque converter pump and then fit the stator into the pump followed by the serrated thrust washer.
27 Clean the grooves on the pump body thoroughly and then install new 'O' rings and fit the turbine to the pump.
28 Install the thrust washer to the turbine.
29 Fit the torque converter cover to the pump making sure to align the mating marks. Locate the starter ring gear so that the flat side is towards the cover and then tighten the securing bolts in the sequence shown in Fig. 7.42 to a torque of 7 to 10 lb f ft (1.0 to 1.4 kg fm)

Fig. 7.40 Installing the low gear and clutch to the mainshaft (Sec. 5)

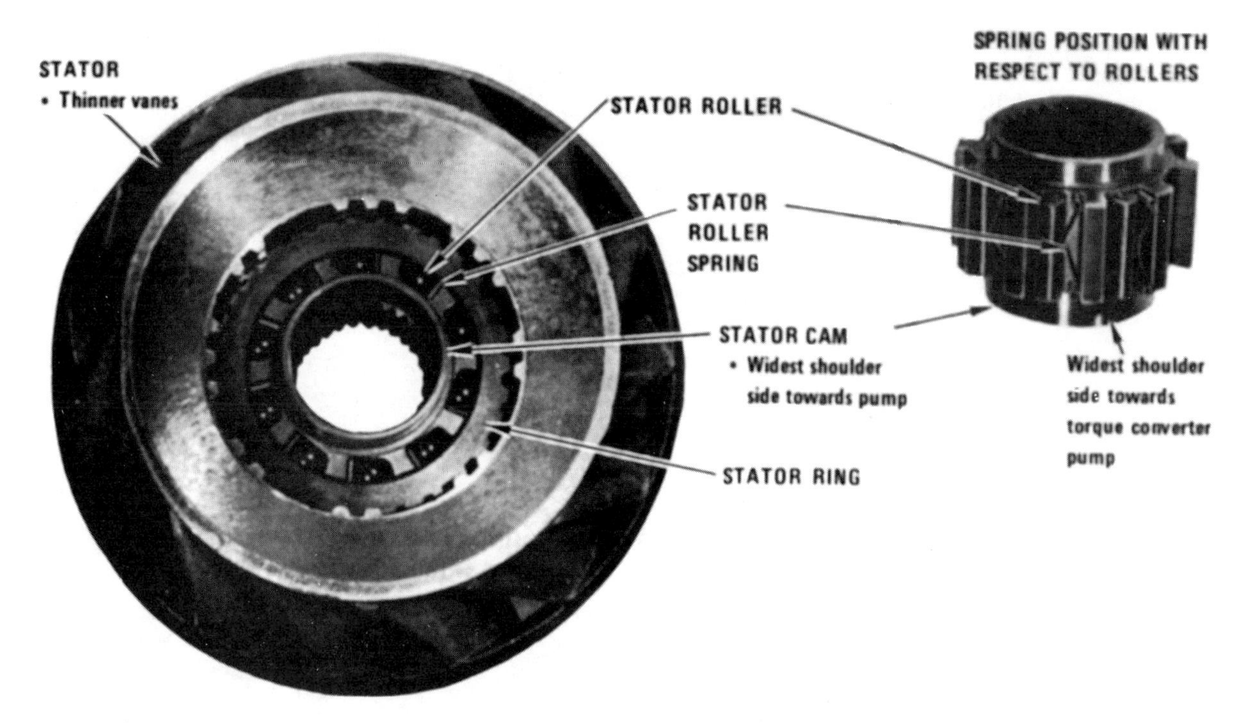

Fig. 7.41 Install the stator ring, cam and rollers (Sec. 5)

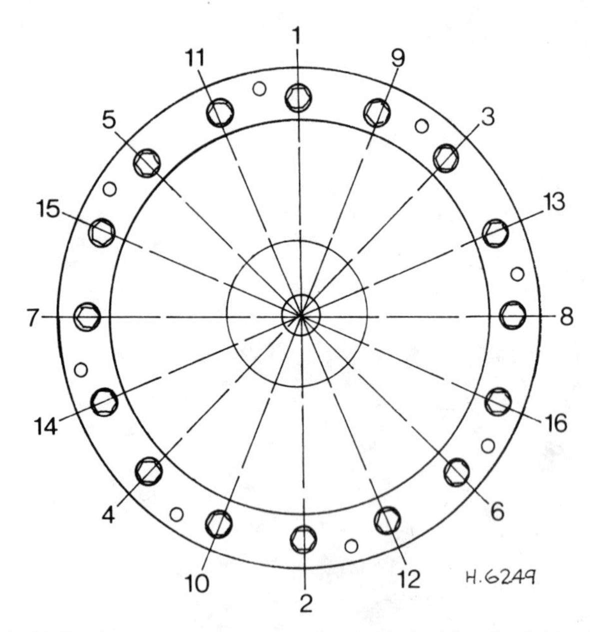

Fig. 7.42 Torque converter cover retaining bolt tightening/loosening sequence (Sec. 5)

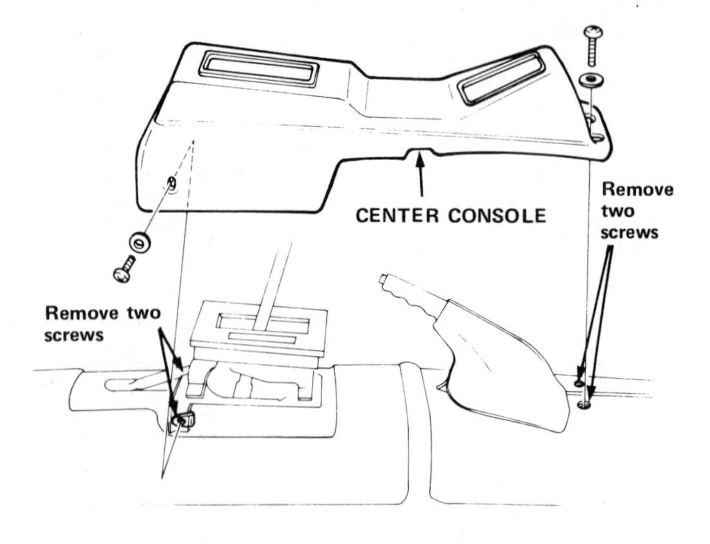

Fig. 7.43 The centre console retaining screw positions (Sec. 6)

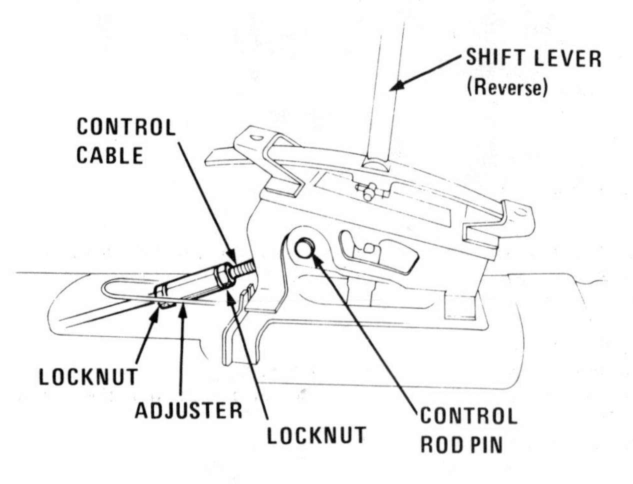

Fig. 7.44 The shift lever to control cable pin and adjuster positions (Sec. 6)

6 Control cable - adjustment, removal and refitting

Adjustment

1 Start the engine and position the selector lever in reverse to ensure correct engagement.

2 Turn off the engine and remove the central console which is retained by two screws at the front and two screws at the rear (Fig. 7.43).

3 Position the shift lever into reverse and extract the clip and clevis pin securing the cable to the base of the speed selector lever.

4 Check that the clevis pin is a sliding fit when inserted through the holes of the cable end and the selector lever. If force is required, loosen the adjuster locknuts and rotate the adjuster accordingly to align the cable end and selector lever clevis pin holes. Insert the pin and tighten the locknuts whilst retaining the adjuster in the set position.

5 Replace the clevis pin clip and refit the console. Start the engine and check that the respective gears are operational.

Removal and refitting

6 To remove the control cable, follow the instructions given in Section 2, paragraph 16 and paragraphs 2 to 3 in this Section. Refitting is a direct reversal of removal but check the cable adjustment as in paragraph 4.

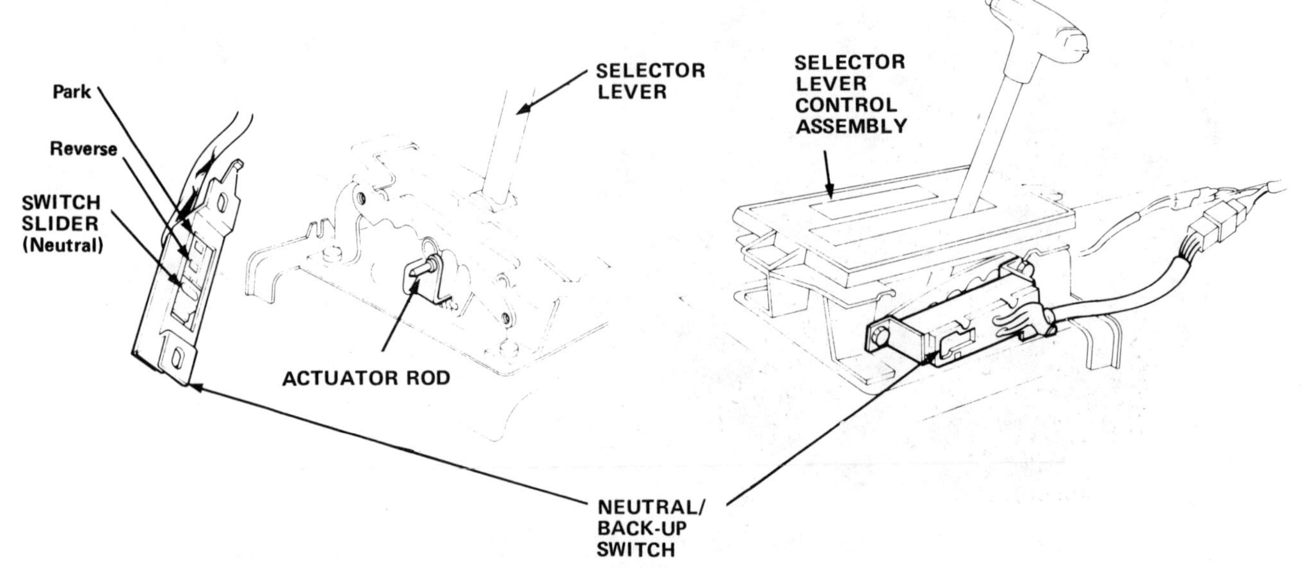

Fig. 7.45 The neutral/reverse switch location (Sec. 7)

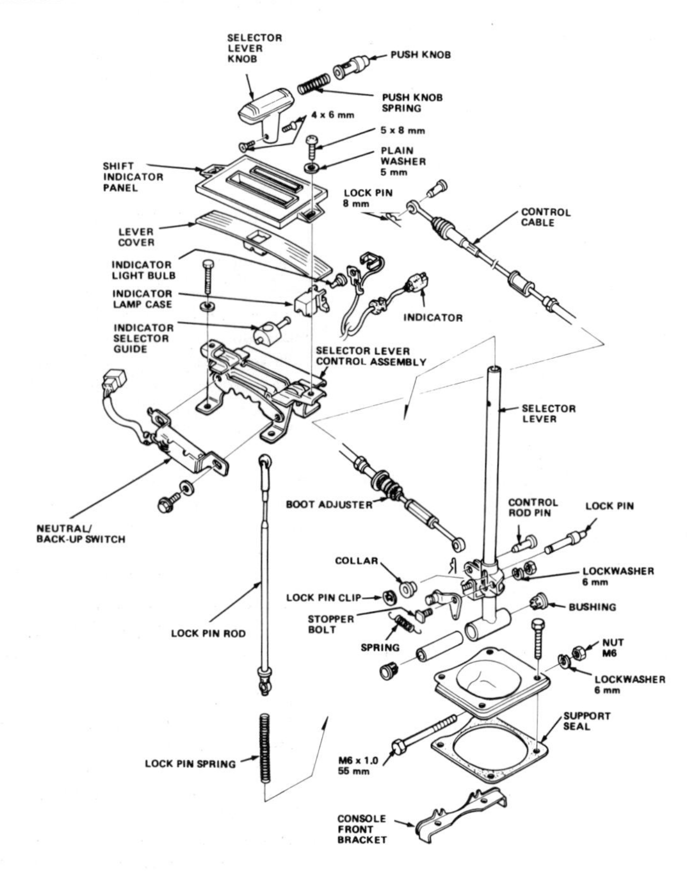

Fig. 7.46 The gear shift selector components

7 Neutral/reverse switch and indicator lamp - removal and refitting

Neutral/reverse switch

1 Remove the centre console inside the car and engage the selector lever in neutral.

2 Unscrew and remove the two bolts retaining the switch unit. Unhook the switch bracket from the forward end of the selector lever control unit, and remove the switch from the selector lever actuator rod.

3 Refitting is the reversal of removal but ensure that the selector lever actuating rod and the switch slides are fully engaged in the neutral position.

Indicator lamp

4 Remove the centre console inside the car.

5 Detach the indicator light unit from the projection on the selector guide.

6 Unclip and remove the bulb.

7 Refit in reverse order.

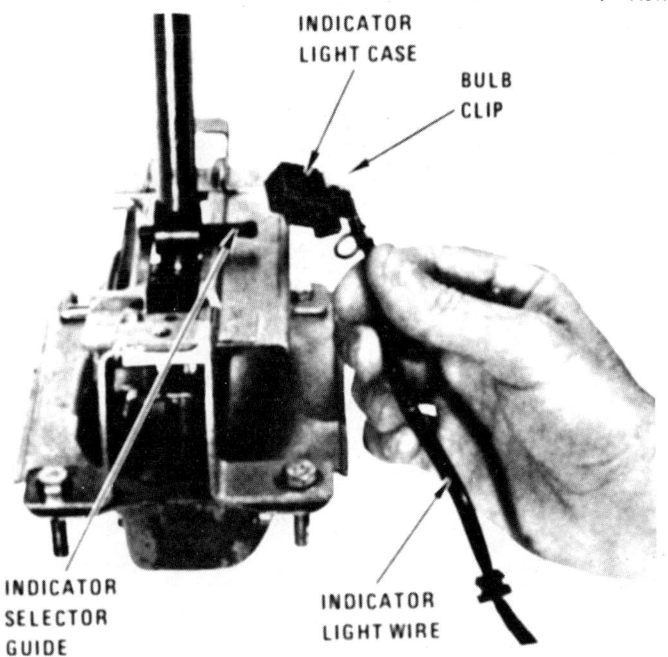

Fig. 7.47 The indicator light (Sec. 7)

8 Fault diagnosis - Hondamatic transmission

Symptom	Reason/s
No drive in any gear	Low fluid level. Selector linkage out of adjustment. Defective servo valve piston. Defective reverse gear selector spline. Converter pump inner hub slipping. Worn pump drivegear splines.
Slip in all drive gears	Low fluid level. Selector linkage out of adjustment. Torque converter pump inoperative. Clogged pump strainer. Defective regulator in valve body.
Engine stalls on acceleration with no drive in forward or reverse	Low fluid level. Selector linkage out of adjustment. Throttle control cable out of adjustment. Defective reverse idler gear. Defective one-way clutch in torque converter.
No drive or slippage in L	Low fluid level. Incorrect selector linkage adjustment. Defective low clutch.
Stall in R on acceleration	Low fluid level. Incorrect selector linkage adjustment. Loose countershaft locknut.
Slip in R	Low fluid level. Incorrect selector linkage adjustment. Defective servo valve piston. Defective reverse gear selector splines. Defective drive clutch.
Poor acceleration	Low fluid level. Incorrect selector linkage adjustment. Defective drive clutch. Defective low clutch. Defective converter one-way clutch.
Grinding in R	Low fluid level. Incorrect linkage adjustment. Defective servo valve piston. Faulty reverse/idler gear. Servo piston sticking in transmission housing recess.
Slip in L and speedometer not working	Loose countershaft locknut.
Buzzing in forward drive selector positions	Faulty torque converter pump. Loose countershaft locknut.
Engine will not turn by hand	Oil pump driven gear seized to separator plate.

If the following symptoms occur after major overhaul, the causes are probably due to incorrect reassembly as indicated.

Symptom	Reason/s
Loud noise in all gear selector positions with engine running	Oil pump gear fitted upside down.
Drive in L but hesitation in Drive (*)	Low gear thrust washer incorrectly assembled. Burrs on mainshaft.
Drive in (*) but hesitation in L	Burrs on mainshaft. Drivegear thrust washer incorrectly assembled.
No drive in any gear	Countershaft low gear fitted backwards. Reverse gear hub fitted upside down.
Acceleration limited to 30 mph (48 kmh)	Torque converter stator assembled backwards.
Vibration in all drive positions	Torque converter not fully installed causing distortion of flexplate.

Note: It cannot be over emphasised that before deciding that the transmission has developed a serious internal fault due to failure of a component, the fluid level should be checked and the adjustment of the speed selector cable inspected. Rupture of one of the flexible oil cooler hoses can cause immediate overheating and loss of drive and should these symptoms occur on the road, inspect these hoses first.

Chapter 8 Final drive and driveshaft

For modifications, and information applicable to later models, see Supplement at end of manual

Contents

Specifications

Type	Mainshaft pinion gear and crownwheel through open driveshafts of unequal lengths incorporating constant velocity joints to the front roadwheels

Final drive reduction ratio

Manual gearbox	4.266 : 1
Hondamatic transmission	4.117 : 1
Lubrication	Jointly with gearbox oil or automatic transmission fluid

Side gear to pinion backlash

Standard	0.003 - 0.006 in (0.08 - 0.15 mm)
Wear limit	0.008 in (0.2 mm)

Differential side clearance	0.004 - 0.008 in (0.10 - 0.20 mm)

Torque wrench settings	**lb f ft**	**kg f m**
Crownwheel bolts (left-hand thread)	65 to 69	9.0 to 9.5
Driveshaft end nut	86 to 130	12 to 18
Transmission casing to clutch housing bolts	16 to 22	2.3 to 3.1
*Transmission housing to torque converter housing bolts:		
Large	17 to 22	2.3 to 3.1
Small	7 to 10	1.0 to 1.4
Oil drain plug	30	4.0
Clutch housing to engine	35	4.8
* Torque converter housing to engine	29 to 36	4 to 5
Suspension arm lower swivel joint nut	25 to 36	3.5 to 5.0

* *Automatic transmission*

1 General description and maintenance

The differential and final drive assembly is located within the transmission casing and the layout is basically the same for both the manual and automatic transmissions.

The drive pinion is an integral part of the countershaft in the gearbox. The pinion meshes with the crownwheel which is bolted to the differential carrier. The differential components are of a conventional type and provide the drive to the front roadwheels via the driveshafts which are of unequal lengths.

The differential unit is lubricated by oil within the manual transmission unit (or special fluid in the Hondamatic).

Maintenance

The final drive unit is lubricated by the transmission oil, and therefore the gearbox or automatic transmission must be regularly checked and topped up as required at the intervals specified in the 'Routine Maintenance' Section. This will automatically service the final drive unit. In addition, the transmission lubricant must be drained and renewed at the specified intervals.

The driveshaft inner joint is normally only lubricated during overhaul.

The driveshaft outer joint is a sealed unit and if worn or damaged in any way, the complete driveshaft must be renewed.

The front hub bearings are normally only lubricated during reassembly after overhaul, when they must be repacked with grease of the correct grade.

2 Final drive - removal, overhaul and refitting

1 Refer to Chapter 6 or 7 accordingly and remove the manual or automatic transmission unit. In both cases the transmission unit can be removed with or without the engine.

2 Having removed the transmission unit from the car, clean off the transmission casing using a suitable solvent or paraffin (kerosene) applied with a stiff brush. Hose off with water and wipe away.

3 To remove the differential unit it is first necessary to dismantle the gearbox, therefore refer to Chapter 6 or 7 accordingly.

Manual gearbox - *Chapter 6, Section 3*
Hondamatic transmission - *Chapter 7, Section 3*

4 The differential and crownwheel assembly should now be the only major item left in the clutch or torque converter housing.

5 Using a tubular drift, applied to the differential carrier bearing which is located in the transmission housing, release the bearing from its seat and then lift out the final drive assembly.

6 The bearings can be removed from both sides of the differential

using a conventional puller as in Fig. 8.1.

7 Secure the differential carrier in the jaws of a vice and then unscrew **(left-hand thread)** the bolts which secure the crownwheel to the differential carrier. Release the bolts half a turn at a time in a diagonally opposite sequence.

8 After the crownwheel has been removed on Hondamatic versions only, the snap-ring must be prised from the differential carrier and the speedometer drivegear and dowel pin removed. Drive out the tension pin which holds the bevel pinion shaft in place in the differential.

9 Drive out the pin by applying the drift to the side opposite to the differential carrier as shown in Fig. 8.3. Extract the shaft and the bevel pinion gears.

10 Once the bevel pinion gears and their shaft have been removed, the side gears can be extracted by moving them into the centre of the differential carrier and out of the aperture in the carrier.

11 With the differential and final drive fully dismantled, thoroughly clean all components and examine for wear. Pay particular attention to the gear teeth and check the ball bearings for wear, and that they are an interference fit in their transmission casing seats.

12 When reassembling dip each component in clean oil. Commence by installing the side gears into the differential carrier and then insert the pinion gears between the side gears. Rotate the side gears so aligning the pinion gear holes with the shaft holes.

13 Install the thrust washers (one behind each pinion gear) and insert the shaft. If the original components and thrust washers are being refitted insert the shaft tension pin. If new components have been

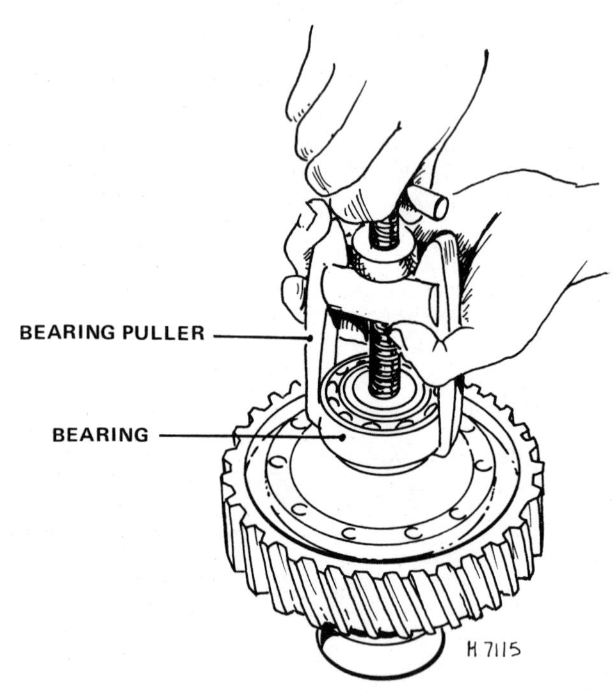

Fig. 8.1. Use a puller to remove the bearings (Sec. 2)

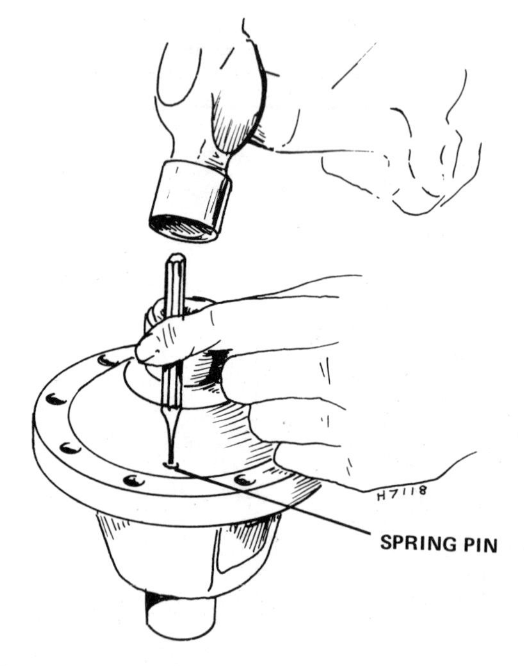

Fig. 8.3. Remove the pinion shaft tension pin using a suitable drift (Sec. 2)

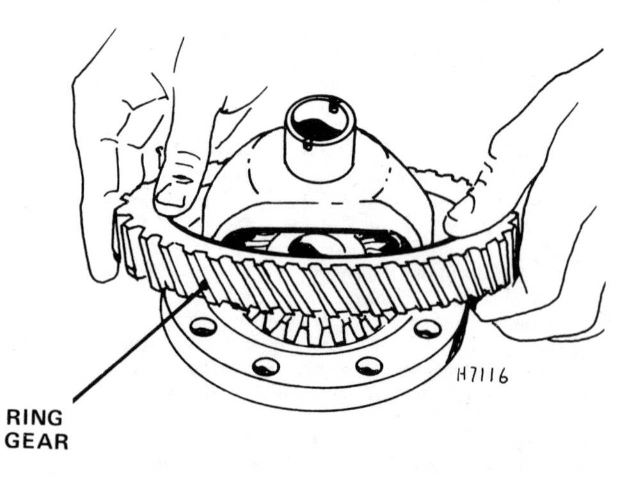

Fig. 8.2. Remove the crownwheel (ring gear) (Sec. 2)

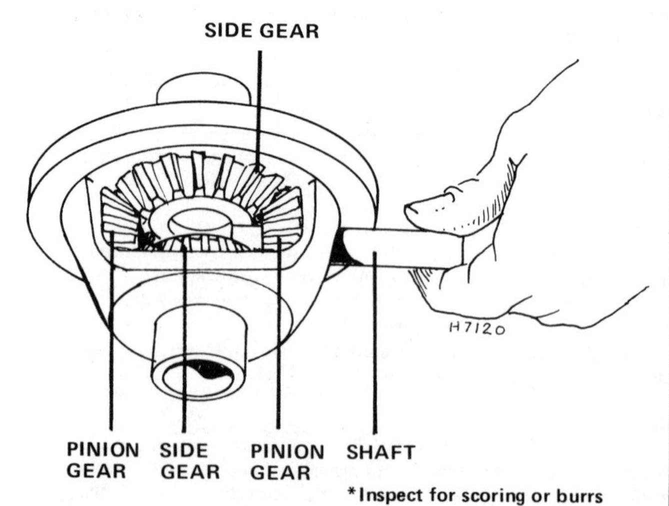

Fig. 8.4. Withdraw the pinion shaft (Sec. 2)

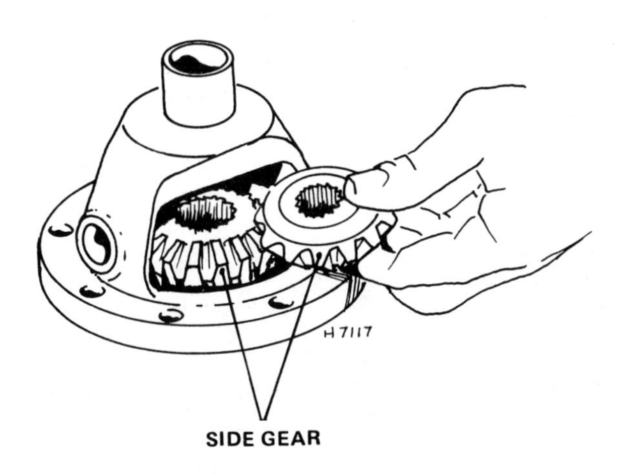
SIDE GEAR
H7117

Fig. 8.5. Installing the differential side gears (Sec. 2)

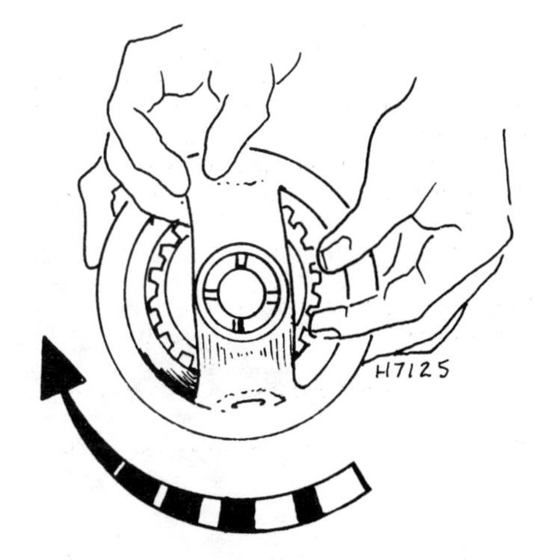
H7125

Fig. 8.6. Rotate the differential side gears to align the pinion gear to shaft holes (Sec. 2)

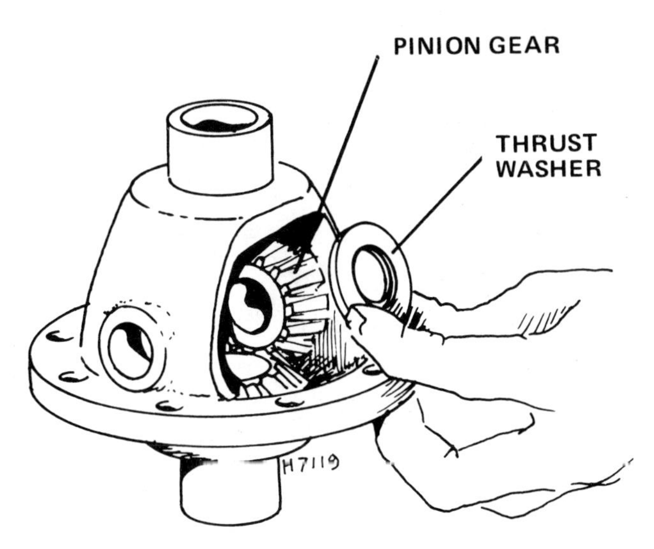
PINION GEAR
THRUST WASHER
H7119

Fig. 8.7. Fit the thrust washers to the pinion gears (Sec. 2)

fitted then, before inserting the tension pin, the backlash between the teeth of the side gears and the bevel pinion gears must be checked. Move the gears carefully by finger pressure and check the backlash using a dial gauge or feeler blades. The tolerance should be between 0.003 and 0.006 in (0.08 and 0.15 mm) with a wear limit of 0.008 in (0.2 mm). If necessary, change the thrust washers for ones of different thickness (three sizes available). The thrust washers on opposite sides must be of equal thickness. When adjustment is complete, drive in the shaft tension pin.

14 If the differential carrier bearings have been removed install the new ones, driving them home with a tubular drift.

15 Install the crownwheel, tightening the securing bolts to the specified torque and remembering that they have left-hand threads (photo). Note the difference in fitting of the crownwheel used with manual gearbox and Hondamatic transmission vehicles (Fig. 8.8)

16 Remove the oil seals from the clutch (or torque converter) housing and discard them and obtain new ones but do not fit them at this stage.

17 Install the large snap-ring and then tap home the differential assembly into the clutch (or torque converter) housing.

18 Locate a new gasket and fit the transmission housing, using a minimum of four bolts that are spaced equally to secure it. Tighten the bolts to the specified torque.

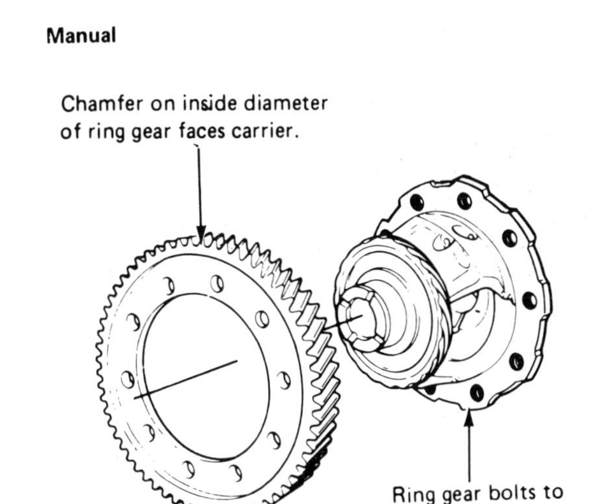
Ring gear bolts have left-hand threads.
Manual
Chamfer on inside diameter of ring gear faces carrier.
Ring gear bolts to left-hand side of carrier.

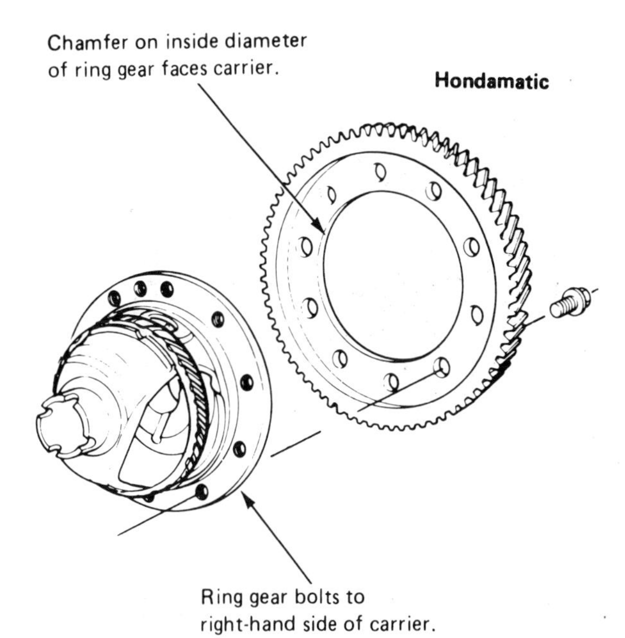
Chamfer on inside diameter of ring gear faces carrier.
Hondamatic
Ring gear bolts to right-hand side of carrier.

Fig. 8.8. Crownwheel installation to differential carrier (Sec. 2)

2.15 The crownwheel assembled to the differential (manual gearbox)

19 Use a drift and hammer to ensure that the differential assembly is bottomed in the transmission housing.
20 Measure the clearance between the large snap-ring and the face of the outer track of the differential case bearing in the clutch (or torque converter) housing. This side clearance should be between 0.004 and 0.008 in (0.10 and 0.20 mm). If it is outside this limit, extract the snap-ring and change it for one of the six alternative thicknesses which are available:

0.096 in (2.45 mm)	*0.100 in (2.55 mm)*
0.104 in (2.65 mm)	*0.108 in (2.75 mm)*
0.112 in (2.85 mm)	*0.116 in (2.95 mm)*

21 The transmission housing should now be removed and the final drive lifted from the clutch (or torque converter) housing and new oil seals installed. With both oil seals, the part numbers on them should be visible when installed.
22 Final reassembly and refitting operations may now be carried out by reversing the dismantling and removal procedure.

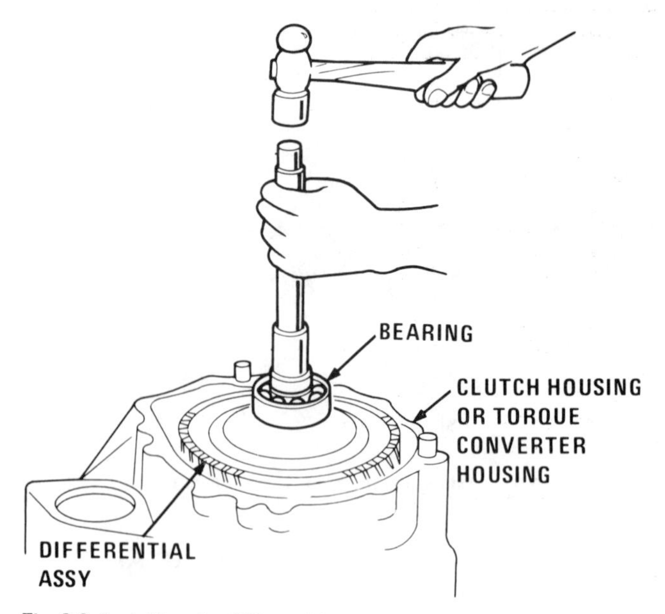

Fig. 8.9 Installing the differential assembly into the clutch or torque converter housing

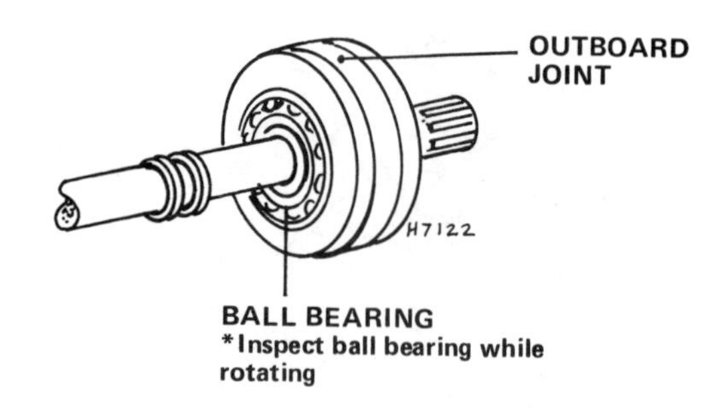

Fig. 8.10 The outer driveshaft and constant velocity joint (Sec. 3)

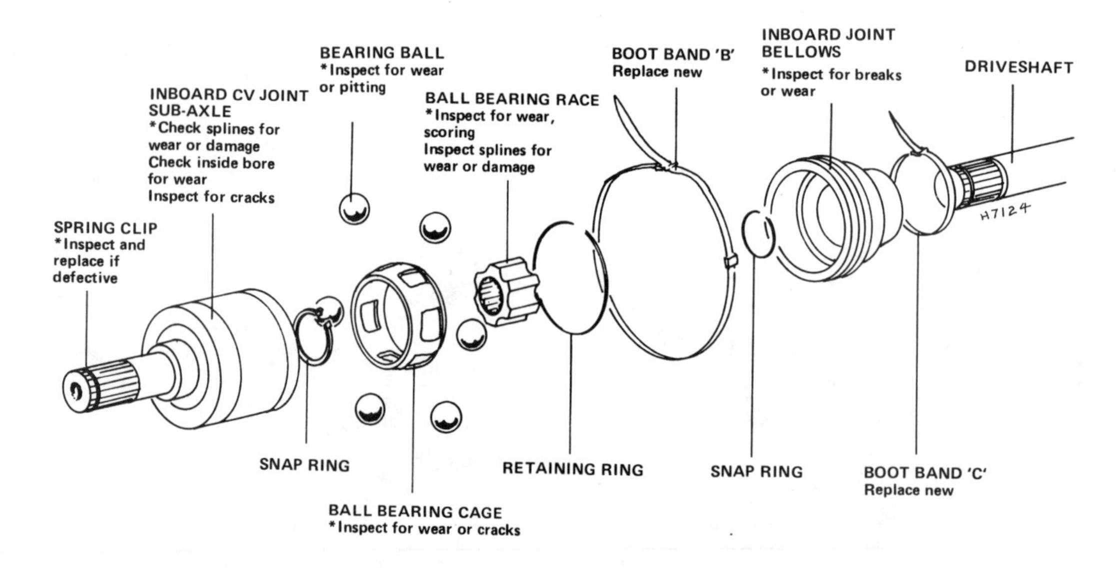

Fig. 8.11 The inner driveshaft and constant velocity (CV) joint components (Sec. 3)

3 Driveshaft - removal and refitting

1 The driveshafts are of unequal length with constant velocity joints incorporated at each end. The inboard end of the shaft is splined and fits into the centre of the output bevels of the differential; the outboard end is splined as well, to accept the front wheel mounting flange. Each constant velocity joint comprises 6 steel balls caged between conformable joint halves.
2 This Section describes the removal and refitting of the driveshafts; if the joints on the shafts are known to be faulty, check the availability of spares before dismantling the shaft assemblies.
3 Prise the centre cap from the wheel hub and then extract the split pin from the driveshaft spindle and nut. Unscrew and remove the spindle nut.
4 Loosen the front roadwheel nuts and then raise the front of the car and support it on chassis stands positioned beneath the strengthened bodyshell areas to the rear of the front wheel arches. Remove the roadwheels.
5 Drain the transmission oil.
6 Extract the split pin from the suspension arm to steering knuckle balljoint and unscrew the castle nut.
7 Detach the front suspension arm balljoint from the steering knuckle using a balljoint separator or forked wedges. If both driveshafts are to be removed, repeat operation on the other side. Unscrew and remove the anti-roll bar bolts.
8 Using a long screwdriver or suitable lever, initially prise the driveshaft inner CV joint from the transmission casing by approximately ½ in (12.7 mm) and then, when the shaft is freed from the inner securing snap-ring, it can be removed completely.
9 Using a soft-faced mallet, drive the splined end of the driveshaft inwards to remove from the steering knuckle.
10 Refitting is a direct reversal of removal but ensure that the CV joint inboard shaft is fully seated when mated to the differential unit in the transmission. Liberally grease the respective splines prior to assembly and tighten all bolts and nuts to the specified torque wrench settings. Always use new split pins.

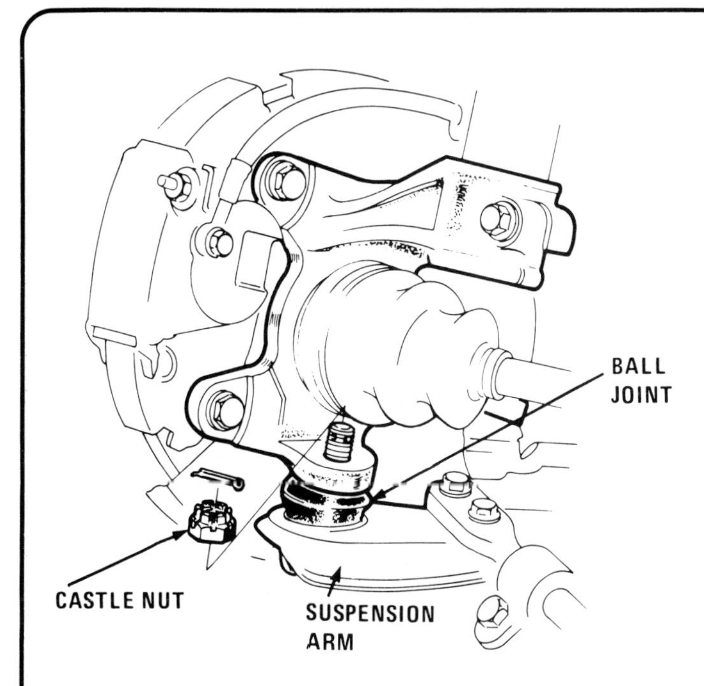

Fig. 8.12. Separate the steering knuckle to suspension arm ball joint (Sec. 3)

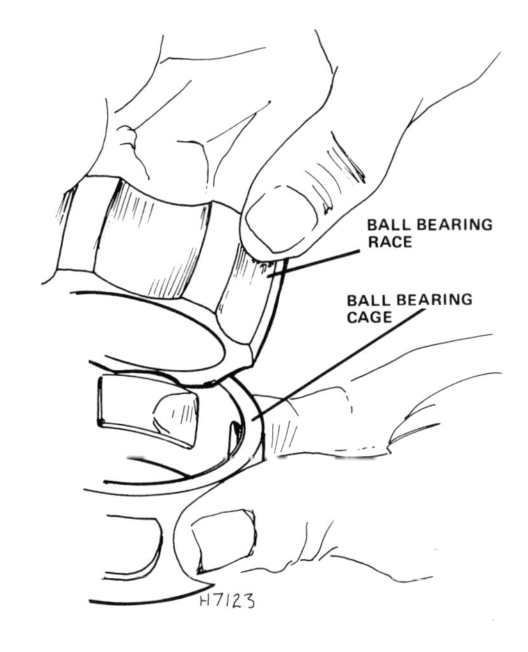

Fig. 8.14. Fit ballrace chamfered edge towards the smaller end of cage (Sec. 5)

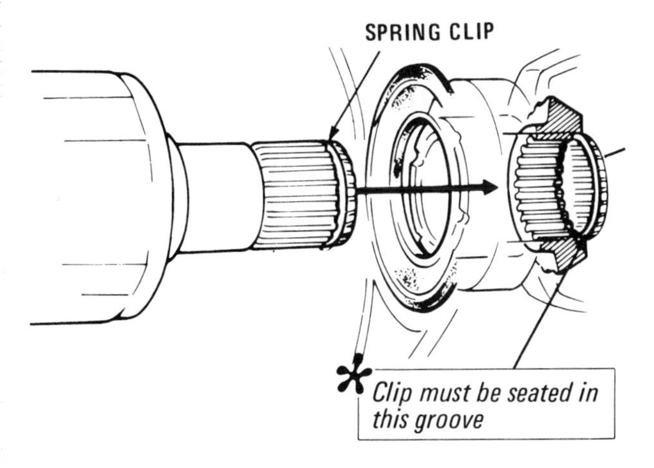

Fig. 8.13. Ensure that the driveshaft is fully located and retained by the spring clip within the transmission (Sec. 5)

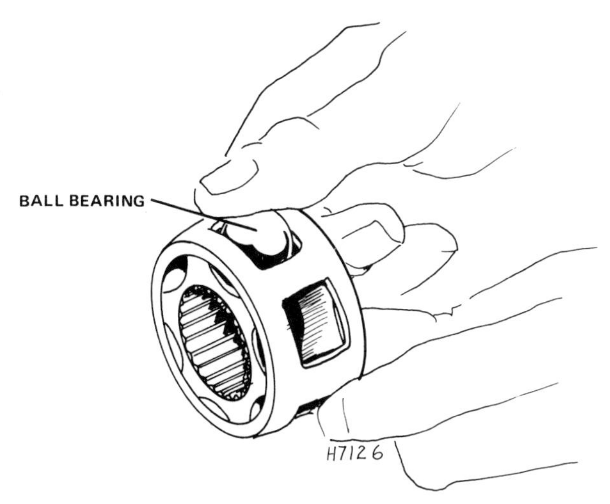

Fig. 8.15 Insert the inner driveshaft joint balls (Sec. 5)

4 Driveshaft outer joint bellows - renewal

1 If, when carrying out the visual inspection of the driveshaft dust excluding bellows recommended in the 'Routine Maintenance' Section, the bellows are found to be split or damaged then they must be renewed.
2 Remove the driveshaft as described in the preceding Section.
3 Before the bellows on the outer joint can be removed, the inner joint must first be dismantled as described in the next Section.
4 With the inner joint removed, cut the securing bands from the bellows on the outer joint and slide the bellows from the driveshaft.
5 Clean away any dirt and old grease from the joint and slide the new bellows up the driveshaft. Before locating the bellows over the outer joint, pack it liberally with specified grease and then slide the bellows over the joint and fit two new securing clips.
6 The outer driveshaft joint cannot be overhauled or dismantled and in the event of wear, the driveshaft must be renewed complete.

5 Driveshaft inner joint - overhaul

1 Remove the driveshaft, as described in Section 3.
2 Cut both securing clips from the inner joint bellows and slide the bellows off the joint down the driveshaft.
3 Extract the large ring on the inside of the joint housing and draw the housing from the joint.
4 Wipe away all grease to expose the snap-ring on the end of the driveshaft. Extract this snap-ring and withdraw the joint cage from the driveshaft.
5 The ball race can be separated from the cage by driving the race out with a tubular drift. Make sure that the cage is supported on a piece of tubing of such a diameter that pressure is not applied to the balls. When driving out the race, apply the drift to the smaller diameter of the race.
6 Draw off the bellows and renew them if necessary together with any inner joint components which are worn or damaged.
7 Commence reassembly by sliding the bellows on to the driveshaft.
8 Install the ball race to the cage so that the chamfered end of the race is towards the smaller end of the cage.
9 Press in the balls until they are firmly seated.
10 Reassemble the joint to the driveshaft by reversing the dismantling process.
11 Pack the joint liberally with specified grease and then draw the bellows over the joint and fit new securing clips.

6 Fault diagnosis - final drive and driveshaft

Symptom	Reason/s
Vibration	Roadwheels out of balance. Worn driveshaft joints. Bent driveshaft.
Knock on taking up drive or on overrun	Worn driveshaft splines. Loose roadwheel nuts. Worn front suspension balljoints. Worn driveshaft joints.

Chapter 9 Braking system

For modifications, and information applicable to later models, see Supplement at end of manual

Contents

Specifications

System type	Hydraulic, Servo assisted self-adjusting discs front and drum rear. Mechanical parking brake

Lining surface area

Total (4 wheels)	158.5 sq in (1022.6 sq cm)

General brake dimensions and clearances

Disc diameter (effective)	7.4 in (187 mm)
Drum inside diameter (effective)	7.1 in (180 mm)
Brake pedal free play	0.039 to 0.197 in (1 to 5 mm)
Pedal to floor height	7.24 in (184 mm)
Disc pad thickness wear limit	0.039 in (1.0 mm) minimum
Shoe lining thickness wear limit	0.079 in (2.0 mm) minimum
Disc minimum thickness (after regrind)	0.449 in (11.4 mm)
Drum maximum internal diameter (after regrind)	7.126 in (181 mm)
Master cylinder to piston clearance	
standard	0.0008 to 0.0039 in (0.02 to 0.10 mm)
wear limit	0.0059 in (0.15 mm)

Torque wrench settings	**lb f ft**	**kg f m**
Master cylinder retaining nuts	11 to 15	1.5 to 2.0
Master cylinder stop bolt	9	1.2
Rear back plate retaining bolts	13 to 18	1.9 to 2.5
Rear spindle nut (final)	1.1 to 3.6	0.15 to 0.5
Rear spindle nut (initial)	18	2.5
Servo unit retaining nuts	5 to 9	0.7 to 1.25
Caliper mounting support bolts	58 to 66	8 to 9
Bleeder screw	6.5 to 9.5	0.9 to 1.3
Hydraulic hose to caliper bolt	7 to 10	1.0 to 1.4
Handbrake retaining bolt	13 to 18	1.9 to 2.5
Cable equaliser castle nut	7 to 14	1.0 to 2.0
Handbrake cable location clamp bolts	5 to 8.7	0.7 to 1.2
Hub to disc bolts	36 to 43	5.0 to 6.0

1 General description and maintenance

The braking system consists of disc brakes on the front wheels and drum brakes at the rear, all of which are hydraulically operated with servo power assistance.

The disc brakes are self-adjusting, but the drum brakes require periodic adjustment at the specified intervals or earlier depending upon the driving conditions.

Adjustment of the rear brakes automatically adjusts the handbrake (park brake) although separate adjustment for the handbrake can be made by tightening or loosening the adjustment nut on the cable equalizer.

Pressure regulating valves are incorporated in the hydraulic circuits to prevent locking of the rear roadwheels before the front ones, when the brakes are applied heavily.

Warning switches are provided for fluid level and pressure, handbrake and stop lamps, but all these devices may not necessarily be installed due to varying territorial regulations enforced in the countries to which the cars are sold.

Maintenance

It cannot be emphasised too much that diligent inspection and maintenance of the braking system is essential to retain your safety in the car.

Every week remove the hydraulic fluid cap(s) and check the level of fluid which should be just in the 'max' mark on the side of the reservoir (photo). Check that the vent hole in the cap is clear. Any need for regular topping-up regardless of quantity should be viewed with suspicion, and the whole braking hydraulic system should be inspected for signs of leakage.

Every 5000 miles (8000 km)

Closely examine all the flexible brake hoses, and hose connections. Use a mirror to inspect all parts of the hose, and remember to move the flexible hose so that cracks or other surface deterioration will be revealed. Renew any hoses which are not in anything but perfect condition, immediately. There is no way of knowing how dangerous a crack in a hose is.

Inspect all fixed metal brake pipes for corrosion and surface deterioration. These pipes are stressed by the fluid pressure in the braking system. Any corrosion on the outer surface can generate and propagate cracks in the metal which will lead ultimately to the sudden failure of the pipe.

The thickness of friction material on both front and rear brake mechanisms should be checked. The capability of the friction material to withstand heat is dependent on the thickness of the friction material on the brake pad or shoe. If the material has worn too thin, there is a risk that the material will disintegrate when hot with the consequent loss of braking.

On the front disc brake pads, the thickness of the friction material should not fall below 0.04 in (1 mm).

On the rear drum brakes, the thickness of the friction material on the brake shoes should not fall below 0.08 in (2 mm) if the shoe linings are bonded.

Alternatively, if the linings are riveted to the shoes, the friction material thickness should not be allowed to fall below the point when the rivet heads begin to be worn.

Never interchange worn shoes or pads to even out wear, try and determine the reason for the uneven wear.

Ensure that the disc calipers operate freely.

Check the rear brake adjustment.

Lubricate and examine the handbrake cable and linkage - adjust if necessary.

Every 25,000 miles (40,000 km)

Renew the hydraulic fluid in the braking system. The condition of the fluid in the brake pipes and slave cylinders deteriorates in time and old fluid is liable to boil when the brakes are in hard usage. The vapour in the brake lines will lead to inconsistency of braking effort.

It is good practice every 2 to 3 years to renew seals and hoses in the brake system as a 'preventative' maintenance.

If you have just acquired a secondhand car, it is strongly recommended that the whole brake system, drums, shoes, discs, pads, hoses, pipes, slave and master cylinders, are thoroughly examined. Even though the effectiveness of the braking system may be excellent, the friction material may be near the end of its useful life, and it will be as well to renew this without delay.

The hydraulic lines, cylinders and flexible pipes should be carefully examined for leaks, external corrosion and chafing. Faults should be rectified immediately.

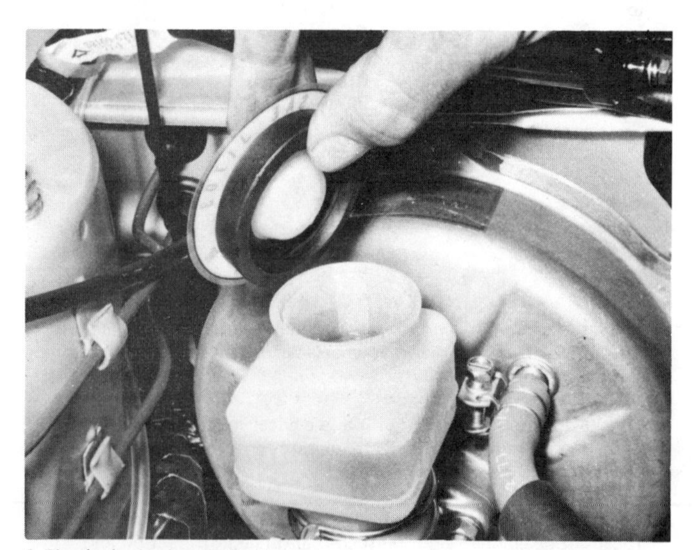

1 Check the hydraulic fluid level

2 Hydraulic system - bleeding

1 The system should need bleeding only when some part of it has been dismantled which would allow air into the fluid circuit; or if the reservoir level has been allowed to drop so far that air has entered the master cylinder.

2 Ensure that a supply of clean non-aerated fluid of the correct specification is to hand in order to replenish the reservoir during the bleeding process. It is advisable, if not essential, to have someone available to help, as one person has to pump the brake pedal while the other attends to each wheel. The reservoir level also has to be continuously watched and replenished. Fluid bled out should not be reused. A clean glass jar and a 9 - 12 inch length of 1/8 inch internal diameter rubber tube that will fit tightly over the bleed nipples, is required.

3 Bleed in the sequence of one front brake and its diagonally opposite rear one. If only one brake circuit has been broken then only this circuit needs to be bled.

4 Make sure the bleed nipple is clean and put a small quantity of fluid in the bottom of the jar. Fit the tube onto the nipple and place the other end in the jar under the surface of the liquid. Keep it under the surface throughout the operation.

5 Unscrew the bleed nipple one half a turn and have your assistant depress the brake pedal slowly to the floor. Have him release the pedal quickly and then repeat the operation until you see no more air bubbles emerging from the submerged end of the tube in the jar. Tighten the bleed nipple while the pedal is held fully depressed.

6 Remove the bleed tube and connect it to the next bleed nipple which is to be bled. Replenish the fluid in the master cylinder reservoirs.

7 When all four wheels have been satisfactorily bled depress the foot

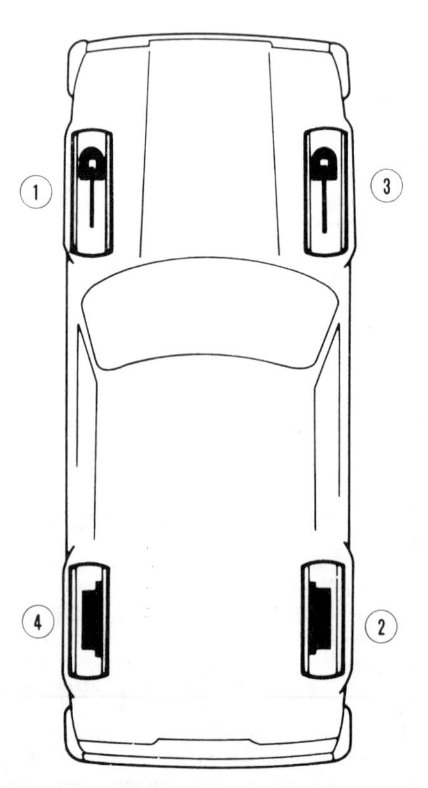

Fig. 9.1. The sequence for bleeding the brakes (Sec. 2)

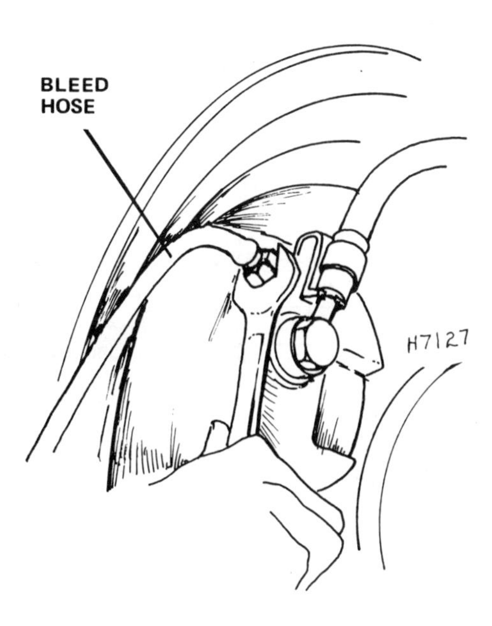

Fig. 9.2. Loosen the bleed nipple (Sec. 2)

pedal which should now offer a firmer resistance with no trace of 'sponginess'. The pedal should not continue to go down under sustained pressure. If it does there is a leak or the master cylinder seals are defective.

8 Always discard fluid ejected into the bleed jar or keep it only for bleed jar purposes.

9 During the foregoing operations, the piston in the brake pressure warning switch will be displaced continually but when both hydraulic circuits have been satisfactorily bled, the switch will automatically be reset in its neutral position and the warning lamp will go out.

3 Disc brake pads - removal, inspection and refitting

1 To check the thickness or wear of the disc brake pads, raise the front of the car and remove the roadwheels. The pads can be checked without removal from the caliper. Generally the pads will only require renewal if the existing ones are worn beyond the specified thickness or have become contaminated with oil or grease.

2 If the pad is to be removed, first withdraw the side plate retaining clips. A pair of snap-ring pliers (photo) are ideal to prise the clips free.

3 Slide the side plate from the caliper unit (photo).

4 Withdraw the caliper body (A) and support it by tying a piece of cord to it and suspending from a suitable point on the body. This prevents the hydraulic hose to the caliper from being distorted or damaged (photo).

5 Detach the anti-rattle clip (B) (photo 3.4) and remove the pads.

6 With the pads removed, clean them off and measure the friction material thickness. Examine the surface areas for any black polished areas which indicate oil contamination. If the pads are to be removed, obtain a complete set of four pads.

7 The brake disc should also be examined whilst the pads are removed. If badly scored or excessively worn they should be renewed at this stage. Measure the thickness of the disc and compare it against the service limit given in the specifications at the beginning of this Chapter, and renew if necessary.

8 Refitting of the disc pads is a direct reversal of the removal procedure. When fitting new pads, the slave cylinder pistons will need to be pushed carefully back within their cylinders in order to expand the pistons to disc clearance, which is necessary to accommodate the new pads.

9 When the pistons are pushed into their cylinders, brake fluid will be displaced and returned to the master cylinder reservoir. A small amount of fluid should therefore be siphoned from the master cylinder reservoir prior to pushing in the pistons.

10 Renew the side plate retaining clips if they are rusted badly or distorted. On completion operate the brake pedal several times and inspect the master cylinder reservoir to ensure that the fluid level is up to the mark.

4 Disc caliper - removal, overhaul and refitting

1 To remove the disc caliper, jack up the appropriate side and remove the roadwheel. If both calipers are to be overhauled, place chassis stands under the strengthened panels to the rear of the front wheel arches. When dismantling the calipers, keep the components of each caliper separate as they must not be interchanged.

2 Remove the disc pads as detailed in Section 3.

3 Raise and secure the bonnet (hood). Unscrew the appropriate cap on the brake fluid reservoir and stretch a thin piece of polythene over the top of the reservoir and refit the cap. This prevents the excessive loss of brake fluid when the brake pipe is disconnected from the caliper.

4 Disconnect the hydraulic hose from the caliper cylinder body taking care not to distort the hose. Plug the end of the hose to prevent leakage and the ingress of dirt.

5 To remove the caliper mounting support detach the anti-rattle pad clip (Fig. 9.3) and unscrew the mounting retaining bolts (Fig. 9.4).

6 Remove the caliper to the work bench and clean off the external surfaces. Place on a clean work area for inspection.

7 Compress and remove the snap-ring retaining the piston boot, then extract the boot.

8 The piston can now be removed from the caliper. The best method of removal is to apply air pressure to the brake hydraulic connection aperture. It may be possible to extract the piston from the caliper using the fingers.

9 Finally, withdraw the piston seal. Do not scratch or damage the cylinder bore.

10 Clean out the cylinder bore using hydraulic fluid. Examine the piston and cylinder bore surfaces. If there are any signs of scoring, scratching or 'bright' wear areas renew the caliper as a complete unit.

11 Check the condition of the clips, springs and snap-ring. Renew any

3.2 Remove the side plate retaining clips

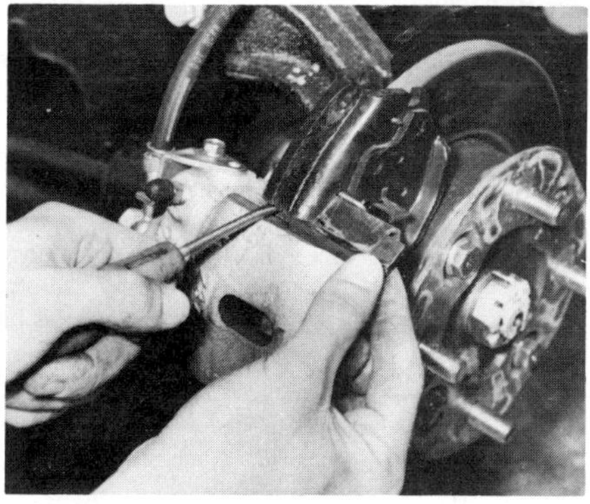

3.3 Withdraw the side plate

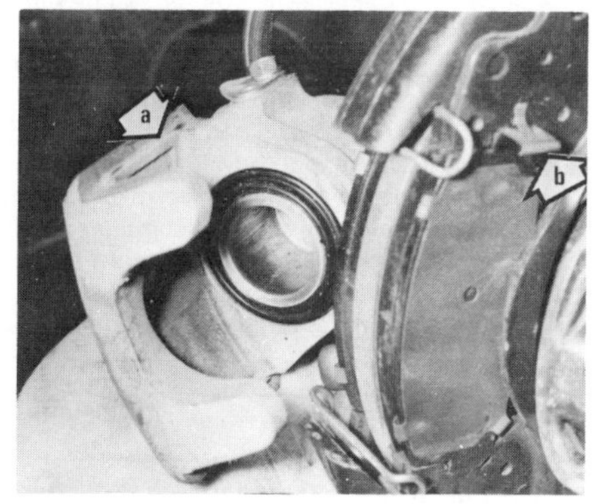

3.4 The caliper body A and anti-rattle clip B

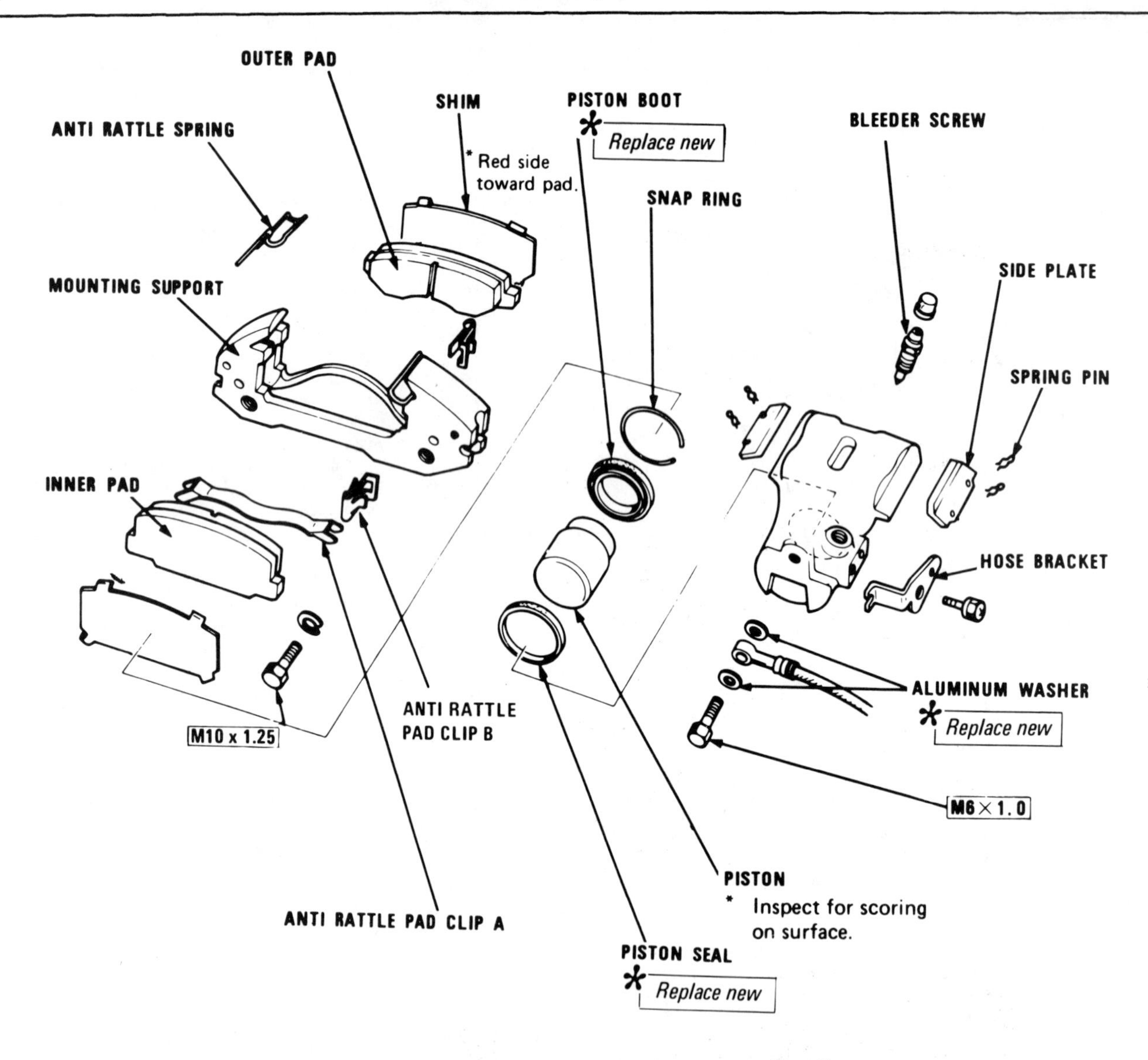

Fig. 9.3. The disc brake caliper and pad components (Sec. 3)

suspect, worn or rusted components. Always renew the piston seal, boot and hydraulic hose connection aiuminium washers.
12 Commence assembly by lubricating the new piston seal with hydraulic fluid, then insert it carefully into position in its groove in the cylinder bore so that the narrower inside diameter is towards the centre of the car as shown in Fig. 9.4.
13 Carefully press the piston into the caliper bore having first lubricated it with hydraulic fluid. Apply an even pressure to the piston and take care not to damage the bore or seal by mis-alignment when fitting.
14 The remaining refitting procedures are a reversal of dismantling. If the mounting support has been removed the retaining bolts must be retightened to a torque of 58 to 66 lb f ft (8 to 9 kg f m), and the hydraulic hose connection bolt is tightened to 7 to 10 lb f ft (1 to 4 kg f m). Ensure that the hose is correctly located and does not bind on any of the steering or suspension components.
15 On completion of reassembly, remove the polythene from the hydraulic fluid reservoir. Top up if necessary with new brake fluid and bleed the system as detailed in Section 2.

5 Rear brake - adjustment

1 The state of the brake adjustment will affect the amount of brake pedal movement when it is applied.
If the pedal travel becomes excessive, adjust the rear brakes as given below. If on adjustment there is still excessive pedal travel, then the rear drum brake linings and the front disc pads must be inspected for wear. In addition the brake hydraulic circuit may want bleeding in which case refer to Section 2.
2 Each rear brake operates from a single slave cylinder and the shoe position adjustment is accomplished at the lower common pivot point. Both shoes pivot in a block at the base of the brake mechanism, the pivot geometry is altered by a tapered head bolt.
3 Jack-up the rear wheels and chock the front wheels so that it is safe to operate the brakes inside the car. Press the brake pedal several times and then check that the wheels are free to turn, having fully released the handbrake.
4 Use a standard adjuster screw socket to turn the screw clockwise until the wheels no longer turn, and then back off the adjuster by two clicks. Press the brake pedal several times, and then check that the wheels are free to turn.
5 If the brake shoes are felt to be dragging on the drum, turn the adjuster screw back by one more 'click'.
6 Once the brakes have been adjusted, the brake pedal and handbrake should require only a relatively small movement to operate the brakes.

6 Rear brake shoes - removal, inspection and refitting

1 Jack-up the car and remove the roadwheel from the brake to be examined. Chock the wheels at the opposite end of the car, and release

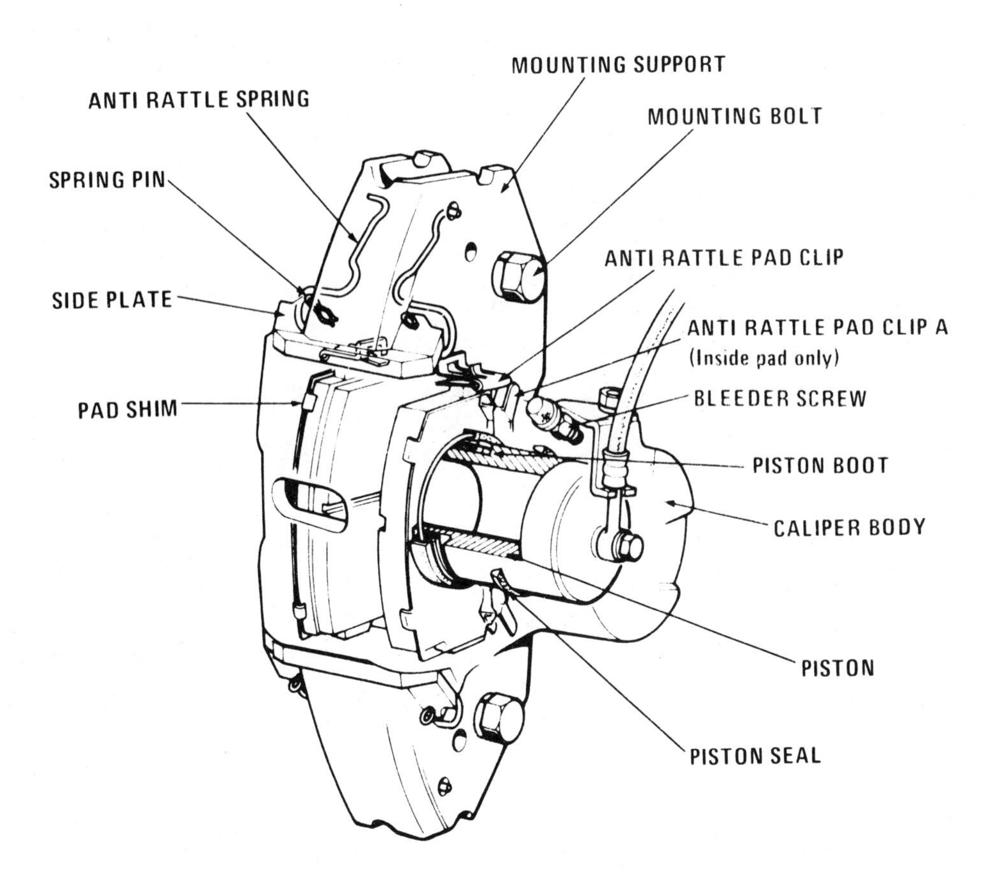

Fig. 9.4 The disc brake caliper components assembled (Sec. 3)

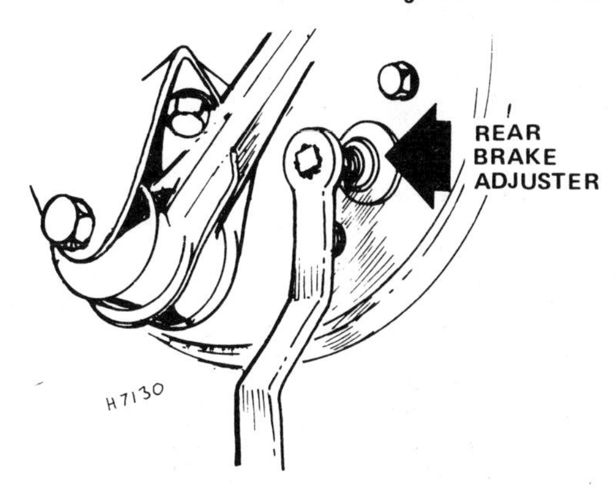

Fig. 9.5 The rear brake adjuster (Sec. 5)

the handbrake.

2 Remove the roadwheel, and then slacken off the adjuster on that brake.

3 Remove the brake drum after first removing the dust cap, split pin, nut lock, the spindle nut and washer. A sharp tug should be all that is required to free the drum/hub unit from the brake assembly. If not, tap it off with a plastic-faced hammer.

4 Once the brake drum has been removed, the brake shoes are fully exposed and can be inspected (photo).

5 Examine the friction linings for signs of oil/grease contamination (black glazed areas), and check the thickness of the linings. Refer to the specifications at the beginning of this Chapter for the minimum thickness of the brake shoe lining permitted.

6 Examine the inside surfaces of the brake drum and watch for scoring and excessive wear. Again refer to the specifications at the beginning of this Chapter for major dimensions and limits for wear before having the interiors of the drums reground.

6.4 The brake layout with the drum removed

7 Always brush all the brake dust from the drum and brake assembly before reassembly or shoe removal. **Do not inhale the dust.**

8 Having inspected the brake shoes and decided on renewing the shoes,

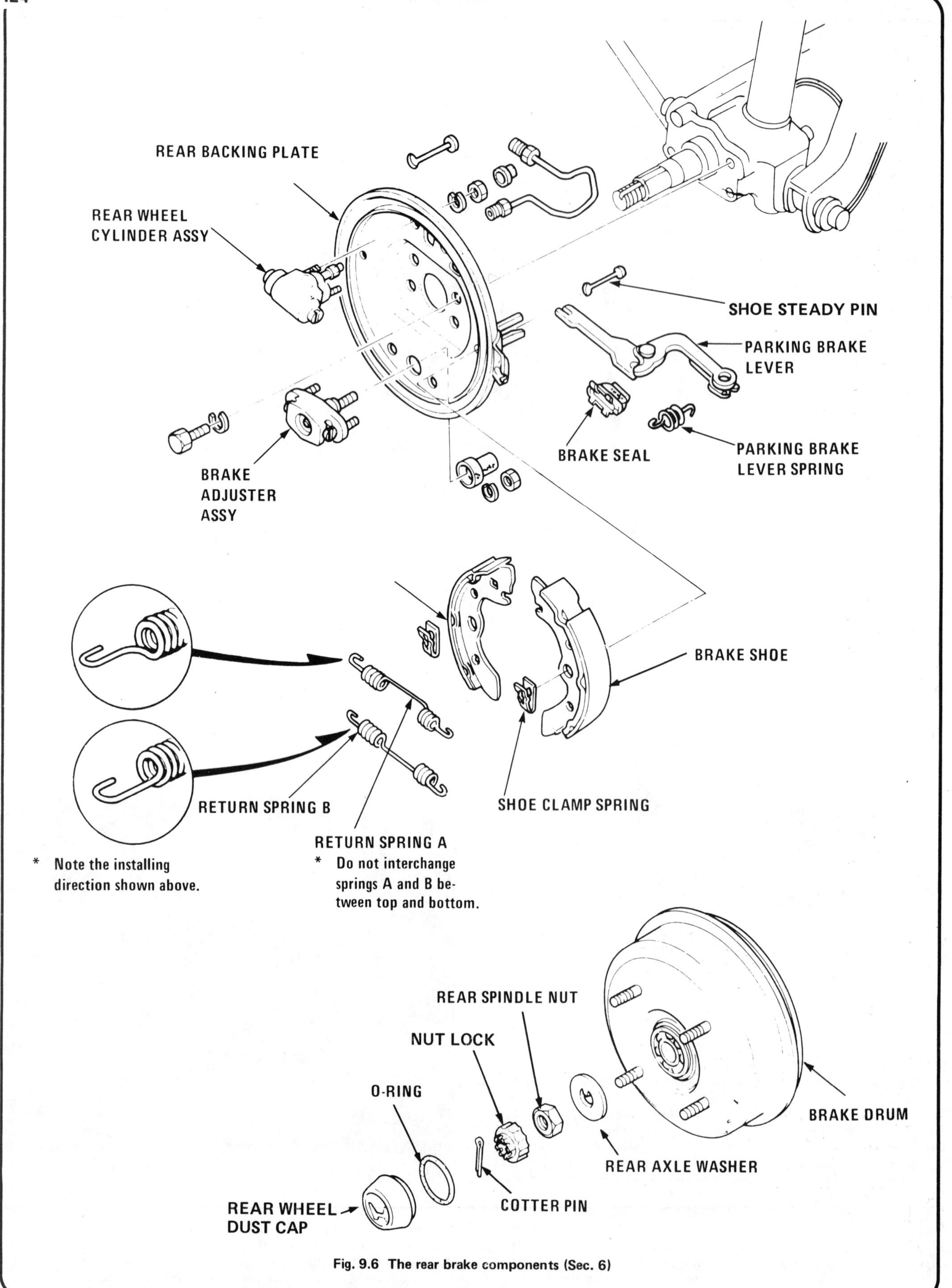
REAR BACKING PLATE
REAR WHEEL CYLINDER ASSY
SHOE STEADY PIN
PARKING BRAKE LEVER
BRAKE SEAL
PARKING BRAKE LEVER SPRING
BRAKE ADJUSTER ASSY
BRAKE SHOE
RETURN SPRING B
SHOE CLAMP SPRING
RETURN SPRING A
* Note the installing direction shown above.
* Do not interchange springs A and B between top and bottom.
REAR SPINDLE NUT
NUT LOCK
O-RING
BRAKE DRUM
REAR AXLE WASHER
COTTER PIN
REAR WHEEL DUST CAP

Fig. 9.6 The rear brake components (Sec. 6)

proceed as follows:

a) *Remove the mid-shoe steady pins. Grip the head of the 'T' ended pin and turn through 90° to permit removal of the pin (photo).*
b) *Take a particular note of the position and orientation of the two shoe return springs, and do not interchange them on assembly.*
c) *Use a screwdriver to lever one of the shoes off the wheel cylinder pistons, and once clear, remove both shoes with springs still in position.*

9 Before fitting new shoes check that the brake wheel cylinder(s) is securely bolted to the brake backplate. Also check that the pistons in the brake cylinder move freely, and that there are no fluid leaks.

6.8 Twist the steady pins

10 The rubber boots on the ends of the cylinder should be clean and renewed if there are any breaks or splits in the rubber.

Finally, handle the new shoes with clean hands and tools to prevent contaminating the new linings.

11 The refitting of the brake shoes follows the reversal of the removal procedure. Be careful if you use a screwdriver or something similar to ease the shoes back around the actuating cylinders next to the backplate, so as not to damage the brake linings or the rubber boots on the slave cylinders.

12 The refitting procedure is as follows:

a) *Turn the adjusters back to the minimum throw position and slacken the parking brake adjustment nut.*
b) *Couple the shoes with the lower spring first and position the shoes around the lower brake adjuster.*
c) *Fit the forward shoe into the wheel cylinder and hold in position with the mid-position retainer pin, and shoe clamp spring.*
d) *Ensure that the handbrake lever and shoe strut are in position, and then refit the upper shoe return spring and pull or lever the rearward shoe into position on the cylinder.*
e) *Secure the rear shoe with the shoe steady pin, and shoe clamp spring.*

13 Once the shoes are back in position, visually position the shoes so that the linings are concentric with the wheel axle and backing plate.

14 Refit the brake drum which incorporates the hub. Position the thrust washer against the bearing and tighten the rear spindle nut against the washer to a torque of 18 lb f ft (2.5 kg f m). Slacken the nut and retighten to a torque of 1.1 to 3.6 lbf ft (0.15 to 0.5 kg m) or finger-tight until all endfloat has disappeared.

15 The nut lock is now located with its slots aligned with the pin hole in the spindle. The spindle nut may be marginally tightened beyond the torque setting to align the hole and nut lock slots. Install the cotter pin to secure (Fig.9.8).

16 Press the brake pedal a few times to centralize the brake shoes to the drums, then adjust the brakes as described in Section 5.

17 If, on adjustment the brake pedal feels spongy, the brakes will need bleeding and this operation is detailed in Section 2.

18 When the brakes have been relined, they must be readjusted after a few hundred miles when the linings will have bedded in.

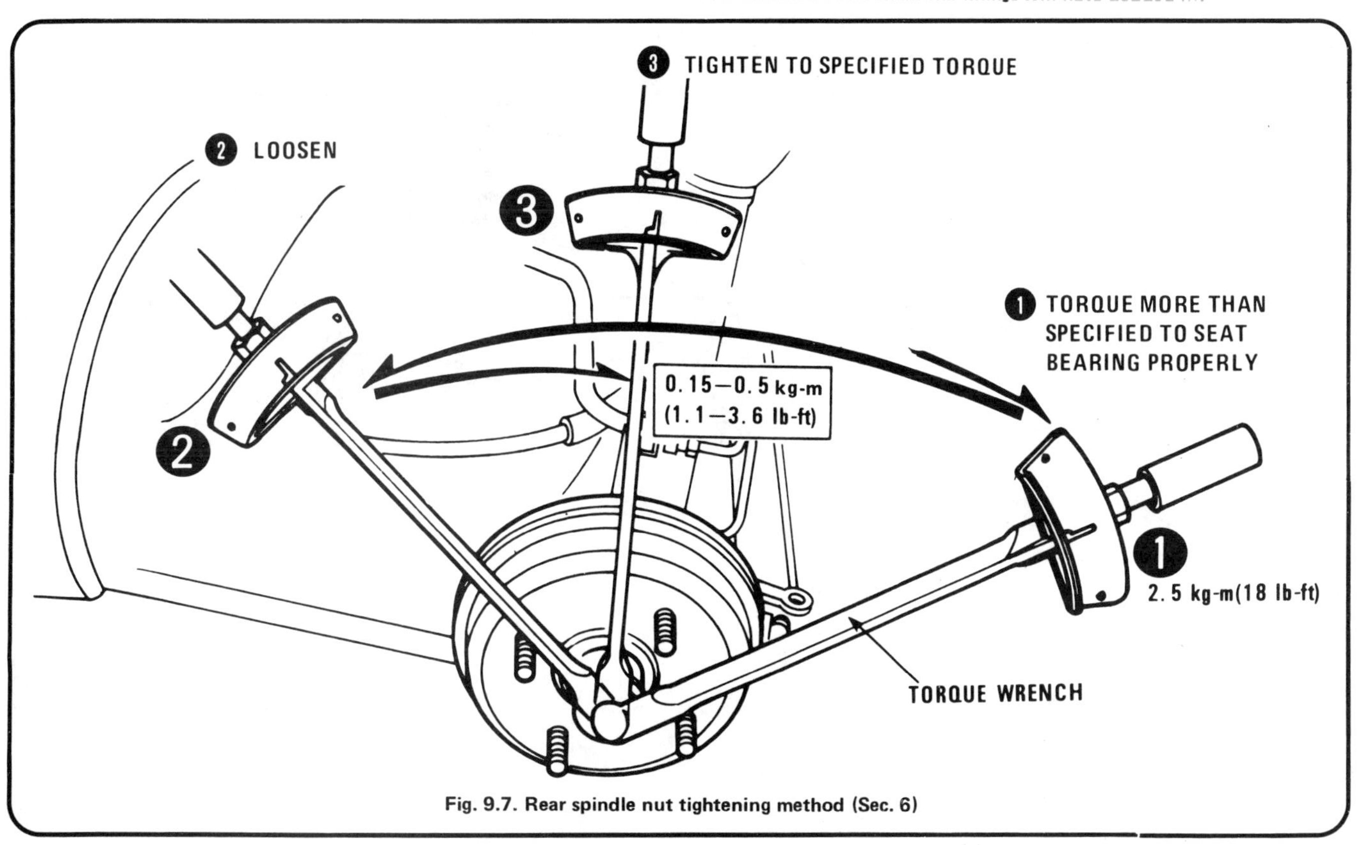

Fig. 9.7. Rear spindle nut tightening method (Sec. 6)

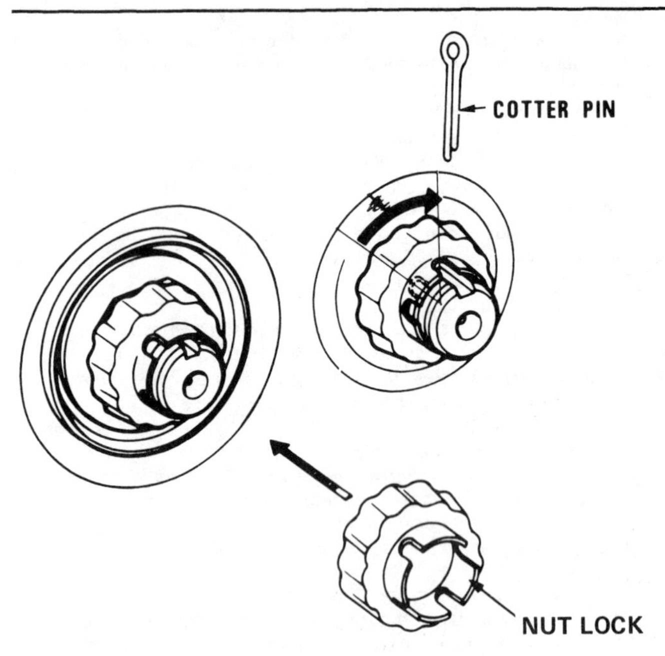

Fig. 9.8. The nut lock and cotter pin (Sec. 6)

7 Rear wheel cylinder - removal, overhaul and refitting

1 The rear wheel brake cylinders have two opposing pistons.
2 If it is suspected that one, or more, of the wheel slave cylinders is malfunctioning, jack-up the suspected wheel and remove the brake drum as detailed in Section 6 of this Chapter.
3 Inspect for signs of fluid leakage around the wheel cylinder, and if there is any, proceed to paragraph 6, of this Section.
4 Next, get an assistant to press the brake pedal very gently and a small distance (engine not running).
5 Watch the wheel slave cylinder and check whether the pistons move out a little. On no account let them come right out or the slave cylinder assembly will have to be reassembled and the brake system bled. On releasing the brake pedal, make sure that the retraction of springs on the shoes moves the pistons back without delay. If both pistons move, all is well; but if only one piston moves, only one shoe has been effective and repair is necessary.
6 If there is a hydraulic fluid leakage or the piston does not move (or only moves a little under pressure), then the piston seals will need renewal at the very least.
7 Begin by removing the brake shoes as detailed in Section 6 of this Chapter. Then remove the fluid reservoir cap(s) and stretch a thin sheet of polythene over the reservoir and refit the cap(s). This measure will prevent excessive loss of hydraulic fluid when hydraulic connections are subsequently undone.
8 Unscrew the fixed brake pipe from the rear of the brake slave cylinder, cover the end of the pipe to prevent ingress of foreign matter into the pipe.
9 Remove the cylinder from the backing plate by undoing the two screws from the rear side of the backing plate. Once the fixing screws have been removed, withdraw the cylinder assembly from the backing plate.
10 Work on a clean bench, and pull out the pistons from the cylinder, complete with seals (and springs if fitted). Discard the seals - they **must not** be reused.
11 Wash the pistons and cylinders in methylated spirits or clean brake fluid. Examine the piston and cylinder for signs of wear or scoring and if there are any, the whole assembly should be renewed. If the piston and cylinder are in good condition only new seals need be fitted.
12 Dip new seals in clean hydraulic fluid and refit the piston seals so that the lip faces away from the centre of the piston. Coat the piston with hydraulic fluid as it is eased back into the cylinder. Refit the dust seals and then bolt the cylinder back onto the backplate.
13 Recouple the fixed brake pipe to the slave cylinder then refit the brake shoes as detailed in Section 6 of this Chapter.
14 Fit the brake drum and bleed the brakes as detailed in Section 2 of this Chapter.
15 Finally check the adjustment of the brake shoes.

8 Master cylinder - removal, overhaul and refitting

Cautionary note

It will be observed from the following text and illustrations that the positions of the primary and secondary pistons are not as annotated or identified using the accepted method for other master cylinders. This reversed terminology used by Honda has been retained in order to maintain consistency with Honda servicing and parts literature.

The master cylinder for the 1977 models differs from the earlier type in that it has a single fluid reservoir in lieu of the twin reservoirs fitted previously. Apart from this feature the master cylinder is identical and the overhaul procedure is the same.

1 Disconnect the fluid level switch leads at their connections to the master cylinder reservoir caps.

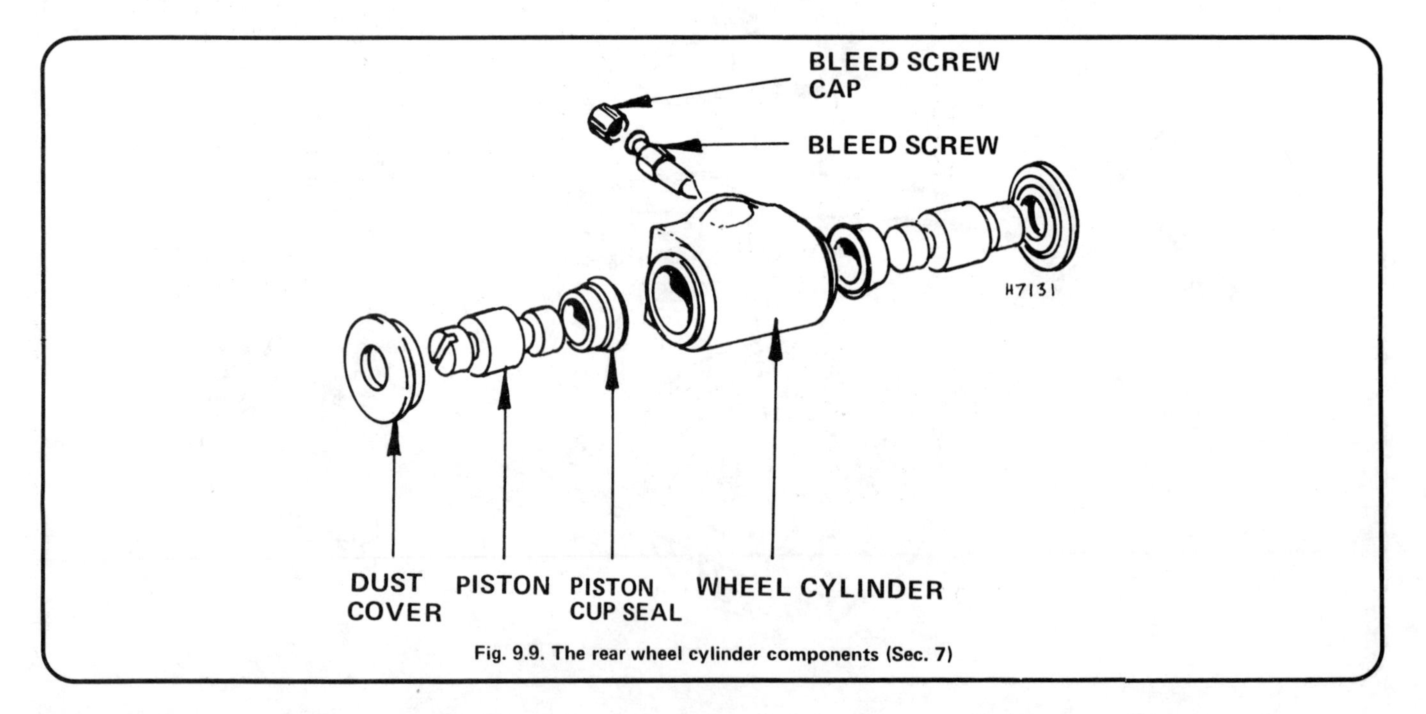

Fig. 9.9. The rear wheel cylinder components (Sec. 7)

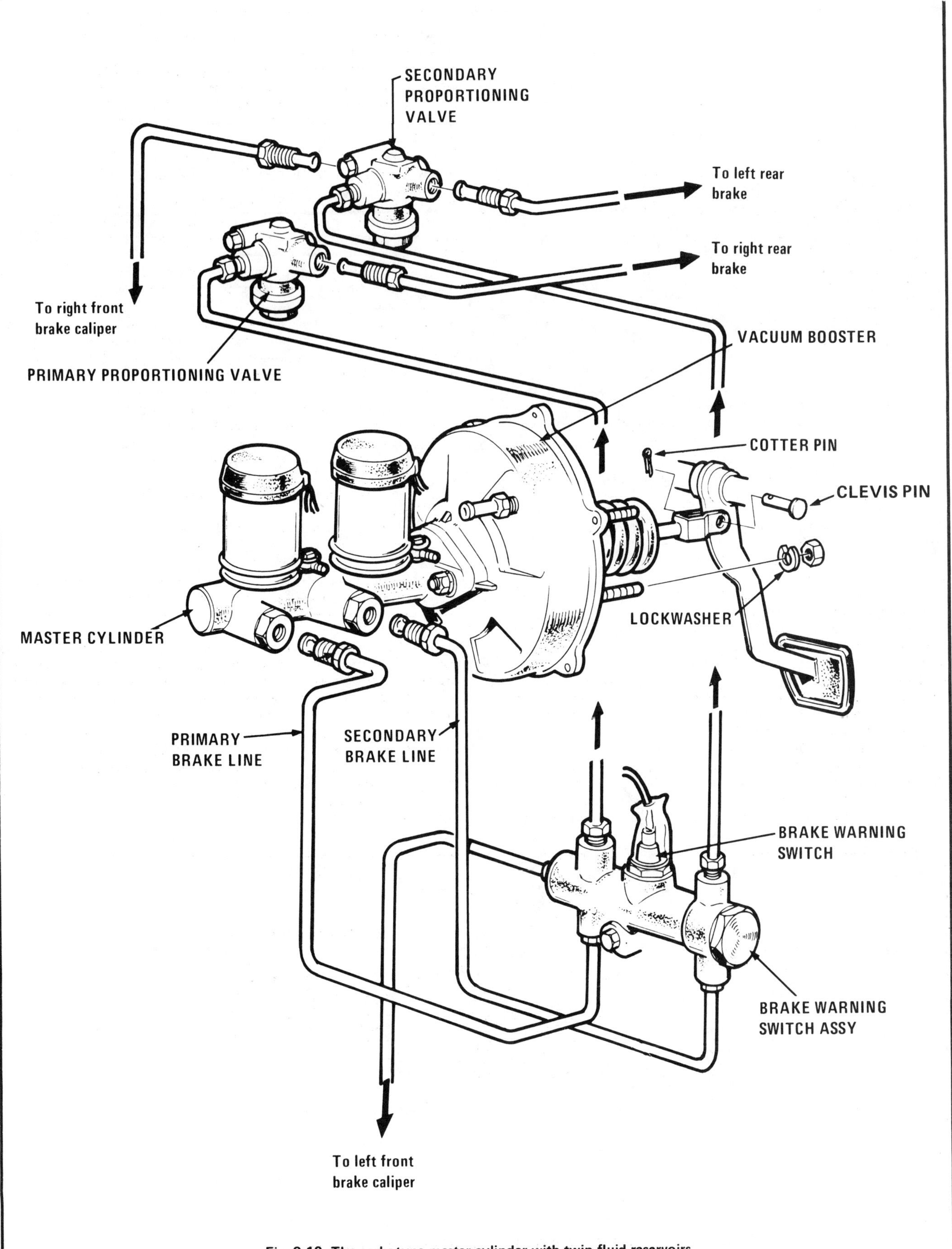

Fig. 9.10 The early type master cylinder with twin fluid reservoirs
(Sec. 8)

2 Disconnect the fluid lines from the master cylinder, catch any hydraulic fluid which runs from the unions and plug the ends of the fluid lines to prevent entry of dirt.
3 Unbolt and remove the master cylinder from the front face of the vacuum servo unit.
4 Unscrew the two fluid reservoir caps and tip out the fluid. Clean the external surfaces of the master cylinder body.
5 From the end of the cylinder body, extract the snap-ring, stop plate and the secondary piston.
6 Unscrew and remove the stop bolt.
7 Apply air pressure from a tyre pump to the brake line union at the end of the master cylinder body while at the same time covering the other union with a finger. The remaining (primary) piston assembly will be ejected.
8 Examine the surfaces of the pistons and the cylinder bore for scoring or 'bright' wear areas. Where these are evident, renew the master cylinder complete. Where the components are in good condition, remove and discard the seals and obtain a repair kit. Note carefully the direction of the seal lips before removing the seals.
9 Unscrew the respective brake pipe unions and extract the check

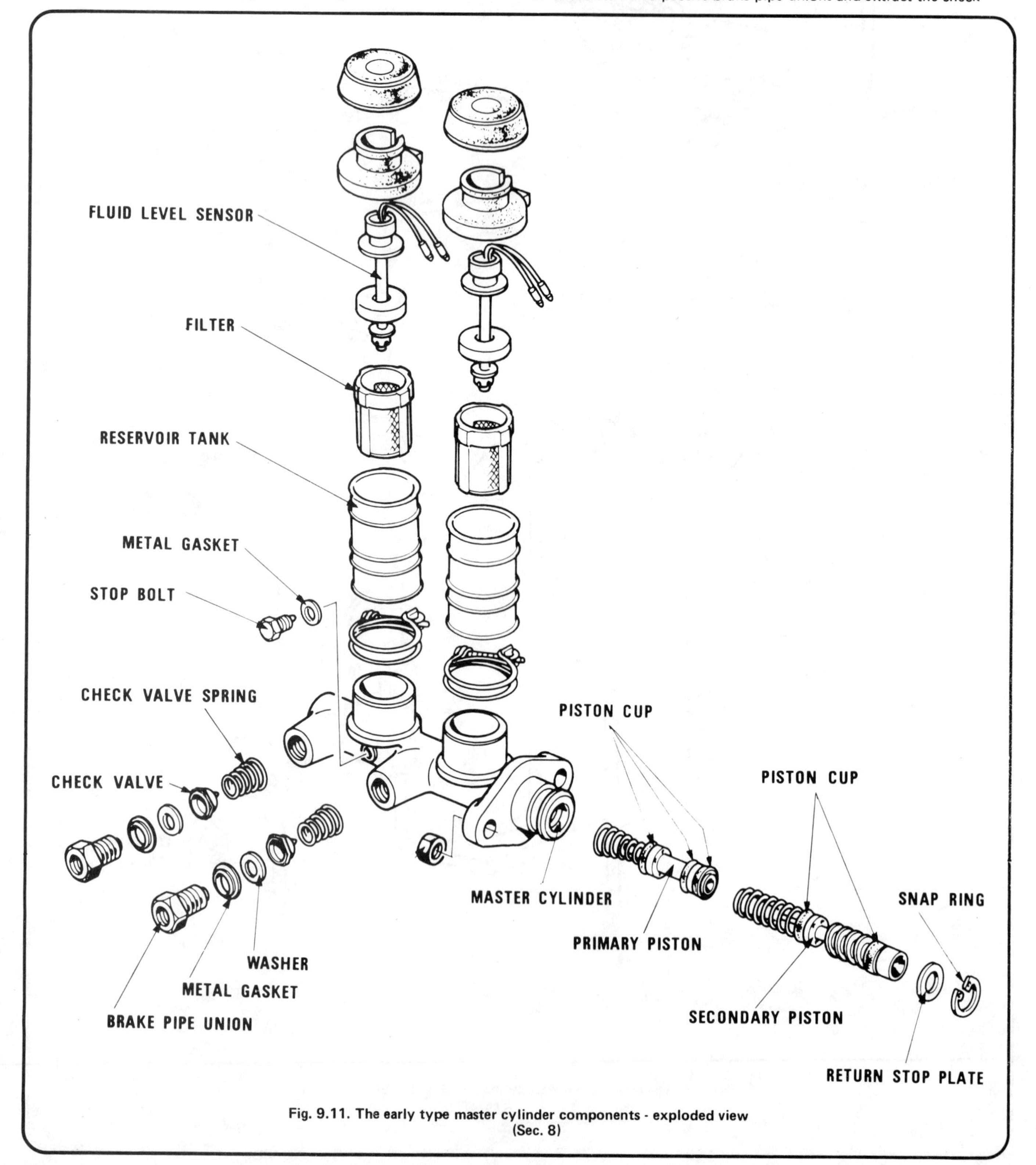

Fig. 9.11. The early type master cylinder components - exploded view (Sec. 8)

valves and springs. Clean and inspect the valves and springs. Renew if they are showing signs of wear or distortion.

10 Refit the springs, valve, washer, metal gasket and union. Ensure that the springs are correctly positioned with the large diameter of the taper towards the cylinder.

11 Manipulate the new seals into position on the pistons using the fingers only and then dip the piston assemblies in clean hydraulic fluid before fitting them.

12 Assemble the springs.

13 Insert the primary piston and spring into the cylinder bore. Lubricate the cylinder bore with clean hydraulic fluid then push the primary piston and spring down the bore using a suitable tool.

14 Refit the stop bolt with metal gasket, tightening it to 9 lb f ft (1.2 kg f m).

15 Refit the secondary piston, compress the spring and refit the stop plate and circlip.

16 Install the master cylinder to the front face of the vacuum booster and reconnect the brake lines and fluid level switch leads.

17 Bleed the hydraulic system, as described in Section 2 and when finally refitting the reservoir caps, make sure that the vent holes are clear.

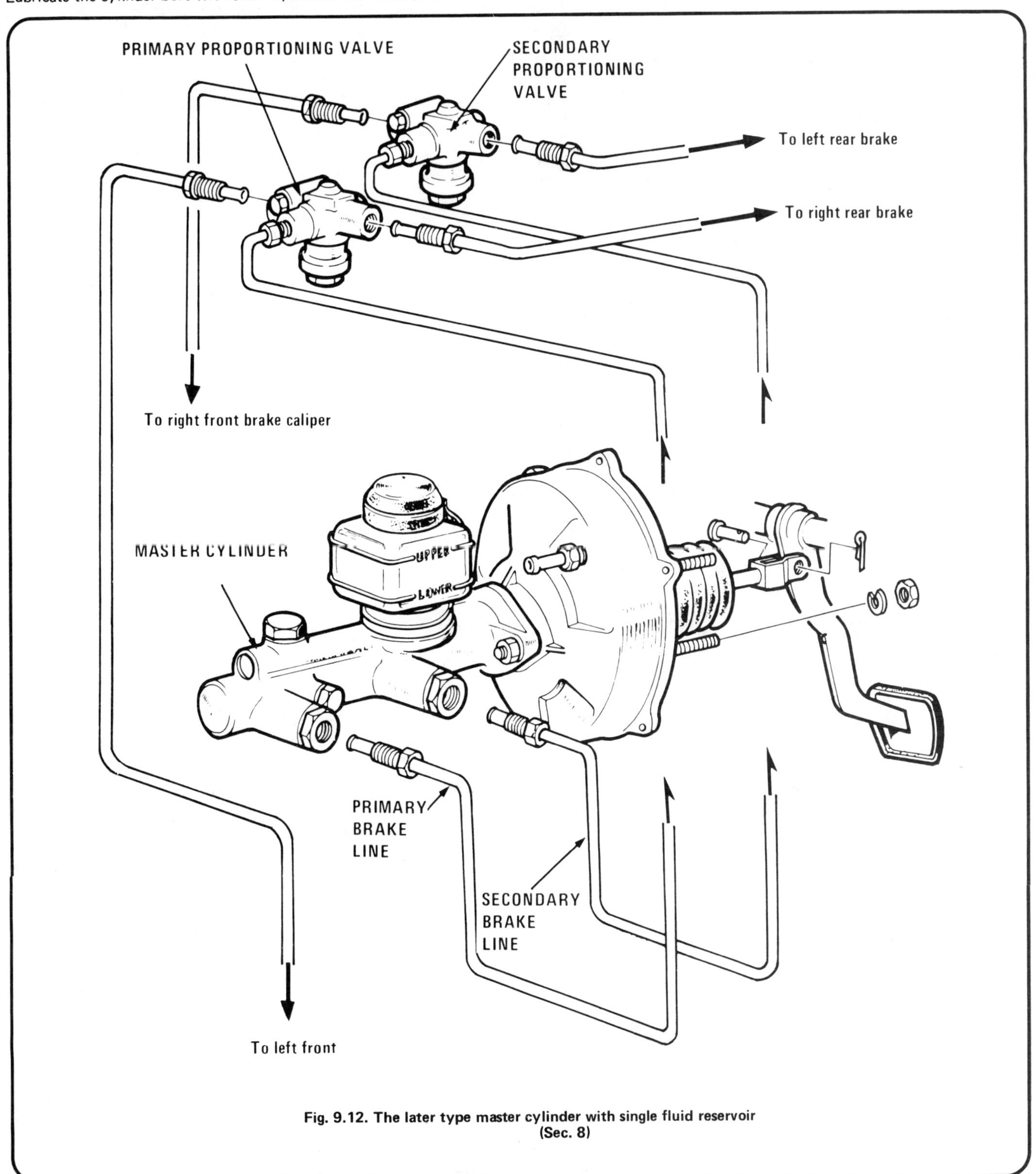

Fig. 9.12. The later type master cylinder with single fluid reservoir (Sec. 8)

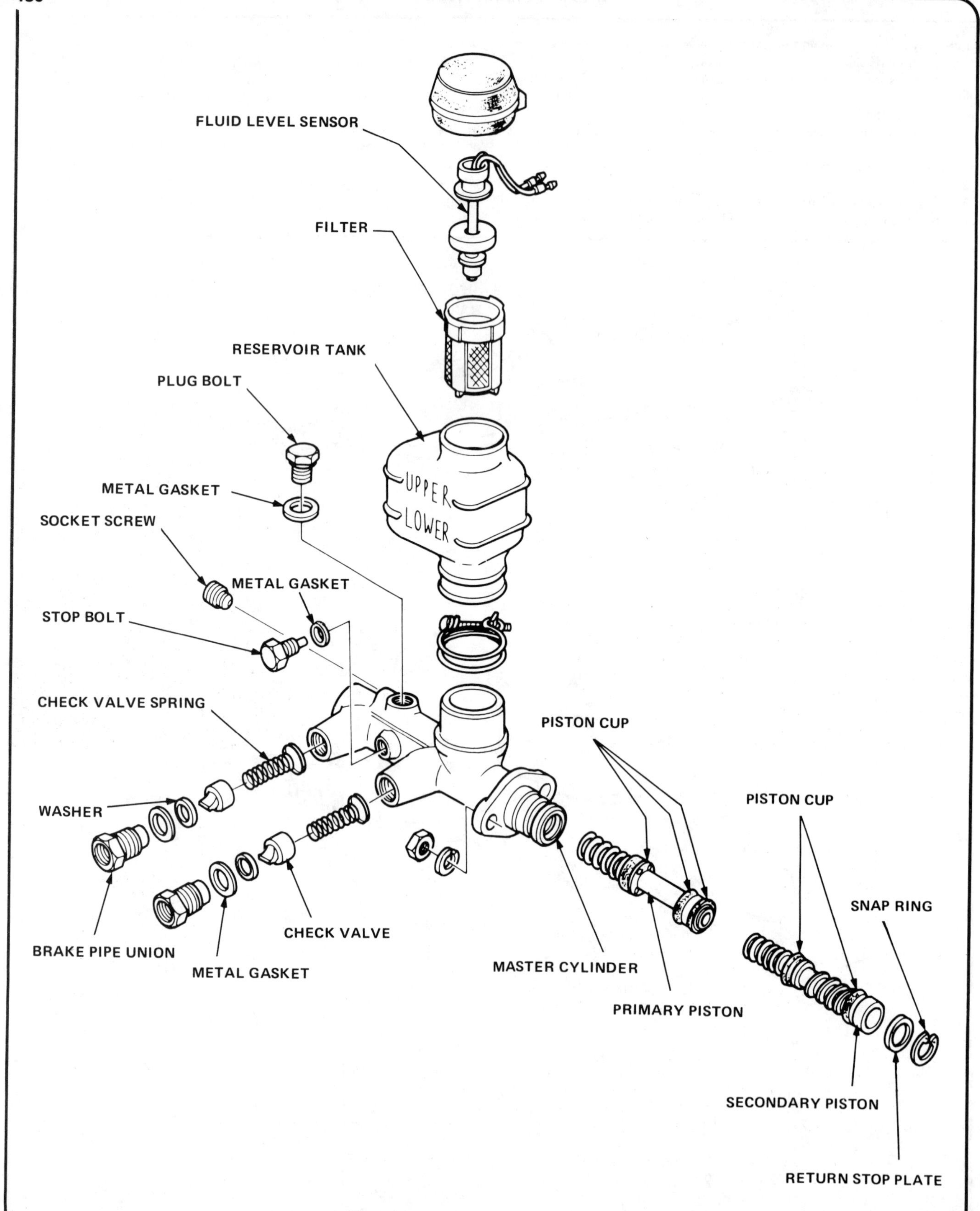

Fig. 9.13 The later type master cylinder component parts (Sec. 8)

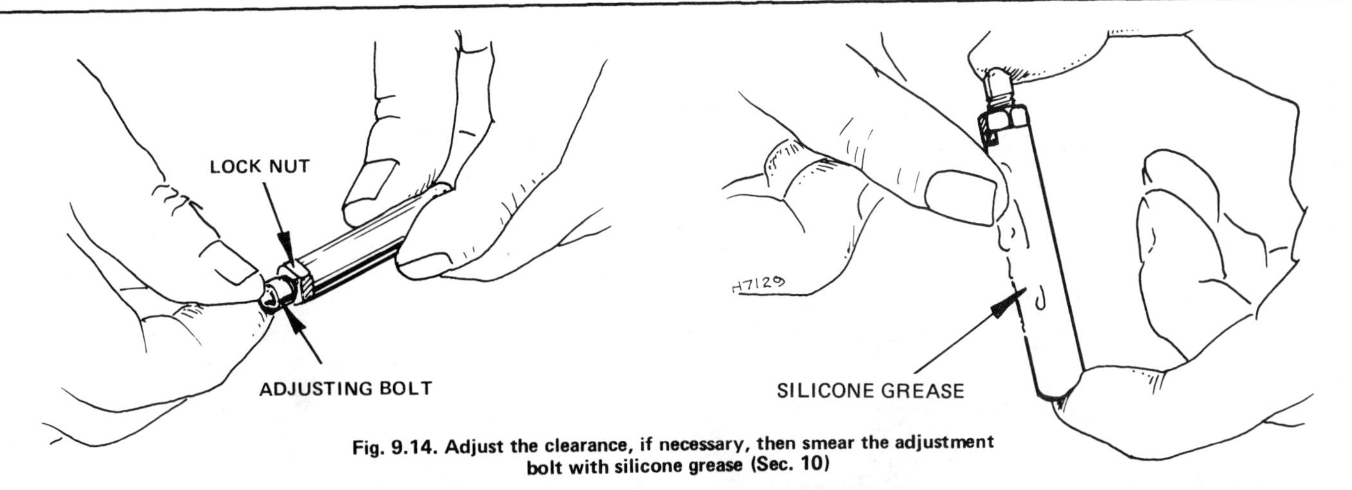

Fig. 9.14. Adjust the clearance, if necessary, then smear the adjustment bolt with silicone grease (Sec. 10)

9 Brake servo unit - description

The vacuum servo unit is fitted into the brake system in series with the master cylinder and brake pedal to provide power assistance to the driver when the brake pedal is depressed with the engine running.

The unit operates by vacuum obtained from the induction manifold and comprises basically a booster diaphragm and a non-return valve.

The servo unit and hydraulic master cylinder are connected together so that the servo unit pushrod acts as the master cylinder pushrod. The driver's braking effort is transmitted through another pushrod to the servo unit piston and its built in control system.

The servo unit piston does not fit tightly into the cylinder but has a strong diaphragm to keep its periphery in contact with the cylinder wall so assuring an airtight seal between the two parts. The forward chamber is held under vacuum conditions created in the inlet manifold of the engine and during the period when the engine is not in use the controls open a passage to the rear chamber so placing it under vacuum. When the brake pedal is pressed, the vacuum passage to the rear chamber is cut off and the chamber is opened to atmospheric pressure. The consequent rush of air into the rear chamber pushes the servo piston forward into the vacuum chamber and operates the push-rod to the master cylinder. The controls are designed so that assistance is given under all conditions. When the brakes are not required, vacuum is re-established in the rear chamber when the brake pedal is released.

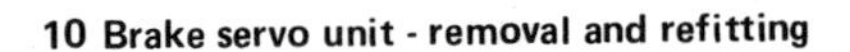

10 Brake servo unit - removal and refitting

1 Refer to Section 8 of this Chapter, and remove the brake master cylinder.
2 Slacken the hose clip and remove the vacuum hose from the inlet manifold and from the union on the forward face of the servo unit.
3 Next remove the small pin that joins the servo pushrod to the pedal lever. Separate the pushrod and pedal lever.
4 The servo is held to the bulkhead by four nuts which are screwed onto the studs attached to the servo projecting through to the pedal side of the bulkhead.
5 Undo the four nuts, and lift the vacuum servo unit away.
6 Before installing a new servo unit it is important to check that there is clearance between the end of the vacuum servo unit pushrod and the end of the end face of the secondary piston in the master cylinder. Obviously this cannot be measured when the master cylinder is bolted to the servo unit and some form of depth gauge must be used to measure the depth of (a) the end of the secondary piston below the mounting flange of the master cylinder and (b) the height of the end of the pushrod above the mounting flange on the front face of the servo unit. Compare the dimensions, when the servo unit one should be shorter by 0.004 to 0.024 in (0.1 to 0.6 mm). If this is not so, release the locknut on the servo unit pushrod and screw the adjustable section in or out. Tighten the locknut and recheck the dimension. If it now matches specifications then the necessary clearance will be provided when the master cylinder is bolted to the vacuum servo unit.
7 Having set and checked the adjustment, coat the adjustment bolt with silicone grease prior to assembly.
8 Refitting is a reversal of the removal procedure.

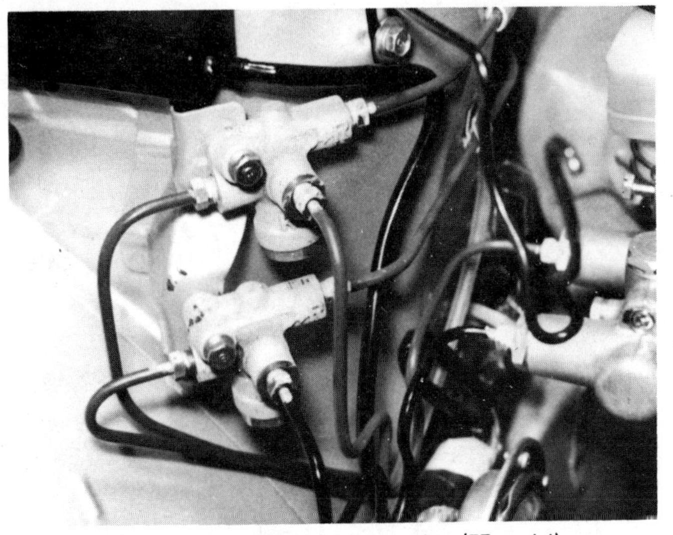

11.1 The primary and secondary regulating valves (77 model)

11 Pressure regulating valve

1 One of these valves is located in each of the two hydraulic braking circuits. They are positioned within the engine compartment (photo).
2 The purpose of these valves is to regulate the hydraulic pressure in the two independent braking circuits to compensate for differing characteristics of the front and rear brakes and for different vehicle loads. The devices also prevent rear wheel lock under severe braking applications.
3 The valves can be dismantled and cleaned in hydraulic fluid. New seals and rubber components can be fitted but the valves should be renewed completely if the intricate valves or the body are worn, scored or corroded.
4 If the valves are removed, the hydraulic circuits must be bled after refitting them (see Section 2).

12 Brake pressure (differential) warning switch - early models only

1 This is located adjacent to the pressure regulating valves within the engine compartment.
2 It is essentially a piston which is normally kept 'in balance' by the equal pressures in the two independent hydraulic braking circuits. In the event of a fault developing in one circuit with consequent loss of pressure, the piston is then displaced and completes an electrical circuit which illuminates a warning lamp.
3 The switch assembly can be dismantled, if necessary, for the renewal of internal components.
4 Whenever the warning lamp lights up, investigate the reason for the

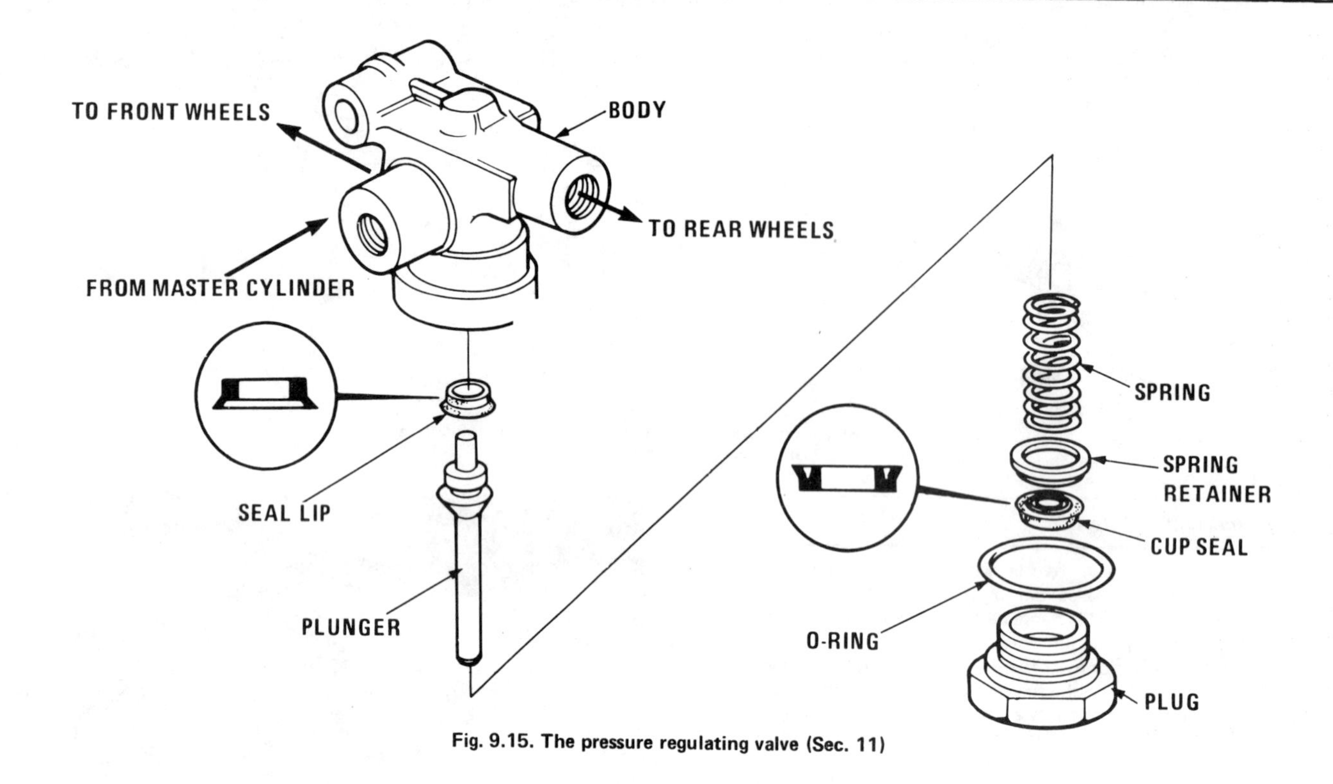

Fig. 9.15. The pressure regulating valve (Sec. 11)

CENTERING VALVE LIMITER
CENTERING VALVE LIMITER
CAP SCREW
O-RING
CENTERING VALVE
O-RING
WASHER
CIRCLIP
BRAKE WARNING SWITCH BODY
BRAKE WARNING SWITCH

Fig. 9.16. The brake warning switch components (Sec. 12)

drop in pressure in one of the hydraulic circuits. This will probably be due to a faulty caliper or wheel cylinder seal or to a leaking brake pipe line. The circuits are split diagonally.

13 Hydraulic pipes - inspection and renewal

1 Examine first all the unions for signs of leaks. Then look at the flexible hoses for signs of fraying and chafing (as well as for leaks). This is only a preliminary inspection of the flexible hoses, as exterior condition does not necessarily indicate interior condition which will be considered later.

2 The steel pipes must be examined equally carefully. They must be thoroughly cleaned and examined for signs of dents or other percussive damage, rust and corrosion. Rust and corrosion should be scraped off, and, if the depth of pitting in the pipes is significant, they will need renewal. This is most likely in those areas underneath the chassis and along the rear suspension arms where the pipes are exposed to the full force of road and weather conditions.

3 If any section of pipe is to be removed, first take off the fluid reservoir cap, line it with a piece of polythene film to make it airtight and screw it back on. This will minimise the amount of fluid dripping out of the system when the pipes are removed. This is not possible where cap floats are fitted.

4 Rigid pipe removal is usually quite straightforward. The unions at each end are undone and the pipe drawn out of the connection. Any clips which hold it to the car body are bent back and it is then removed. Underneath the car the exposed union can be particularly stubborn, defying all efforts of an open ended spanner. As few people will have the special split ring spanner required, a self-grip wrench (mole) is the only answer. If the pipe is being renewed, new unions will be provided. If not, then one will have to put up with the possibility of burring over the flats on the union and of using a self-grip wrench for refitting also.

5 Flexible hoses are always fitted to a rigid support bracket where they join a rigid pipe, the bracket being fixed to the chassis or rear suspension arm. The rigid pipe unions must first be removed from the flexible union. Then the locknut securing the flexible pipe to the

bracket must be unscrewed, releasing the end of the pipe from the bracket. As these connections are usually exposed they are, more often than not, rusted up and a penetrating fluid is virtually essential to aid removal. When undoing them, both halves must be supported as the bracket is not strong enough to support the torque required to undo the nut and can be snapped off easily.

6 Once the flexible hose is removed, examine the internal bore. If clear of fluid it should be possible to see through it. Any specks of rubber which come out or there are signs of restriction in the bore, mean that the inner lining is breaking up and the pipe must be renewed.

7 Rigid pipes which need renewal can usually be purchased at your local garage where they have the pipe, unions and special tools to make them up. All that they need to know is the pipe length required and the type of flare used at the ends of the pipe. These may be different at each end of the same pipe. It is a good idea to take the old pipe along as a pattern.

8 Refitting of pipes is a straightforward reversal of removal. Any acute bends should be put in by the garage on a bending machine, otherwise there is the possibility of kinking the pipe and restricting the bore area and fluid flow.

9 With the pipe refitted, remove the polythene from the reservoir cap and bleed the system, as described in Section 2.

14 Handbrake - adjustment

1 The handbrake is normally only adjusted to compensate for stretch and wear in the handbrake system or when new brake linings have been fitted to the rear. Always check the rear brake adjustment before adjusting the handbrake cable.

2 A cable equalizer is fitted and hinges from the rear chassis cross-member to which the rear suspension arms are pivoted. Compensation of the cable is made by turning the adjustment nut on the equalizer accordingly.

3 To adjust the cable, raise the rear of the vehicle and secure with chassis stands positioned under the strengthened plates under the sills to the rear of each door. Place wheel chocks under each of the front wheels and engage first gear. Release the handbrake.

4 Slacken off the equalizer adjustment nut and then engage the handbrake lever onto its first notch (photo).

5 Now tighten the adjustment nut on the equalizer until the rear wheels are felt to drag slightly when rotated.

6 Fully release the handbrake and check that the rear wheels can spin freely without the brakes binding.

7 Fully apply the handbrake lever and check that the rear wheels are locked before removing the chassis stands.

15 Handbrake cable - renewal

1 The handbrake system comprises a lever assembly inside the car, a single cable which connects the lever assembly to the equalizer lever mounted underneath the car between the rear wheels, and finally another cable which runs across between each rear brake and through the equalizer.

2 The single cable is retained to the handbrake lever by a single pin, and to the equalizer by the special adjusting nut. The removal and refitting task is accomplished from beneath the car.

3 The second cable which runs between rear brakes is the one most likely to stretch and wear. It operates in the worst environment and undergoes a greater amount of flexing by the equalizer.

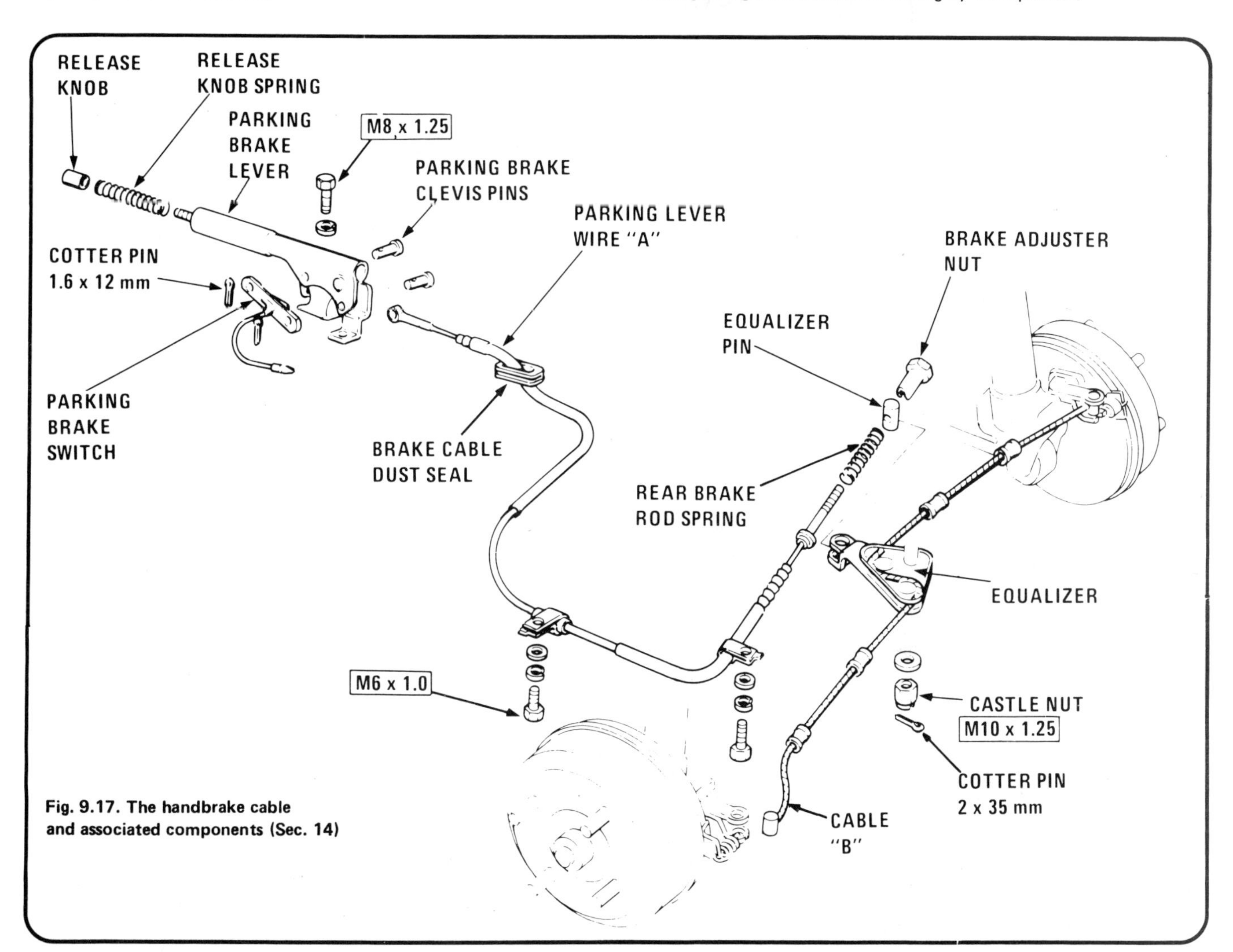

Fig. 9.17. The handbrake cable and associated components (Sec. 14)

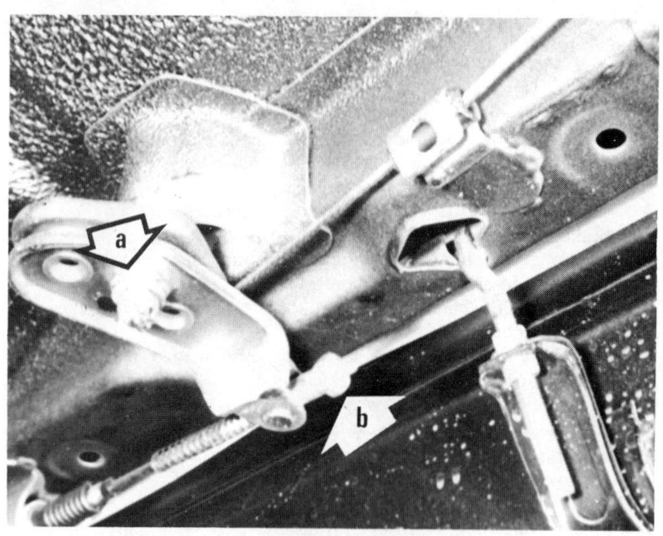

14.4 The equalizer A and adjustment nut B

15.5 The transverse cable to lever connection - note the return spring

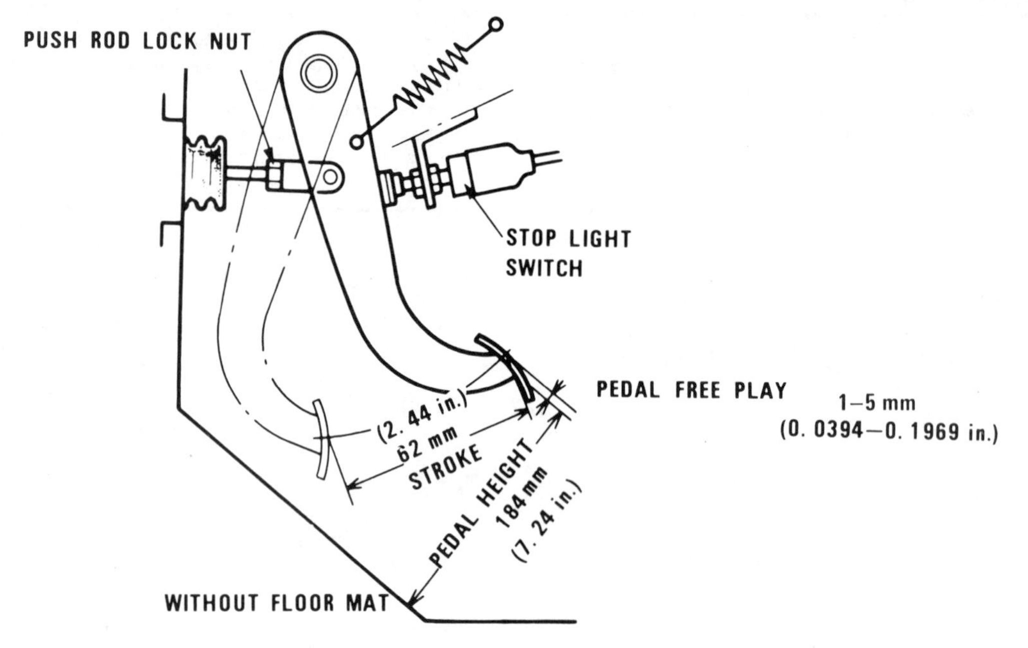

Fig. 9.18 Pedal adjustment (Sec. 16)

4 The equalizer comprises two pulleys around which the cable runs. The equalizer bracket is turned by the cable from the lever to effectively shorten and apply a tension to the transverse cable between rear brakes.

5 The equalizer is retained to its pivot on the underside of the body-shell by a single nut locked by a split pin. The transverse cable is terminated in cylindrical blocks on the end of the shoe lever protruding from each rear brake (photo).

6 Renewal of the transverse cable requires the removal of the equalizer and then the removal of the cable ends from the brake levers at each end.

Lift the cable from the pulleys in the equalizer. Refitting the cable follows the reversal of the removal procedure.

7 When either cable is renewed, readjust the brake cable linkage as per Section 14.

8 Give the cables liberal coatings of grease to prevent corrosion and reduce fretting between strands in the cables.

16 Brake pedal - adjustment and dismantling

1 The brake pedal is of the pendant type and its design differs

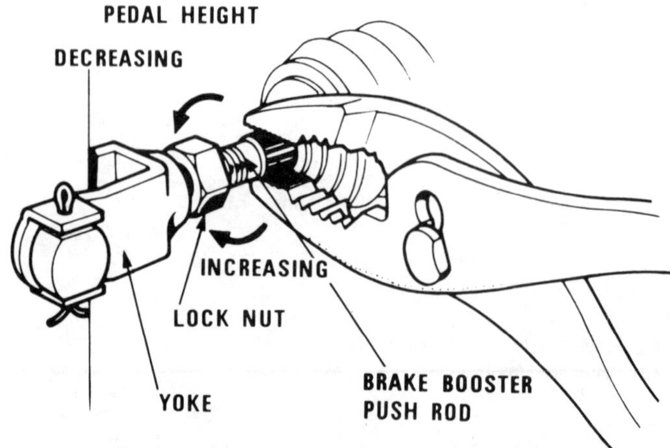

Fig. 9.19 Adjusting the pedal height (Sec. 16)

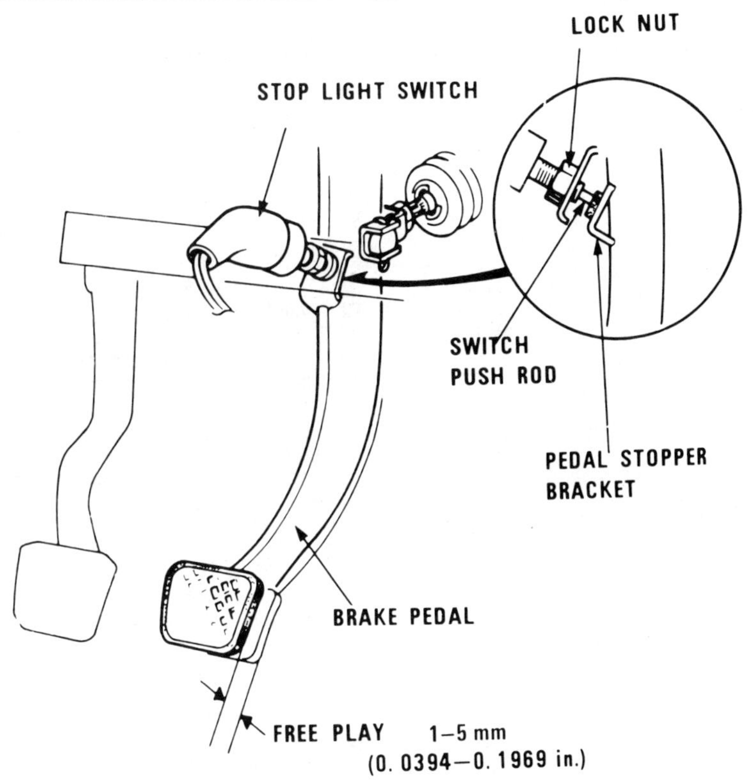

Fig. 9.20. The pedal free play (Sec. 16)

according to whether the vehicle is left-hand or right-hand drive and whether it is equipped with manual or automatic transmission.

2 The brake pedal must be set so that the distance from the floor to its underside is 7.24 in (184 mm). Adjustment is provided by releasing the locknuts on the brake stop lamp switch and moving the position of the switch.

3 With the brake pedal correctly set for height, depress the pedal pad with the fingers. A free-movement at the pedal pad of between 0.040 and 0.196 in (1.0 and 5.0 mm) should be felt.

4 The brake pedal is retained to its bracket by either a pivot bolt or a snap-ring. Dismantling can be carried out by removing the securing device according to type, detaching the pedal return spring and disconnecting the pushrod from the pedal arm.

5 The clutch pedal should be adjusted so that it is level with the brake pedal (see Chapter 5, Section 2)

See overleaf for 'Fault diagnosis - Braking system'

18 Fault diagnosis - braking system

Symptom	Reason/s
Brake grab	Out of round drums. Excessive run-out of discs. Rust on drum or disc. Oil stained linings or pads.
Brake drag	Faulty master cylinder. Foot pedal return impeded. Reservoir breather blocked. Seized caliper or wheel cylinder piston. Incorrect adjustment of handbrake. Weak or broken shoe return springs. Crushed, blocked or swollen pipe lines.
Excessive pedal effort required	Linings or pads not yet bedded-in. Drum, disc or linings contaminated with oil or grease. Scored drums or discs. Faulty vacuum servo unit.
Brake pedal feels hard	Glazed surfaces of friction material. Rust on disc surfaces. Seized caliper or wheel cylinder piston.
Excessive pedal travel	Low reservoir fluid level. Disc run-out excessive. Worn front wheel bearings. Air in system. Worn pads or linings. Rear brakes require adjustment.
Pedal creep during sustained application	Fluid leak. Internal fault in master cylinder. Faulty servo unit non-return valve.
Pedal "spongy"	Air in system. Perished flexible hose. Loose master cylinder mounting nuts. Cracked brake drum. Faulty master cylinder. Reservoir breather blocked. Linings not bedded-in.
Fall in reservoir fluid level	Normal, due to pad or lining wear. Leak in hydraulic system.

Chapter 10 Electrical system

For modifications, and information applicable to later models, see Supplement at end of manual

Contents

Specifications

System type ... 12V negative earth (ground), battery and alternator

Battery ... 12V 45 ah European models
12V 47 ah - USA models
12V 40 ah - all other models

Alternator

Output	12V 50 ah
Direction of rotation	Counterclockwise (clockwise on air conditioned models)
Brush length	
New	0.610 in (15.5 mm)
Wear limit	0.216 in (5.5 mm)
Brush spring pressure	300 to 500 g
Polarity	Negative earth
Drive belt tension	0.47 to 0.67 in (12. to 17 mm) @ 19.8 to 24 lbs (9 - 11 kg) loading

Voltage regulator

Range	13.5 to 14.5 volts
Point gap	0.016 to 0.047 in (0.4 to 1.2 mm)
Armature gap - maximum	0.020 in (0.5 mm)
Contact spring deflection	0.008 to 0.023 in (0.2 to 0.6 mm)
Angle gap	0.020 in (0.5 mm)

Voltage relay

Rated voltage	4.5 to 5.8V
Point gap	0.016 to 0.047 in (0.4 to 1.2 mm)
Contact spring deflection (contracted)	0.008 to 0.023 in (0.2 to 0.6 mm)

Starter motor - standard

Type	12V - 0.7 kw pre-engaged
Rotation	Clockwise viewed from pinion
Minimum brush length	0.39 in (10.0 mm)
Pinion to stopper clearance	0.012 to 0.06 in (0.3 to 1.5 mm)

Starter motor - reduction gear type

Type	12V, 0.8 kw
Brush length	
New	0.551 in (14.0 mm)
Wear limit	0.354 in (9.0 mm)

Spring pressure (new)	3.3 to 4.2 lbs (1.5 to 1.9 kg)
Commutator outside diameter	
New	1.181 in (30.0 mm)
Wear limit	1.142 in (29.0 mm)
Commutator run out wear limit	0.003 in (0.08 mm)
Mica depth wear limit	0.078 in (0.20 mm)

Bulbs

Headlights	12V, 45/50W, 45W - European models 12V, 37.5/50W, 37.5W - Other models
Front indicator/marker lights	12V, 21/5W
Panel lights	12V, 3.4/1.2W
Indicator signal light	12V, 1.2W
Warning lights	12V, 1.2W
Steering illumination light	12V, 2W
Rear window defrost pilot light	12V, 1.2W
Glovebox light	12V, 2W
Interior light	12V, 2W
Tailgate light	12V, 5W
Side turn signal light	12V, 4W
Rear turn signal light	12V, 21/21/5W
Reversing lights	12V, 21W
License plate lights	12V, 10W

Fuses

Main fuse	55A
Hazard light/horn/stoplight	15A
Interior light/clock/cigarette lighter	10A
Tail light/license light/meter light	15A
Headlight/dip (low beam)	15A
Turn signal light/reverse light/fuel meter	10A
Regulator/fuel gauge	10A
Wiper washer	10A
Air conditioning	10A
Radio/rear window defroster	15A
Heater	15A

Torque wrench settings

	lb f ft	kg fm
Starter motor housing bolt	7 to 10	1.0 to 1.4
Starter motor to transmission bolts	29 to 36	4 to 5
Alternator retaining bolt	29 to 36	4 to 5
Alternator adjustment bolt	17 to 20	2.3 to 2.8
Alternator through bolts	29 to 36	4 to 5
Alternator pulley nut	22 to 36	3 to 5

1 General description

The electrical system is of the 12 volts negative earth type. The principal components comprise a lead acid type battery, an alternator which is belt driven from the crankshaft pulley; and a pre-engaged starter motor.

The ignition system is supplied with a steady current from the battery, which is in turn charged by the alternator. The battery also supplies current to the various electrical accessories and therefore a voltage regulator adjusts the charge rate to the battery according to demand.

2 Battery - maintenance

1 Check the battery electrolyte level weekly by lifting off the cover or removing the individual cell plugs. The tops of the plates should be just covered with the liquid. If not, add distilled water so that they are just covered. Do not add extra water with the idea of reducing the intervals of topping-up. This will merely dilute the electrolyte and reduce charging and current retention efficiency. On batteries fitted with patent covers, troughs, glass balls and so on, follow the instructions marked on the cover of the battery to ensure correct addition of water (photo).

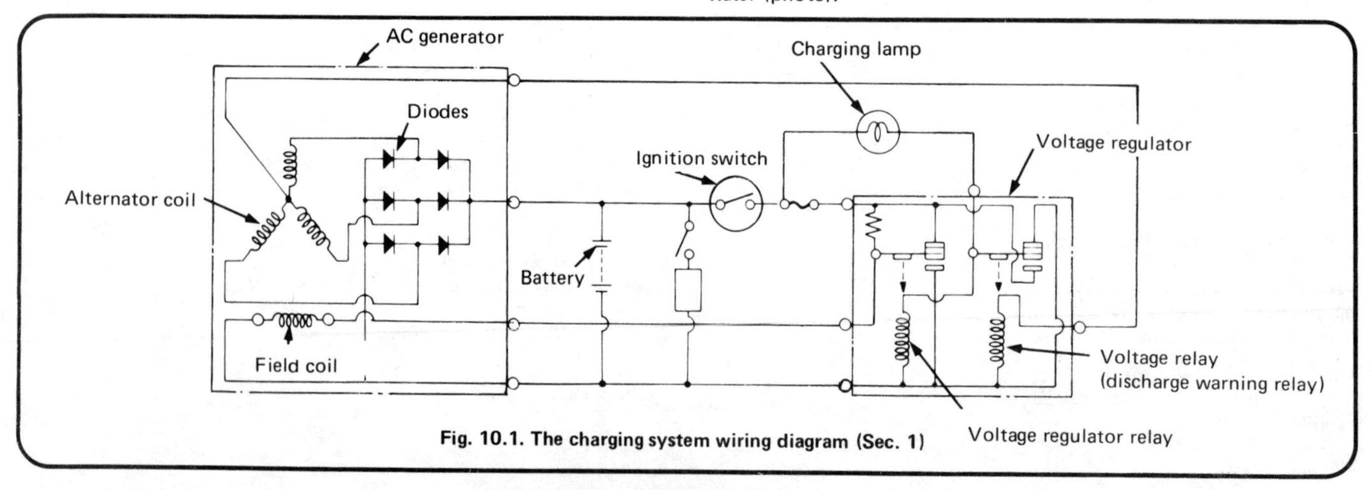

Fig. 10.1. The charging system wiring diagram (Sec. 1)

2 Keep the battery clean and dry all over by wiping it with a dry cloth. A damp top surface could cause tracking between the two terminals posts with consequent draining of power.

3 Every three months remove the battery and check the support tray clamp and battery terminal connections for signs of corrosion - usually indicated by a whitish green crystalline deposit. Wash this off with clean water to which a little ammonia or washing soda has been added. Then treat the terminals with petroleum jelly and the battery mounting with suitable protective paint to prevent the metal being eaten away. Clean the battery thoroughly and repair any cracks with a proprietary sealer. If there has been any excessive leakage, the appropriate cell may need an addition of electrolyte rather than just distilled water.

4 If the electrolyte level needs an excessive amount of replenishment but no leaks are apparent, it could be due to overcharging as a result of the battery having been run down and then left to recharge from the vehicle rather than from an outside source. If the battery has been heavily discharged for one reason or another, it is best to have it continuously charged at a low amperage for a period of many hours. If it is charged from the car's system under such conditions the charging will be intermittent and greatly varied in intensity. This does not do the battery any good at all. If the battery needs topping-up frequently, even when it is known to be in good condition and not too old, then the voltage regulator should be checked to ensure that the charging output is being correctly controlled. An elderly battery, however, may need topping-up more than a new one because it needs to take in more charging current. Do not worry about this provided it gives satisfactory service.

5 When checking a battery's condition a hydrometer should be used. On some batteries where the terminals of each of the six cells are exposed, a discharge tester can be used to check the condition of any one cell also. On modern batteries the use of a discharge tester is no longer regarded as useful as the renewal or repair of cells is not an economic proposition. The following table gives the hydrometer readings for various states of charge. A further check can be made when the battery is undergoing a charge. If, towards the end of the charge, when the cells are meant to be 'gassing' (bubbling), one cell appears not to be, then it indicates that the cell or cells in question are probably breaking down and the life of the battery is limited.

	Climate below 80°F (26.7°C)	*Climate above 80°F (26.7°C)*
Fully charged	*1.270 - 1.290*	*1.210 - 1.230*
Half charged	*1.190 - 1.210*	*1.120 - 1.150*
Discharged completely	*1.110 - 1.130*	*1.050 - 1.070*

Note: If the electrolyte temperature is significantly different from 60°F (15.6°C) then the specific gravity reading will be affected. For every 5°F (2.8°C) it will increase or decrease with the temperature by 0.002.

3 Battery - charging and electrolyte replenishment

1 Occasionally it may be required to recharge the battery from an external source. This is usually the case when the vehicle has not seen regular usage, the battery is nearing the end of its life or during the winter when the load in the battery cannot be recuperated, dependent on accessory usage and daily mileage. Charging the battery from an external source is best done overnight at a 'trickle' rate of 1 to 1.5 amps. Alternatively, a 3 to 4 amp rate can be used over a reduced period of 3 to 4 hours. Check the specific gravity in the latter case and stop the charge when the reading is correct. Most modern charging sets reduce the rate automatically when the fully charged state is neared. Rapid boost charges of 30 - 60 amps or more may get you out of trouble or can be used on a battery that has seen better days. They are not advisable for a good battery that may have run flat for some reason.

2 Electrolyte replenishment should not normally be necessary unless an accident or some other cause such as contamination arises. If it is necessary then it is best first to discharge the battery completely and then tip out all the remaining liquid from all cells. Then acquire a quantity of mixed electrolyte from a battery shop or garage according to the specifications in the table given. The quantity required will depend on the type of battery but 3 - 4 Imp. pints (1.7 to 2.3 litres) should be more than enough for most. When the electrolyte has been put into the battery a slow charge not exceeding one amp - should be given for as long as is necessary to fully charge the battery. This could be up to 36 hours.

Specific gravities for hydrometer readings (check each cell) - 12 volt batteries - are given in Fig. 10.3.

2.1 Check the battery electrolyte level

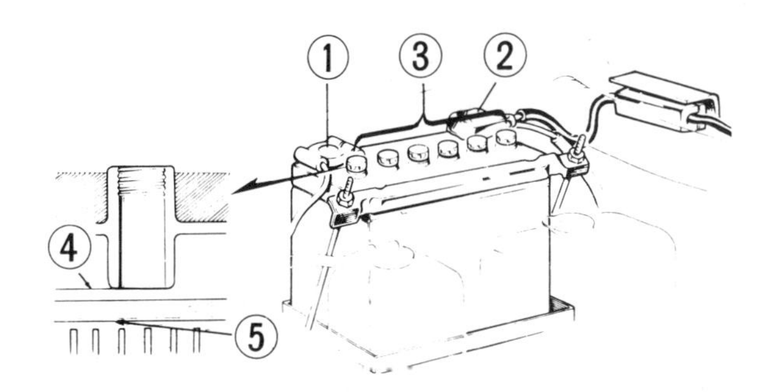

Fig. 10.2 The battery connections and electrolyte level (Sec. 2)

1 Negative terminal (–)
2 Positive terminal (+)
3 Filler caps
4 Upper level
5 Lower level

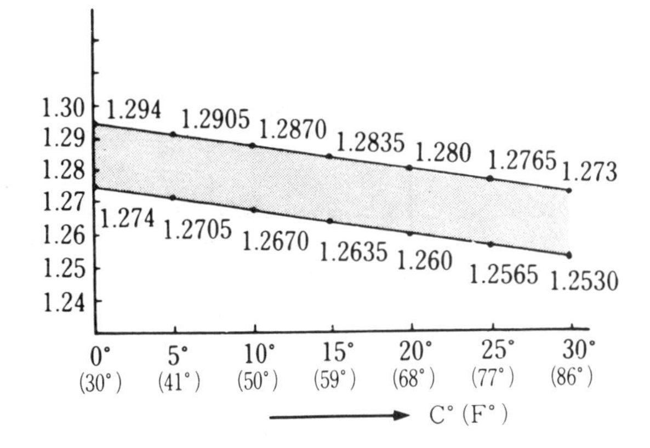

Fig. 10.3 The specific gravity check chart (Sec. 3)

4 Battery - removal and refitting

1 The battery is located within the engine compartment on the right-hand side. It is held in place by two tie-rods and a pressed steel angle strip.
2 To remove the battery, begin by disconnecting the negative earth lead from the battery and bodyshell. Then disconnect the positive lead from the battery.
3 Once the leads have been removed, undo and remove the two wing nuts which tension the tie-rods onto the angle strip which secures the battery. Lift the angle strip aside once the rod nuts have been undone.
4 Lift the battery from its seating in the bodyshell, taking great care not tc spill any of the highly corrosive electrolyte.
5 Refitting follows the reversal of the removal procedure. Refit the positive lead first and smear the clean terminal posts and lead clamp assembly beforehand with petroleum jelly in order to prevent corrosion. **Do not use ordinary grease,** it does not prevent corrosion of the terminal and does not conduct electricity.

5 Alternator - general description

The main advantage of the alternator lies in its ability to provide a relatively high power output at low revolutions. Driving slowly in traffic with a dynamo means a very small charge or even no charge at all, reaching the battery.

The alternator is of the rotating field, ventilated design and comprises principally a laminated stator on which is wound a 3 phase output winding, and a twelve pole rotor carrying the field windings.

Each end of the rotor shaft runs in ball race bearings which are lubricated for life. Aluminium end housings hold the bearings and incorporate the alternator mounting lugs. The rear housings support the silicone diode rectifier pack which converts the AC output of the alternator to a DC output, for battery charging and output to the voltage regulator.

The alternator is belt driven from the engine crankshaft pulley through a pulley keyed to the rotor shaft. A special centrifugal action fan adjacent to the pulley, draws cool air through the machine. This fan forms an integral part of the alternator specification. It has been designed to provide adequate airflow with the minimum of noise at all speeds of rotation of the machine - rotation is anticlockwise when viewed from the drive end for standard models or clockwise on models fitted with air conditioning.

The rectifier pack of silicone diodes is mounted on the inside of the rear end casing, the same mounting is used by the brushes which contact slip rings on the rotor to supply the field current. The slip rings are carried on a small diameter moulded drum attached to the rotor. By keeping the circumference of the slip rings to a minimum, the contact speed and therefore the brush wear is minimised.

6 Alternator - maintenance and precautions

Maintenance

1 Maintenance consists of occasionally wiping the outside of the alternator free from dirt and grease and checking the security of the electrical connections.
2 Correct tensioning of the drivebelt is essential to maintain the proper power output from the alternator and a deflection of ½ in (12.7 mm) must be provided at the centre point of the longest run of the belt (photo).
3 To adjust the tension, release the alternator mounting bolts and the adjuster link bolt and pivot the alternator either towards or away from the engine as necessary. Retighten the bolts on completion of adjustment.

Precautions

4 Take extreme care when making circuit connections to a vehicle fitted with an alternator and observe the following:

When making connections to the alternator from a battery always match correct polarity.

Before using electric arc welding equipment to repair any part of the vehicle, disconnect the connector from the alternator and disconnect the positive battery terminal.

Never start the car with a battery charger connected.

Always disconnect both battery leads before using a mains charger.

If boosting from another battery, always connect in parallel using heavy cable.

6.2 Check the alternator drivebelt tension

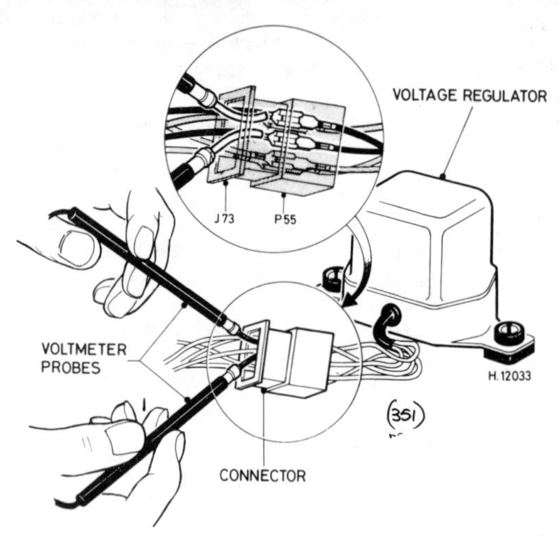

Fig. 10.4 Testing the alternator and voltage regulator (Sec. 7)

7 Alternator - testing (in position), removal and refitting

Testing

Prior to testing, ensure that the battery is in a fully charged condition.

1 If, when the ignition is switched on, the warning lamp does not come on, check that the bulb is not blown and the fuse is sound (fuse no. 3, see Section 16).
2 Unplug the connector J73 at the voltage regulator connection P55 and short pin '3' to earth. If the warning lamp comes on, the voltage regulator is faulty and should be renewed.
3 If having started the engine, the ignition warning lamp does not go out even when the engine speed is increased, a voltmeter should be connected across pins '2' and '1' of the connectors at the voltage regulator. Leave the connector plugs connected for this test and insert the probes from the back of the connector 'J73' as shown in Fig. 10.4 If the voltmeter indicates 7 volts then the alternator is serviceable and the voltage regulator is at fault and must be renewed.

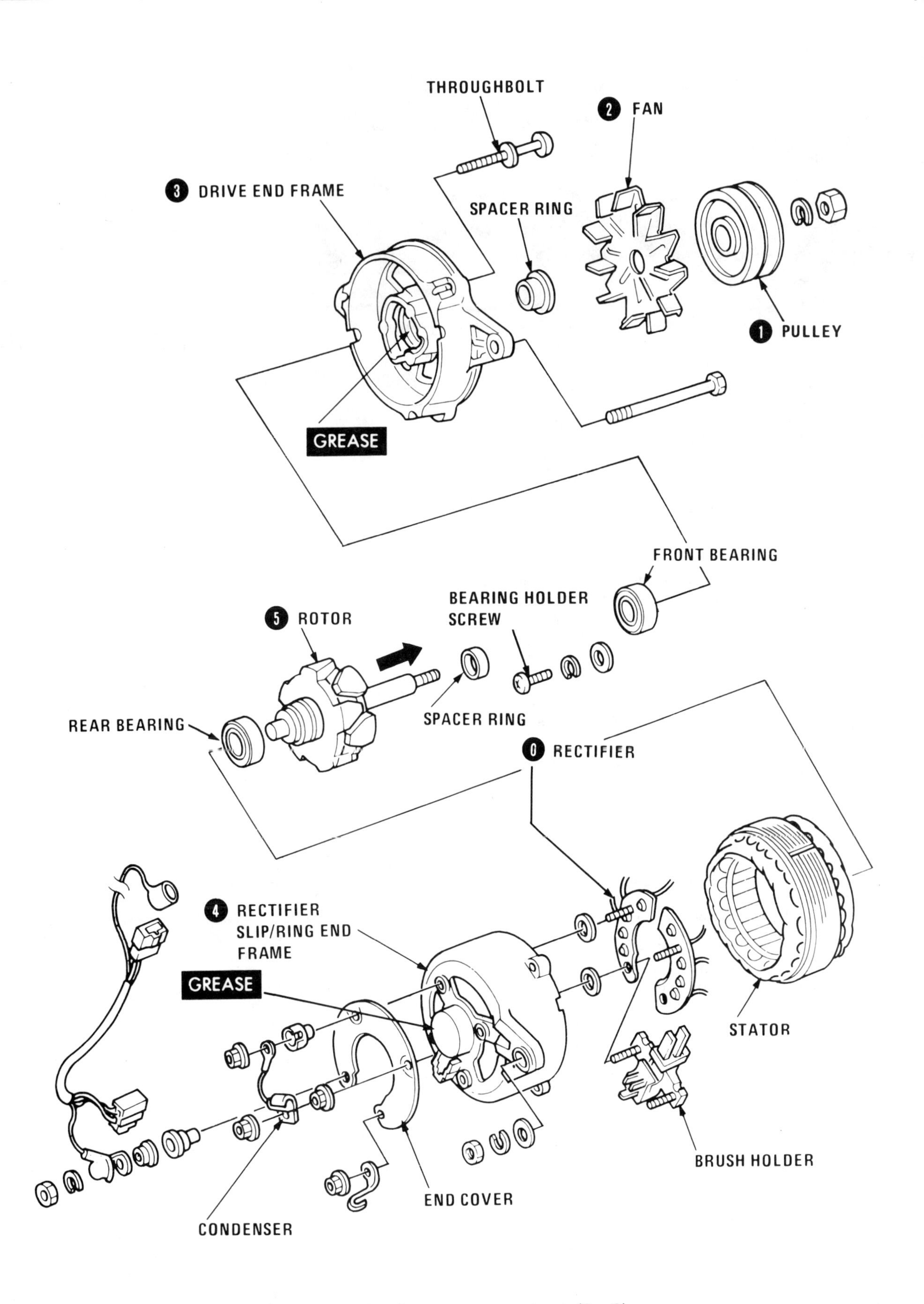

Fig. 10.5 The alternator component parts (Sec. 8)

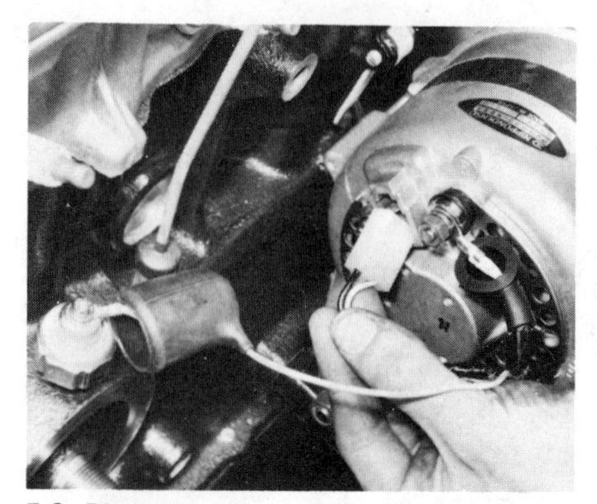

7.6a Disconnect the alternator wiring connector

7.6b Remove the retaining bolts to lift the alternator clear

Fig. 10.6 Remove the end pulley nut using ring spanner and 6 mm Allen key (Sec. 8)

4 If the voltage is not within one volt of half output voltage (14 volts) then the alternator probably has faulty diodes or stator.
5 To verify the output of the alternator, disconnect the plug 'J73' from 'P55' at the voltage regulator. Connect a jumper lead from the battery positive terminal to pin '6' of 'J73'. If the alternator output is not shown on the test instruments in accordance with specifications (engine running) then check the lead between the alternator and the regulator, also the lead from the alternator to the 55 amp fuse. If these are in order, remove the alternator for overhaul or renewal.

Removal and refitting

6 Begin by removing both battery cable terminals and stow the cables carefully so that they do not inadvertently come into contact with the battery posts. Detach the 'E', 'F' and 'N' plug from the alternator. Slacken the alternator mounting bolts and move the unit towards the engine. Remove the drivebelt which is now loose. Finally completely undo and remove the alternator mounting bolts so that the unit may be lifted clear (photos).
7 The procedure for fitting the alternator is the reversal of the removal procedure, but the following tasks should also be completed:

(i) Clean electrical connections.
(ii) Adjust drivebelt tension so that there is just half-an-inch lateral movement midway along the belt between the alternator and crankshaft pulleys.

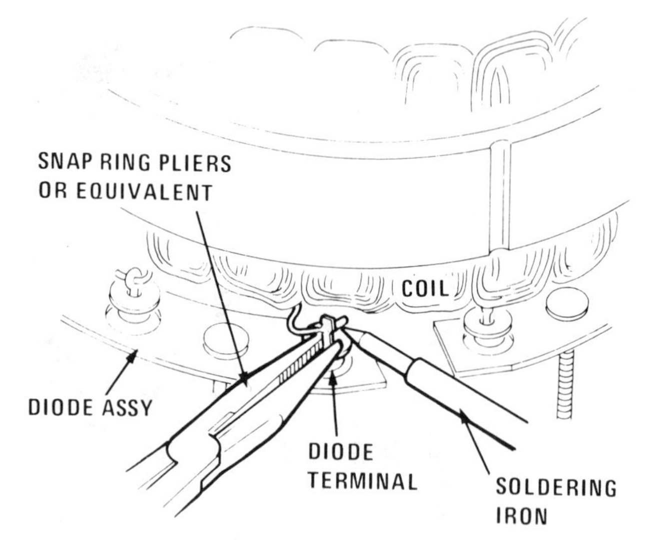

Fig. 10.7 Unsolder the stator leads and brush terminals (Sec. 8)

8 Alternator - dismantling and reassembly

1 This task should only be attempted if specialist equipment and expertise is available.
2 Remove the end pulley by undoing the retaining nut whilst holding the shaft with a 6 mm Allen key. Use a suitable puller to remove the pulley from the shaft.
3 Make alignment marks on the end members and centre part of the alternator with a centre punch, to ensure correct alignment on assembly.
4 Undo and remove the three long bolts which hold the alternator together. Separate the two ends and stator assembly gently, only use gentle taps with a light mallet to loosen the ends.
5 Note the position of the washers and spacers, and insulators. It is essential to fit them back correctly.
6 Unsolder the brush holder lead and separate the brush holder from the stator. Label the leads with tags to ensure correct reassembly.
7 Unsolder the stator leads from the rectifier diodes; be careful not to overheat the diodes. Hold their terminals with long nose pliers to absorb the soldering iron heat (Fig. 10.7).
8 Check the continuity of the rotor field windings and check for shorting to the rotor cone and shaft.
9 Measure the length of the brushes, they should not be less than 7/32 in (5.5 mm). New brushes may be fitted by unsoldering the worn ones, inserting the new brushes and resoldering the wires to the new brushes.
10 Check the functioning of each diode. If any diodes show high resistance in both directions or low resistance in both directions they are defective.
11 When resoldering leads to diodes, be as quick as possible, use a 100 to 120 watt iron, and sink the terminal heat into long nose pliers. Diodes on the plate have a red stripe and those on the negative earthed plate have a black stripe.
12 If the bearings are being renewed, unscrew the three retaining screws with lock washers and flat washers. On reassembly renew the felt washer and lubricate with oil prior to fitting.
13 When installing the rotor into the rear casing, raise the brushes in the holders and hold by pushing a pin through the rear casing and brushes. The pin will hold the brushes so that there is little likelihood of them getting damaged as the rotor and slip rings pass into the rear casing.
14 After refitting, remove the pin to allow the brushes to rest on the slip rings.
15 Once assembled, tighten the pulley nut to its specified torque of 22 to 36 lb f ft (3 to 5 kg fm) and check the rotor for easy rotation.

9 Voltage regulator - description, removal and refitting

1 The voltage regulator unit comprises two main components, the voltage regulator and the ignition/battery discharge warning light relay (Figs. 10.10, 10.11 and 10.12).
2 The voltage regulator governs the current that is fed into the alternator field coils. When the engine is not running or when it is running very slowly and the alternator is not developing more than 12 volts, the regulator relay coil remains weak and the field coils receive a full field current.
3 Once the alternator voltage reaches 14 volts, the regulator relay switches off the direct supply of full field current to the alternator, and switches the supply through a series or resistor. This limits the field current, and hence the voltage developed by the alternator.

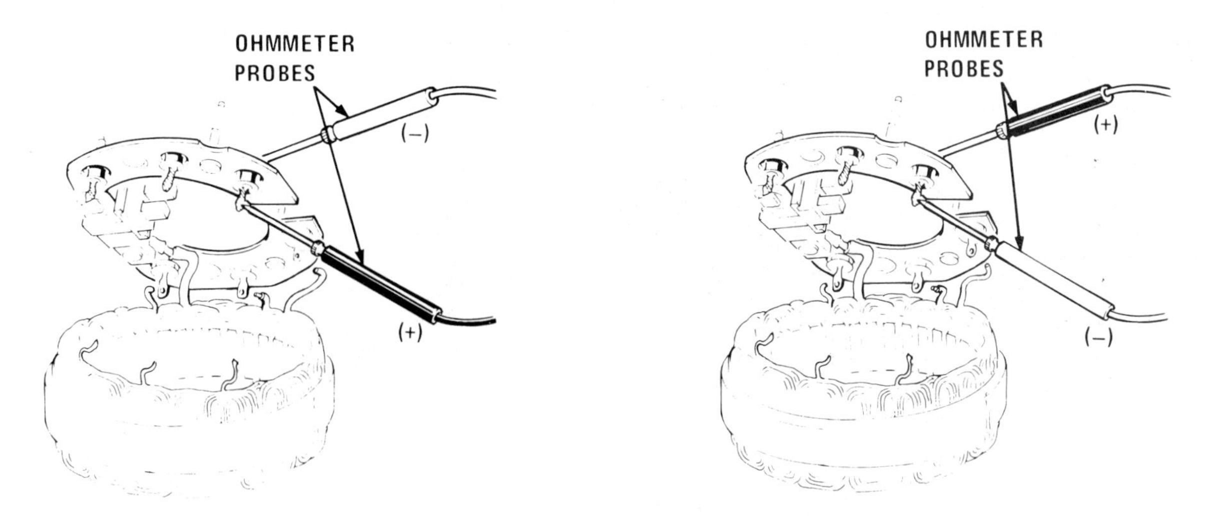

Fig. 10.8 Check the diodes (Sec. 8)

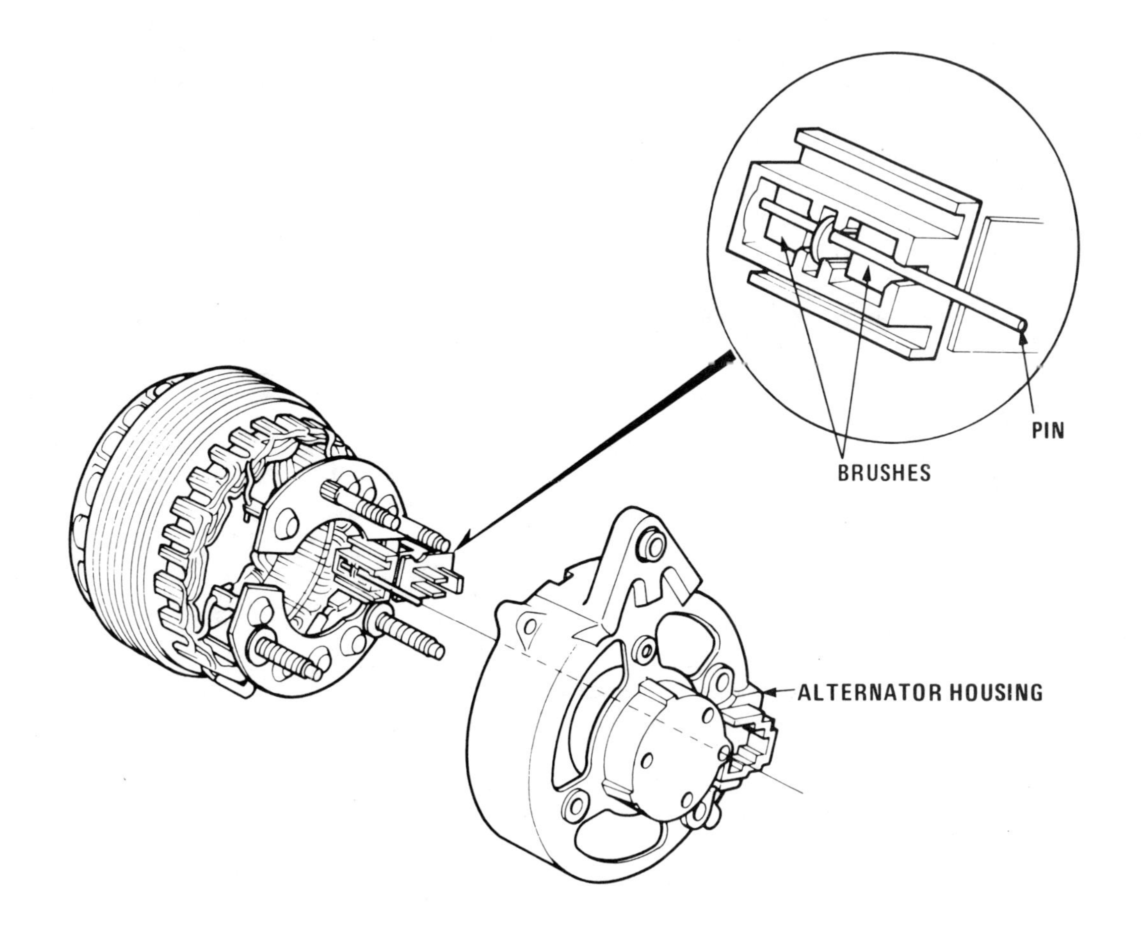

Fig. 10.9 The brushes and pin location (Sec. 8)

4 The battery charging lamp relay operates off the full return current to the alternator. It is connected directly to the centre point of the star wound output windings of the three phase alternator. The relay coil is therefore a low resistance device and functions to switch the ignition warning light return.

5 Although it is possible to adjust the operation of both regulator relay and warning light relay, it is not a task that can be recommended without specialist knowledge and equipment.

6 If, therefore, the regulator has been found faulty, the unit should be removed, and a new one put in its place.

7 This task involves disconnecting the electrical leads from the regulator. Finally undo and remove the screws retaining the regulator to the bodyshell. Refitting follows the reversal of the removal procedure.

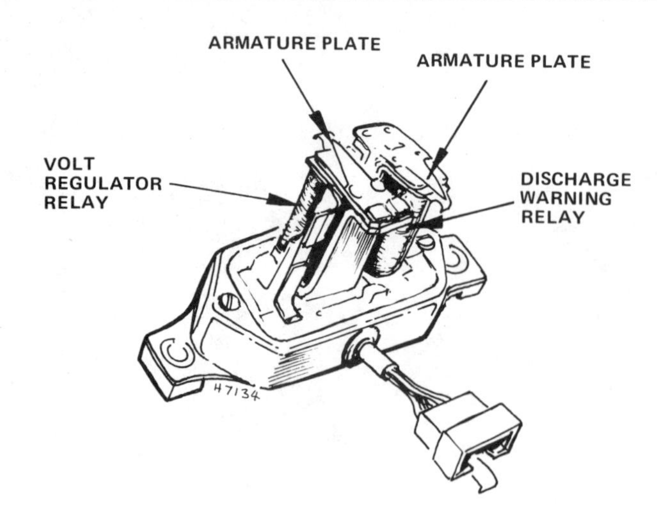

Fig. 10.10. The voltage regulator cover removed (Sec 9)

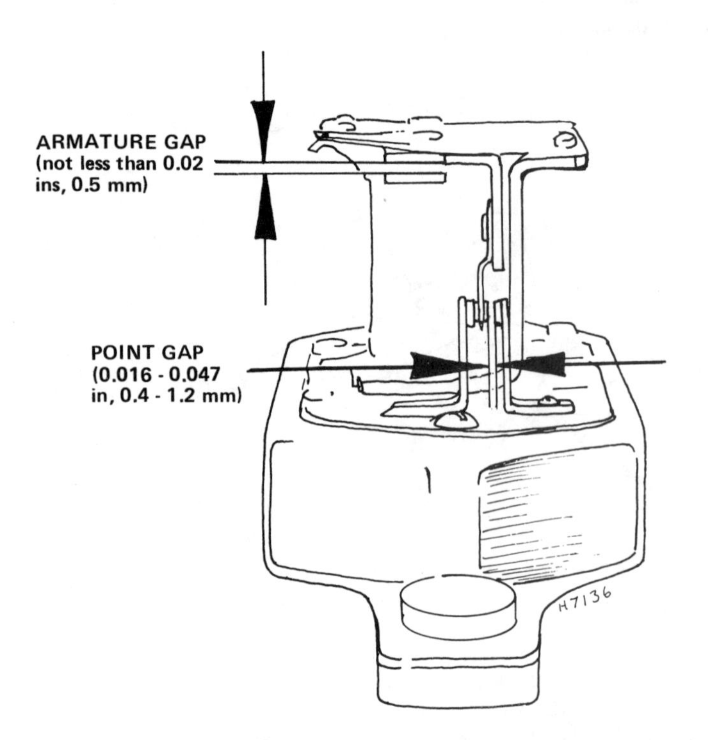

Fig. 10.11. The regulator point and armature gaps (Sec. 9)

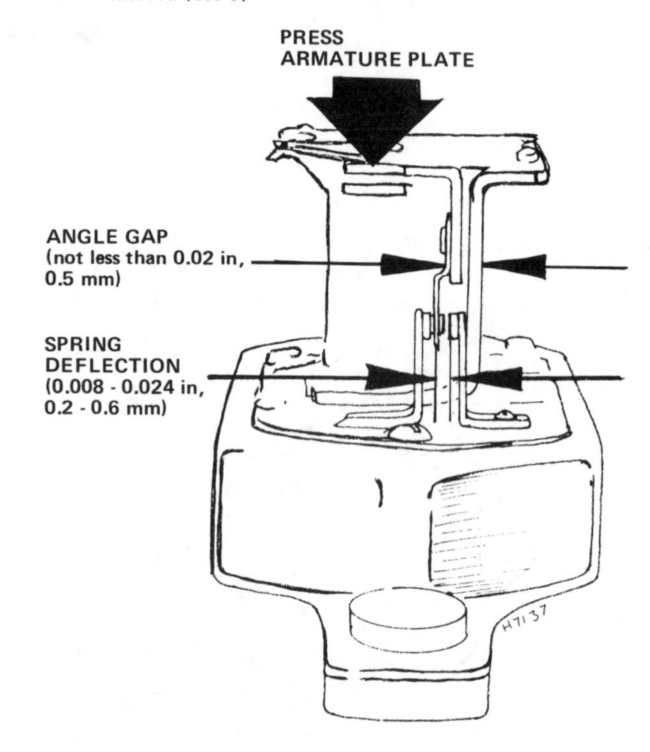

Fig. 10.12. The regulator armature gap and spring deflection (Sec. 9)

10 Starter motor - general description

The starter motor fitted to the standard engine is a 12 volt pre-engaged unit. It comprises a DC series wound motor switched by a solenoid mounted on the motor casing. The solenoid also serves to move the motor pinion into engagement with the ring gear on the periphery of the flywheel, before the main switch contacts are closed to supply electrical power to the starter motor.

The motor pinion is mounted on a carriage which engages a spiral spline on the motor shaft. The carriage incorporates an overspeed clutch which allows the pinion gear to be driven at speeds greater than the starter motor speed when the engine starts.

Once the engine has started, and when the start switch is released, the solenoid cuts off the power from the motor and moves the pinion and carriage back from engagement with the flywheel ring gear. The starter fitted to CVCC engines has a different internal construction.

11 Starter motor - testing in car

1 If the starter motor fails to turn the engine, when the switch is operated there are four possible reasons why:

a) The battery is flat.
b) The electrical connections between the switch, solenoid, battery and starter motor are failing to pass the necessary current from the battery through to the starter motor and earth.
c) The solenoid switch is defective.
d) The starter motor is either jammed or electrically defective.

2 The test procedure for the starter system is as follows:

a) Remove the battery connections, starter/solenoid power connections and the engine earth strap - and thoroughly clean and refit them. Smear petroleum jelly around the battery connections to prevent corrosion. Corroded connections are the most frequent cause of electrical system malfunctions.

b) If the starter still doesn't work check the battery as follows: Switch on the headlights, if they go dim after a few seconds, the battery is definitely at fault. If the lights shine brightly, operate the starter switch and watch what happens to the lights. If they go dim, then you know that power is reaching the starter motor but failing to turn it. In this event check that the motor is not jammed. Place the car in gear and rock the car to-and-fro. If the starter system still does not operate properly, proceed to the next test.

c) Note whether a clicking noise is heard each time the starter switch is operated. This is the solenoid operating, but it doesn't necessarily follow that the main contacts are closing properly. If a click is not heard from the solenoid, it will most probably be defective. The solenoid contact can be checked by putting a voltmeter or bulb across the main cable connection on the starter side of the solenoid and earth. When the switch is operated there should be a reading of 12 volts or the bulb should light up. **Do not put a bulb across the two solenoid power connections.** *If there is no reading or the bulb does not light the solenoid unit is faulty and should be renewed. Finally, if it is established that the solenoid is not faulty, and 12 volts are getting to the starter, then the motor should be removed for inspection.*

12 Starter motor - removal and refitting

1 The starter motor is quite accessible with the engine in place in the car; it can be found on the transmission end of the engine, above the gearbox. It is held to the engine by two large bolts, one of which passes right through the clutch bellhousing and cylinder block flange and is secured by a nut. The other bolt screws into the cylinder block (photo).
2 Remove the earth (negative) lead from the battery and then proceed to disconnect the solenoid and motor electrical connections. Identify the leads as necessary to ensure correct refitment.
3 Remove the two bolts (one secured by a nut) which secure the solenoid-motor assembly to the engine. The motor can now be lifted clear.
4 Refitting follows the reversal of the removal procedure, except that attention should be paid to the following points:

(i) Tighten the securing bolts to the specified torque.
(ii) Ensure all electrical connections are tight and clean.

13 Starter motor solenoid (standard engine) - removal and refitting

1 The solenoid is retained to the starter block by two bolts. Undo the electrical connection between the starter and solenoid switch from the solenoid. Then undo and remove the two solenoid retaining bolts, and lift the solenoid away. Take care to unhook the solenoid plunger from the pinion carriage lever. Recover the return spring retainer plate.
2 The solenoid is not repairable, and no attempt should be made to dismantle it. If it has been proven faulty, it should be renewed. If the solenoid only is suspected, the coiled resistance may be checked by connecting a multimeter across the 'S' and 'M' terminals on the solenoid. If an open circuit is found (infinite resistance) the solenoid is definitely faulty.
3 To refit the solenoid, ensure that the plunger is properly hooked onto the pinion carriage lever, and that the plate which retains the plunger and lever return spring is in position.
4 Make sure that the electrical connections are clean and secure.

14 Starter motor (standard engine) - dismantling and reassembly

1 It will be necessary to dismantle the starter motor in order to complete the following tasks:

(i) Brush removal and renewal.
(ii) Armature and commutator inspection.
(iii) Pinion gear and overspeed clutch inspection.
(iv) Pinion gearshift mechanism inspection.

12.1 The starter motor location - standard engine

2 Begin the starter motor dismantling by removing the solenoid as detailed in the previous Section.
3 Prise off the rear dust cover with a screwdriver and then lever off the 'C' clip from the end of the motor shaft. Remove the thrust washers.
4 Continue then to undo the two small screws in the end cover which secure the brush holder plate to the inside of the end cover.
5 Next undo the two through bolts which hold the gear and shift lever case to the starter motor. Once the two bolts have been removed, tap the rear cover with a light mallet and lift it off the motor. The brush plate should remain in position around the commutator.
6 Finally dislodge the gear and shift lever case, and then extract the armature and brushes.
7 To remove the pinion gear from the armature, hold the armature shaft in a vice fitted with soft jaws, the pinion and carriage downwards to the armature. Near the end of the shaft there is the travel stop ring which limits pinion movement. Drive back the stop plate to expose the ring.
8 Pull the ring out of its groove in the shaft with pliers, and then lift the gear and carriage off the shaft.
9 The motor is now dismantled and the parts should be laid out on a clean bench for inspection.
10 Having first dismantled the motor, proceed to remove the brushes.
11 Extract the brushes from the holders mounted on the holder support plate.
12 Measure the length of the brushes which should not be less than 0.16 in (4.0 mm).
13 If possible check the brush spring load when deflected to an equivalent position to when the brush is installed.
14 Use a multimeter set to read electrical resistance, to check the insulation between brushes and brush holder support plate. Renew the holder if there is a low resistance recorded on any of the four brush holders.
15 If the brushes have worn too short, they are renewed as follows: De-solder the brushes from the connecting wires; take care when soldering new wires not to allow the solder to flow up the wires and bind the individual strands.
16 Refitting is simply the reversal of removal.
17 Clean the commutator with solvent and a non-fluffy cloth, scrape away any metal deposits from between the copper segments of the commutator. The commutator surface must be smooth, clean and free from scores and scratches.
18 The armature should then be checked for electrical insulation. Again use a multimeter to measure the electrical resistance between each segment of the commutator and the motor shaft. The resistance should be infinity. If a low resistance is measured the armature is faulty and should be renewed.
19 Examine the pinion gearteeth; if any are damaged the pinion/clutch assembly should be renewed.
20 Check the freedom of movement of the gear and clutch assembly

along the spiral spline on the motor shaft.
21 If any binding is felt, renew the pinion clutch unit, it is improbable that the fault lies with the spiral spline.
22 Finally check the operation of the overspeed clutch. Hold the pinion gear and turn the motor shaft clockwise when viewed from the pinion end. The clutch should not slip and the turning effort exerted on the shaft should be felt at the pinion. However, it should be possible to turn the pinion clockwise relative to the motor shaft. Renew the pinion/clutch assembly if it does not operate as required.
23 The starter assembly technique is basically the reversal of the dismantling procedure, except that the following points should be noted:

(i) *Take care to assemble the pinion shaft correctly in the shaft casing.*
(ii) *After assembly check the pinion carriage to travel stop clearance when the solenoid is energised to move the pinion into its engaged position. Apply 12 volts across the solenoid to activate it.*

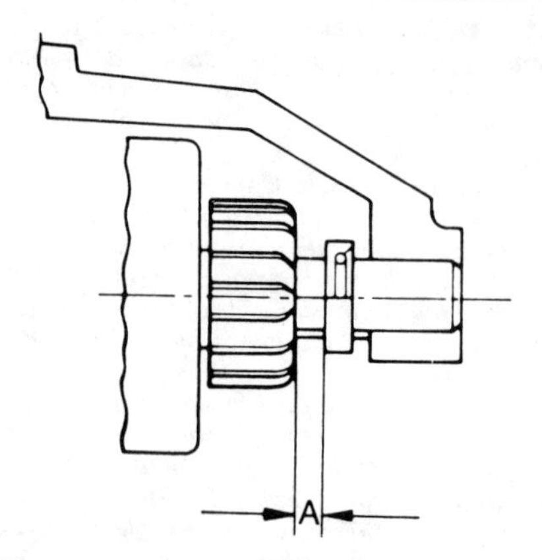

Fig. 10.13 Check the starter drive pinion endfloat (standard engine) (Sec. 14)

A = 0.012 to 0.06 in (0.3 to 1.5 mm)

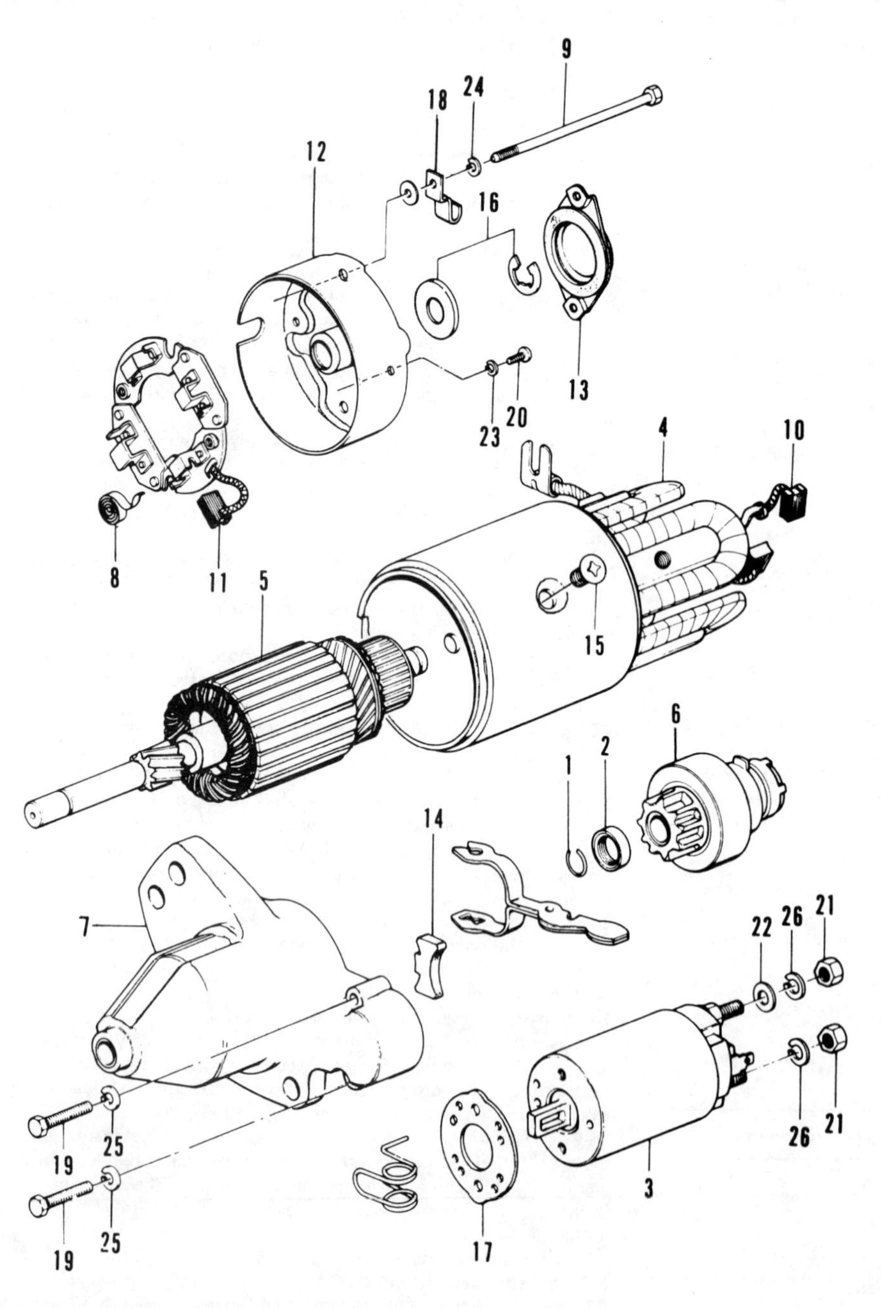

Fig. 10.14 The standard engine starter motor components (Sec. 14)

1 Jump ring
2 Pinion stop plate
3 Solenoid
4 Field coil
5 Armature
6 Drive pinion assembly
7 Gear case
8 Brush spring
9 Tie bolt
10 Positive brush
11 Negative brush
12 Cover
13 Dust excluder
14 Dust excluder
15 Pole screw
16 Thrust washer and clip
17 Dust excluder
18 Cable clip
19 Bolt
20 Screw
21 Nut
22 Washer
23 to 26 Spring washers

15 Starter motor (reduction gear type) - removal, overhaul and reassembly

1 The starter motor fitted to USA models with the CVCC engine and to Canadian models (cold climate) differs from the standard type as can be seen from Fig.10.15 and 10.16. The principal differences are that the starter solenoid is mounted in line with the starter drive pinion and the field frame assembly is located at the side and bolted to the common starter housing. Drive to the drive pinion clutch assembly is via an idler gear which runs in roller bearings on a shaft incorporated in the front of the starter solenoid housing.

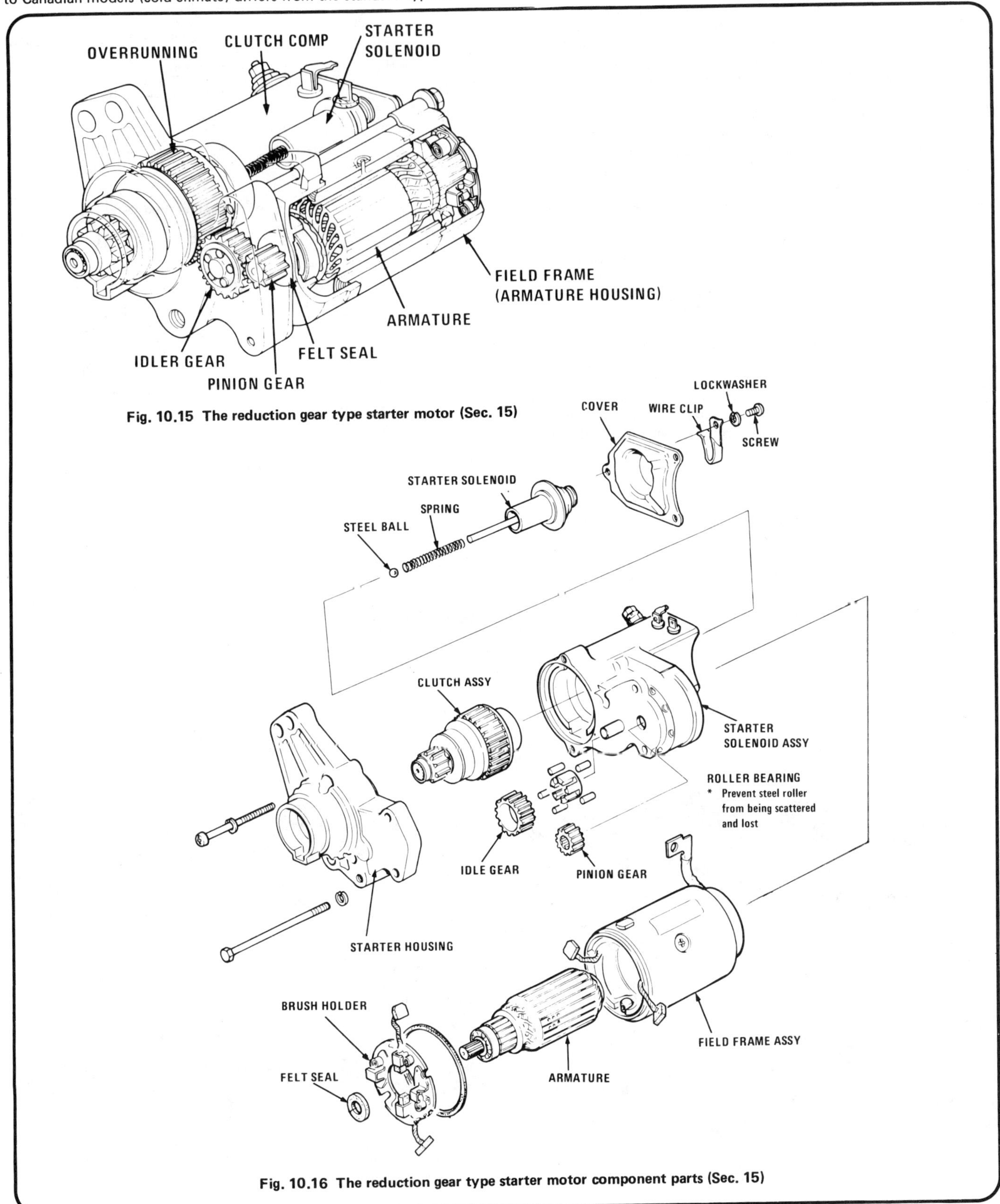

Fig. 10.15 The reduction gear type starter motor (Sec. 15)

Fig. 10.16 The reduction gear type starter motor component parts (Sec. 15)

2 Although the basic construction features are the same, the 1977 models have a more powerful starter motor than the earlier models and therefore, when ordering spare parts, be sure to quote the model number so that the correct parts are obtained. The removal, dismantling and overhaul procedures are otherwise much the same.
3 To remove the starter motor unit, detach the negative (ground) cable from the battery terminal and the starter cable from the positive terminal. Disconnect the respective wiring from the starter motor.
4 The starter motor is retained by two bolts, one from the front of the clutch housing (short bolt) and one from the starter motor side (long bolt). Unscrew the two bolts and withdraw the starter motor.
5 To withdraw the field frame unit, unscrew the retaining bolts from the starter housing and pull the unit clear.
6 To remove the solenoid, undo the retaining screws and remove them with the lockwashers, noting to which screw the wire clip is fitted. Withdraw the solenoid and cover taking care not to lose the solenoid spring and ball.
7 The starter pinion and clutch assembly, also the idler gear are accessible on removal of the starter housing from the starter solenoid housing.
8 Further dismantling is dependent on the nature of the fault, but in any case, all parts so far dismantled should be cleaned and examined for excessive wear or damage.
9 Examine the brushes and armature as described in Section 14, paragraphs 11 to 18. The minimum brush length allowable is 0.35 in (9 mm). If the brushes have worn down to this length or less they must be renewed. Do not under any circumstances interchange the respective brushes.
10 Check that the overspeed clutch moves freely on the pinion shaft. To remove the pinion gear, press it down the shaft and remove the retaining circlip and stopper ring. If the pinion or pinion spring is worn or distorted they must be renewed. If the overspeed clutch does not move freely on the shaft or the clutch is known to slip when the armature is rotated whilst the pinion gear is retained, the unit must be renewed.
11 Check the solenoid contact points and contraction face on the plunger. If they are pitted or burnt they can be refaced using 500 or 600 grade glasspaper. If they are severely damaged or marked, renew the solenoid and points.
12 Reassembly of the starter motor is basically a reversal of the removal sequence but note the following:

a) Ensure that all parts are perfectly clean before assembly.
b) Grease the bearings.
c) Tighten the retaining bolts to the specified torque.

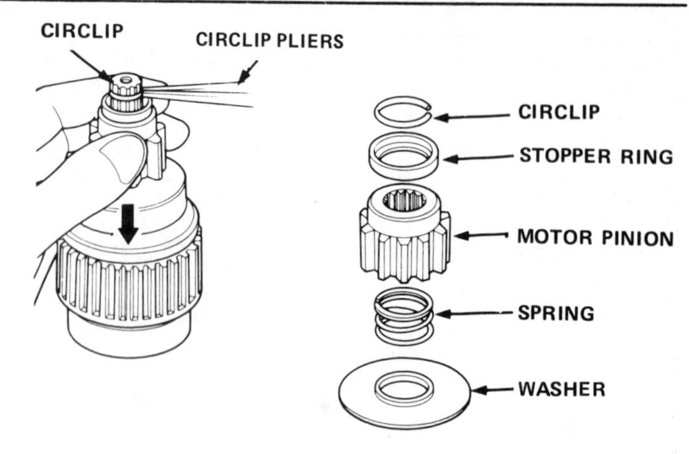

Fig. 10.17 Pinion gear removal method (Sec. 15)

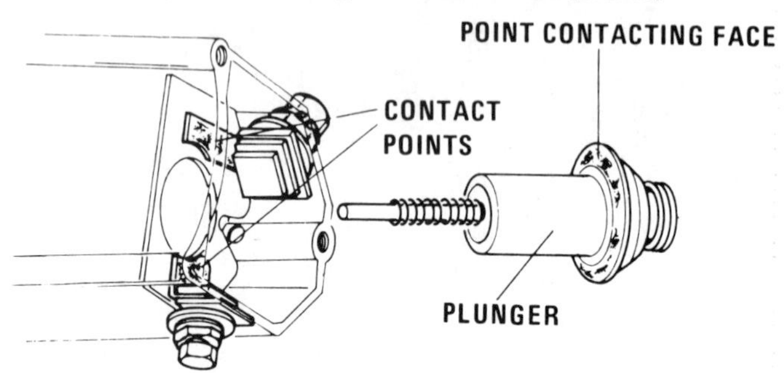

Fig. 10.18 Check the solenoid contact points and face for pitting or signs of burning (Sec. 15)

16 Fuses

1 The fuse block is located under the instrument panel on the right-hand side (photo). The ratings of the fuses and the circuits protected are given in the Specifications Section.
2 Always renew a blown fuse with one of the same rating and if it blows twice in quick succession, find the reason (usually faulty

16.1 The fuse block hinged down to show respective fuses

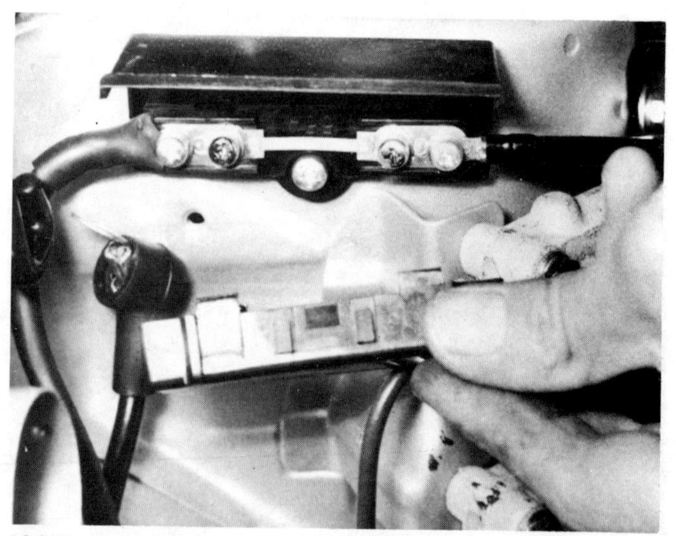

16.3 The heavy capacity fuse with cover removed for inspection

insulation in the wiring) before renewing the fuse again.
3 A heavy capacity fusible link (55A) is incorporated in the lead from the positive terminal of the battery and in the event of this blowing and the complete electrical system becoming dead, then your Honda dealer should be consulted before any attempt is made to repair the circuit (photo).

17 Bulbs - renewal

Headlamps

1 Detach the headlamp trim, press the headlamp unit and twist it to release from the spring loaded screws.
2 Disconnect the headlamp wiring connector plug (photo). Refit the new lamp unit by reversing the removal procedure.
3 Providing the headlamp adjustment screws have not been disturbed, beam realignment should not be necessary.

Front combination light

4 Remove the front lens by unscrewing the two retaining screws.
5 Push and twist the bulb to remove it from the socket.
6 If necessary, the light housing may also be removed once the lens is off, although to remove completely, the wiring to socket will have to be disconnected (photo).
7 Refitting is the reversal of removal but always ensure that the electrical connections are clean and secure. Also ensure that the water seals are in good condition and correctly located.

Side marker lamps (USA) - direction indicator repeater lamps (Europe)

8 Access to the bulbs is obtained by removing the two lens retaining screws and withdrawing the lens from the body. The bulb is then easily removed from the socket. Refitting is the reverse of the removal

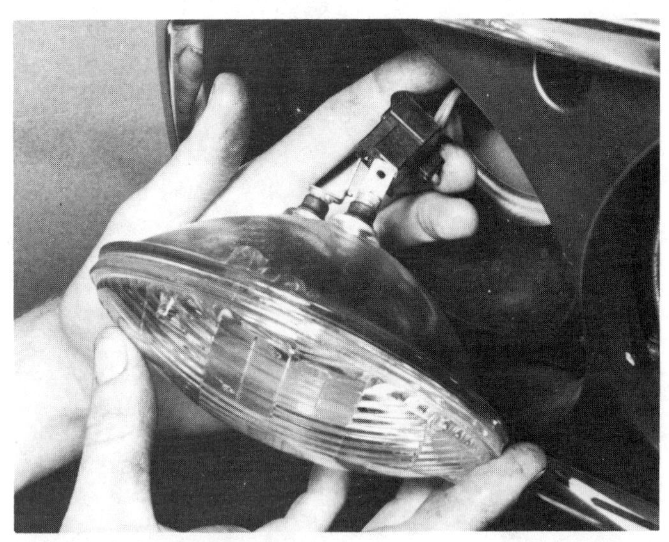

17.2 Detach the wire connector

procedure, but ensure that the sealing gaskets are in good condition and correctly fitted (Fig. 10.21).

Rear combination lamp

9 To gain access to the bulbs, lift the rear tailgate and prise the rear panel free. The bulb and socket can then be twisted and withdrawn from the socket holder (photo). Push, twist and then pull, the bulb from the socket. Refitting is the reverse of the removal procedure.

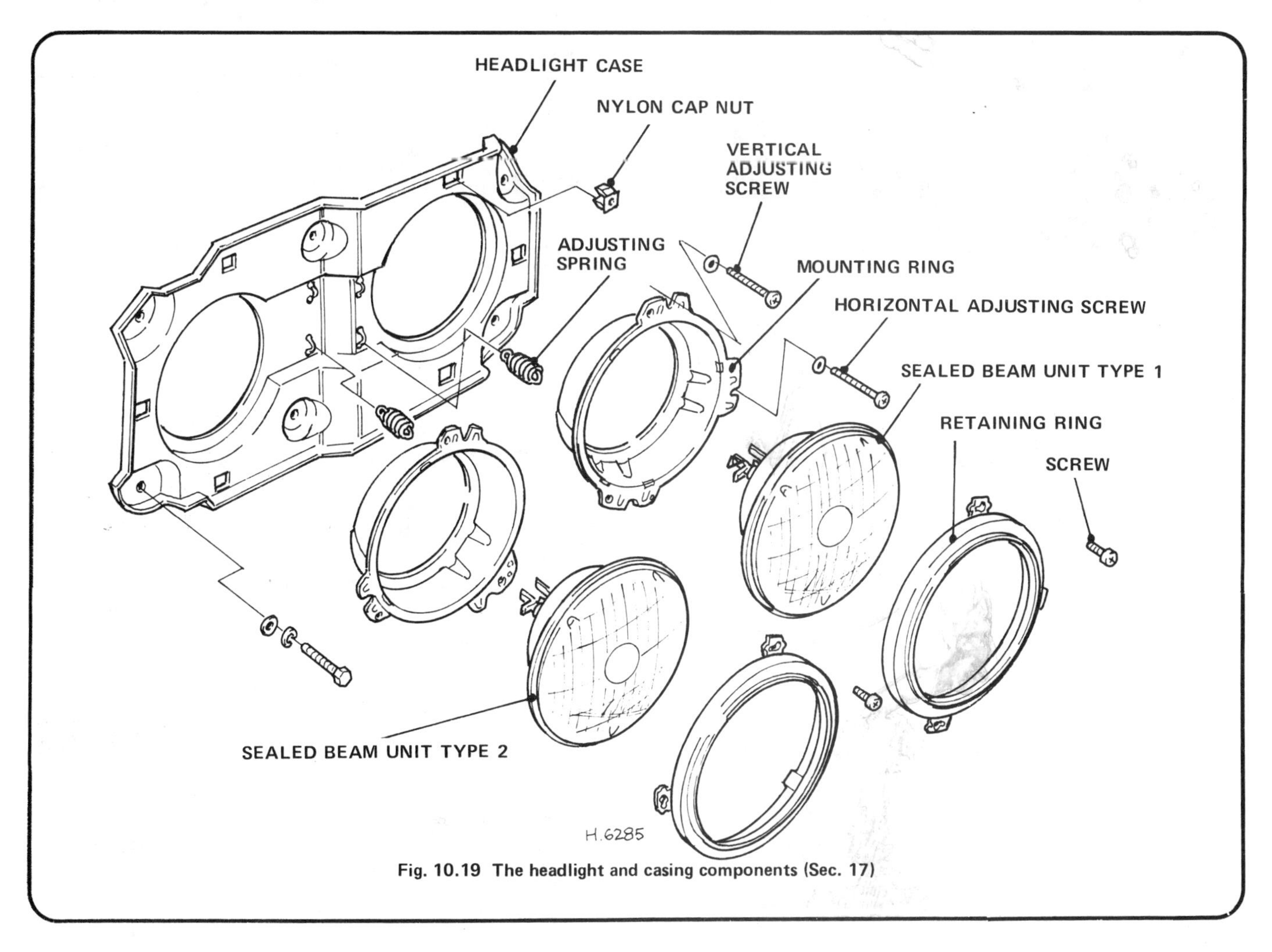

Fig. 10.19 The headlight and casing components (Sec. 17)

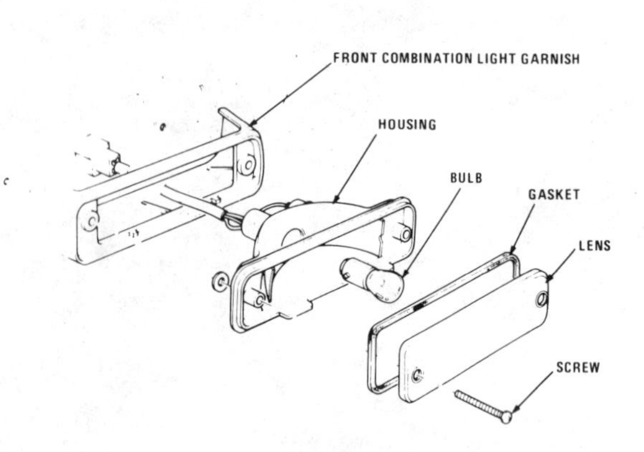

Fig. 10.20. The front combination light components (Sec. 17)

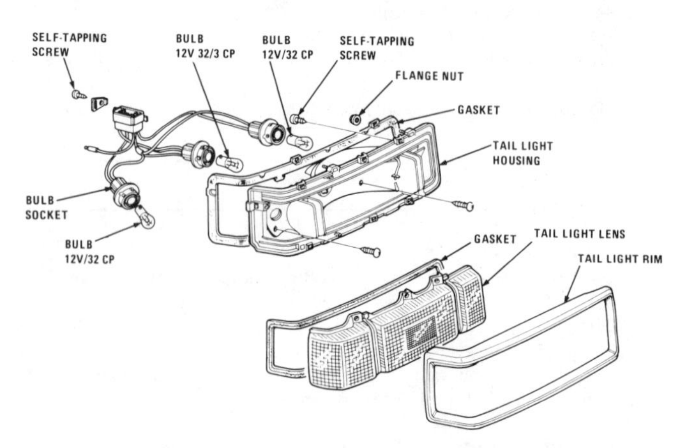

Fig. 10.22. The rear combination light (Sec. 17)

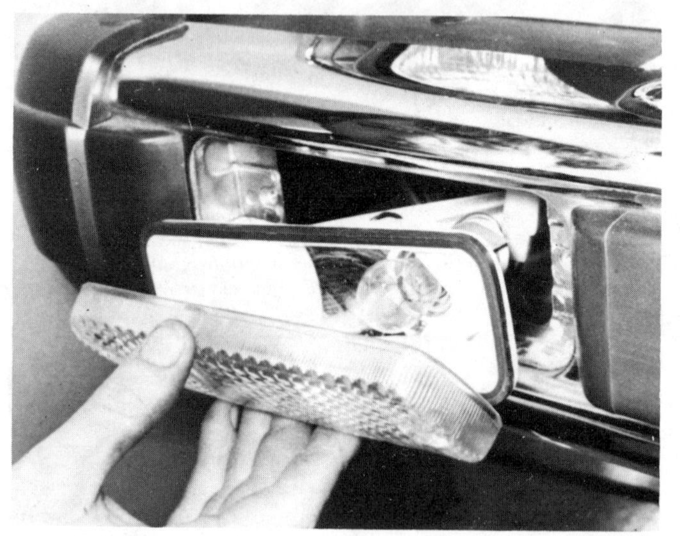

17.6 The front combination light removal

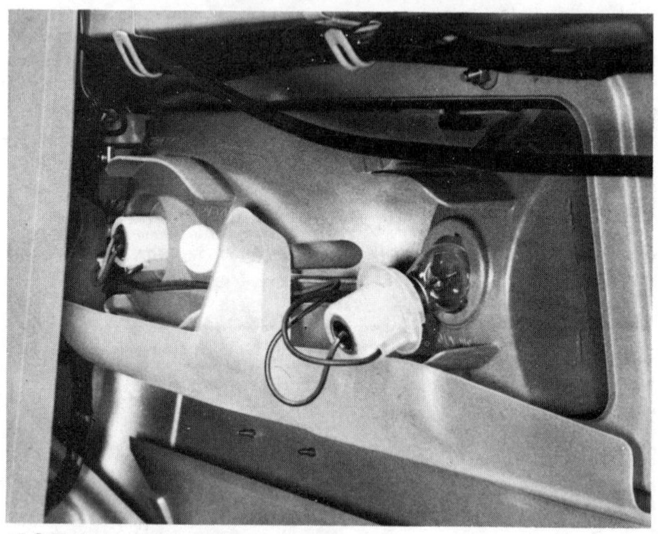

17.9 Twist the bulb holder to remove

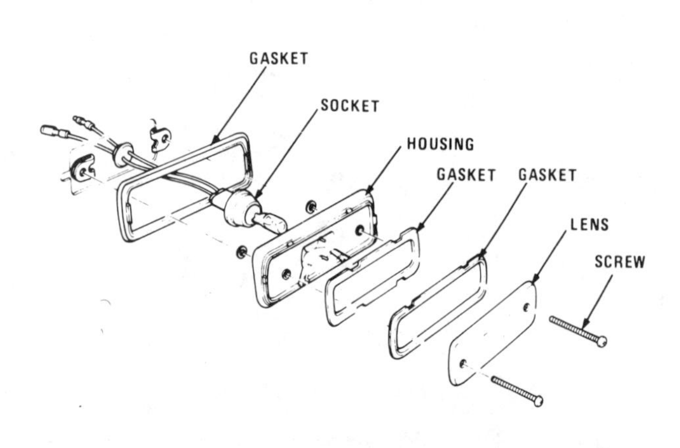

Fig. 10.21. The side marker light (Sec. 17)

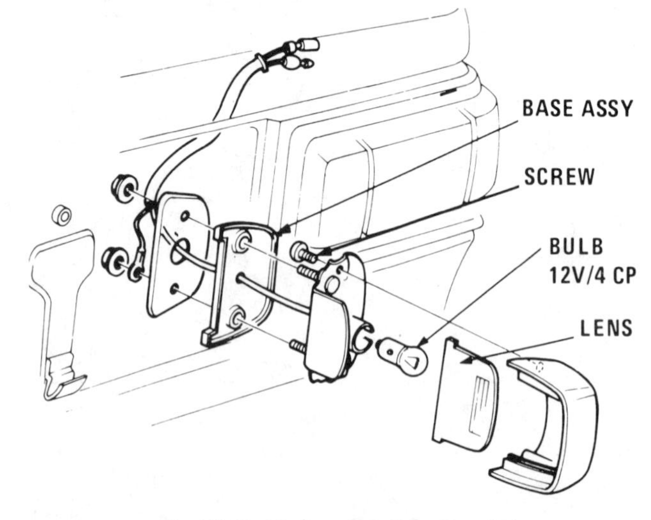

Fig. 10.23. Licence plate light (Sec. 17)

Rear license plate lamp

10 To change the bulb or remove the lamp unit/s, unscrew the two retaining screws and remove the lens and cover. The bulb may now be removed from its socket. To remove the bulb holder unit, disconnect the wire connectors, unscrew the retaining nuts and withdraw the unit complete with socket and wire. Reverse the procedure to refit (photo).

Interior lamp

11 To remove the bulb, carefully prise the lens from the lamp base, then withdraw the bulb (photo).

17.10 The licence plate light

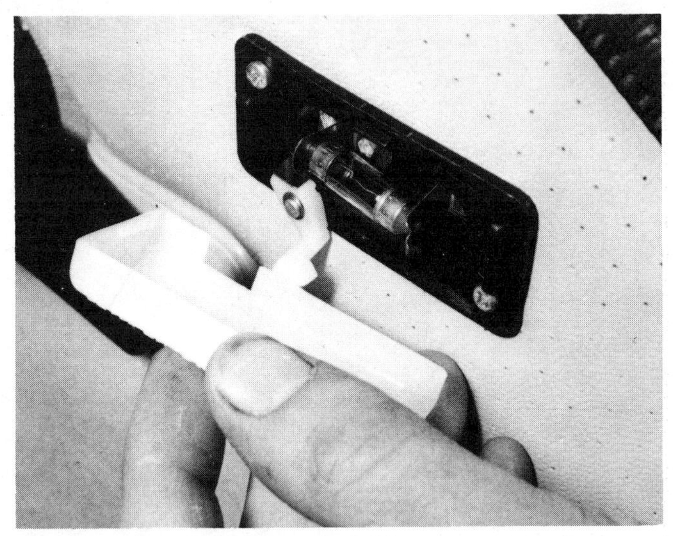
17.11 The interior light with lens removed

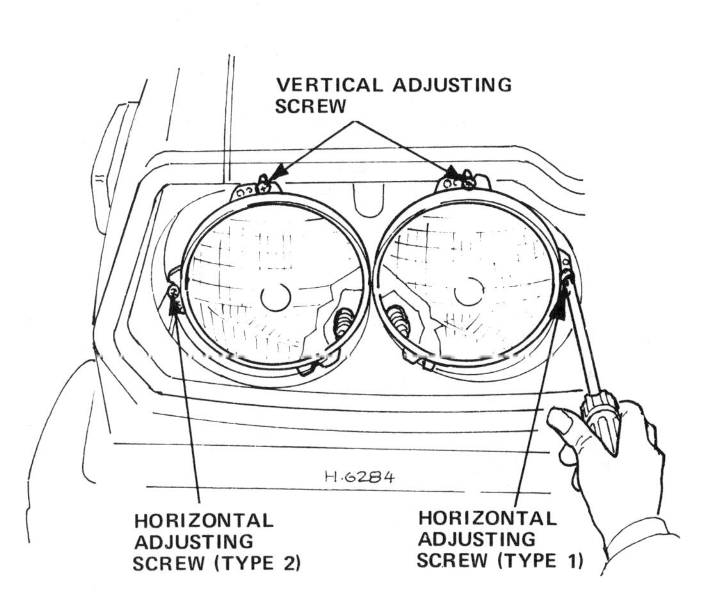

Fig. 10.24 Headlight alignment adjustment points (Sec. 18)

Warning and indicator lamps

12 The bulbs for these lamps are accessible from the rear of the instrument panel. Dependent on location, it is usually easier to change the respective bulbs by first removing the instrument panel as described in Section 27.

18 Headlamps - alignment

1 Accurate setting of the headlamp alignment is essential to comply with local regulations. It is generally recommended that they are adjusted by your local Honda dealer, who has the optical beam setting equipment necessary.
2 In an emergency, the horizontal and vertical adjustment screws can be turned by passing a screwdriver through the front grille.

19 Ignition switch - removal and refitting

1 Removal and refitting of the combined ignition switch and steering

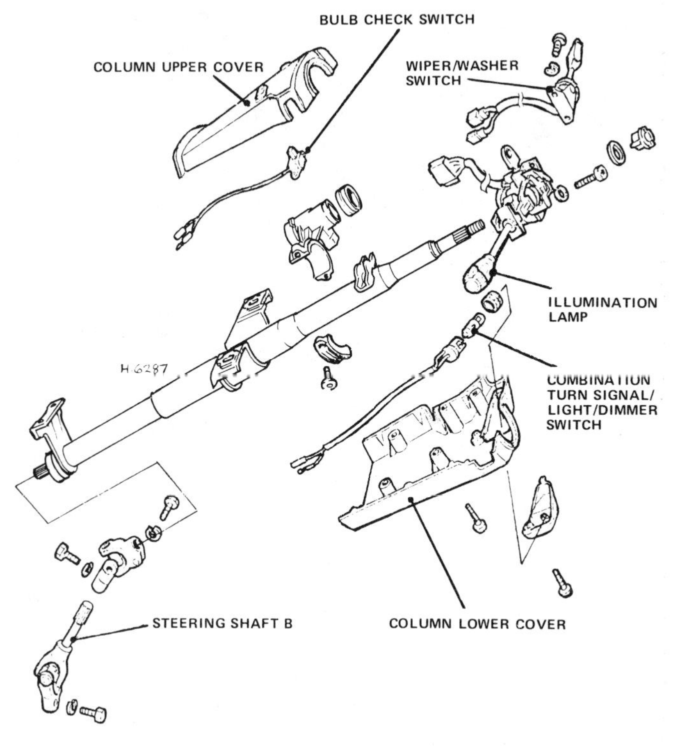

Fig. 10.25 The combination switch and steering column components (Sec. 20)

column lock is detailed in Chapter 11.

20 Combination switch - removal and refitting

1 The combined light/demister/direction indicator switch which is fitted to the top end of the steering column can be removed in the following way.
2 Remove the steering wheel, as described in Chapter 11.
3 Unscrew and remove the screws which secure the two sections of the steering column shroud and remove the sections, see Fig. 10.25.
4 Extract the signal switch cancelling key from the top of the column followed by the thrust washer.
5 Disconnect the multi-connector plugs from the combination switch and the washer/wiper switch.

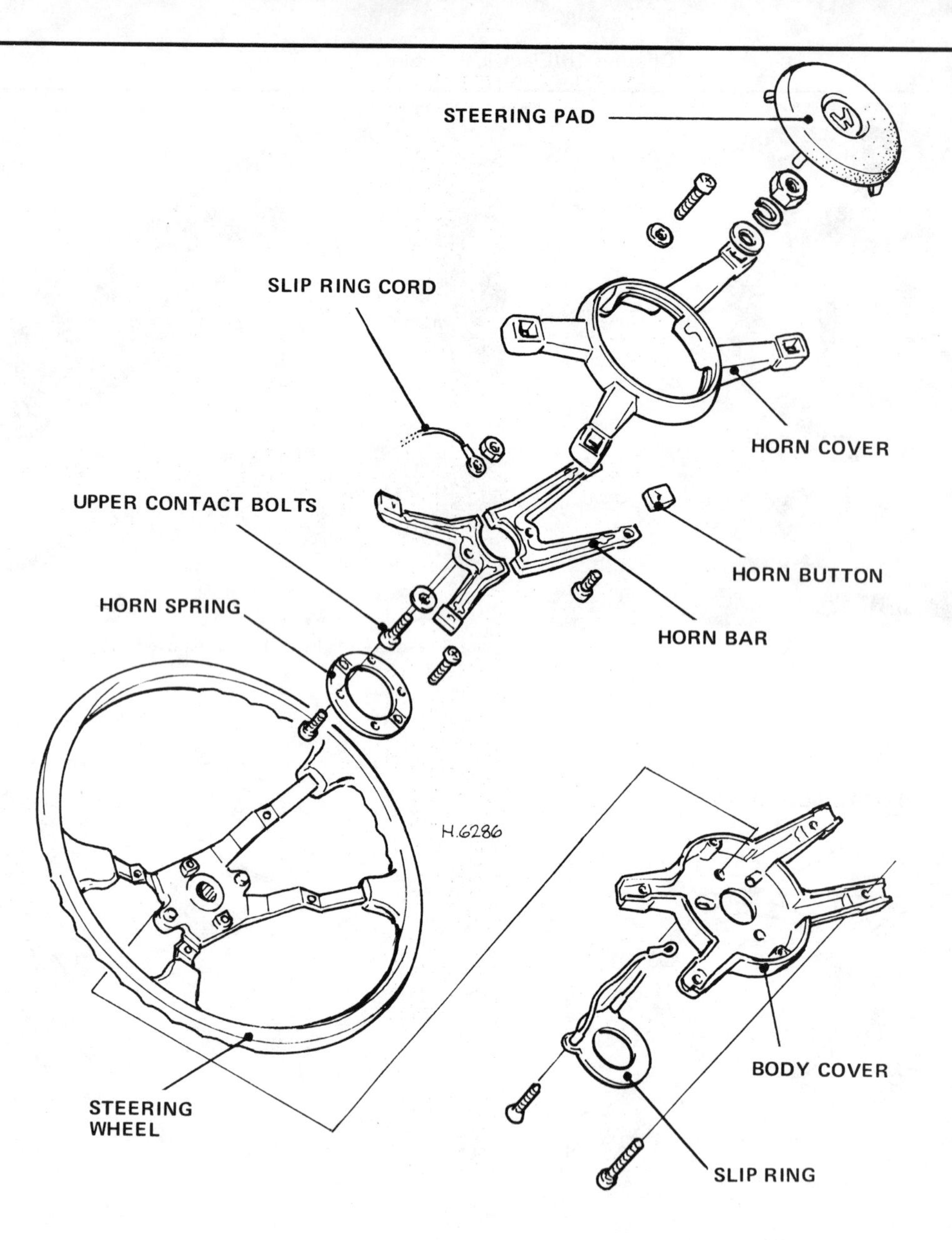

Fig. 10.26 The horn bar to steering wheel components (Sec. 22)

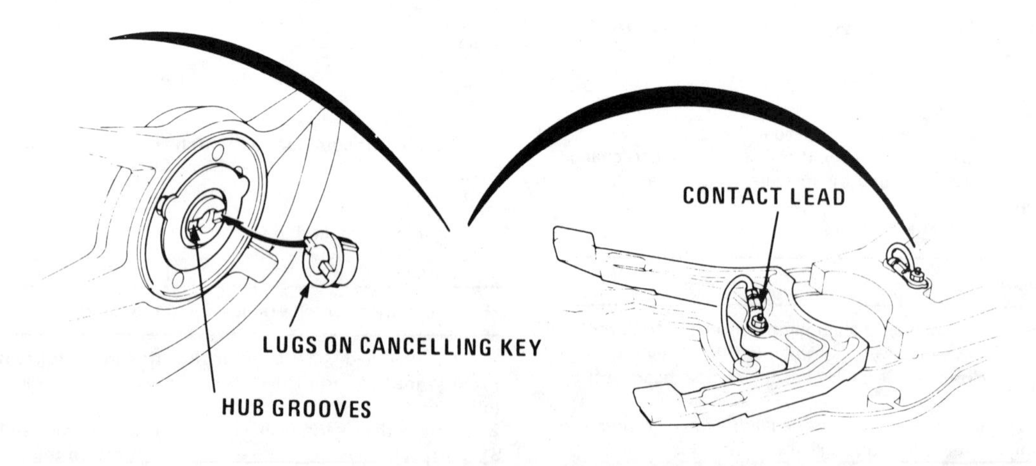

Fig. 10.27 The cancelling key lugs and contact lead positions (Sec. 22)

6 Unscrew and remove the switches from the steering column.
7 Refitting is a reversal of removal but when installing the combination switch to the column, make sure that the lugs on the switch engage with the grooves in the steering column. Fit the cancelling key so that the raised keys are uppermost. The thrust washer must be fitted beneath the cancelling key.

21 Switches (general) - removal and refitting

1 To remove a switch, first disconnect the multi pin plug on the switch harness.
2 Some switch knobs are retained by a small grub screw on the underside of the knob and this can be seen on inspection.
3 Other switch knobs are clipped onto the spindle of the switch. With these, prise out the switch knob blanking disc and then pinch the exposed clips together with a pair of long-nosed pliers and withdraw the knob.
4 The switch retaining nut can then be unscrewed and the switch withdrawn rearwards.
5 Reverse the removal procedure to refit the switches.

22 Horns and horn switch

1 The horns are not built to enable adjustments or repairs to be made to them. In the event of a fault developing, check the connecting leads and the fuse in the main block.
2 A horn button is incorporated in each of the steering wheel spokes. These are accessible after prising off the safety pad from the centre of the steering wheel and removing the horn pad retainer and the horn wires from the spokes.

23 Windscreen wiper blades and arms - removal and refitting

1 The wiper blades should be renewed whenever they are seen not to wipe the screen clearly.
2 To remove a wiper blade, pull the arm away from the glass, lift the small catch with the finger nail and slide the wiper blade assembly from the wiper arm (photo).
3 To remove a wiper arm, unscrew the retaining nut and pull the arm from the driving spindle. On some models a nut is not used, the arm fitting direct to the spindle splines (photo).
4 When installing an arm make sure that the wiper motor is in the parked position having been switched off using the wiper switch and not the ignition key. Position the arm/blade assembly so that the end of the blade is between 3/8 and 3/4 in (10.0 to 20.0 mm) from the windscreen lower rubber surround.
5 Do not overtighten the spindle nut.

24 Windscreen wiper motor and linkage - removal and refitting

1 Remove the blades and arms as detailed in the previous Section.
2 Carefully prise the air scoop from the body in front of the windscreen. Lift the bonnet for access to the securing clips, which are located in the rubber seal (Fig. 10.29).
3 Disconnect the wiring.
4 Detach the connecting rod from the wiper motor pivot and disconnect the rod (photo).
5 Unscrew the wiper motor mounting attachment bolts and then remove the wiper motor.
6 The two connecting rods may be removed from the pivots after detaching the respective caps and unscrewing the retaining nuts with washers and rubber cushions.
7 Refitting is the reversal of removal.

25 Rear window wiper motor - removal and refitting

1 Detach the wiper arm and blade as detailed in Section 23.
2 Unscrew and remove the special nut and washer from the driveshaft.
3 Raise the tailgate and remove the tailgate plastic inner panel by prising the clips free with a screwdriver (photo).

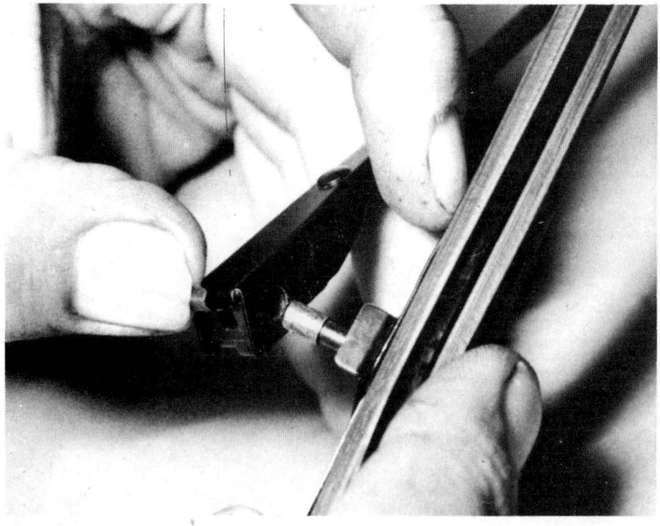

23.2 Method of removing the wiper blades

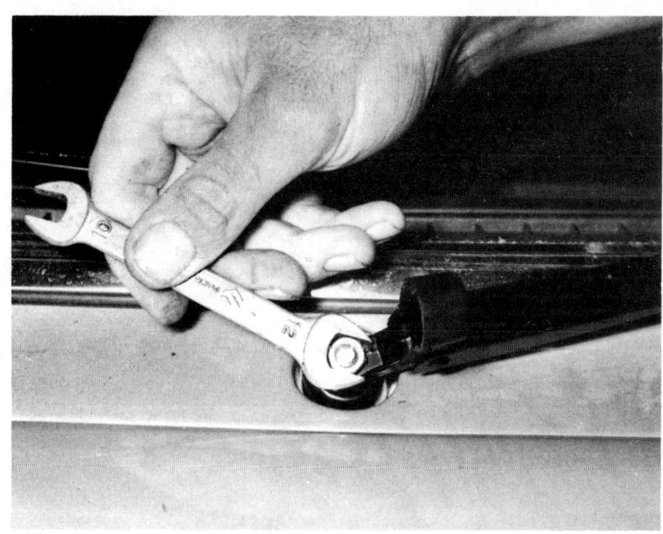

23.3 The wiper arm retaining nut

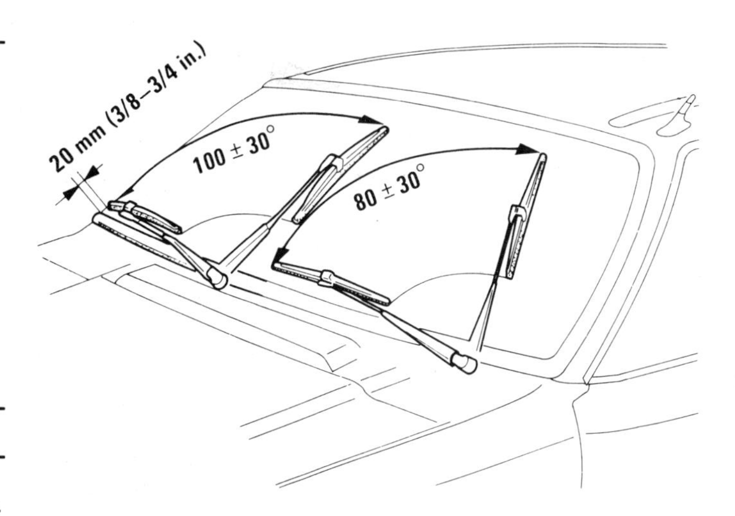

Fig. 10.28. The wiper arm adjustment (Sec. 23)

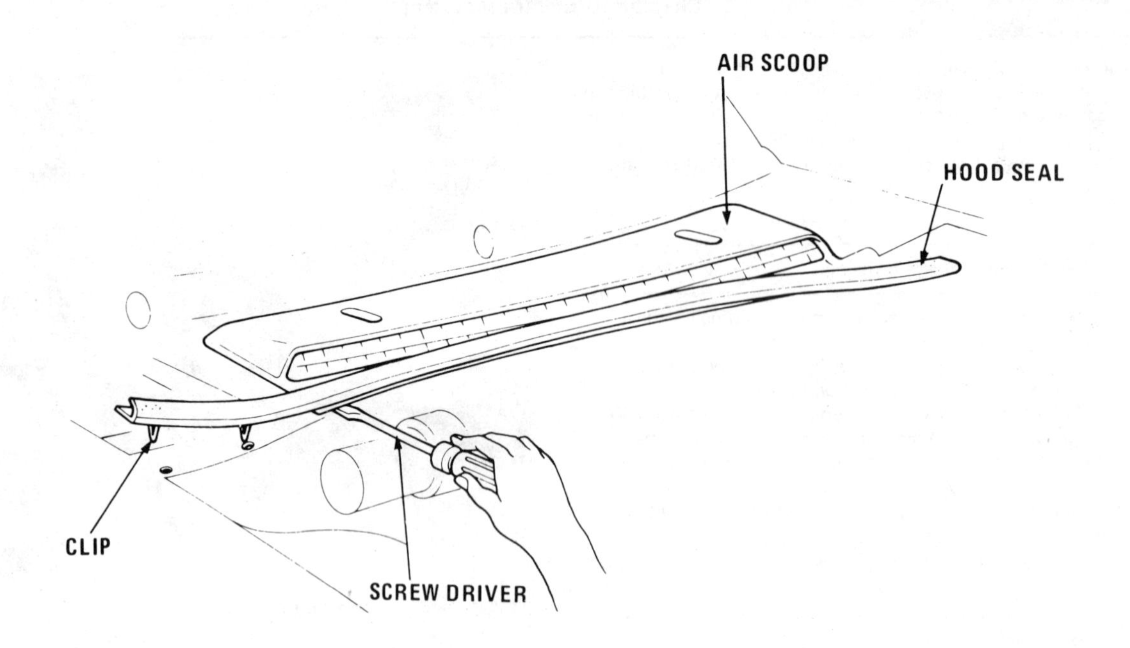

Fig. 10.29. Method of removing air scoop (Sec. 24)

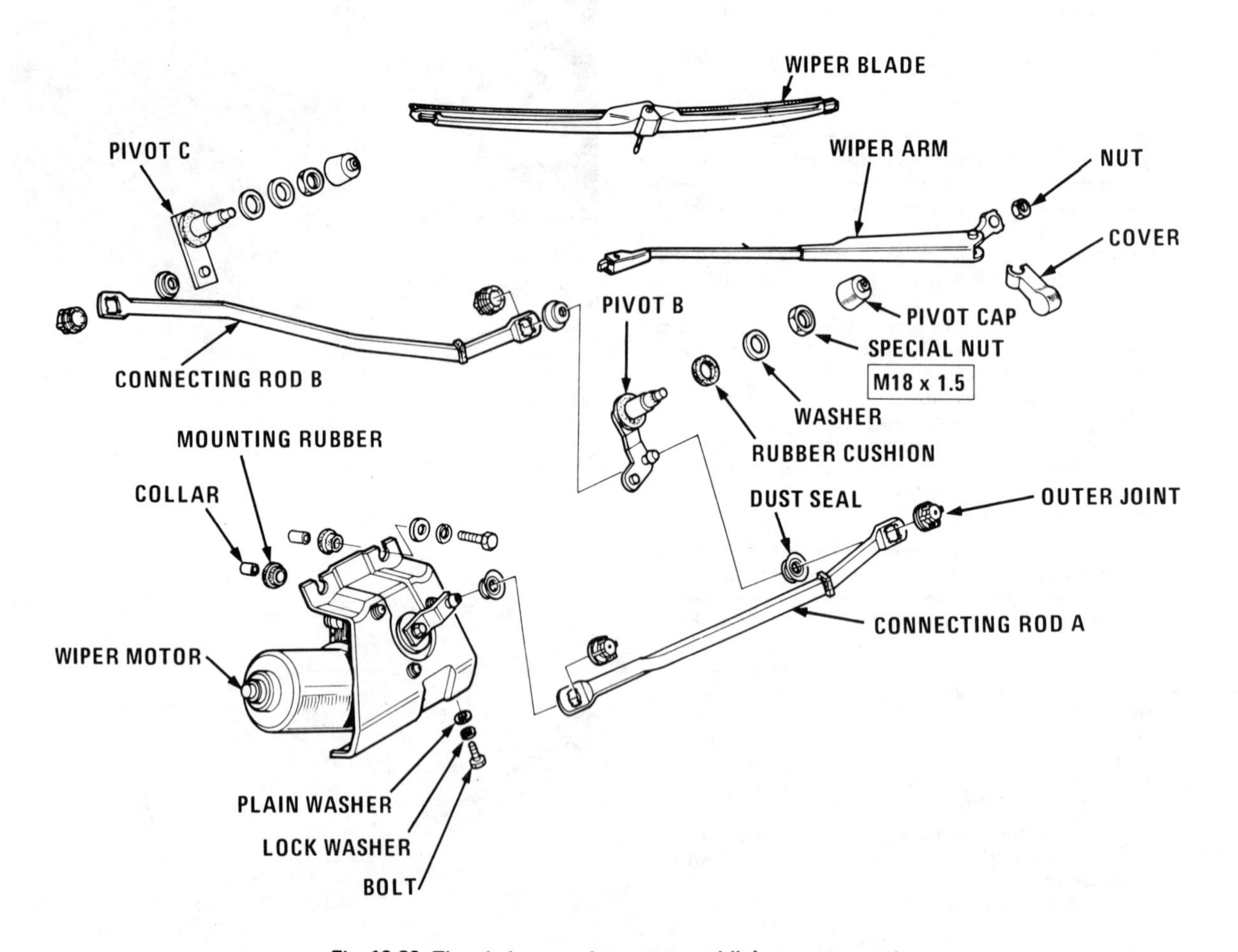

Fig. 10.30. The windscreen wiper motor and linkage components (Sec. 24)

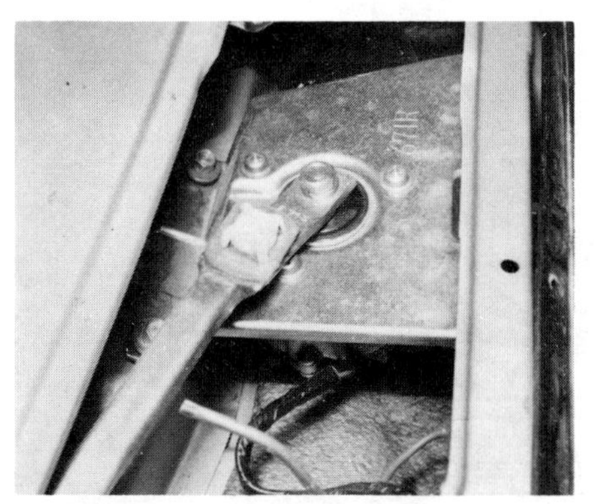

24.4 The wiper motor and connecting rod

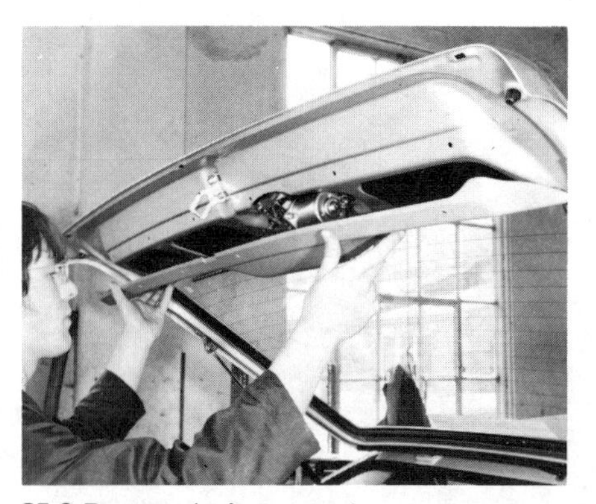

25.3 Remove the inner panel

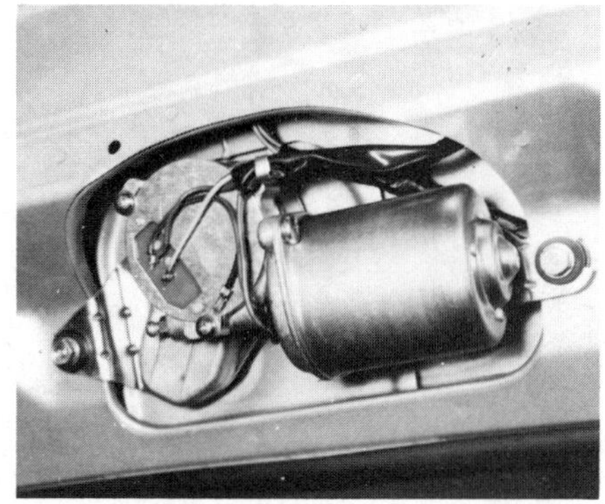

25.5 The rear screen wiper motor location

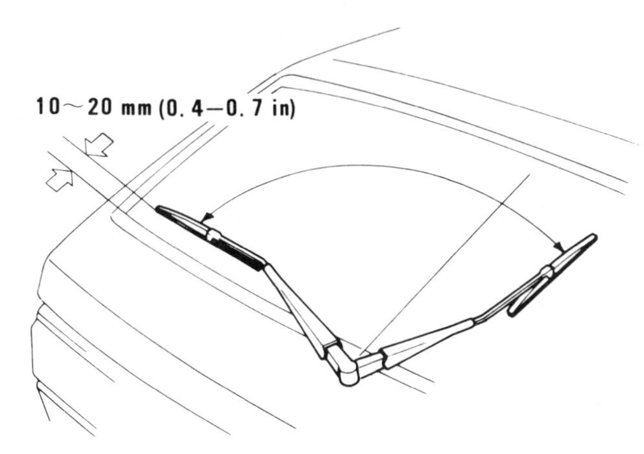

Fig. 10.31 The rear window wiper arm adjustment (Sec. 25)

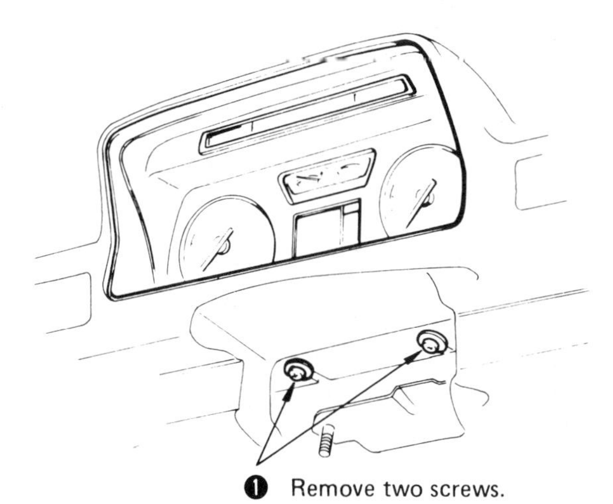

Fig. 10.32 Remove the two screws (Sec. 27)

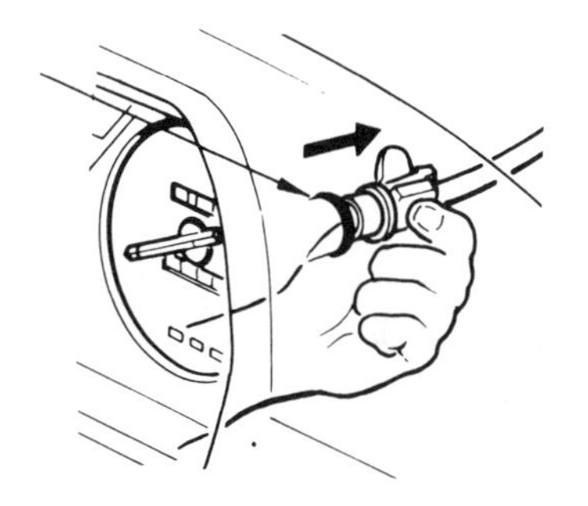

Fig. 10.33 Detach the speedometer cable (Sec. 27)

4 Detach the wiring coupling.
5 Unscrew the motor retaining bolts and withdraw the unit from the tailgate (photo).
6 Refitting is the reversal of removal but when refitting the wiper arm allow a gap of 0.4 to 0.7 in (10 to 20 mm) between the wiper blade and the base of the window as shown in Fig. 10.31.

26 Windscreen washer nozzle - adjustment

1 The two nozzles are located within the recess covered by the air scoop forward of the windscreen.
2 To adjust the nozzles insert a suitable piece of thin steel rod into each nozzle and move the nozzle accordingly but do not damage the nozzle orifice.

27 Instrument panel - removal and refitting

1 Remove the steering column as described in Chapter 11.
2 Refer to Fig. 10.32 and remove the two screws from underneath the panel
3 Carefully withdraw the panel sufficiently to disconnect the speedometer cable (Fig. 10.33) and the respective wire harness connectors. Remove the panel (Fig. 10.34).
4 Refitting is a direct reversal of the removal sequence.

28 Facia panel - removal and refitting

1 Remove the instrument panel as detailed in the previous Section.
2 Prise the speaker grille from the top of the facia, remove the screws retaining the clock panel and lift out the clock. Detach the wire connector.
3 Detach the heater control knobs and withdraw the control bezel from the facia. The wiring coupler should be carefully detached by spreading the locking tabs.
4 Unscrew and remove the three screws retaining the centre panel (Fig. 10.35).
5 With both doors open, prize the plastic side covers free between the facia and door hinge pillar. Then unscrew the retaining bolts.
6 Unscrew and remove the two retaining bolts located under the radio panel.
7 With the clock removed from its panel, unscrew the centre facia panel bolt (Fig. 10.36).
8 Carefully remove the facia panel.
9 Refitting is the reversal of removal, but ensure that all wiring connections are good, and note that when pushing the heater switch knob back into position, do not use too much force or the switch connection directly behind the facia may be detached (Fig. 10.37).

29 Radio equipment - removal and refitting

Radio

1 Unscrew the central lower lid retaining screws (located beneath

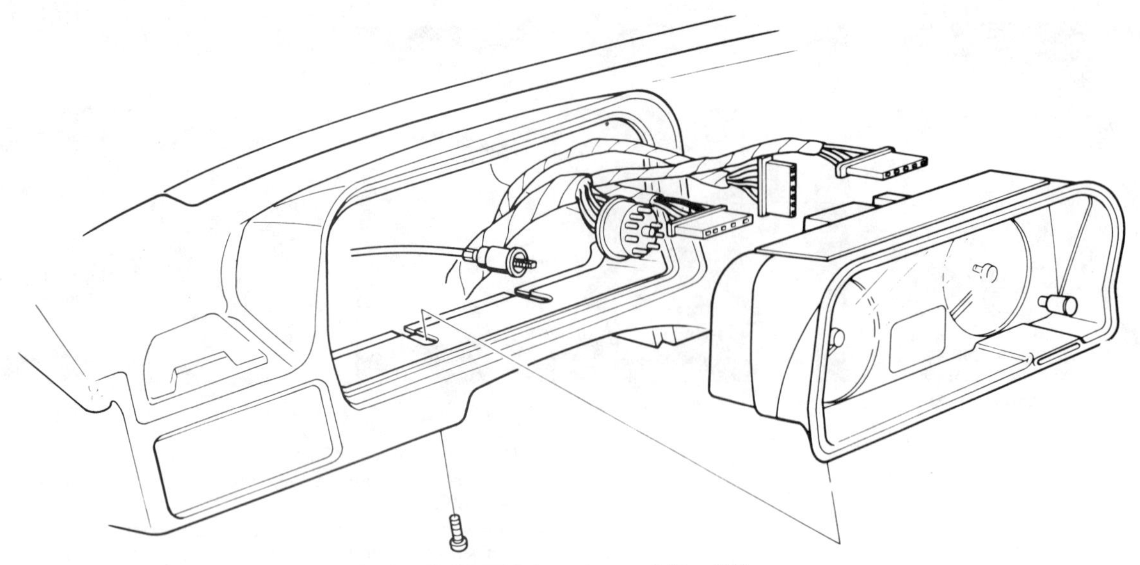

Fig. 10.34 Withdraw the panel (Sec. 27)

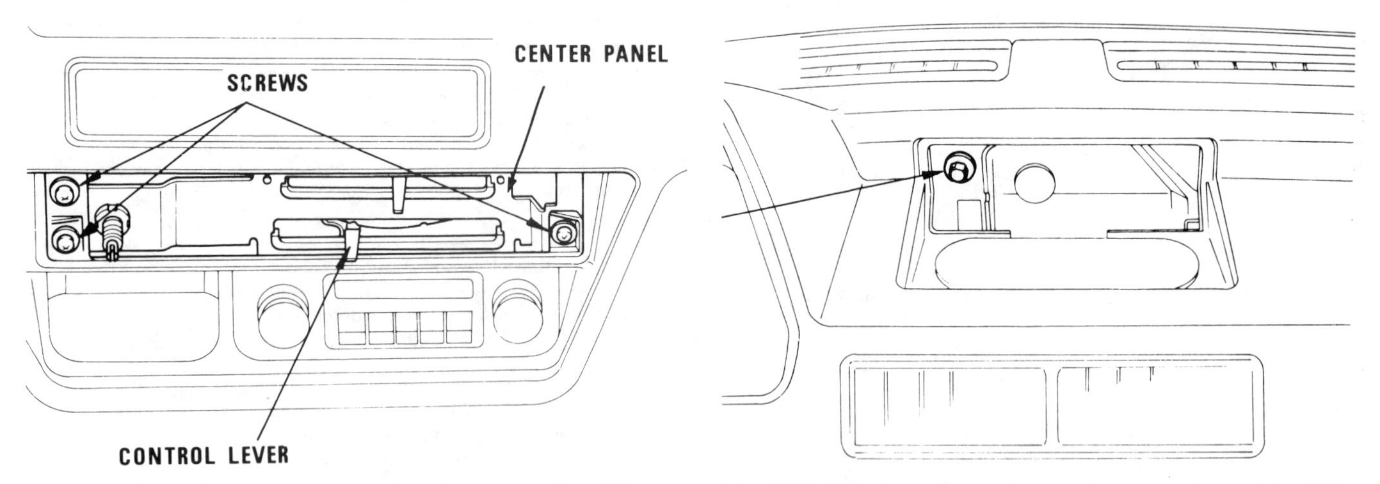

Fig. 10.35 Remove the centre panel retaining screws (Sec. 28)

Fig. 10.36 With the clock panel removed, unscrew the retaining bolt arrowed (Sec. 28)

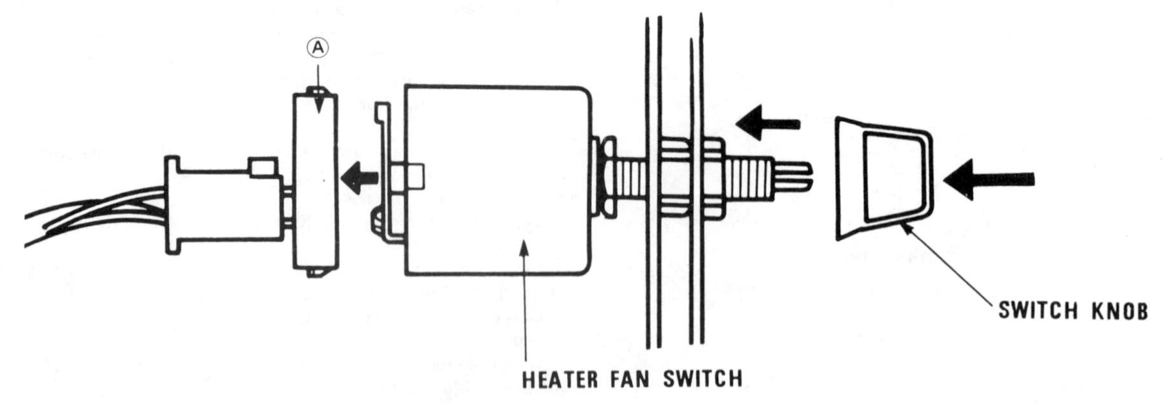

Fig. 10.37 The heater fan switch knob (Sec. 28)

the radio) and remove the lid. Now unscrew and remove the three radio securing screws.

2 Detach the radio control knobs and nuts.

3 Detach the heater fan switch knob and heater lever knob. Remove the heater control bezel, undoing from the left side first, then, when free, detach the wiring release coupler by prising open the lock tabs.

4 Unscrew the centre panel retaining screws (three) and partially withdraw to enable the cigar lighter leads to be disconnected. Now remove the panel.

5 Withdraw the radio and disconnect the aerial and lead connections.

6 Refitting of the radio is a reversal of removal but ensure that the respective wire connections are good prior to refitting the panels.

Speaker

7 This is located under the grille panel on the top of the facia. Remove as follows:

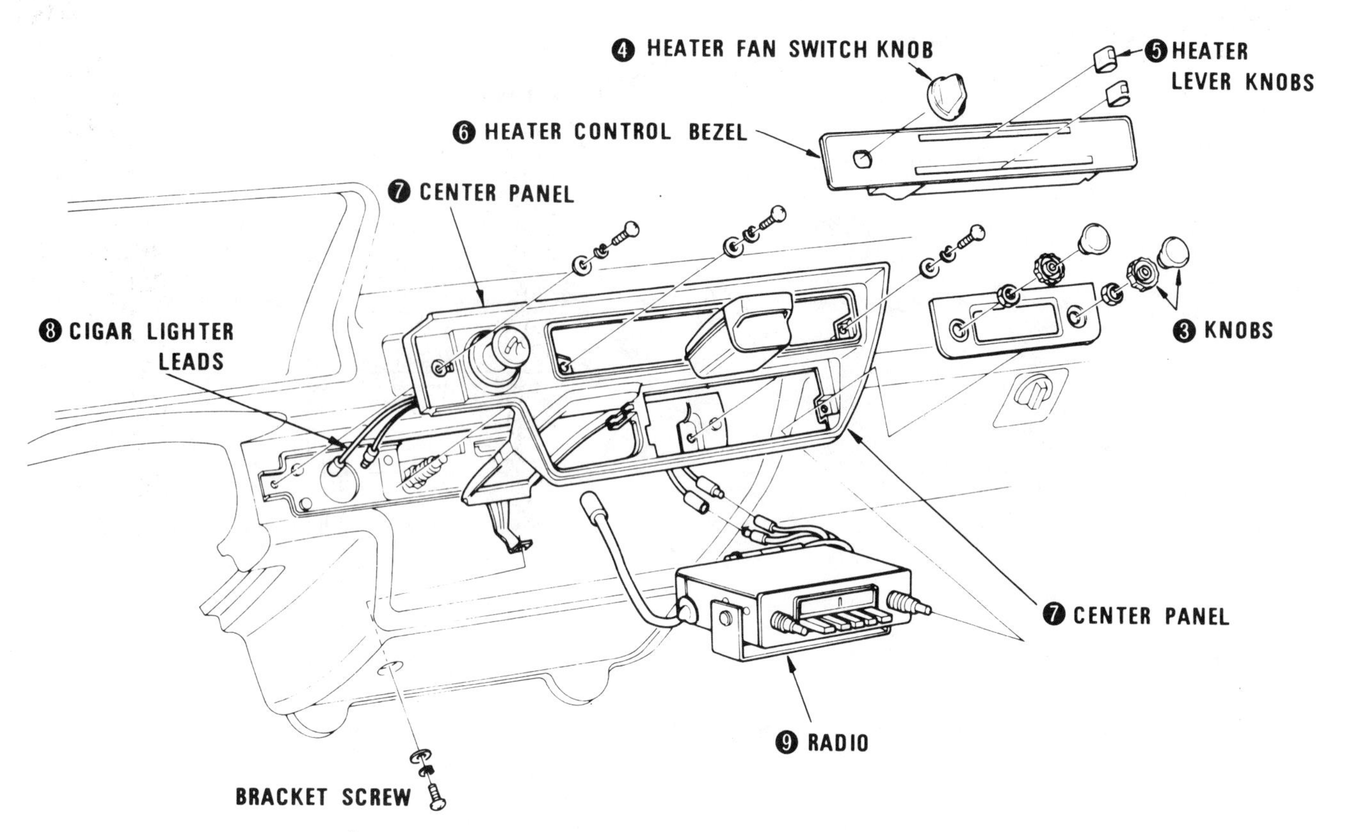

Fig. 10.38 The radio and panel components (Sec. 29)

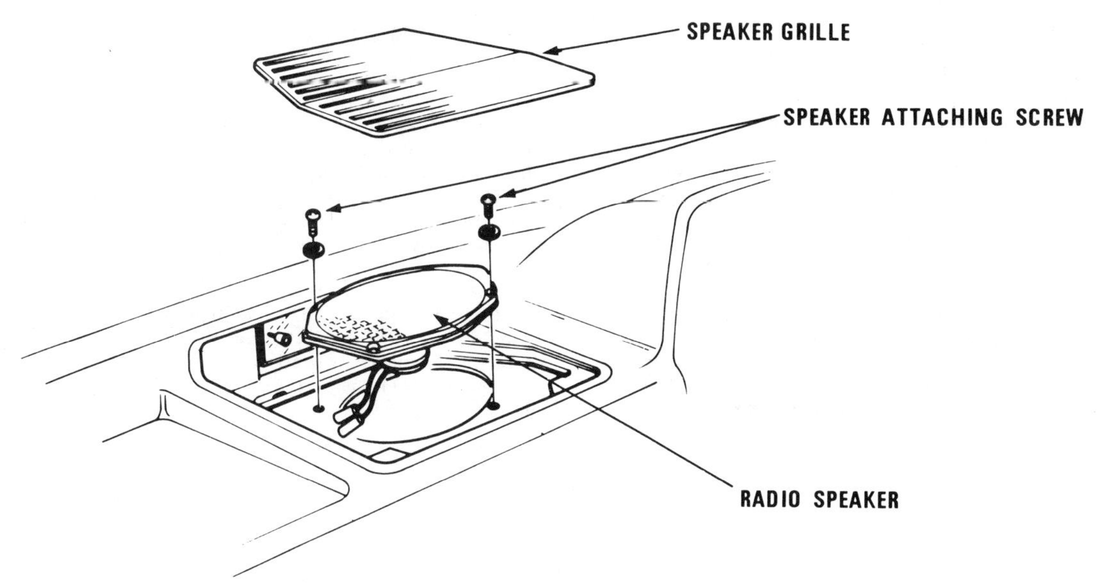

Fig. 10.39 The speaker and grille (Sec. 29)

8 Prise the grille free using a screwdriver, applying pressure from the rear so that it is released at the forward (windscreen) end.
9 Unscrew and remove the speaker unit securing screws. Lift the speaker and disconnect the wire connectors.
10 Refitting is a reversal of the removal procedure.

Aerial (antenna)
11 Unscrew the two retaining screws from the roof and then disconnect the lead from the 'sub cable' beneath the facia panel. Pull the aerial from the body and carefully feed the cable through the pillar channel (Fig. 10.40).
12 Refitting is a reversal of the removal procedure.

30 Clock - removal and refitting

1 Remove the radio speaker grille - see previous Section.
2 Unscrew the clock panel retaining screws, lift the panel clear and withdraw the clock sufficiently to detach the wiring from the connector. Remove the clock.
3 Refitting is the reverse of removal.

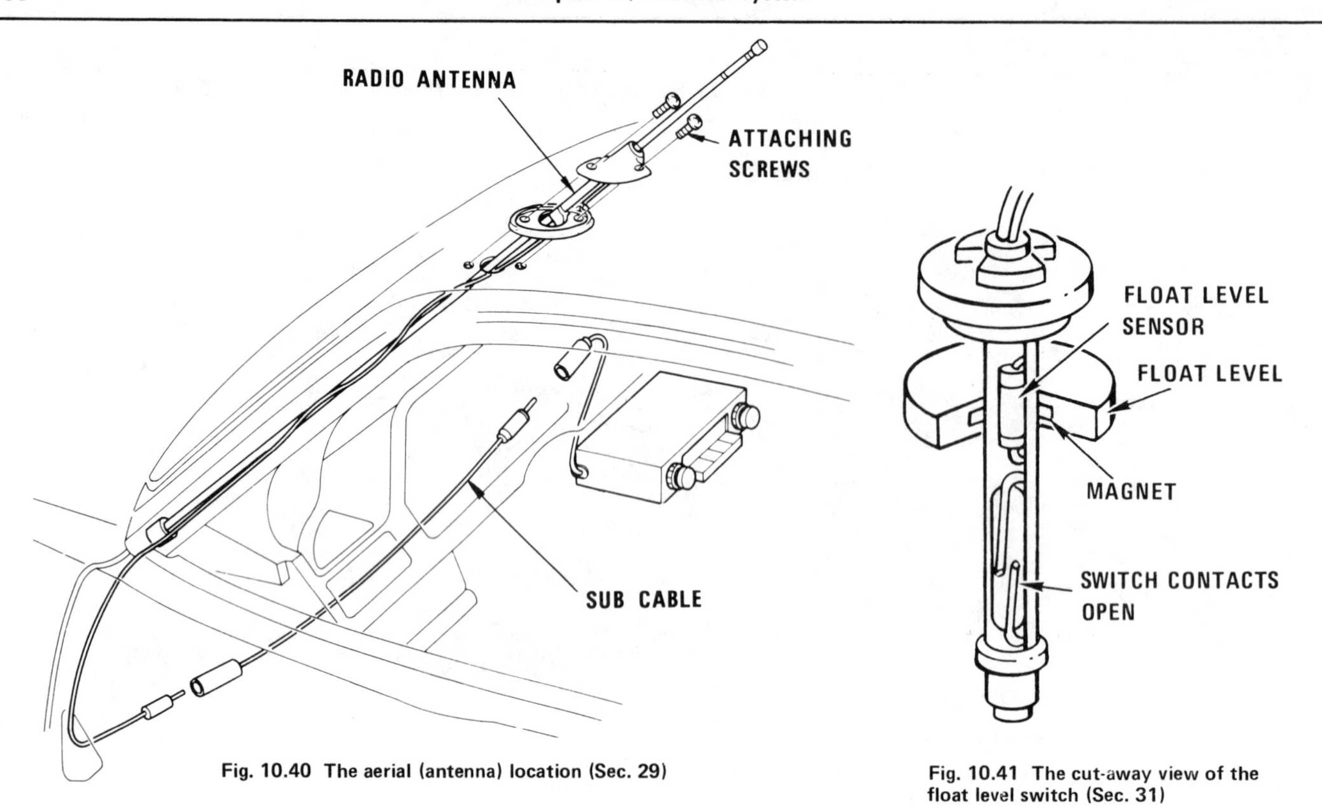

Fig. 10.40 The aerial (antenna) location (Sec. 29)

Fig. 10.41 The cut-away view of the float level switch (Sec. 31)

31 Brake warning system switch - testing

1 A brake failure warning system is incorporated into the braking circuit on some models and is activated if the fluid in the master cylinder reservoir/s drops below the required level, when there is unequal pressure in the hydraulic system, or when the handbrake is in the 'on' position with the ignition switched on.
2 The master cylinder reservoir/s incorporate a fluid level sensor and when the fluid level drops, the sensor/s detect this and activate the warning light. To check the fluid level switch, turn on the ignition, release the handbrake, remove the float level switch from the reservoir and if the warning light stays on then the switch is in working order.
3 If a brake warning switch is fitted, it can be checked for correct functioning by first detaching the wire to the switch, then release the handbrake and turn on the ignition.

a) If the warning light is off then remove the switch and using an ohmmeter check the continuity between the switch terminal and base. If continuity exists, the switch is faulty. However, when the switch plunger is pressed, continuity should be made. If the switch is faulty it must be renewed as it is not possible to repair it.

b) If the warning light stays on, check the switch wiring for a short circuit or possible damage to the connector.

32 Heated rear window - maintenance

Great care should be taken not to scratch the elements on the interior surface of the rear window. Use only a wet cloth to clean the glass and take care not to scratch the glass with a ring which you may have on a finger.

Many dealers still stick adhesive advertising slogans on the rear window over the elements when the car is supplied to the customer. Always insist on this being removed before taking delivery and test the operation of the heater. If it has been damaged, have the window renewed.

Damage to the heated rear window elements can be repaired by using special silver conductive paint and this is of course much cheaper than purchasing a new window.

Always check the circuit fuse if the heated rear window does not function.

33 Fault diagnosis - electrical system

Symptom	Reason/s
Starter motor fails to turn engine	
No electricity at starter motor	Battery discharged. Battery defective internally. Battery terminal leads loose or earth lead not securely attached to body. Loose or broken connections in starter motor circuit. Starter motor switch or solenoid faulty.
Electricity at starter motor: faulty motor	Starter motor pinion jammed in mesh with flywheel gear ring. Starter brushes badly worn, sticking, or brush wires loose. Commutator dirty, worn or burnt. Starter motor armature faulty. Field coils earthed.
Starter motor turns engine very slowly	
Electrical defects	Battery in discharged condition. Starter brushes badly worn, sticking, or brush wires loose. Loose wires in starter motor circuit.
Starter motor operates without turning engine	
Mechanical damage	Pinion or flywheel gear teeth broken or worn. Battery in discharged condition.
Starter motor noisy or excessively rough engagement	
Lack of attention or mechanical damage	Pinion or flywheel gear teeth broken or worn. Starter motor retaining bolts loose.
Battery will not hold charge for more than a few days	
Wear or damage	Battery defective internally. Electrolyte level too low or electrolyte too weak due to leakage. Plate separators no longer fully effective. Battery plates severely sulphated.
Insufficient current flow to keep battery charged	Battery plates severely sulphated. Drivebelt slipping. Battery terminal connections loose or corroded. Alternator not charging. Short in lighting circuit causing continual battery drain. Regulator unit not working correctly.
Ignition light fails to go out, battery runs flat in a few days	
Alternator not charging	Drivebelt loose and slipping or broken. Brushes worn, sticking, broken or dirty. Brush springs weak or broken. Commutator dirty, greasy, worn or burnt. Alternator field coils burnt, open, or shorted. Commutator worn. Pole pieces very loose.
Regulator or cut-out fails to work correctly	Regulator incorrectly set. Cut-out incorrectly set. Open circuit in wiring of cut-out and regulator unit.
Horn	
Horn operates all the time	Horn push either earthed or stuck down. Horn cable to horn push earthed.
Horn fails to operate	Blown fuse. Cable or cable connection loose, broken or disconnected. Horn has an internal fault.
Horn emits intermittent or unsatisfactory noise	Cable connections loose. Horn incorrectly adjusted.
Lights	
Lights do not come on	If engine not running, battery discharged. Sealed beam filament burnt out or bulbs broken. Wire connections loose, disconnected or broken. Light switch shorting or otherwise faulty.

Symptom	Reason/s
Lights come on but fade out	If engine not running battery discharged. Light bulb filament burnt out or bulbs or sealed beam units broken. Wire connections loose, disconnected or broken. Light switch shorting or otherwise faulty.
Lights give very poor illumination	Lamp glasses dirty. Lamp badly out of adjustment.
Lights work erratically - flashing on and off, especially over bumps	Battery terminals or earth connection loose. Light not earthing properly. Contacts in light switch faulty.
Wipers	
Wiper motor fails to work	Blown fuse. Wire connection loose, disconnected, or broken. Brushes badly worn. Armature worn or faulty. Field coils faulty.
Wiper motor works very slowly and takes excessive current	Commutator dirty, greasy or burnt. Armature bearings dirty or unaligned. Armature badly worn or faulty.
Wiper motor works slowly and takes little current	Brushes badly worn. Commutator dirty, greasy or burnt. Armature badly worn or faulty.
Wiper motor works but wiper blades remain static	Wiper motor gearbox parts badly worn.
Wipers do not stop when switched off or stop in wrong place	Auto-stop device faulty.

See pages 162 - 165 for Wiring Diagrams

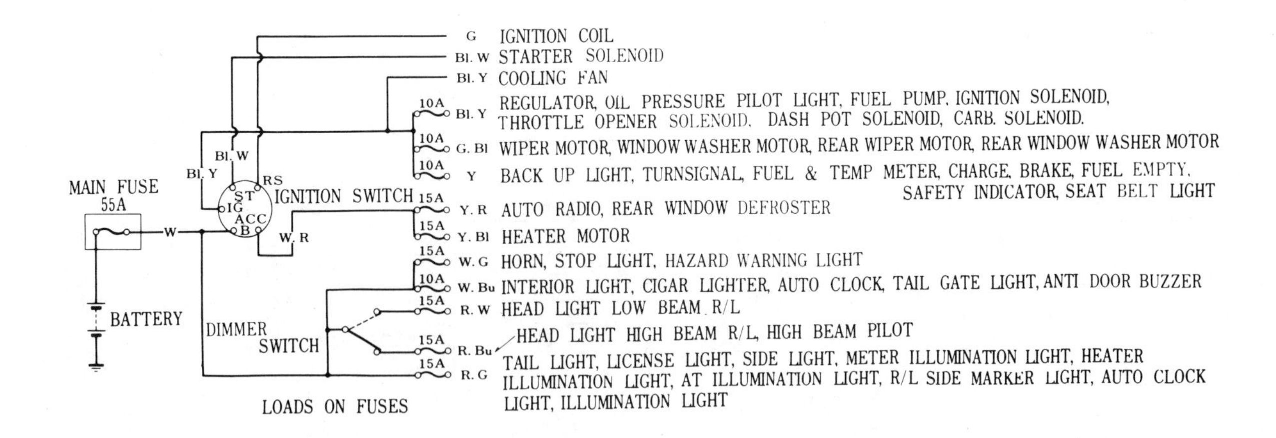

Fuse ratings and supply circuit for Honda Accord 1976 models

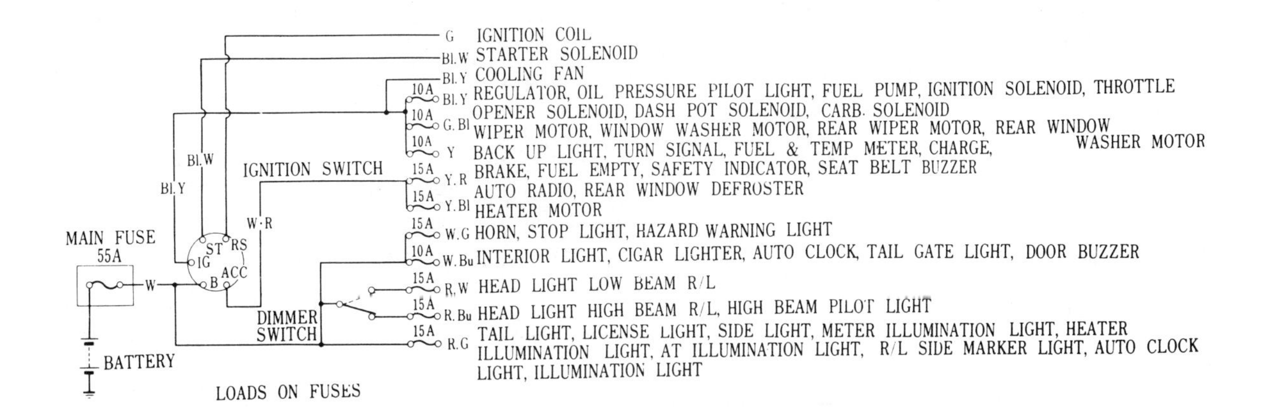

Fuse ratings and supply circuit for Honda Accord 1977 models

W.	: White	Bu.	: Blue	G. W	: Green/white stripe
W. R	: White/red stripe	Bu. R	: Blue/red stripe	G. Y	: Green/yellow stripe
W. Y	: White/yellow stripe	Bu. W	: Blue/white stripe	L G	: Light Green
W. Bu	: White/blue stripe	Bu. Y	: Blue/yellow stripe	LG. Bl	: Light Green/black stripe
W. G	: White/green stripe	Bl.	: Black	R.	: Red
Y.	: Yellow	Bl. W	: Black/white stripe	R. Bl	: Red/black stripe
Y. Bl	: Yellow/black stripe	Bl. Y	: Black/yellow stripe	R. Bu	: Red/blue stripe
Y. R	: Yellow/red stripe	G.	: Green	R. G	: Red/green stripe
Y. W	: Yellow/white stripe	G. Bl	: Green/black stripe	R. Y	: Red/yellow stripe
Y. G	: Yellow/green stripe	G. Bu	: Green/blue stripe	R. W	: Red/white stripe
		G. R	: Green/red stripe		

Colour code used for 1976 and 1977 Wiring Diagrams

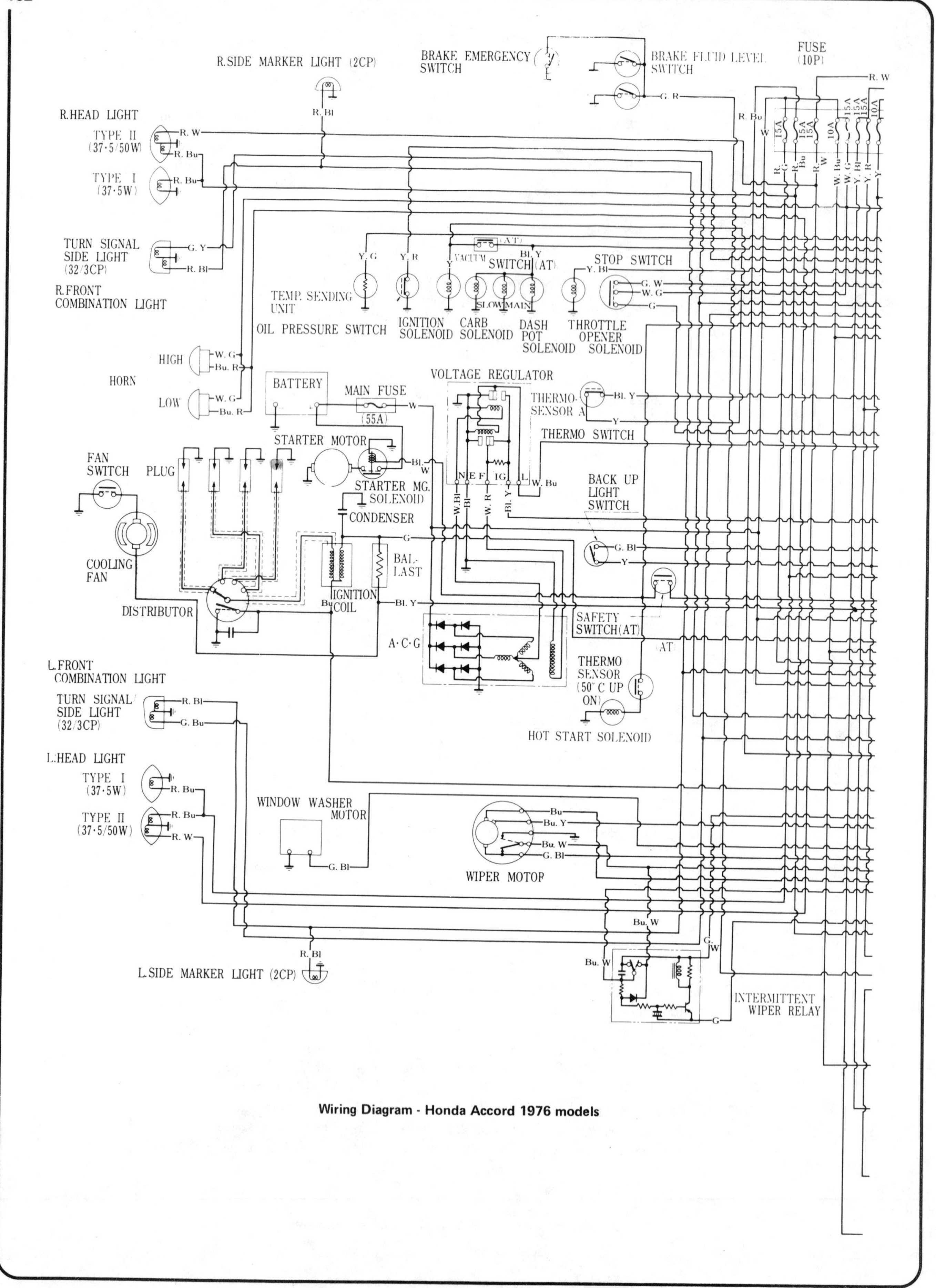

Wiring Diagram - Honda Accord 1976 models

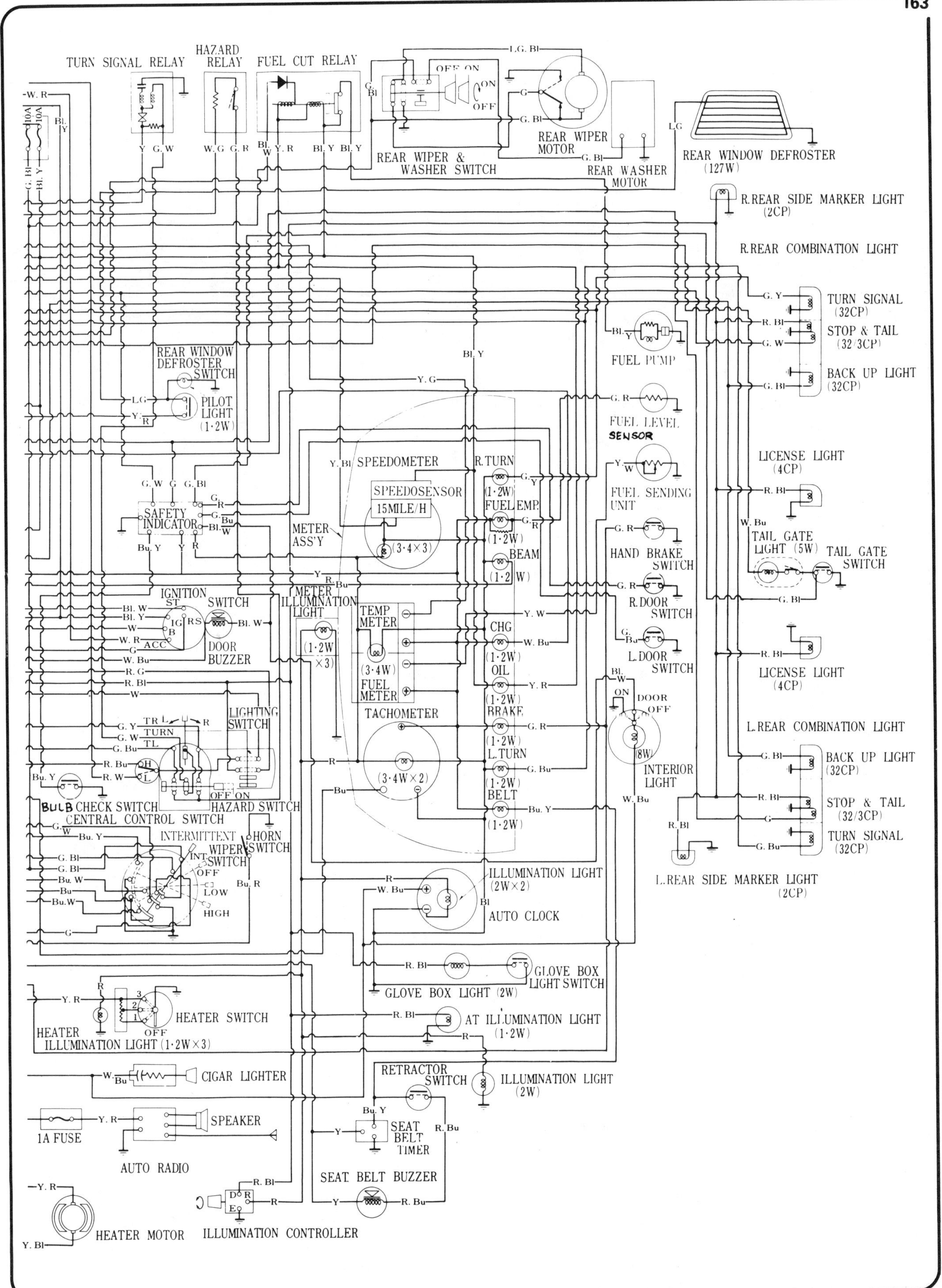
TURN SIGNAL RELAY
HAZARD RELAY
FUEL CUT RELAY
REAR WIPER & WASHER SWITCH
REAR WIPER MOTOR
REAR WASHER MOTOR
REAR WINDOW DEFROSTER (127W)
R.REAR SIDE MARKER LIGHT (2CP)
R.REAR COMBINATION LIGHT
TURN SIGNAL (32CP)
STOP & TAIL (32/3CP)
BACK UP LIGHT (32CP)
FUEL PUMP
FUEL LEVEL SENSOR
FUEL SENDING UNIT
REAR WINDOW DEFROSTER SWITCH
PILOT LIGHT (1·2W)
SPEEDOMETER
SPEEDOSENSOR
15MILE/H
METER ASS'Y
SAFETY INDICATOR
R.TURN
FUEL EMP.
BEAM
LICENSE LIGHT (4CP)
TAIL GATE LIGHT (5W)
TAIL GATE SWITCH
HAND BRAKE SWITCH
R.DOOR SWITCH
L.DOOR SWITCH
IGNITION SWITCH
DOOR BUZZER
METER ILLUMINATION LIGHT
TEMP METER
FUEL METER
CHG
OIL
BRAKE
L.TURN
BELT
TACHOMETER
LIGHTING SWITCH
HAZARD SWITCH
BULB CHECK SWITCH
CENTRAL CONTROL SWITCH
INTERMITTENT WIPER SWITCH
HORN SWITCH
INTERIOR LIGHT (8W)
L.REAR COMBINATION LIGHT
L.REAR SIDE MARKER LIGHT (2CP)
ILLUMINATION LIGHT (2W×2)
AUTO CLOCK
GLOVE BOX LIGHT (2W)
GLOVE BOX LIGHT SWITCH
HEATER SWITCH
HEATER ILLUMINATION LIGHT (1·2W×3)
AT ILLUMINATION LIGHT (1·2W)
CIGAR LIGHTER
RETRACTOR SWITCH
ILLUMINATION LIGHT (2W)
SPEAKER
1A FUSE
AUTO RADIO
SEAT BELT TIMER
SEAT BELT BUZZER
HEATER MOTOR
ILLUMINATION CONTROLLER

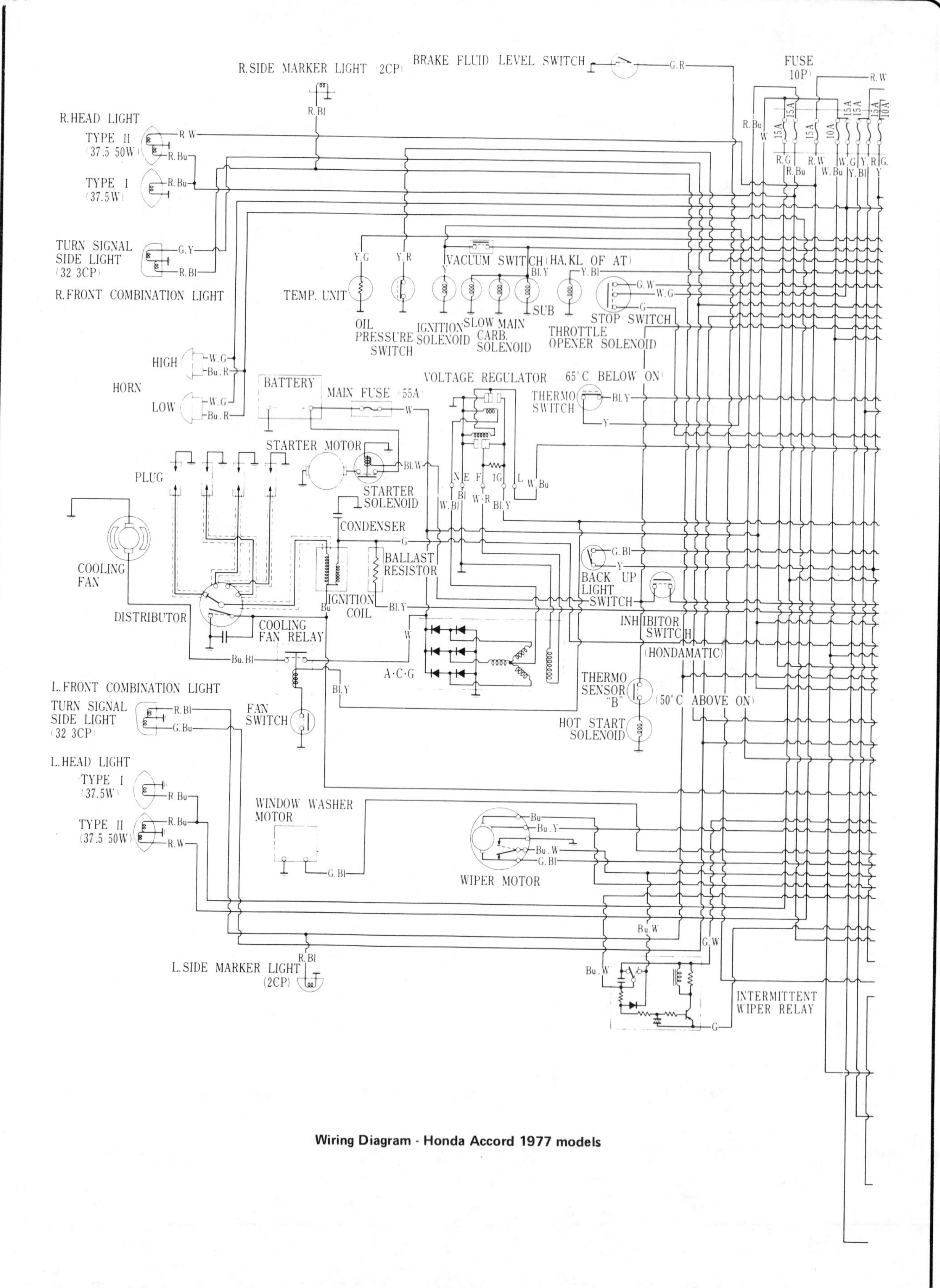

Wiring Diagram - Honda Accord 1977 models

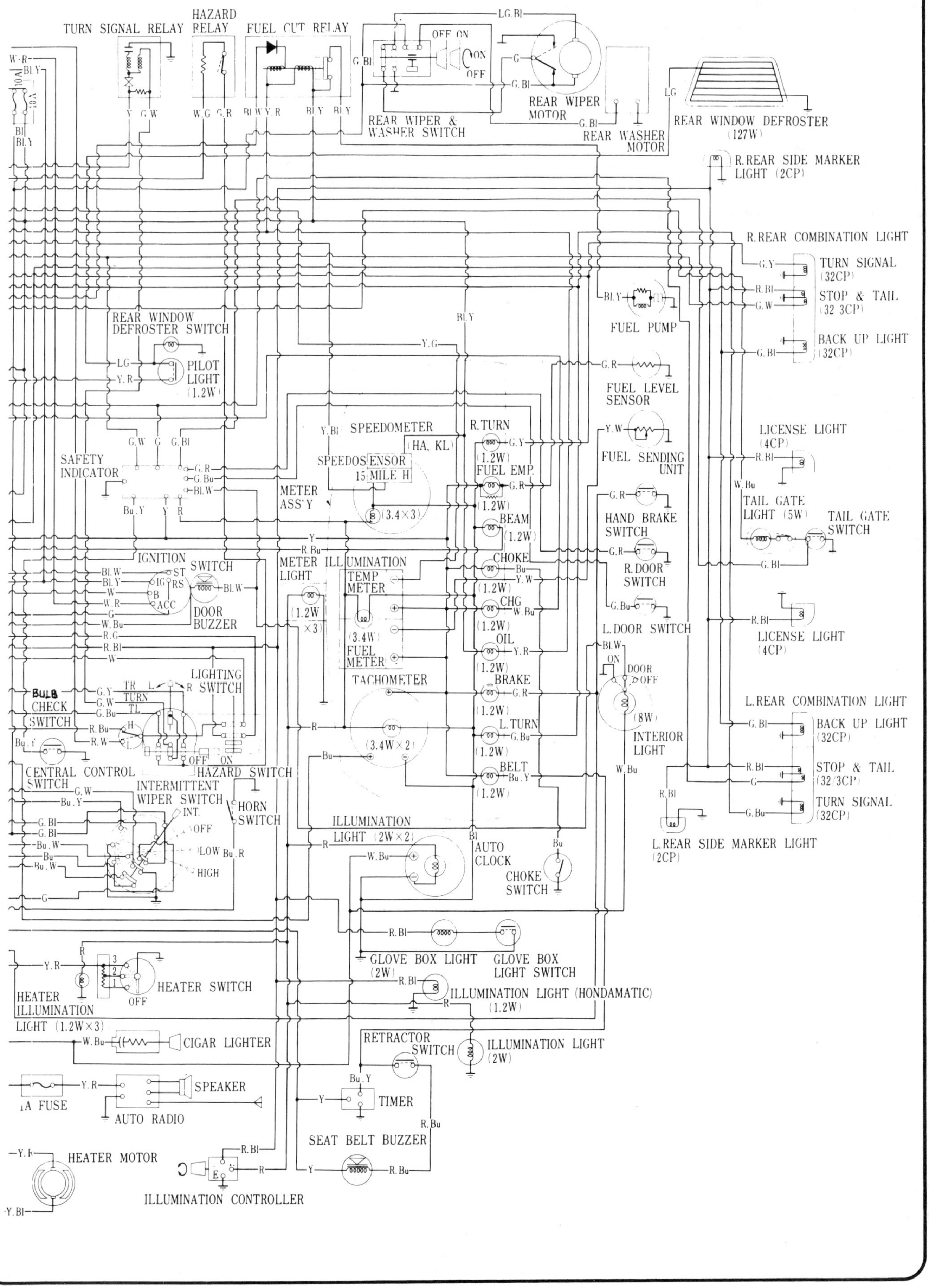

TURN SIGNAL RELAY
HAZARD RELAY
FUEL CUT RELAY
REAR WIPER & WASHER SWITCH
OFF ON
ON
OFF
REAR WIPER MOTOR
REAR WASHER MOTOR
REAR WINDOW DEFROSTER (127W)
R. REAR SIDE MARKER LIGHT (2CP)
R. REAR COMBINATION LIGHT
TURN SIGNAL (32CP)
STOP & TAIL (32 3CP)
BACK UP LIGHT (32CP)
FUEL PUMP
REAR WINDOW DEFROSTER SWITCH
PILOT LIGHT (1.2W)
FUEL LEVEL SENSOR
SPEEDOMETER (HA, KL)
SPEEDOSENSOR 15 MILE H
R. TURN (1.2W)
FUEL EMP. (1.2W)
BEAM (1.2W)
CHOKE (1.2W)
CHG (1.2W)
OIL (1.2W)
BRAKE (1.2W)
L. TURN (1.2W)
BELT (1.2W)
SAFETY INDICATOR
FUEL SENDING UNIT
LICENSE LIGHT (4CP)
TAIL GATE LIGHT (5W)
TAIL GATE SWITCH
HAND BRAKE SWITCH
R. DOOR SWITCH
L. DOOR SWITCH
METER ASS'Y
IGNITION SWITCH
ST IG RS B ACC
DOOR BUZZER
METER ILLUMINATION LIGHT (1.2W ×3)
TEMP METER
FUEL METER
(3.4W)
(3.4×3)
TACHOMETER (3.4W×2)
LIGHTING SWITCH
TR TURN TL
OFF ON
BULB CHECK SWITCH
CENTRAL CONTROL SWITCH
HAZARD SWITCH
INTERMITTENT WIPER SWITCH
INT. OFF LOW HIGH
HORN SWITCH
ILLUMINATION LIGHT (2W×2)
AUTO CLOCK
CHOKE SWITCH
INTERIOR LIGHT (8W)
ON DOOR OFF
LICENSE LIGHT (4CP)
L. REAR COMBINATION LIGHT
BACK UP LIGHT (32CP)
STOP & TAIL (32/3CP)
TURN SIGNAL (32CP)
L. REAR SIDE MARKER LIGHT (2CP)
GLOVE BOX LIGHT (2W)
GLOVE BOX LIGHT SWITCH
HEATER SWITCH
OFF
HEATER ILLUMINATION LIGHT (1.2W×3)
ILLUMINATION LIGHT (HONDAMATIC) (1.2W)
CIGAR LIGHTER
RETRACTOR SWITCH
ILLUMINATION LIGHT (2W)
1A FUSE
SPEAKER
AUTO RADIO
TIMER
SEAT BELT BUZZER
HEATER MOTOR
ILLUMINATION CONTROLLER

Chapter 11 Suspension and steering

For modifications, and information applicable to later models, see Supplement at end of manual

Contents

Specifications

Front suspension ... Independent, MacPherson strut and coil spring

Rear suspension ... Independent, MacPherson strut and coil spring

Steering ... Rack and pinion, collapsible steering wheel column and shaft

Front wheel steering angles

Toe out	0.04 in (1 mm) ± 0.118 in (3 mm)
*Caster	1° 50′ ± 1°
*Camber	0° 40′ ± 1°
*King pin inclination	12° 10′ ± 30′

Rear wheel alignment

Toe out	0.04 in (1 mm) ± 0.079 in (2 mm)
*Camber	0° 20′

* *Non-adjustable*

Steering rack guide spring

Free length (new)	1.02 in (26 mm)
Minimum free length (used)	0.944 in (24 mm)

Front track ... 55.1 in (1400 mm)

Rear track ... 54.7 in (1390 mm)

Turning circle ... 32 ft 5 in (9.8 m)

Wheels and tyres

Rim size	4½ J
Tyre type and size	Tubeless radial 155 x 13
Tyre pressures front and rear (cold)	24 lbf/in^2

Torque wrench settings

	lb f ft	kg f m
Front suspension		
Engine support beam retaining bolt	25 to 31	3.5 to 4.3
Centre beam retaining bolt	13 to 18	1.9 to 2.5
Stabilizer bar bush bolts	13 to 18	1.9 to 2.5
Radius rod locknuts	29 to 34.7	4.0 to 4.8
Radius rod bolts	36 to 43	5.0 to 6.0
Front hub nut	86 to 130	12 to 18
Steering knuckle strut bolt	43 to 51	6.0 to 7.0
Front hub to disc bolts	36 to 43	5.0 to 6.0
Lower arm pivot bolt	25 to 36	3.5 to 5.0
Brake hose clamp bolt	5 to 8	0.7 to 1.2
Strut upper mounting nuts	29 to 36	4 to 5
Rear suspension		
Strut upper mounting nuts	7 to 12	1.0 to 1.6
Strut spindle nuts	22 to 25	3.0 to 3.5
Lower suspension arm outer pivot bolt castle nut	54 to 65	7.5 to 9.0
Stub axle carrier bolt	36 to 43	5.0 to 6.0
Rear wheel hub carrier to radius rod bolt	47 to 54	6.5 to 7.5
Rear wheel backing plate bolts	14 to 18	1.9 to 2.5
Lower suspension arm inner pivot bolt	25 to 36	3.5 to 5.0
Radius rod pivot bolt	43 to 54	6.0 to 7.5

Torque wrench settings

Steering	lb f ft	kg f m
Steering box mounting bracket bolts	13 to 18	1.9 to 2.5
Steering shaft connector pinch bolts	34 to 50	4.8 to 6.8
Steering shaft connector bolt	20 to 23	2.8 to 3.2
Steering column mounting bracket bolts	13 to 18	1.9 to 2.5
Steering column retaining nuts	7 to 11	1.0 to 1.6
Track rod end balljoint nuts	29 to 35	4.0 to 4.8

1 General description and maintenance

The independent front suspension is of the MacPherson strut type. The strut is located between the inner wing panel at the top and the steering knuckle at the bottom.

The steering system is of the rack and pinion type, actuated by a universally jointed steering shaft which is collapsible as is the steering column. The steering column incorporates a locking device.

The track rods are adjustable to correct the front wheel alignment if required. An added safety feature to the front suspension is a stabilizer bar, which is attached to the bodyshell and to the lower suspension arm, as is the radius rod.

The rear suspension is also independent and of the MacPherson strut type. Wheel alignment at the rear is adjusted by means of the radius rod.

Regular maintenance is essential to maintain the steering and suspension in good condition and to ensure that the safety of the car is preserved. The components that will require particular attention are as follows:

a) Lower knuckle balljoint
b) Steering tie-rod balljoints
c) Top anchorage for the MacPherson struts
d) Anchorages and bushes for anti-roll bar
e) The suspension struts for leaks.
f) Lower control arm pivot bushes

All of these points should be tested with a stout lever or screwdriver to see whether there is any movement between them and the fixed components. Checks on the suspension should always be made with the car jacked up and supported on chassis stands. It will be easier to detect small amounts of wear and movement when normal imposed loads are not acting on the suspension members. Together with the mechanical tests on the suspension and steering joints, the components themselves should be checked for serviceability, particularly the:

a) Steering rack mounting bolts tightness
b) Steering column shaft couplings
c) Steering column retention bolts
d) Steering wheel retention
e) Front and rear wheel hub bearings

There should be no play - or failure - in any single part of any of the aforementioned components. It is dangerous to use a vehicle in a doubtful condition of this kind.

Finally, all parts should be kept clean and rust free, and if rust is found, remove it and use a rust proof paint to restore the parts to a good condition. Rust left can cause cracks and possibly failure of that suspension member.

2 Front hubs, bearings and steering knuckle - dismantling, overhaul and reassembly

The front wheel hub is bolted to the brake disc. The centre of the hub is splined and mates with the splines of the driveshaft, thus transmitting the drive to the roadwheels. Two ball bearings support the hub and are located by the outer races to the steering knuckle (stub axle carrier). There is no facility for adjustment and therefore once wear is detected in the bearings they must be renewed, together with the dust seals.

1 Commence by raising the front of the car and supporting it on chassis stands, placed beneath the strengthened body areas to the rear of the front wheel arches. Remove the front wheels.

2 Unscrew and remove the front brake caliper retaining bolts and detach the caliper from the knuckle. Support the caliper by suspending it by a piece of wire from the suspension unit so that the flexible brake hose is not strained in any way.

3 Withdraw the split pin which locks the spindle nut, then unscrew and remove the nut. A socket wrench and extension will be required to remove the nut.

4 Attach a slide hammer puller to the wheel nut studs on the hub to remove the hub from the driveshaft spindle and clear of the bearings in the steering knuckle.

5 When the hub and disc are removed from the knuckle, undo the four bolts which retain the hub to the disc and separate the two components.

6 The bearings should be an interference fit in the knuckle and it will be necessary to remove the knuckle in order to press out the two bearings. The new bearings must have been obtained prior to the removal of the old ones; bearings should not be re-used once they have been withdrawn from the knuckle.

7 To remove the steering knuckle, disconnect the track rod ends and use a conventional balljoint separator to detach the two components, taking care not to damage the joint seals.

8 Unscrew and withdraw the knuckle to shockabsorber retaining bolt. With a soft headed mallet, tap the knuckle downwards to separate it from the shock absorber.

9 Extract the split pin and unscrew the lower suspension arm to knuckle joint retaining nut. Lever the suspension arm from the knuckle whilst tapping the knuckle to the joint pin to loosen the taper and free the pin.

10 Withdraw the knuckle from the driveshaft and support the driveshaft so that it is not removed from the final drive unit or there will be a loss of oil.

11 Clean off the steering knuckle and take it to the workbench.

12 Prise the dust seals from the centre of the inboard side of the knuckle.

13 Unscrew and remove the four bolts securing the retainer and disc shield to the knuckle. Prise out the outer seal.

14 The two bearings are now ready to be removed from the knuckle. Ideally the knuckle should be supported on a base beneath a hydraulic press and a suitable driver used to push the bearing from the knuckle. Whatever method is used to remove the bearings, ensure that the knuckle is supported as close to the periphery of the bearings as possible without interfering with them.

15 Discard the old bearings and oilseals and install new ones.

16 Reassembly is a reversal of the dismantling procedure but note the following:

17 Each bearing must be packed with the correct grade of grease prior to fitting in the knuckle. Each bearing must be fitted so that the manufacturers marking(s) are facing towards each other as in Fig. 11.2.

18 When pressing the bearings into position in the knuckle use a

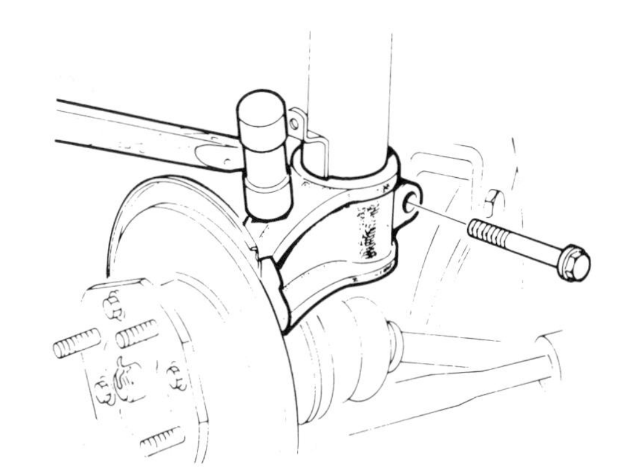

Fig. 11.1. Tap the knuckle downwards (Sec. 2)

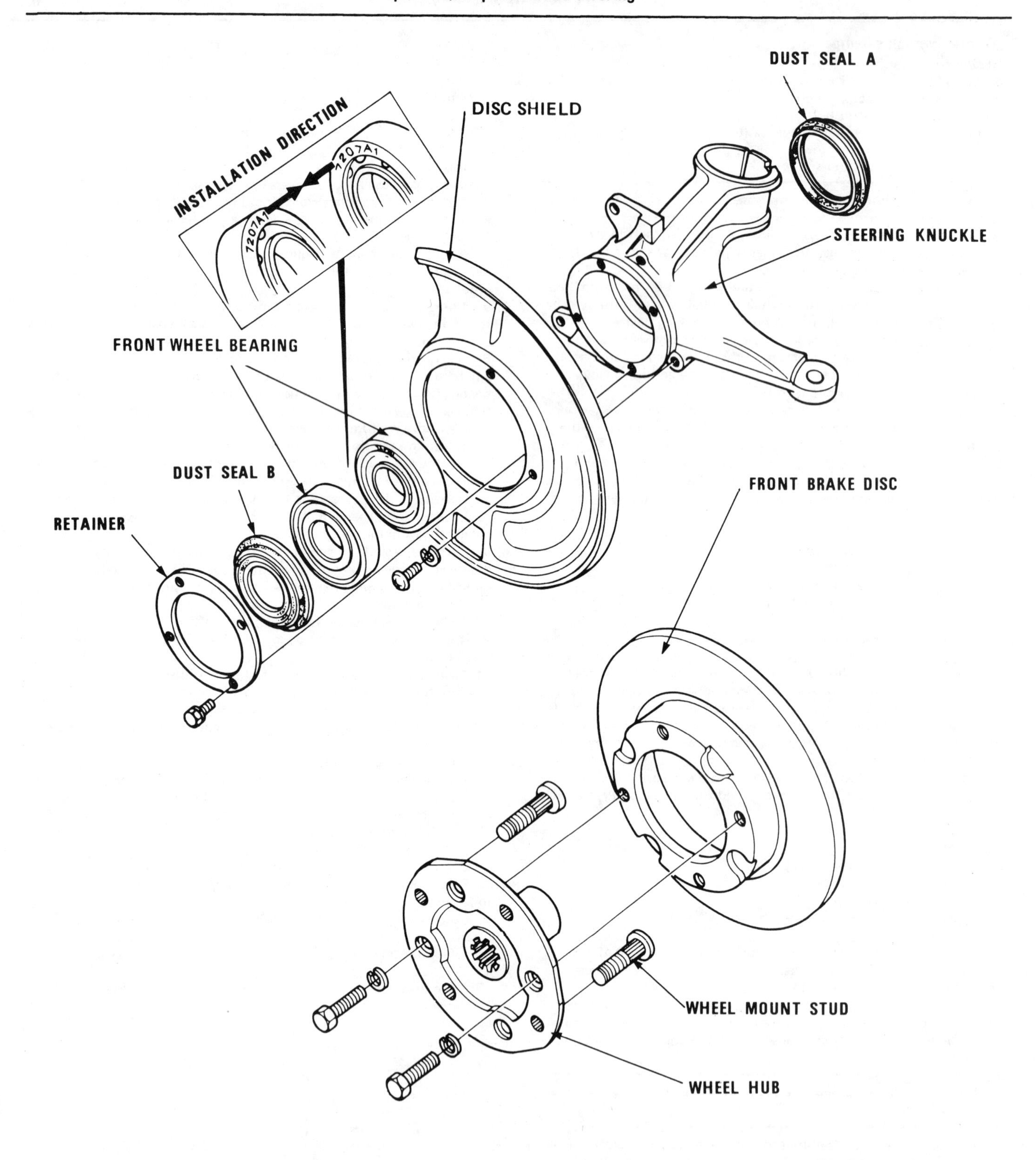

Fig. 11.2. The front hub and knuckle components (Sec. 2)

suitable tubular drift which locates on the bearing outer race only. It is important not to load the ball bearings during assembly.

19 Assemble the wheel hub onto the bearings and knuckle prior to refitting the knuckle unit to the suspension.

20 Tighten all nuts and fasteners to the specified torque wrench settings.

3 Front suspension stabilizer bar, track control arm and radius rod - removal and refitting

1 Place the car on level ground, and apply the handbrake.

2 Removal of the lower control arm proceeds as follows: Raise the

car onto chassis stands placed beneath the suspension subframes. Remove the roadwheels.
3 Support the front wheel hub, whilst removing the control arm balljoint from the base of the knuckle member.
4 Extract the split pin which locks the nut on the balljoint pin, then undo and remove the nut.
5 Use a separator to disconnect the balljoint and remove the pin from the knuckle.
6 Next remove the stabilizer bar, by undoing the bolts which retain the middle brackets to the front subframe and then the band and bush to the radius arm between the front subframe and major lower control arm (photo).
7 Once the anti-roll bar has been removed, undo and remove the nut and rubber bushes which secure the radius rods to the brackets on the front subframe.
8 Finally, undo and remove the pivot bolt at the anchorage of the lower control arm.
9 The lower control arm is a complete assembly and the balljoint cannot be separated from the arm, so that when wear is found the arm/balljoint assembly should be renewed.
10 The pivot bushing is an interference fit in the end of the control arm.Use a broad cylindrical drift to force the bushing from the arm if its condition is suspect.
11 Reassembly follows the reversal of the dismantling procedure. Pay particular attention to the following:

a) The condition of the lower arm balljoint seal
b) Grease the taper pins of the balljoints prior to assembly
c) The tightening torques of the pivot bolts, anti-roll bar bolts, radius arm nut and the balljoint pin nut
d) Use a new split pin to lock the ball pin nut

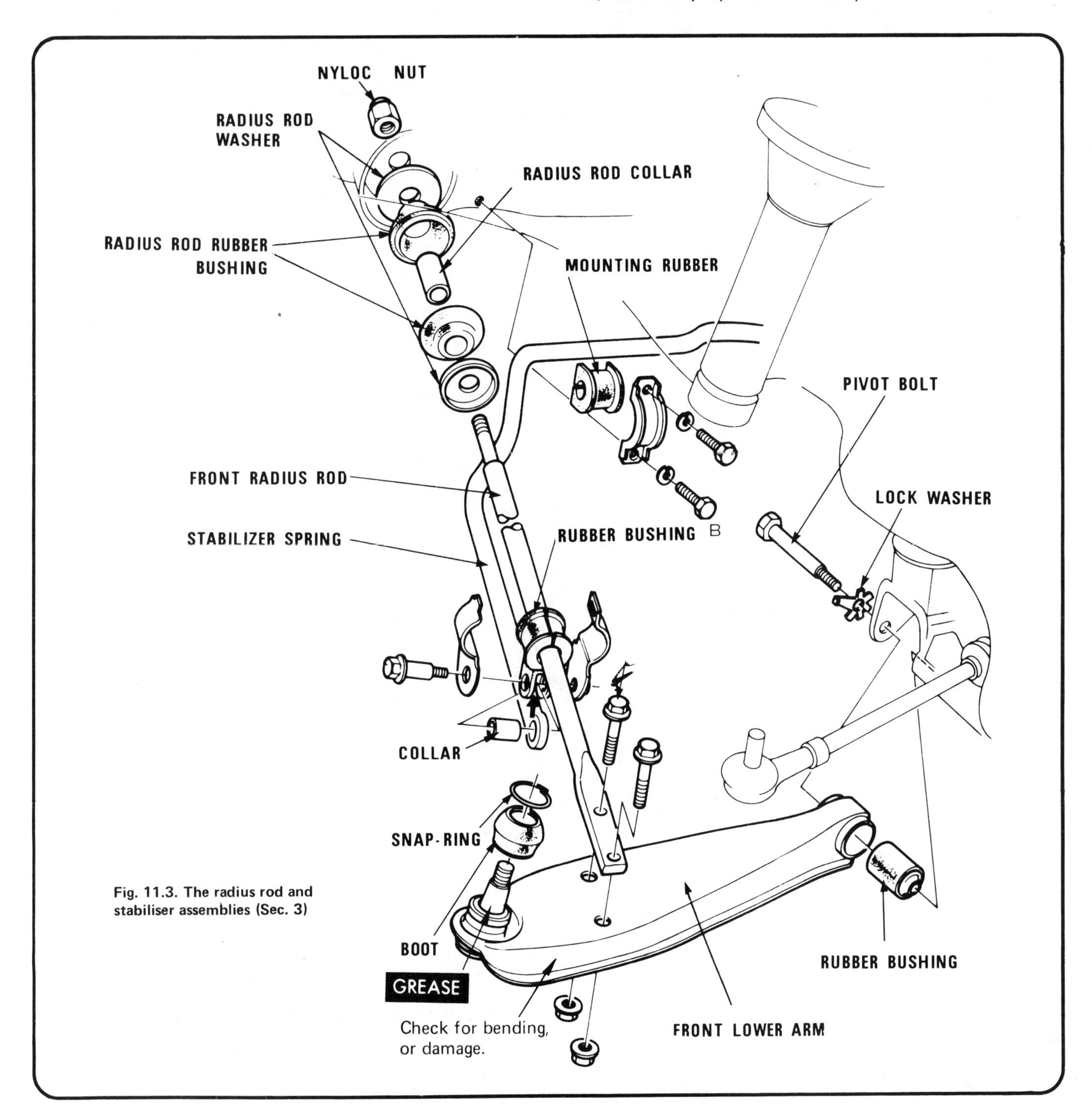

Fig. 11.3. The radius rod and stabiliser assemblies (Sec. 3)

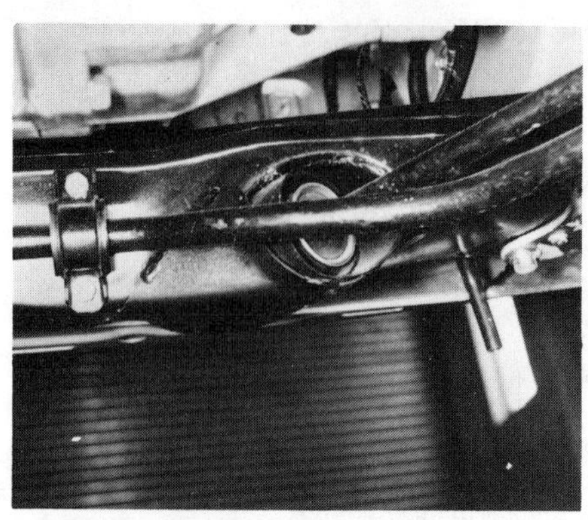

3.6 The radius rod and stabilizer bar to front subframe attachment points

4.4 Removing the steering knuckle from the suspension strut

4.10 View showing the alignment dowel and slot

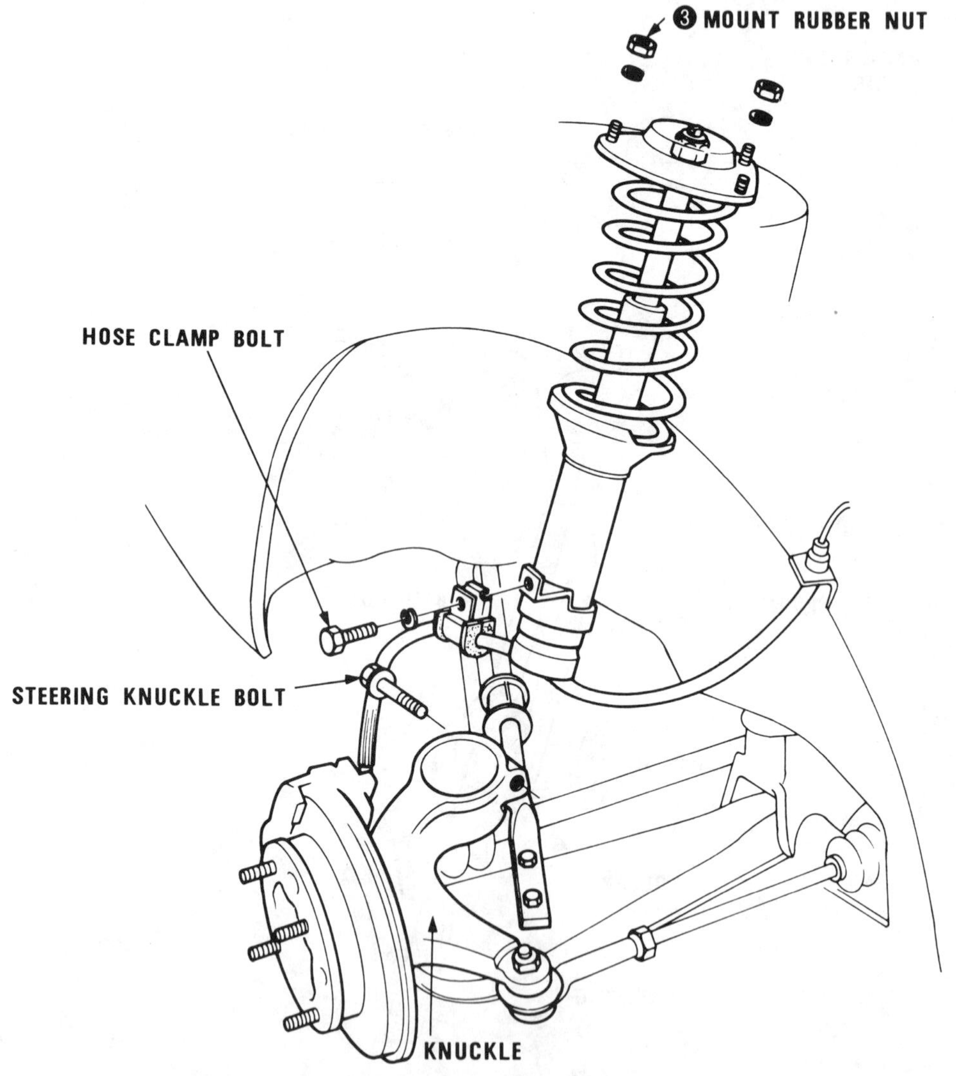

Fig. 11.4 The steering knuckle and suspension strut (Sec. 4)

12 When refitting is complete, check the front wheel alignment (see Section 16).

4 Front suspension strut and spring - removal, overhaul and refitting

1 Fit spring compressors to the coils of the front road springs.

2 Jack up the front of the car and position chassis stands beneath the subframe. Remove the roadwheels.

3 Unscrew the flexible hydraulic brake hose clamp bolt from the suspension strut. Position the hose out of the way temporarily.

4 Unscrew and withdraw the steering knuckle to strut bolt. With a soft headed mallet, drive the knuckle downwards to separate it from the strut. Support the knuckle to prevent the hydraulic hose from being distorted or over stretched (photo).

5 Unscrew the three nuts securing the strut upper end to the body-shell and lower the strut from the car.
6 The spring (still compressed) can be removed after the self-locking nut has been unscrewed and removed from the top of the strut and the mounting components withdrawn.
7 If the strut assembly is faulty, it should be renewed with one of exactly similar type, alternatively a new hydraulic cartridge can be obtained which can be inserted after carefully following the manufacturer's instruction. The latter method will prove more economical as the original strut casing can be re-used.
8 If the original spring is to be refitted, the compressors should not be released until the spring has been refitted to the strut and the strut fitted to the car.
9 Refit the strut by reversing the removal process and then tighten all the bolts to the specified torque and finally check the front wheel alignment (Section 16). When fitting the piston self-locking nut, the piston rod should be prevented from turning by making up a suitable lever with a 'D' shaped hole in it to fit the flat at the upper end of the rod. On no account grip the rod or threads.
10 When refitting the knuckle to the strut ensure that the alignment dowel and slot are correctly located (photo). Ensure that the flexible hydraulic brake hose does not bind against any surrounding components when it is relocated.

5 Rear hubs and bearings - overhaul

1 The rear wheel hub bearings are of the taper roller type. Each hub has two taper bearings opposed to each other and located in the brake drum and over the stub axle. Adjustment of the bearings is by means of a hub nut which is locked in position by a holder and split pin.
2 To remove the hub and bearings, jack up the rear of the car and support it on chassis stands. Chock the front wheels. Remove the rear wheel/s.
3 Prise the hub dust cap free using a suitable screwdriver, taking care not to damage the 'O' ring.
4 Withdraw the split pin (photo) and remove the nut lock.
5 Unscrew and remove the hub nut and washer, and withdraw the

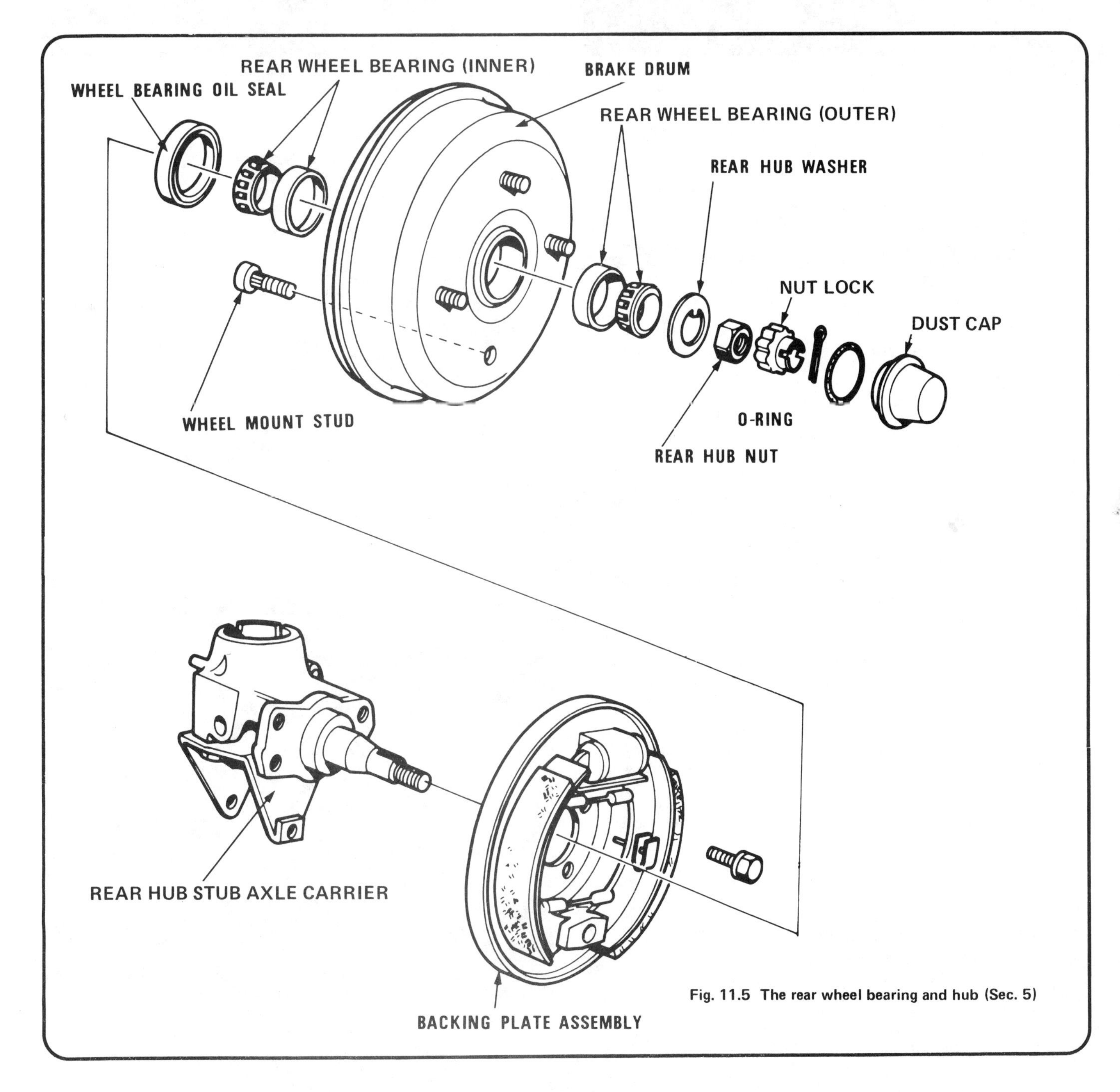

Fig. 11.5 The rear wheel bearing and hub (Sec. 5)

5.4 Withdraw the split pin

5.5 Remove the washer and outer bearing cone

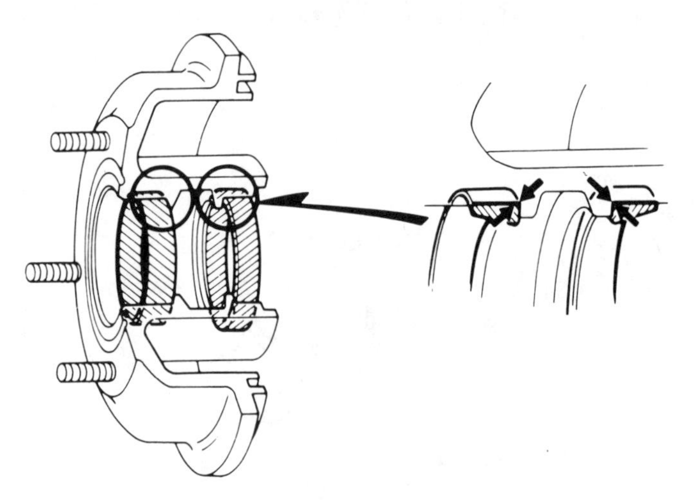
Fig. 11.6. The bearing cups (outer races) must be seated correctly (Sec. 5)

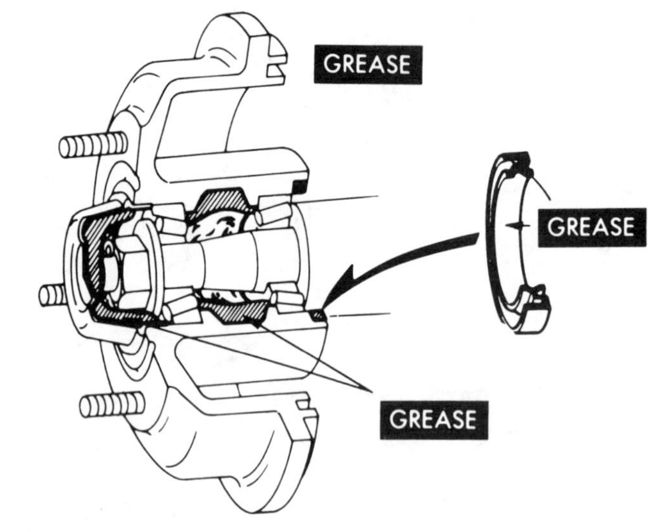

Fig. 11.7. The lubrication points in the hub (Sec. 5)

outer bearing cone (photo).

6 Pull the drum hub and bearings from the stub axle. If the drum is reluctant to move, check that the handbrake is off and that the brakes are not binding. A conventional puller bolted to the wheel studs on the drum and acting against the stub axle may be necessary; or try tapping it off with a plastic- faced mallet.

7 Having removed the drum, take it to the workbench for the removal of the bearings. First prise the oil seal free from the inner face and extract the inner bearing cone (photo).

8 To remove the bearing cups (outer races), use a suitable drift and drive the cups from the drum, noting the direction and location of each cup. Tap the bearing cups evenly to avoid being driven askew in their seatings.

9 The bearings can now be cleaned and inspected for signs of excessive wear, pitting or damage, in particular to the rollers and cage. Renew as required.

10 Refitting is a reversal of the removal procedure but note the following:

- a) *Ensure that the new bearing cups are fully located within the drum as in Fig. 11.6.*
- b) *Pack grease between the two bearings as in Fig. 11.7. Also grease the bearing cones, the oil seal and drum cap prior to assembly.*
- c) *On refitting the drum refer to Chapter 9, Section 6, paragraph 14 and 15 for adjustment of the hub bearings. Readjust the brakes if they have been slackened.*
- d) *Check that the hub rotates freely.*

5.7 Removing oil seal

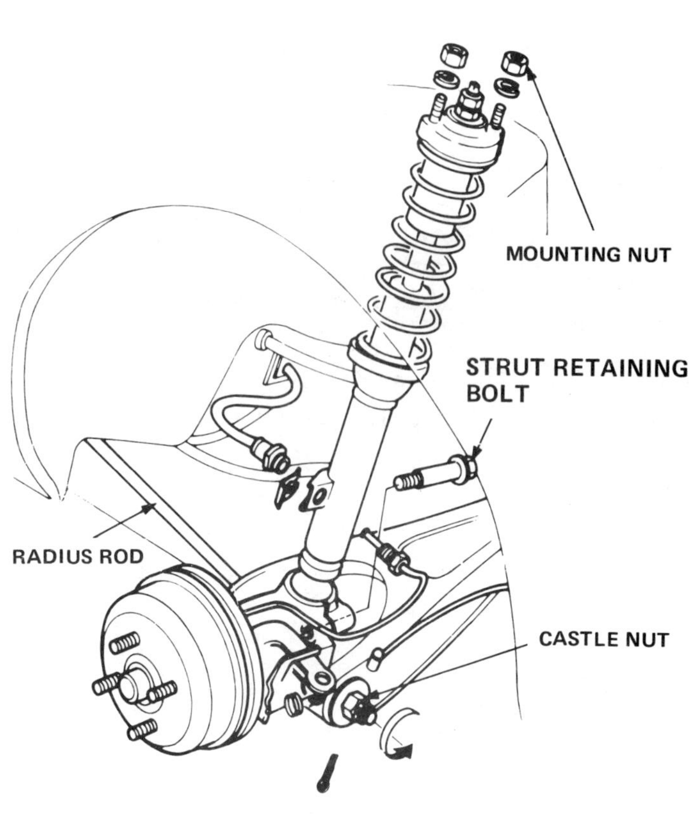

Fig. 11.8. The rear suspension strut location (Sec. 6)

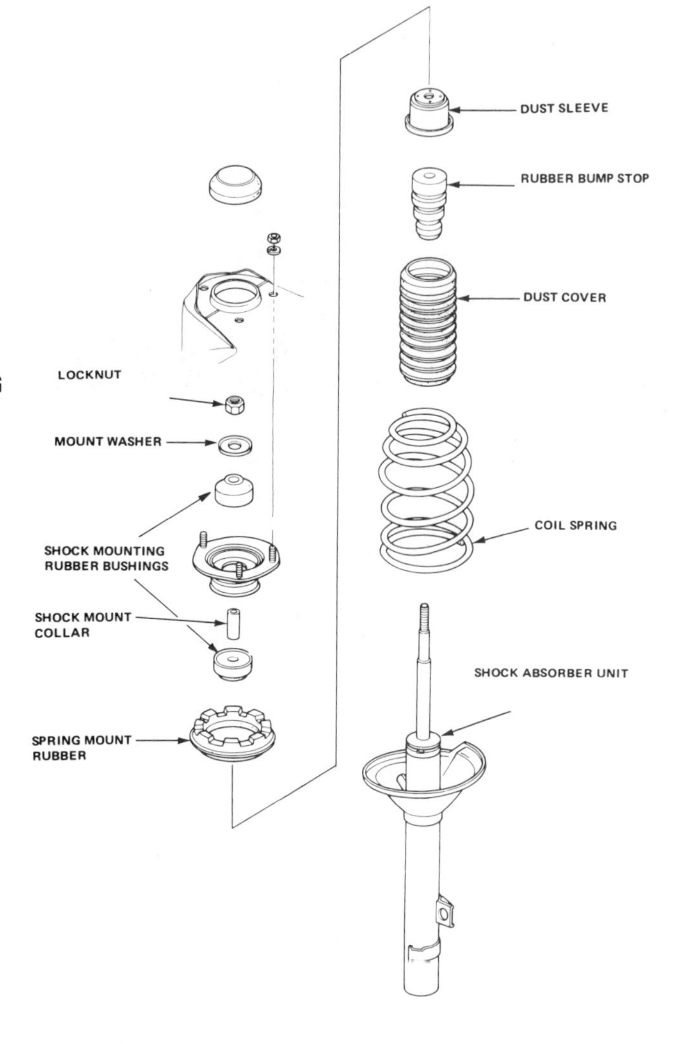

Fig. 11.8A Rear strut components (later models) (Sec. 6)

6 Rear suspension strut - removal and refitting

1 Raise the rear of the car and support it securely on axle stands under the jacking points.
2 Remove the road wheel.
3 Disconnect the hydraulic brake line and quickly cap the end of the hose to prevent loss of fluid.
4 Disconnect the anti-roll bar from the suspension lower arm (later models).
5 Refer to Chapter 9 or the Supplement and remove the brake drum. Then disconnect the handbrake cable.
6 Unscrew the self-locking pinch-bolt which holds the base of the suspension strut to the stub axle carrier.
7 Unscrew the strut top mounting nuts. Earlier models have two nuts, later models have three.
8 Withdraw the strut assembly complete with coil spring.
9 If the coil spring is to be removed from the strut, spring compressors must be fitted. These are obtainable from most motor accessory stores. The compressors should be tightened evenly, but only enough to relieve the spring pressure on the top mounting and then unscrew the self-locking type centre (piston rod) nut.
10 If the spring is to be renewed, release the compressors evenly and slowly before removing them.
11 Refitting is a reversal of removal. Make sure that the alignment tab at the base of the strut engages fully in the slot in the stub axle carrier.
12 Tighten all nuts and bolts to the specified torque.
13 Bleed the brake hydraulic system on completion.

7 Rear suspension lower arm and radius rod - removal and refitting

1 Follow the instructions given in paragraphs 2 to 5 in Section 6.
2 Remove the brake drum after extracting the split pin and removing the nut lock, spindle nut and washer. It may be necessary to slacken off the adjustment on the brake concerned to withdraw the drum.
3 Unscrew the retaining bolts and remove the brake backing plate assembly complete with shoes, adjuster unit and hydraulic brake cylinder from the rear wheel hub carrier (Fig. 11.9 and 11.10).
4 Support the hub carrier unit and then extract the split pin from the lower suspension arm to carrier unit bolt. Unscrew the castle nut and withdraw the bolt. Lower the hub carrier unit.
5 Bend up the locking tab of the lower arm pivot bolt lockwasher, unscrew and withdraw the bolt. Remove the lower arm and take it to the workbench for cleaning and inspection.
6 Before removing the radius arm it should be noted that its length is adjusted to allow the toe-out of the rear wheels. The radius arm should therefore not be removed unless it is absolutely necessary.
7 If it has to be removed, note the position of the adjustment bolt and cam plate prior to removal, as a guide for readjustment on assembly.
8 Unscrew and remove the radius arm retaining bolt to the hub carrier. Unscrew and remove the radius rod adjustment bolt and nut and remove the rod for cleaning and inspection.
9 Clean off the respective components and inspect for wear, damage or signs of deterioration. Renew any suspect rubber bushings and other components as required.
10 Refitment of the lower arm and radius rod is a direct reversal of the removal procedure but note the following:

a) Tighten the nuts and bolts to the specified torque wrench settings. The pivot nuts and bolts must be tightened to the specified torque wrench settings, only when the car is standing on level ground and is unladen. Bend over the lower arm pivot bolt lockwasher tab (Fig. 11.11).
b) Check that the hydraulic brake hoses are secure and do not

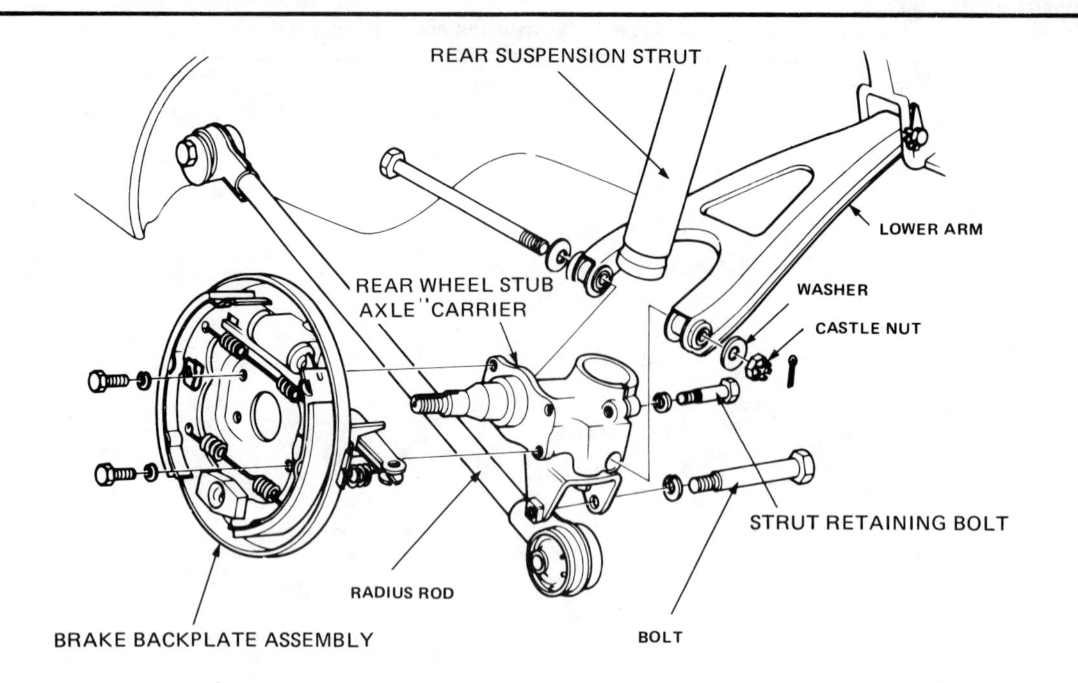

Fig. 11.9. The rear suspension radius rod and lower arm location (Sec. 7)

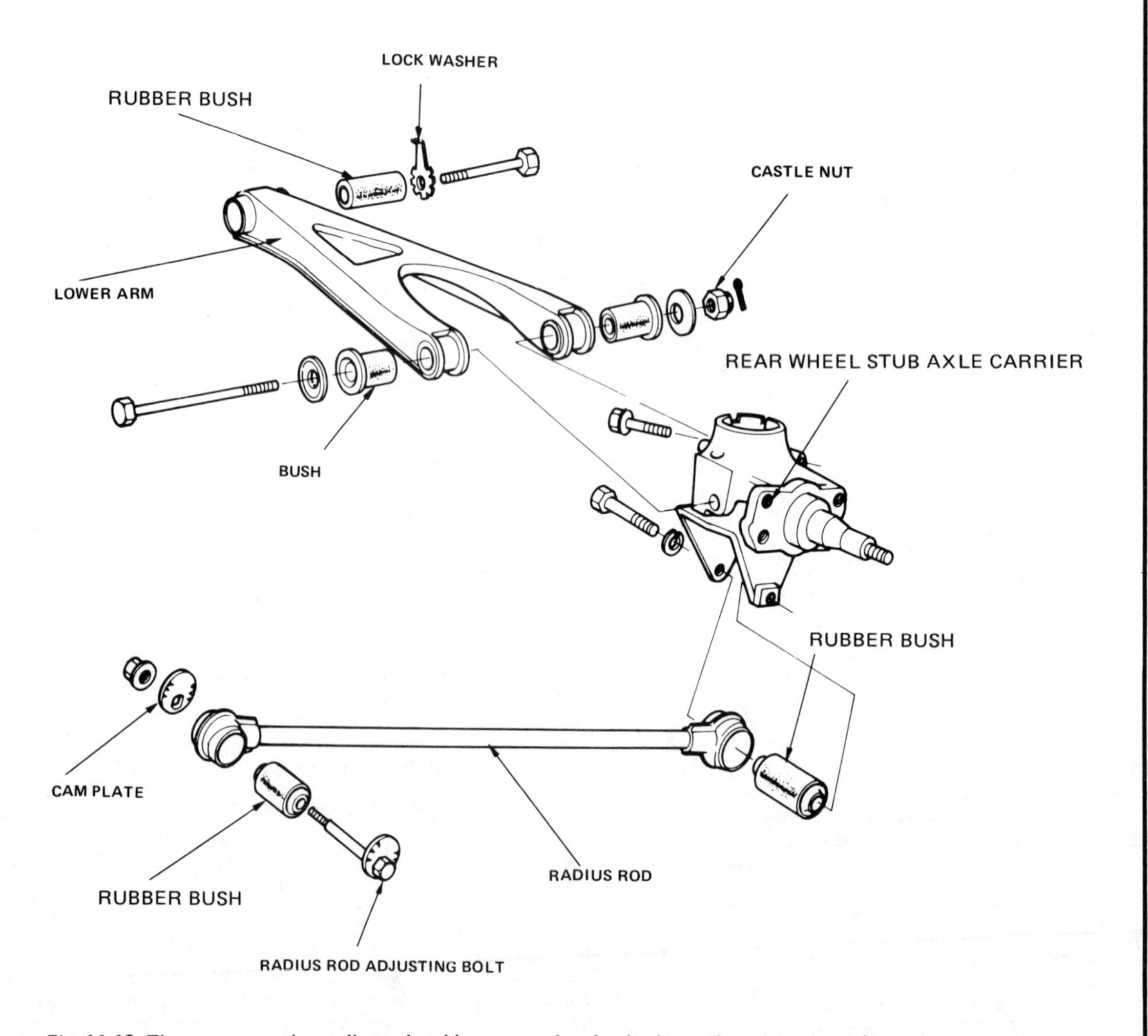

Fig. 11.10. The rear suspension radius rod and lower arm showing bushes and retaining bolts (Sec. 7)

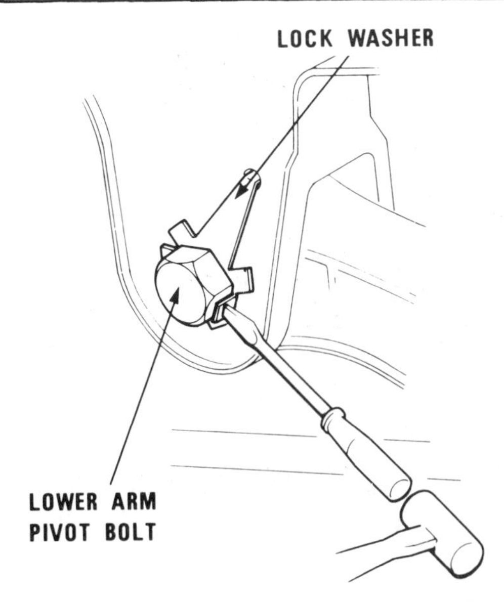

Fig. 11.11. The lower arm pivot bolt and lockwasher (Sec. 7)

10.3 Remove the central crash pad

10.6 Pull the steering wheel to remove

bind against any surrounding components.

c) *Bleed the braking system, top up the reservoir and readjust the brakes as required (see Chapter 9, Section 2).*

d) *Check the alignment - toe -out, of the rear wheels, (see Section 17).*

8 Trackrod end balljoints - removal and refitting

1 Set the steering wheel and the front roadwheels in the 'straight-ahead' position.
2 Using two spanners, hold the trackrod end quite still while the lock-nut is released. Do not unscrew the locknut more than a ¼ of a turn.
3 Withdraw the split pin from the balljoint taper pin and unscrew and remove the castle nut.
4 Using a balljoint separator or forked wedges, separate the trackrod end balljoint from the steering arm.
5 Grip the trackrod to prevent it turning and unscrew and remove the trackrod end from it.
6 If the balljoint taper pins can be easily moved or there is any end-float when the taper pin is pushed or pulled then the trackrod end must be renewed. If the bellows are split or damaged, release their clips and renew them.
7 Again gripping the trackrod to prevent it turning, screw on the new trackrod end and when it is correctly aligned so that it can be re-inserted into the eye of the steering arm, tighten the locknut by the same amount through which it was unscrewed. If this is carried out correctly, the front wheel toe-out will not have been altered too much but even so the front wheei alignment must be checked, as described in Section 6.
8 Connect the balljoint taper pin to the steering arm (do not grease them) screw on and tighten the castle nut to the specified torque and insert a new split pin.
9 Check that the steering rack flexible bellows have not twisted, if they have, straighten them.

9 Steering - checking for wear

1 Apart from visual detection of wear in the steering linkage and joints, time for overhaul can be assumed if the steering wheel can be moved more than 0.39 in (10.0 mm) without transmitting any movement to the front roadwheels.
2 A further test can be carried out by raising the front roadwheels and attaching a spring balance to one of the spokes of the steering wheel. The force required to turn the wheel should not exceed 3.3 lbs (1.5 kg) otherwise check the adjustment of the rack guide screw in the following way.
3 Release the rack guide adjusting screw locknut.
4 Tighten the adjusting screw until it just seats.
5 Now unscrew the adjusting screw 1/8th of a turn and retighten the locknut.
6 Re-check the turning force of the gear again using the spring balance attached to the steering wheel.

10 Steering wheel - removal and refitting

1 Set the roadwheels in the 'straight-ahead' position.
2 Disconnect the lead from the battery negative terminal.
3 Prise off the crash pad from the steering wheel hub (photo).
4 Unscrew the retaining screws (accessible from the rear of the steering wheel spokes) and lift off the horn button covers.
5 Disconnect the horn button connecting leads.
6 The crash pad retainer can now be unscrewed and the steering wheel unbolted from the hub. Alternatively, the centre hub retaining nut can be unscrewed and the complete steering wheel assembly removed from the steering shaft (photo).
7 Whichever method is used, mark the position of the wheel to the hub and the hub to the shaft.
8 Do not jar the hub from the shaft as this may damage the collap-sible type column. No force should be required as the steering wheel is secured by parallel splines not tapered splines as is usually the case.
9 Refitting is a reversal of removal.

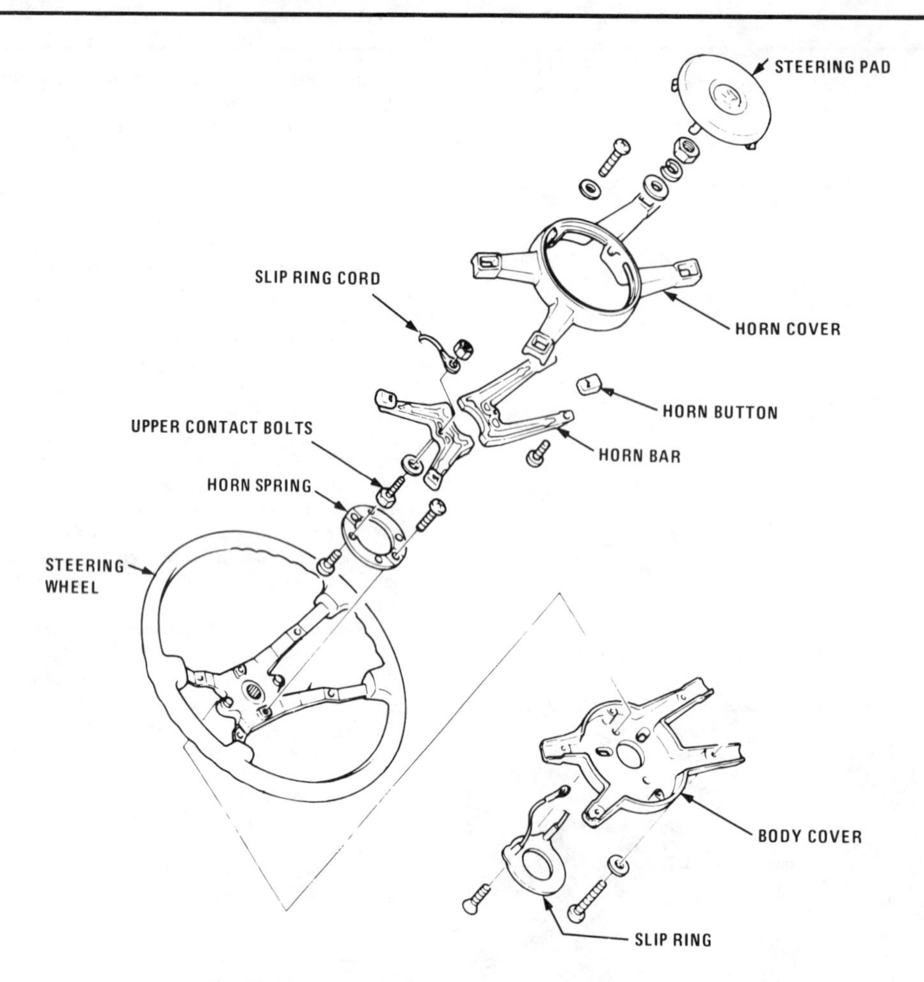

Fig. 11.12 The steering wheel components (Sec. 10)

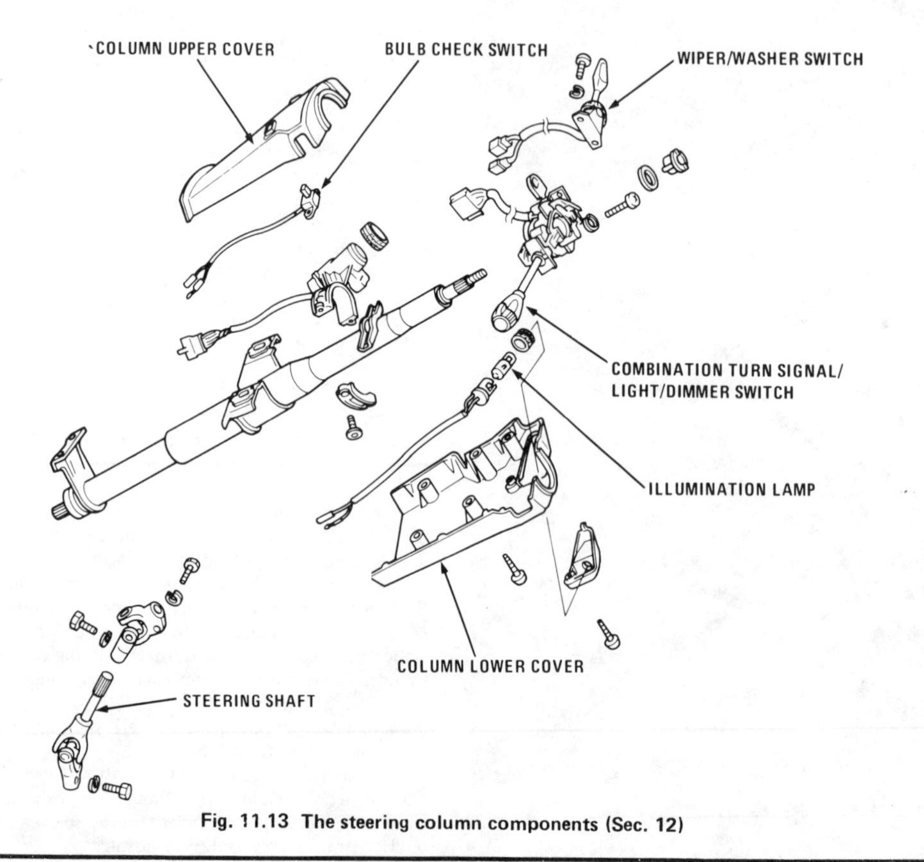

Fig. 11.13 The steering column components (Sec. 12)

11 Steering column lock - removal and refitting

1 Disconnect the lead from the battery negative terminal.
2 Jack up the front roadwheels and turn the steering until the column locks.
3 Remove the lower section of the steering column shroud (four screws).
4 Disconnect the ignition switch wiring connector.
5 The lock/switch assembly is secured to the column by shear bolts and the ends of the bolts will have to be centre-punched and drilled out using a ¼ in (6.35 mm) drill.
6 Install the new lock/switch assembly and screw in the new shear bolts only finger-tight then test the lock for smooth operation by inserting the ignition key and withdrawing it, at the same time turning the steering wheel.
7 If the tongue of the lock is engaging positively in the cut out in the column, then fully tighten the shear bolts evenly, until their heads break off.
8 Reconnect the ignition switch wiring plug and refit the column lower shroud. Lower the jack.

12 Steering column - removal and refitting

1 The column can be removed complete with steering wheel or the steering wheel can be removed first. If the latter method is adopted (see Section 10) then the column must be in the locked position, otherwise the shaft will slip out of the column during removal of the assembly. If the steering column is to be overhauled, it is preferable to remove the steering wheel prior to removing the column.
2 Disconnect the wiring plugs at the side of the column for the ignition switch, the hazard warning switch and the direction indicator, lighting and wiper switches.
3 Set the front roadwheels in the 'straight-ahead' position and then mark the relative alignment of the steering shaft lower universal joint to the pinion shaft.
4 Unscrew and remove the pinch bolt from the lower joint.
5 Unscrew and remove the nuts from the column upper mounting bracket.
6 Unscrew and remove the two bolts from the column lower mounting bracket.
7 Withdraw the steering column assembly into the vehicle interior.
8 Refitting is a reversal of removal. Tighten nuts and bolts to the specified torque and align the marks made before disconnecting the lower joint from the pinion shaft. Ensure that all electrical connections are good prior to refitting the column lower shroud.

13 Steering column - overhaul

1 Having removed the steering column assembly from the vehicle, as described in the preceding Section, remove the steering wheel (if not already removed), as described in Section 10.
2 If damage to the column is suspected due to abuse or previous frontal impact of the vehicle, carry out the following measurements. Renewal of the column bearings or bushes or other components is a waste of time if either the shaft or column do not match specifications as to length. Compare the length of the shaft and column against new ones and if either component measures less, this proves that the component/s have collapsed under impact and must therefore be renewed; no repair is possible.
3 The lower ball bearing can be renewed after removing the universal joint assembly (having marked its relationship to the shaft) and extracting the snap-ring and spacer from the lower end of the column.
4 The upper bush can be removed after withdrawing the combination switch from the column.
5 To reassemble the steering column, first fit the horn earthing ring to the upper end of the column.
6 Fit the corrugated bush and then tap in the plain bush making sure that the flats on the bush align with the slots in the column.
7 Insert the steering shaft into the column from the bottom end.
8 Pack the lower end of the column with grease and fit the ball bearing and snap-ring.
9 Fit the spacer over the bottom end of the steering shaft.
10 Fit the universal joint assembly to the bottom end of the steering shaft so that the marks made before disconnection are aligned.
11 To the top end of the steering column fit the combination switch making sure that the lugs on the switch engage with the slots in the column.
12 Fit the switch cancelling key.
13 The steering wheel can be refitted now or after refitment of the column assembly to the vehicle. Make sure that the steering wheel is correctly aligned to the shaft to give the correct setting of spokes when the front roadwheels are in the 'straight-ahead' position.
14 Tighten all fastenings to the specified torque wrench settings and refer to Section 11 for the fitting procedure of the steering lock, if this has been dismantled. Ensure that the respective switch wires are correctly located prior to refitting the lower shroud.

14 Steering rack and pinion gear - removal and refitting

1 Raise the front of the car and support with chassis stands.
2 Disconnect the trackrod balljoints from the steering knuckle.
3 Disconnect the exhaust pipe from the manifold.

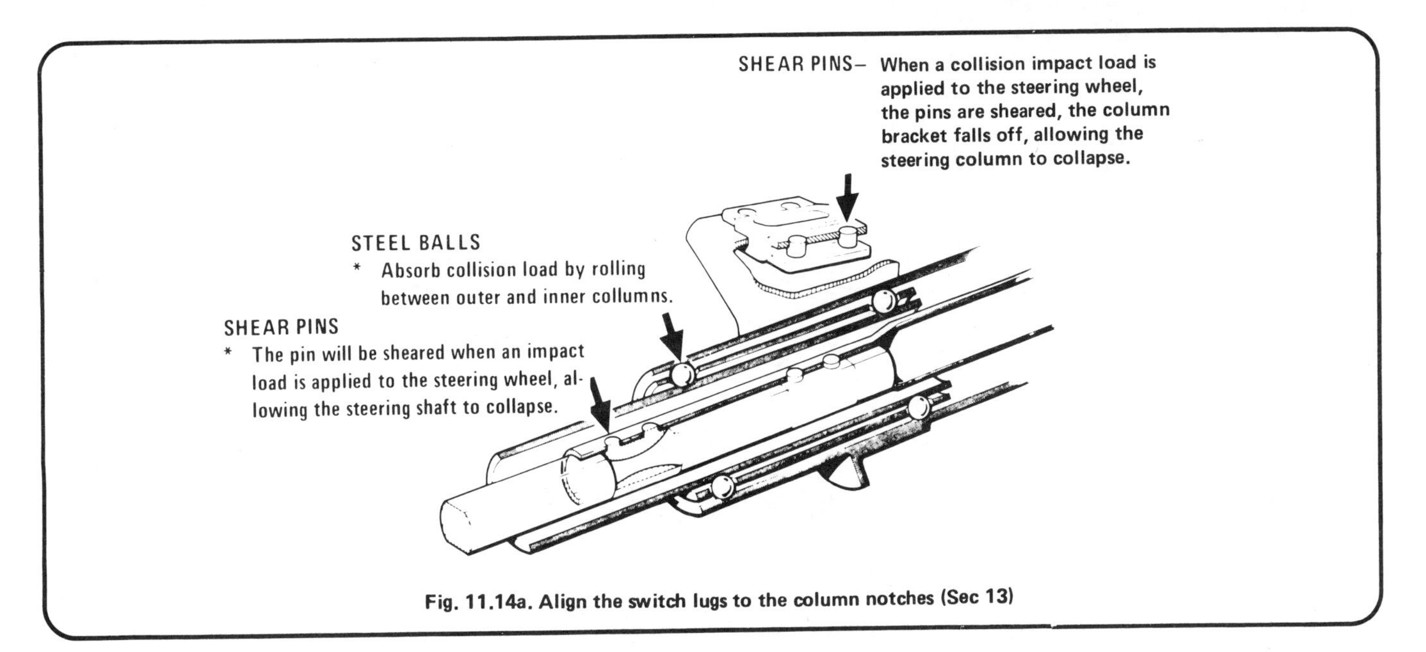
SHEAR PINS– When a collision impact load is applied to the steering wheel, the pins are sheared, the column bracket falls off, allowing the steering column to collapse.
STEEL BALLS
* Absorb collision load by rolling between outer and inner collumns.
SHEAR PINS
* The pin will be sheared when an impact load is applied to the steering wheel, allowing the steering shaft to collapse.

Fig. 11.14a. Align the switch lugs to the column notches (Sec 13)

4 On manual transmission models, disconnect the shift rod linkage by sliding back the spring cover and driving out the location pin using a suitable drift (photo).

5 Unscrew the retaining bolts and remove the engine centre beam (Fig.7.2). Now disconnect the extension torque rod to the gear shift from its engine location.

6 On vehicles fitted with Hondamatic transmission disconnect the speed control cable, and then the splash guard and engine mount.

7 Turn the steering to full right lock, then mark the steering column lower universal joint to the pinion shaft and unscrew and remove the pinch bolt.

8 Unbolt and remove the steering gear mounting brackets.

9 Push the trackrod upwards and tilt the gear from its connection with the lower universal joint. Rotate the gear so that the pinion shaft is pointing downwards and carefully withdraw the assembly from the car.

10 Refitting is the reversal of removal but check the rack adjustment on completion. Tighten all retaining nuts and bolts to the specified torque wrench settings.

15 Steering rack and pinion gear - overhaul

1 Clean the external surfaces of the rack housing.

2 Remove the rack boot air transfer tube, and then undo the boot clamps so that the boots can be moved along the trackrods to expose the trackrod/rack joint.

3 Use a screwdriver to straighten the lockwasher which secures the trackrod/rack joint.

4 Unscrew the trackrods from the end of the rack and recover the rack travel stop washers, and the lockwashers.

5 Turning your attention now to the pinion/rack box, undo and remove the rack adjuster guide screw; the guide screw is locked by a large thin nut and this will have to be loosened before the guide screw can be unscrewed from the rack housing.

6 Recover the rack guide spring, and the guide itself if necessary. Use snap-ring pliers to pull the guide out by gripping the holes in the top of the guide.

7 The pinion assembly can be removed as follows: begin by prising out the pinion shaft oil seal, and then extract the larger snap-ring which retains the pinion shaft assembly in place.

8 The pinion shaft can now be extracted, and once it is out, the small snap-ring on the shaft can be removed so that the ball bearing race can be slid off the shaft. Hold the bearing while lightly tapping the pinion with a light mallet to urge the shaft out of the bearing. Recover the pinion collar.

9 Extract the rack from the rack housing.

10 Lay all the parts out on a clean bench for visual inspection.

11 Examine the teeth of the steering rack and pinion for wear, and if wear is seen, and if when previously in use, the rack movement was felt to be uneven, the only course of action is to renew the whole rack and

14.3 View showing 'A' the shift rod linkage 'B' the extension rod 'C' the steering gear mounting brackets

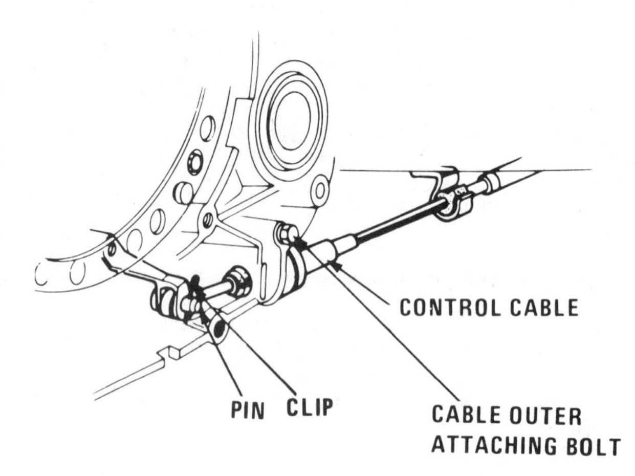

Fig. 11.15. Detach the speed control cable (Hondamatic only) (Sec. 14)

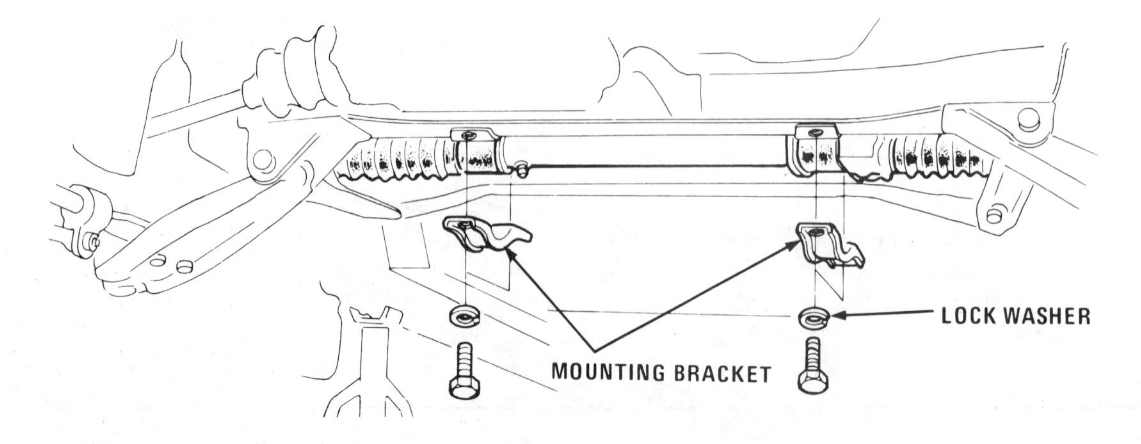

Fig. 11.16. The steering rack mounting brackets (Sec. 14)

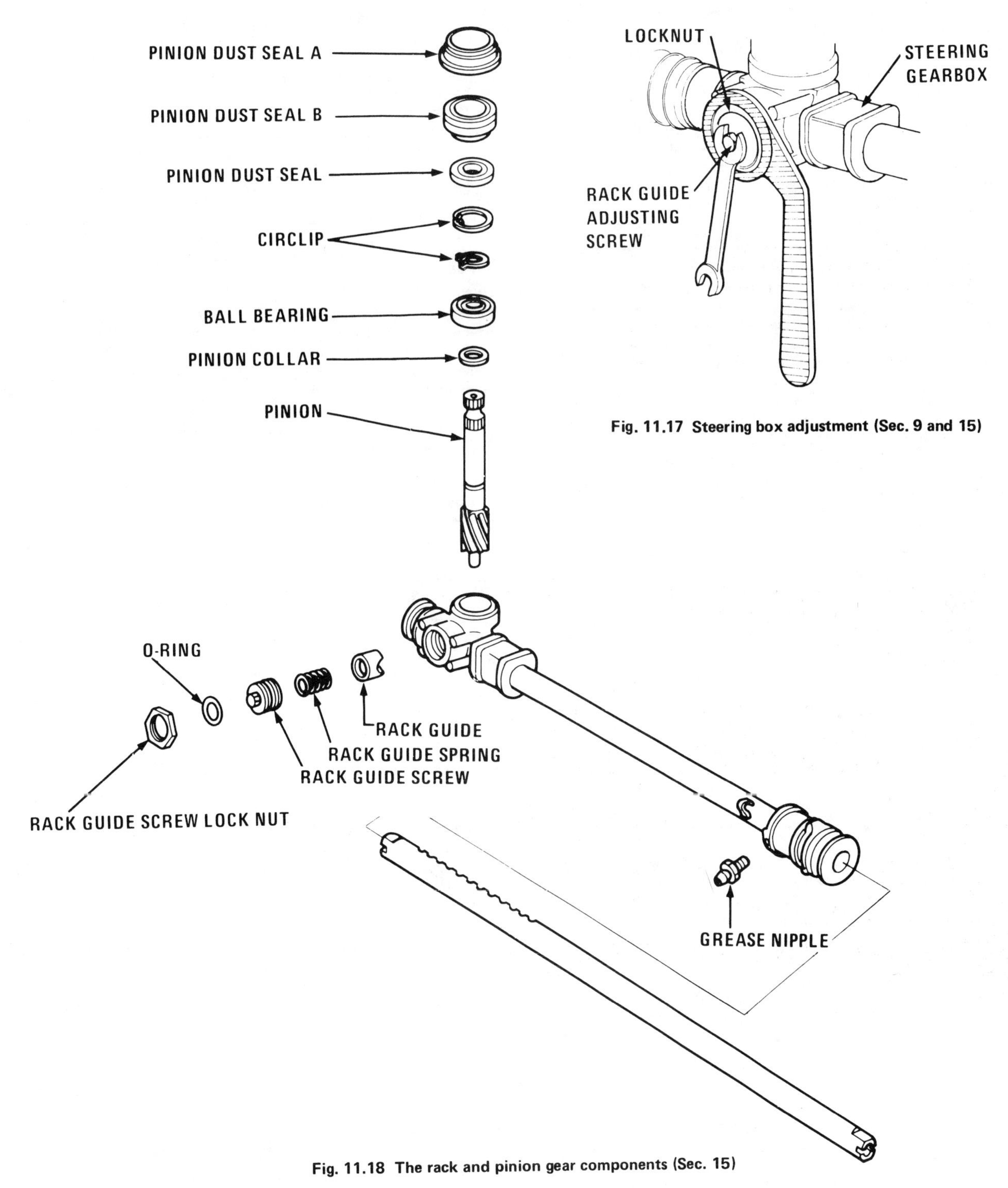

Fig. 11.17 Steering box adjustment (Sec. 9 and 15)

Fig. 11.18 The rack and pinion gear components (Sec. 15)

pinion assembly.

12 Examine the bearing surfaces on the pinion shaft, the ball bearing assembly, and pinion washer - if wear or scoring is seen, renew the appropriate parts.

13 Lastly check the free-length of the rack guide backing spring and if the length does not match with the specification, renew the spring.

Standard length of spring (free)	–	*1.023 in (26 mm)*
Wear limit of spring (free)	–	*0.944 in (24 mm)*

14 The assembly procedure is the reversal of the dismantling sequence, except that the following tasks should be added:

15 Smear all sliding surfaces with grease before assembling in the following sequence. Insert the rack into the rack housing, then assemble the pinion shaft and refit into the rack housing. Once the pinion is engaged with the rack, fit the internal snap-ring which retains the pinion assembly in the rack/pinion housing. Finally fit the grease/dust seal.

16 The next component to be refitted should be the rack guide. Insert it into the rack housing, opposite the pinion shaft; follow it with the backing spring and retaining guide screw. Remember to fit a new 'O' ring to the retaining guide screw, and tighten the guide screw until the rack cannot be moved, then turn the plug back 45° and hold it in that position while the locknut is tightened. The rack should now move smoothly when the steering system has been reassembled. The steering force should be measured at the steering wheel. See Section 9 of this Chapter for steering checks.

17 Having assembled the rack and pinion, the trackrods can be fitted to the rack ends. Fit the travel stop washers and new locking washers.

Make sure that the lockwasher tags engage the slots at each end of the rack, once the trackrod ends have been screwed into the rack and tightened to the specified torque. Finally, the lockwashers should be bent over to lock the trackrod screw.
18 Refit the boots over the rack and trackrod joints and fasten into position, and remember the air transfer tube.
19 The rack and pinion assembly is now ready to be refitted to the car.
20 The grease applied during assembly is the only lubricant required and this should therefore be applied fairly liberally.
21 Every 5000 miles (8000 km) give four or five strokes of the grease gun to the nipple on the rack and pinion housing.

16 Steering angles and front wheel alignment

1 Accurate front wheel alignment is essential for good steering and slow tyre wear. Before considering steering angles, check that the tyres are correctly inflated, that the wheels are not buckled, the hub bearings are not worn and that the steering linkage is in good order without slackness or wear in the joints.
2 Wheel alignment consists of four factors:
Camber, which is the angle at which the wheels are set from vertical when viewed from the front of the vehicle. The camber angle is regarded as positive when the wheels are tilted outwards at the top.
Castor, which is the angle between the steering axis and a vertical line when viewed from the side of the vehicle. The castor angle is regarded as positive when the steering axis is inclined rearward at the top.
Steering axis inclination, which is the angle, when viewed from the front of the vehicle between the vertical and an imaginary line drawn between the upper and lower suspension leg pivots.
Toe-in or toe-out, is the amount by which the wheels deviate from parallel lines drawn through the centre points of the wheel rims. In the case of the vehicles covered by this manual, the front wheel alignment specifies toe-out.
3 All angles except toe-out are set in production and are non-adjustable.
4 It is recommended that front wheel alignment is set by your Honda dealer who will have the necessary setting equipment. However, a reasonably accurate alternative can be carried out in the following way:
5 Place the vehicle on level ground with the wheels in the 'straight-ahead' position.
6 Obtain or make a tracking gauge from metal tubing, having one fixed and one adjustable pointer which will contact the roadwheel outer rims at hub height.
7 Measure the distance between the rim edges at the front of the wheel, withdraw the gauge without altering its setting and push or pull the vehicle until the roadwheel has turned through 180°. Now use the gauge to measure the distance between the rim edges at the rear of the wheel. This dimension should be less by 0.039 in (1.0 mm) than the one previously taken at the front of the wheel and represents the correct toe-out.
8 Where the toe-out is found to be incorrect, slacken the locknuts on each trackrod and rotate each trackrod an exactly equal amount. Turn each trackrod clockwise (when viewed from the centre of the car) to reduce the toe-out or counterclockwise to increase the toe-out.
9 Re-check the alignment using the gauge and then retighten the trackrod end locknuts making sure that the balljoints are in the centre of their arcs of travel and that the rack bellows are not twisted.
10 If after adjustment, the position of the steering wheel spokes has altered, this can be corrected by again releasing the trackrod end locknuts and turning the trackrods, one clockwise and one counter-clockwise, (when viewed from the centre of the vehicle) an exactly equal amount. Retighten the locknuts.

17 Rear wheel alignment

1 The rear roadwheels should be set so that they have the specified toe dimensions.
2 Adjustment is made by releasing the locknuts and adjusting the effective length of the radius rod by turning the camplates equally.
3 It is again recommended that this work is carried out by your Honda dealer unless a tracking gauge can be obtained or made up and used in a similar manner to that described for the front roadwheels in Section 16.
4 Moving the camplates through one notch alters the toe-out by 5 mm (Fig.11.19).

18 Roadwheels and tyres

1 Whenever the roadwheels are removed it is a good idea to clean the insides of the wheels to remove accumulations of mud and in the case of the front ones, disc pad dust.
2 Check the condition of the wheel for rust and repaint if necessary.
3 Examine the wheel stud holes. If these are tending to become elongated or the dished recesses in which the nuts seat have worn or become overcompressed, then the wheel will have to be renewed.
4 With a roadwheel removed, pick out any embedded flints from the tread and check for splits in the sidewalls or damage to the tyre carcass generally.
5 Where the depth of tread pattern is 1 mm or less, the tyre must be renewed.
6 Rotation of the roadwheels to even out wear is a worthwhile idea if the wheels have been balanced off the car. Include the spare wheel in the rotational pattern. With radial tyres, it is recommended that the tyres are moved between front and rear on the same side and not from side to side of the vehicle.
7 If the wheels have been balanced on the car then they cannot be moved round the car as the balance of wheel, tyre and hub will be upset.
8 It is recommended that wheels are re-balanced halfway through the life of the tyres to compensate for the loss of tread rubber due to wear.
9 Finally, always keep the tyres (including the spare) inflated to the recommended pressures and always refit the dust caps on the tyre valves. Tyre pressures are best checked first thing in the morning when the tyres are cold.

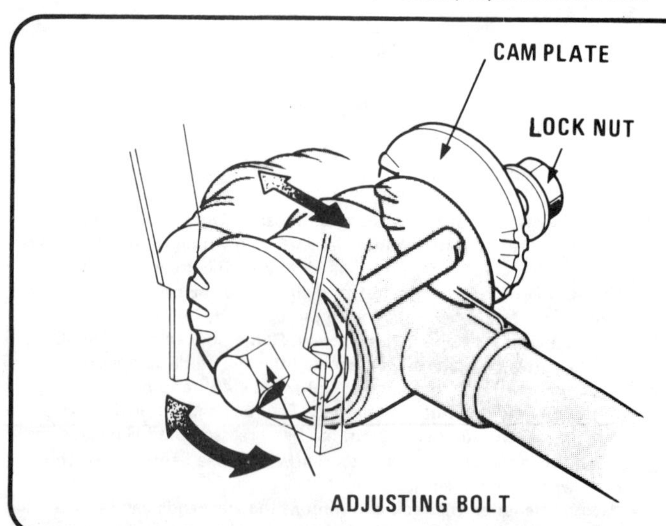

Fig. 11.19. Rear wheel toe-out adjustment (Sec 17).

19 Fault diagnosis - suspension and steering

Symptom	Reason/s
Steering feels vague, car wanders and floats at speed	Tyre pressures uneven. Shock absorbers worn. Spring broken. Steering gear balljoints badly worn. Suspension geometry incorrect. Steering mechanism free play excessive. Front suspension and rear axle pick-up points out of alignment.
Stiff and heavy steering	Tyre pressure too low. Corroded swivel joints. Corroded steering and suspension balljoints. Front wheel toe-out incorrect. Suspension geometry incorrect. Steering gear incorrectly adjusted too tightly. Steering column badly misaligned.
Wheel wobble and vibration	Wheel nuts loose. Front wheels and tyres out of balance. Steering balljoints badly worn. Hub bearings badly worn. Steering gear free play excessive. Front springs weak or broken.

Chapter 12 Bodywork and fittings

For modifications, and information applicable to later models, see Supplement at end of manual

Contents

Specifications

Overall length	162.4 in (4125 mm)
Overall width	63.8 in (1620 mm)
Overall height unladen	52.6 in (1335 mm)
Wheelbase	93.7 in (2380 mm)
Ground clearance	6.9 in (165 mm)
Weight (unladen)	1962 lb (890 kg)

Torque wrench settings	**lb f ft**	**kg fm**
Corner bumper nut	14 to 20	2 to 2.8
Bumper beam mounting bolt	7 to 10	1 to 1.5
Energy absorber mount bolt	13 to 18	2 to 2.5
Energy absorber mount nut	25 to 32	3.5 to 4.5
Bonnet hinge bolts	13 to 19	2 to 2.5

1 General description

The bodyshell and underframe are of a welded all-steel construction. The front wings are attached with bolts and screws and can be removed and refitted economically in the event of damage due to a collision.

Impact absorbing bumpers are fitted front and rear.

Practical clip-on plastic mouldings and panels are extensively used in the interior, and are easily removed for access to the various components.

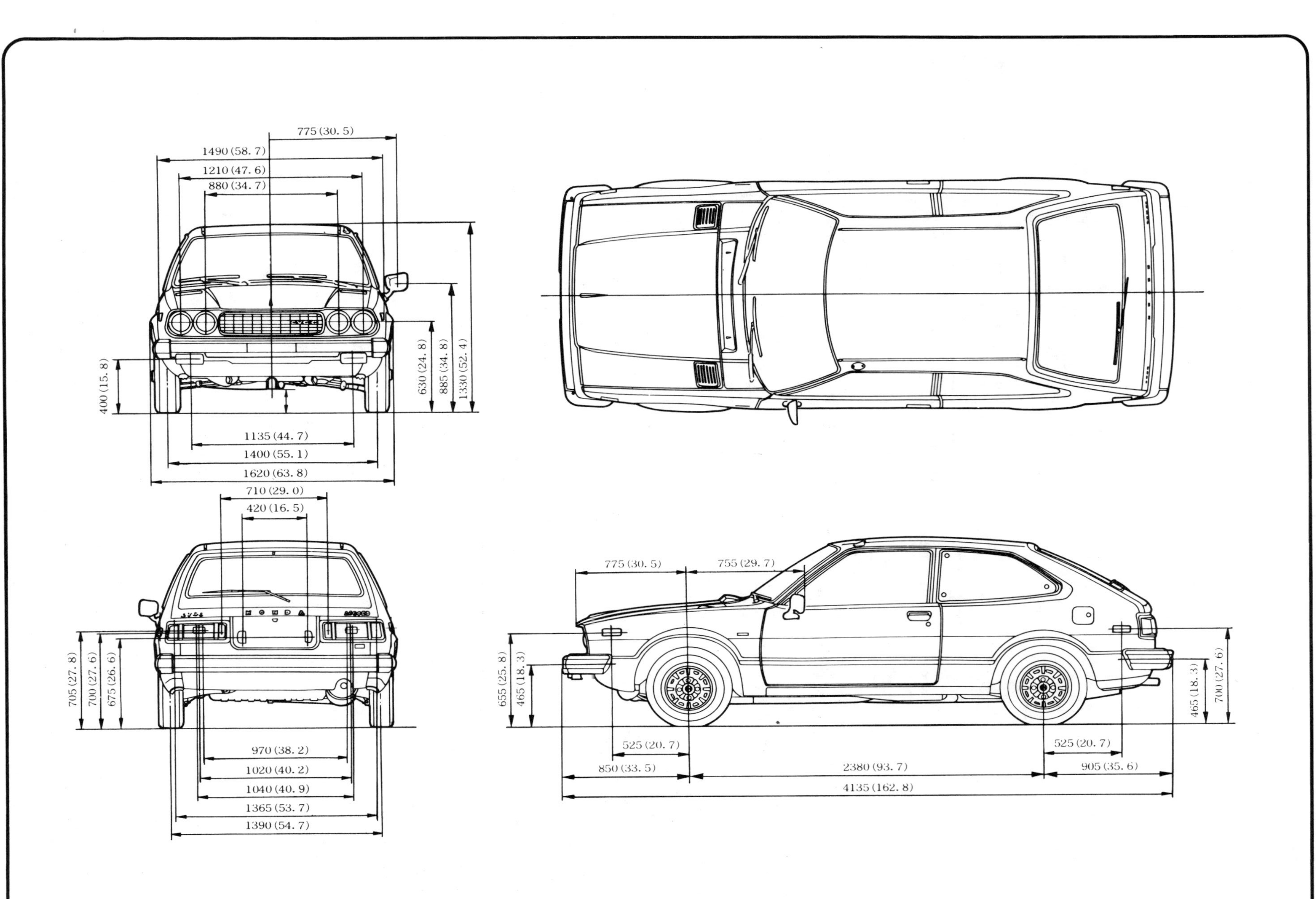

Fig. 12.1. The respective body height and width dimensions (Sec. 1)

2 Maintenance - bodywork and underframe

1 The general condition of a car's bodywork is the one thing that significantly affects its value. Maintenance is easy but needs to be regular. Neglect, particularly after minor damage can lead quickly to further deterioration and costly repair bills. It is important also to keep watch on those parts of the car not immediately visible, for instance, the underframe, inside all the wheel arches and the lower part of the engine compartment.
2 The basic maintenance routine for the bodywork is washing - preferably with a lot of water, from a hose. This will remove all the loose solids which may have stuck to the car. It is important to flush these off in such a way as to prevent grit from scratching the finish. The wheel arches and underframe need washing in the same way to remove any accumulated mud which will retain moisture and tend to encourage rust. Paradoxically enough, the best time to clean the underframe and wheel arches is in wet weather when the mud is thoroughly wet and soft. In very wet weather the underframe is usually cleaned of large accumulations automatically and this is a good time for inspection.
3 Periodically it is a good idea to have the whole of the underframe of the car steam cleaned, engine compartment included, so that a thorough inspection can be carried out to see what minor repairs and renovations are necessary. Steam cleaning is available at many garages and is necessary for removal of the accumulation of oily grime which sometimes is allowed to cake thick in certain areas near the engine, gearbox and back axle. If steam cleaning facilities are not available, there are one or two excellent grease solvents available which can be brush applied. The dirt can then be simply hosed off.
4 After washing paintwork, wipe off with a chamois leather to give an unspotted clear finish. A coat of clear protective wax polish will give added protection against chemical pollutants in the air. If the paintwork sheen has dulled or oxidised, use a cleaner/polisher combination to restore the brilliance of the shine. This requires a little effort, but is usually caused because regular washing has been neglected. Always check that the door and ventilator opening drain holes and pipes are completely clear so that water can be drained out. Bright work should be treated the same way as paintwork. Windscreens and windows can be kept clear of the smeary film which often appears if a little ammonia is added to the water. If they are scratched, a good rub with a proprietary metal polish will often clear them. Never use any form of wax or other body or chromium polish on glass.

3 Maintenance - upholstery and carpets

1 Mats and carpets should be brushed or vacuum cleaned regularly to keep them free of grit. If they are badly stained remove them from the car for scrubbing or sponging and make quite sure they are dry before refitting. Seats and interior trim panels can be kept clean by a wipe over with a damp cloth. If they do become stained (which can be more apparent on light coloured upholstery) use a little liquid detergent and a soft nail brush to scour the grime out of the grain of the material. Do not forget to keep the head lining clean in the same way as the upholstery. When using liquid cleaners inside the car do not over-wet the surfaces being cleaned. Excessive damp could get into the seams and padded interior causing stains, offensive odours or even rot. If the inside of the car gets wet accidentally it is worthwhile taking some trouble to dry it out properly, particularly where carpets are involved. *Do not leave oil or electric heaters inside the car for this purpose.*

4 Minor body damage - repair

The photographic sequence on pages 190 and 191, illustrate the operations detailed in the following sub-Sections.

Repair of minor scratches in the car's bodywork

If the scratch is very superficial, and does not penetrate to the metal of the bodywork, repair is very simple. Lightly rub the area of the scratch with a paintwork renovator, or a very fine cutting paste, to remove loose paint from the scratch and to clear the surrounding bodywork of wax polish. Rinse the area with clean water.

Apply touch-up paint to the scratch using a thin paintbrush, continue to apply thin layers of paint until the surface of the paint in the scratch is level with the surrounding paintwork. Allow the new paint at least two weeks to harden; then, blend it into the surrounding paintwork by rubbing the paintwork, in the scratch area, with a paintwork renovator, or a very fine cutting paste. Finally, apply wax polish.

Where the scratch has penetrated right through to the metal of the bodywork, causing the metal to rust, a different repair technique is required. Remove any loose rust from the bottom of the scratch with a penknife, then apply rust inhibiting paint to prevent the formation of rust in the future. Using a rubber or nylon applicator, fill the scratch with bodystopper paste. If required, this paste can be mixed with cellulose thinners to provide a very thin paste, which is an ideal way of filling narrow scratches. Before the stopper-paste in the scratch hardens, wrap a piece of smooth cotton rag around the top of a finger. Dip the finger in cellulose thinners and then quickly sweep it across the surface of the stopper-paste in the scratch; this will ensure that the surface of the stopper-paste is slightly hollowed. The scratch can now be painted over as described earlier in this Section.

Repair of dents in the car's bodywork

When deep denting of the car's bodywork has taken place, the first task is to pull the dent out, until the affected bodywork almost attains its original shape. There is little point in trying to restore the original shape completely, as the metal in the damaged area will have stretched on impact and cannot be reshaped fully to its original contour. It is better to bring the level of the dent up to a point which is about 1/8 inch (3 mm) below the level of the surrounding bodywork. In cases where the dent is very shallow anyway, it is not worth trying to pull it out at all. If the underside of the dent is accessible, it can be hammered out gently from behind, using a mallet with a wooden or plastic head. Whilst doing this, hold a suitable block of wood firmly against the impact from the hammer blows and thus prevent a large area of the bodywork from being 'belled-out'.

Should the dent be in a section of the bodywork which has a double skin or some other factor making it inaccessible from behind, a different technique is called for. Drill several small holes through the metal inside the dent area - particularly in the deeper sections. Then screw long self-tapping screws into the holes just sufficiently for them to gain a good purchase in the metal. Now the dent can be pulled out by pulling on the protruding heads of the screws with a pair of pliers.

The next stage of the repair is the removal of the paint from the damaged area, and from an inch or so of the surrounding 'sound' bodywork. This is accomplished more easily by using a wire brush or abrasive pad on a power drill, although it can be done just as effectively by hand using sheets of abrasive paper. To complete the preparations for filling, score the surface of the bare metal with a screwdriver or the tang of a file, or alternatively, drill small holes in the affected area. This will provide a really good 'key' for the filler paste.

To complete the repair see the Section on filling and re-spraying.

Repair of rust holes or gashes in the car's bodywork

Remove all paint from the affected area and from an inch or so of the surrounding 'sound' bodywork, using an abrasive pad or a wire brush on a power drill. If these are not available a few sheets of abrasive paper will do the job just as effectively, With the paint removed you will be able to gauge the severity of the corrosion and therefore decide whether to renew the whole panel (if this is possible) or to repair the affected area. New body panels are not as expensive as most people think and it is often quicker and more satisfactory to fit a new panel than to attempt to repair large areas of corrosion.

Remove all fittings from the affected area except those which will act as a guide to the original shape of the damaged bodywork (headlamp shells etc). Then, using tin snips or a hacksaw blade, remove all loose metal and any other metal badly affected by corrosion. Hammer the edges of the hole inwards in order to create a slight depression for the filler paste.

Wire brush the affected area to remove the powdery rust from the surface of the remaining metal. Paint the affected area with rust inhibiting paint; if the back of the rusted area is accessible treat this also.

Before filling can take place it will be necessary to block the hole in some way. This can be achieved by the use of one of the following materials: Zinc gauze, Aluminium tape or Polyurethane foam.

Zinc gauze is probably the best material to use for a large hole. Cut a piece to the approximate size and shape of the hole to be filled, then position it in the hole so that its edges are below the level of the surrounding bodywork. It can be retained in position by several blobs of filler paste around its periphery.

Aluminium tape should be used for small or very narrow holes. Pull a piece off the roll and trim it to the approximate size and shape required, then pull off the backing paper (if used) and stick the tape over the hole; it can be overlapped if the thickness of one piece is insufficient. Burnish down the edges of the tape with the handle of a screwdriver or similar, to ensure that the tape is securely attached to the metal underneath.

Polyurethane foam is best used where the hole is situated in a section of bodywork of complex shape, backed by a small box section (eg, where the sill panel meets the rear wheel arch - most cars). The usual mixing procedure for this foam is as follows: Put equal amounts of fluid from each of the two cans provided in the kit, into one container. Stir until the mixture begins to thicken, then quickly pour this mixture into the hole, and hold a piece of cardboard over the larger apertures. Almost immediately the polyurethane will begin to expand, gushing out of any small holes left unblocked, When the foam hardens it can be cut back to just below the level of the surrounding bodywork with a hacksaw blade.

Bodywork repairs - filling and re-spraying

Before using this Section, see the Sections on dent, deep scratch, rust hole, and gash repairs.

Many types of bodyfiller are available, but generally speaking those proprietary kits which contain a tin of filler paste and a tube of resin hardener are best for this type of repair. A wide, flexible, plastic or nylon applicator will be found invaluable for imparting a smooth and well contoured finish to the surface of the filler.

Mix up a little filler on a clean piece of card or board - use the hardener sparingly (follow the maker's instructions on the packet) otherwise the filler will set very rapidly.

Using the applicator, apply the filler paste to the prepared area; draw the applicator across the surface of the filler to achieve the correct contour and to level the filler surface. As soon as a contour that approximates the correct one is achieved, stop working the paste - if you carry on too long the paste will become sticky and begin to pick up' on the applicator. Continue to add thin layers of filler paste at twenty minute intervals until the level of the filler is just 'proud' of the surrounding bodywork.

Once the filler has hardened, excess can be removed using a metal plane or file. From then on, progressively finer grades of abrasive paper should be used, starting with a 40 grade production paper and finishing with 400 grade 'wet-or-dry' paper. Always wrap the abrasive paper around a flat rubber, cork, or wooden block - otherwise the surface of the filler will not be completely flat. During the smoothing of the filler surface the 'wet-or-dry' paper should be periodically rinsed in water. This will ensure that a very smooth finish is imparted to the filler at the final stage.

At this stage the 'dent' should be surrounded by a ring of bare metal, which in turn should be encircled by the finely 'feathered' edge of the good paintwork. Rinse the repair area with clean water, until all of the dust produced by the rubbing-down operation has gone.

Spray the whole repair area with a light coat of primer - this will show up any imperfections in the surface of the filler. Repair these imperfections with fresh filler paste or bodystopper, and once more smooth the surface with abrasive paper. If bodystopper is used, it can be mixed with cellulose thinners to form a really thin paste which is ideal for filling small holes. Repeat this spray and repair procedure until you are satisfied that the surface of the filler, and the feathered edge of the paintwork are perfect. Clean the repair area with clean water and allow to dry fully.

The repair area is now ready for spraying. Paint spraying must be carried out in a warm, dry, windless and dust free atmosphere. This condition can be created artificially, if you have access to a large indoor working area, but if you are forced to work in the open, you will have to pick your day very carefully. If you are working indoors, dousing the floor in the work area with water will 'lay' the dust which would otherwise be in the atmosphere. If the repair area is confined to one body panel, mask off the surrounding panels; this will help to minimise the effects of a slight mis-match in paint colour. Bodywork fittings (eg, chrome strips, door handles etc.,) will also need to be masked off. Use genuine masking tape and several thicknesses of newspaper for the masking operation.

Before commencing to spray, agitate the aerosol can thoroughly, then spray a test area (an old tin, or similar) until the technique is mastered. Cover the repair area with a thick coat of primer; the thickness should be built up using several thin layers of paint rather than one thick one. Using 400 grade 'wet-or-dry' paper, rub down the surface of the primer until it is really smooth. While doing this, the work area should be thoroughly doused with water, and the 'wet-and-dry' paper periodically rinsed in water. Allow to dry before spraying on more paint.

Spray on the top coat again building up the thickness by using several thin layers of paint. Start spraying in the centre of the repair area and then, using a circular motion, work outwards until the whole repair area and about 2 inches of the surrounding original paintwork is covered. Remove all masking material 10 to 15 minutes after spraying on the final coat of paint.

Allow the new paint at least 2 weeks to harden fully, then, using a paintwork renovator or a very fine cutting paste, blend the edges of the new paint into the existing paintwork. Finally, apply wax polish.

5 Major body damage - repair

1 Because the body is built on the unitary principle, major damage must be repaired by a competent body repairer with the necessary jigs and equipment.
2 In the event of a crash that resulted in buckling of body panels, or damage to the roadwheels, the car must be taken to a Honda dealer or body repairer where the bodyshell and suspension alignment may be checked.
3 Body shell and/or suspension mis-alignment will cause excessive wear of the tyres, steering system and possibly transmission. The handling of the car also will be affected adversely.

6 Doors - tracing and rectifying rattles

1 The most common cause of door rattles is a misaligned, loose or worn striker, but other causes may be:

a) Loose door handles, window winder handles and door hinges.
b) Loose, worn or misaligned door lock components.
c) Loose or worn remote control mechanism.

2 It is quite possible for door rattles to be the result of a combination of these faults, so careful examination must be made to determine the cause of the noise.
3 If the leading edge from the striker loop is worn, and as a result the door rattles, renew it and adjust the position.
4 If the leading edge of the lock pawl is worn, and as a result the door rattles, fit a new door latch assembly.
5 Examine the hinge; it is quite possible that it has worn and caused rattles. Renew the hinge if necessary.

7 Bonnet and latch - removal and refitting

Bonnet

1 Release the bonnet catch but do not raise the bonnet.
2 The bonnet is hinged at the front and the hinge retaining bolts are accessible through the front grille using a socket (box wrench) and extension.
3 On removing the bolts, get an assistant to help lift the bonnet clear and avoid damaging the paintwork.
4 Refitting is the reversal of removal. Refit any hinge shims removed.

Bonnet latch

5 Lift and support the bonnet. Scribe marks around the latch for alignment during reassembly.
6 Unscrew the latch retaining bolts and then disconnect the release cable and remove the latch (photo).

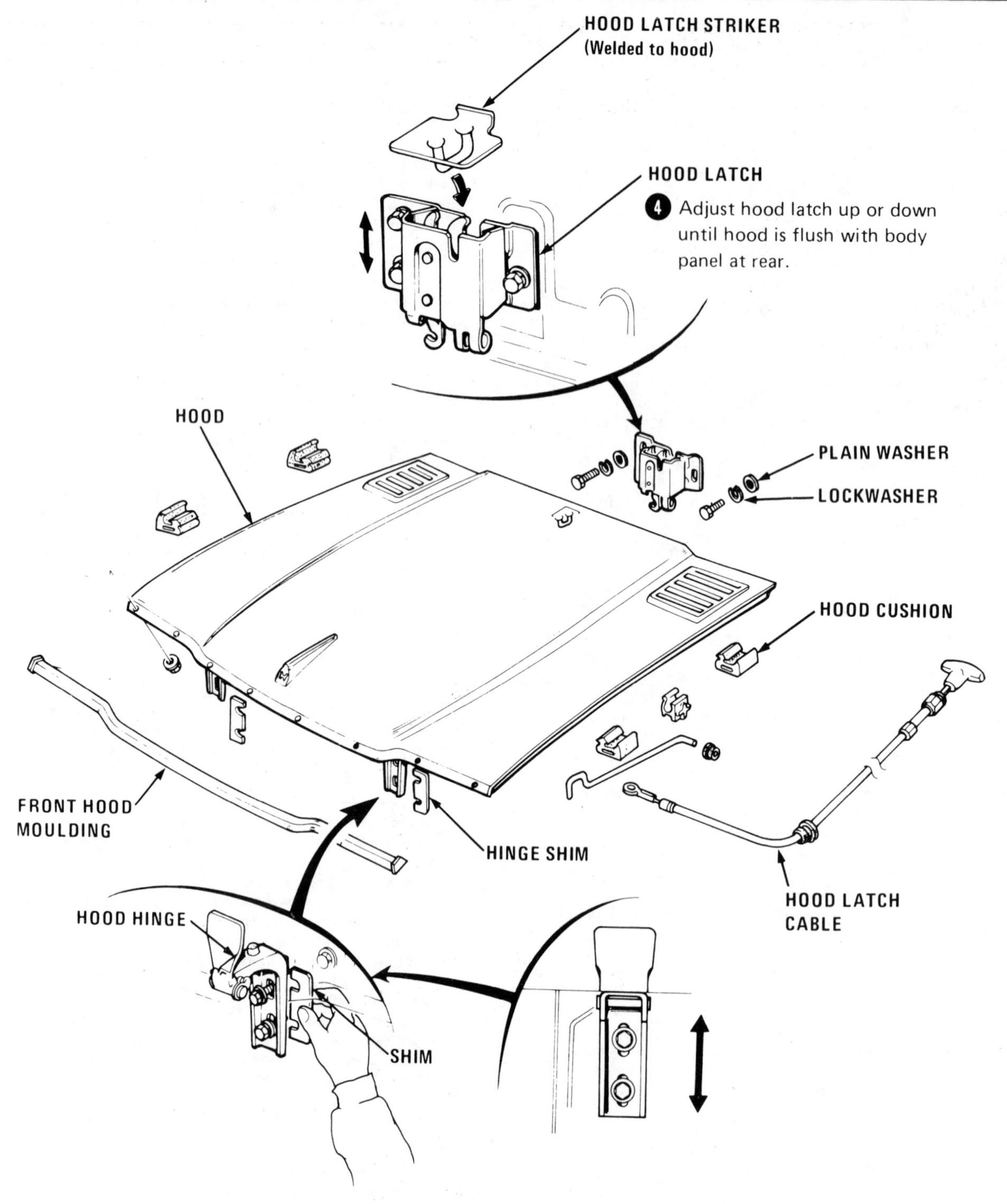

Fig. 12.2. The bonnet and fittings (Sec. 7)

7 Refit the latch in the reverse order but ensure that when refitted, the bonnet is securely locked when closed. Adjust the latch position if necessary.

8 Bumpers - removal and refitting (N. American models)

Front bumper

1 Disconnect the front side and indicator light wiring underneath the bumper.

2 Unscrew the bumper bracket retaining nuts and remove with washers.

3 Unclip the corner bumpers from their locations in the wing panels at the side and remove the bumpers.

4 The bumper can be further dismantled by referring to Fig. 12.3. for the renewal or repair of certain items.

5 Refit in the reverse order to removal.

Rear bumper

6 Unscrew and remove the bumper to mounting bolts. Detach the corner bumpers from the body panel at the side and remove the bumper.

7 The bumper can be further dismantled by referring to Fig. 12.4. for repair or renewal of individual components.

8 Refit in the reverse order to removal.

7.6 The bonnet latch and release cable

9 Front wing - removal and refitting

1 Disconnect the earth (ground) cable from the battery terminal.
2 Remove the bonnet as described in Section 7.
3 Disconnect the side marker light leads.
4 Using a wire brush, clean any dirt and/or underseal from the respective wing retaining bolts, and apply penetrating fluid to assist removal.
5 Mark the wing joint outline position to assist with re-alignment on refitting.
6 Unscrew and remove the front trim chrome retaining screws. Unclip the front corner bumper from the wing panel.
7 Unscrew and remove the wing retaining bolts from the top inner channel, the lower inner edge to lower front panel, the inner wing stay support, the top rear retaining bolt (open the door for access), and the lower bolt at the forward end of the door sill. Remove the wing.
8 Clean away all old mastic and paint any rusty or corroded metal work with protective paint.
9 The new wing will be supplied in primer.
10 Locate a thick bead of mastic on the mating flange of the body and install the wing. Insert and tighten the securing bolts and screws. Do not tighten the bolts until they are all fully located.
11 Reconnect the side marker light.
12 Apply a coating of underseal to the wing panel underneath and refinish the outside to match the rest of the body paintwork.

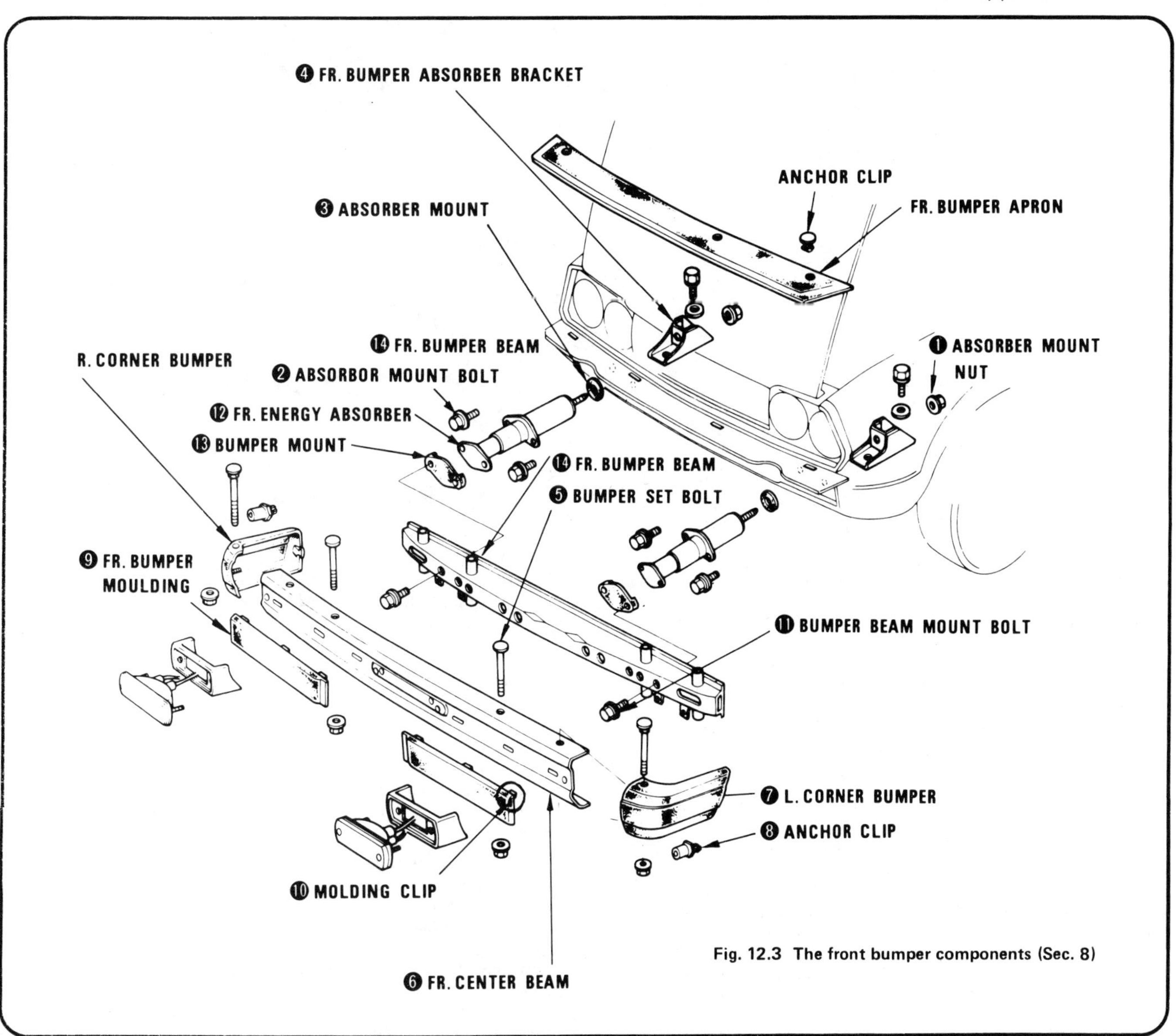

Fig. 12.3 The front bumper components (Sec. 8)

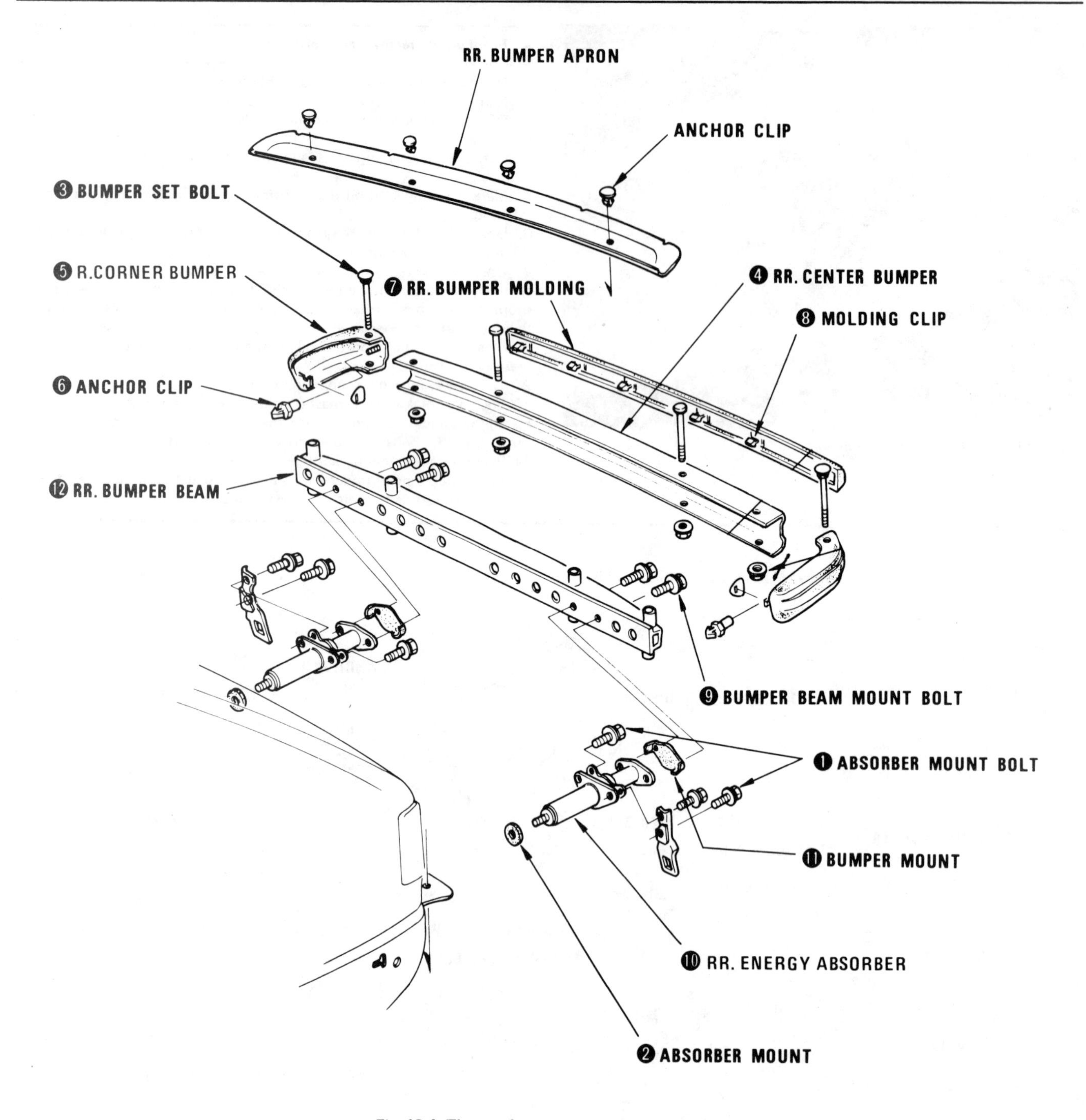

Fig. 12.4. The rear bumper components (Sec. 8)

13 If required the motif can be unclipped from the side of the original wing and refitted to the new one.

10 Front grille - removal and refitting

1 Unscrew the right and left-hand headlamp garnish retaining screws and remove each garnish.
2 Carefully prise the lower grille moulding free taking care not to distort it.
3 Unscrew and remove the front grille retaining screws and lift the grille clear.
4 Refitting the grille is a reversal of the removal sequence.

11 Tailgate, opening support, striker plate and latch - removal, refitting and adjustment

Tailgate and opening support

1 Raise the tailgate and get an assistant to support the tailgate during removal and refitting.
2 Unscrew and remove the tailgate support retaining bolts from the tailgate.
3 Disconnect the rear window demister cable and the rear window washer feed tube.
4 Prise the rear of the headlining free to gain access to the tailgate hinge bolts, then unscrew and remove the bolts. Carefully lift the

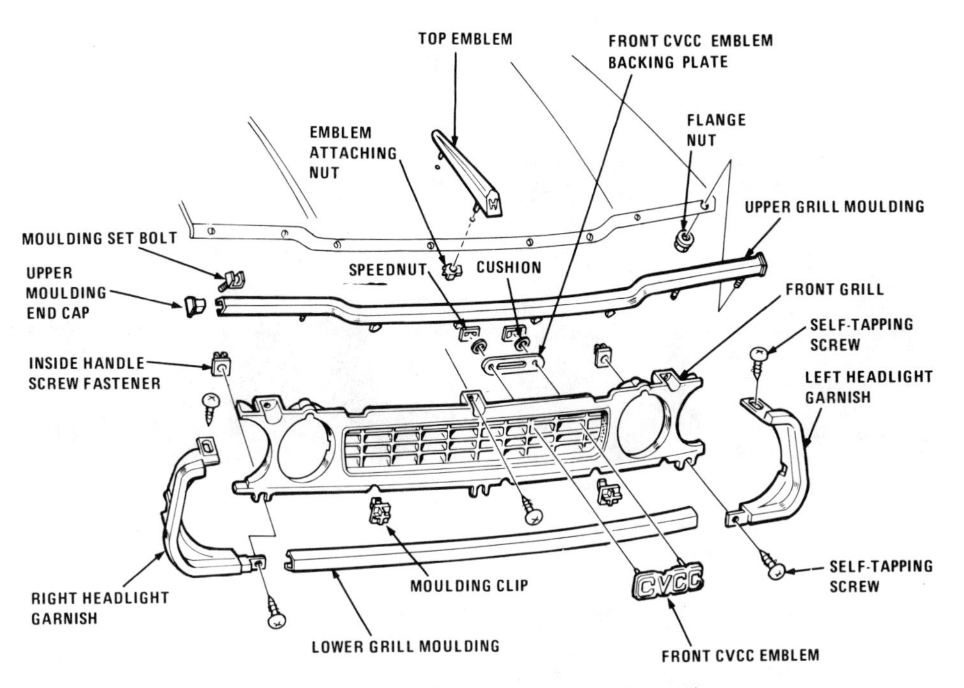

Fig. 12.5. The front grille components (Sec. 10)

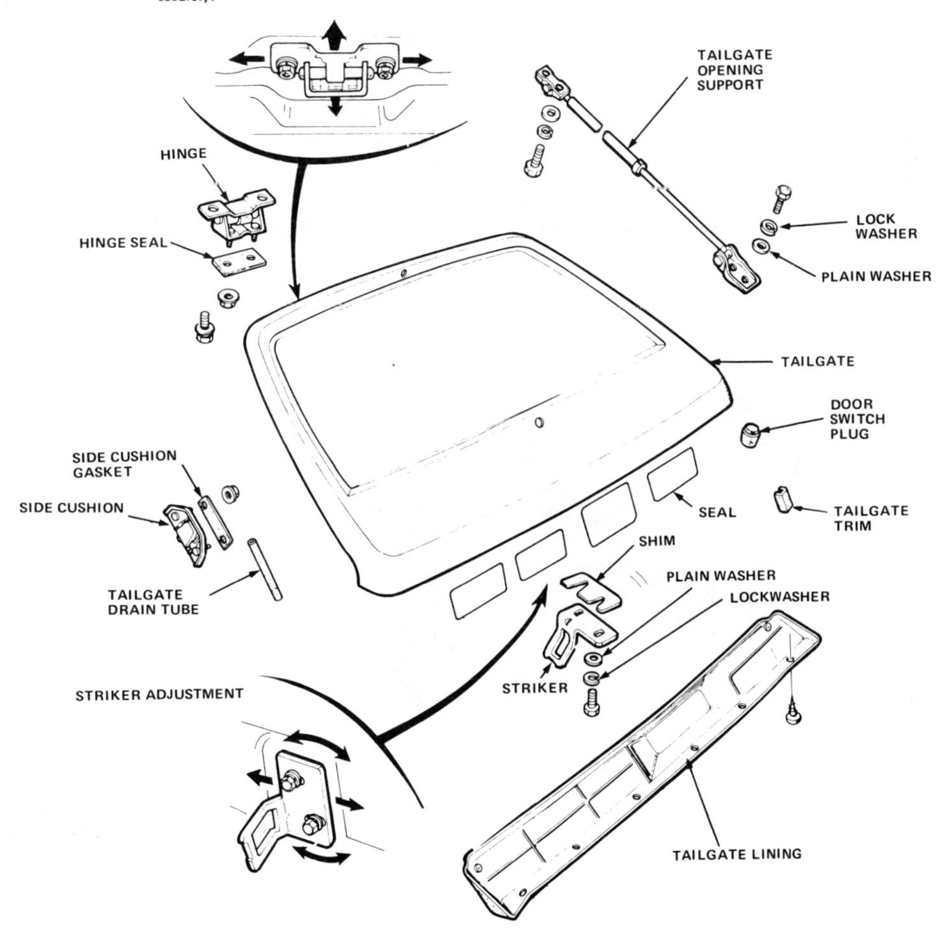

Fig. 12.6 The tailgate and opening support fittings (Sec. 11)

This sequence of photographs deals with the repair of the dent and paintwork damage shown in this photo. The procedure will be similar for the repair of a hole. It should be noted that the procedures given here are simplified – more explicit instructions will be found in the text

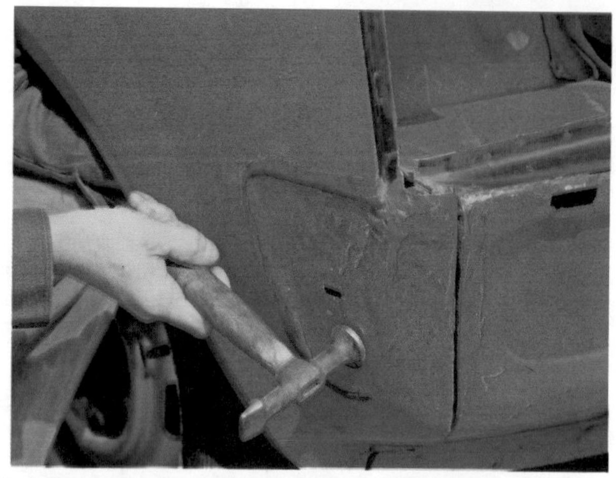

In the case of a dent the first job – after removing surrounding trim – is to hammer out the dent where access is possible. This will minimise filling. Here, the large dent having been hammered out, the damaged area is being made slightly concave

Now all paint must be removed from the damaged area, by rubbing with coarse abrasive paper. Alternatively, a wire brush or abrasive pad can be used in a power drill. Where the repair area meets good paintwork, the edge of the paintwork should be 'feathered', using a finer grade of abrasive paper

In the case of a hole caused by rusting, all damaged sheet-metal should be cut away before proceeding to this stage. Here, the damaged area is being treated with rust remover and inhibitor before being filled

Mix the body filler according to its manufacturer's instructions. In the case of corrosion damage, it will be necessary to block off any large holes before filling – this can be done with aluminium or plastic mesh, or aluminium tape. Make sure the area is absolutely clean before ...

... applying the filler. Filler should be applied with a flexible applicator, as shown, for best results; the wooden spatula being used for confined areas. Apply thin layers of filler at 20-minute intervals, until the surface of the filler is slightly proud of the surrounding bodywork

Initial shaping can be done with a Surform plane or Dreadnought file. Then, using progressively finer grades of wet-and-dry paper, wrapped around a sanding block, and copious amounts of clean water, rub down the filler until really smooth and flat. Again, feather the edges of adjoining paintwork

The whole repair area can now be sprayed or brush-painted with primer. If spraying, ensure adjoining areas are protected from over-spray. Note that at least one inch of the surrounding sound paintwork should be coated with primer. Primer has a 'thick' consistency, so will find small imperfections

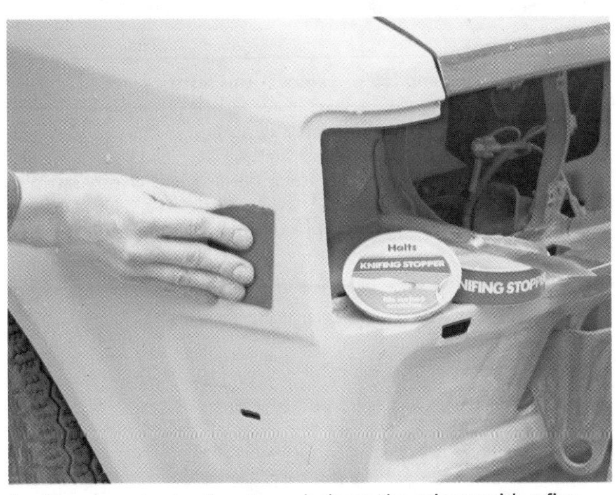

Again, using plenty of water, rub down the primer with a fine grade wet-and-dry paper (400 grade is probably best) until it is really smooth and well blended into the surrounding paintwork. Any remaining imperfections can now be filled by carefully applied knifing stopper paste

When the stopper has hardened, rub down the repair area again before applying the final coat of primer. Before rubbing down this last coat of primer, ensure the repair area is blemish-free – use more stopper if necessary. To ensure that the surface of the primer is really smooth use some finishing compound

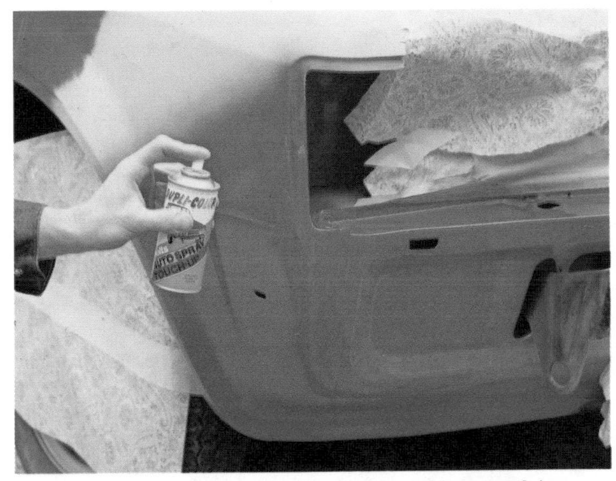

The top coat can now be applied. When working out of doors, pick a dry, warm and wind-free day. Ensure surrounding areas are protected from over-spray. Agitate the aerosol thoroughly, then spray the centre of the repair area, working outwards with a circular motion. Apply the paint as several thin coats

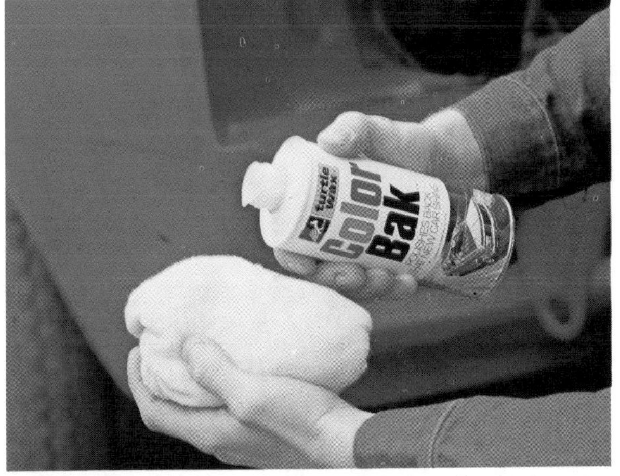

After a period of about two weeks, which the paint needs to harden fully, the surface of the repaired area can be 'cut' with a mild cutting compound prior to wax polishing. When carrying out bodywork repairs, remember that the quality of the finished job is proportional to the time and effort expended

tailgate clear.
5 Refitting is a reversal of removal. Adjust as follows.

Tailgate adjustment
6 With the hinge mounting bolts loosened, align the tailgate evenly with the aperture of the rear of the body and retain in this position whilst tightening the hinge bolts.

Striker plate
7 This is retained by two bolts and shims are fitted if necessary for depth adjustment.
8 Mark the position of the striker plate if it is to be removed to assist alignment on refitting and note the number of shims. Unscrew the two bolts to remove.
9 Refit in the reverse order. If adjustment is required, slacken the retaining bolts and readjust the striker as required. The tailgate should shut flush in alignment with the body at its lower edge.

Tailgate latch
10 Raise and support the tailgate, then remove the inner rear panel. Unscrew the three latch retaining screws.
11 Disconnect the latch to lock connecting rod and detach the cable. Disconnect the warning light cable and remove the latch.
12 Refitting is a reversal of removal.

12 Tailgate cable - removal and refitting

1 Using a screwdriver as a lever, slide the tailgate knob from the lever as in Fig. 12.8.
2 Detach the side garnish.
3 Unscrew the retaining bolts and remove the tailgate opener. Loosen the locknut and remove the cable from the opener.
4 Prise the rear body panel free and remove it. Disconnect the tailgate lock to latch rod and detach the cable from the latch (Fig. 12.9).
5 The cable can now be refitted in the reverse sequence to removal. Adjustment is provided by turning the adjusting nut as required and then tightening the locknut against the opener.

13 Door interior trim panel - removal and refitting

1 Press the bezel which surrounds the window regulator handle inwards and extract the securing clip using a piece of hooked wire or a thin screwdriver (photo).
2 Withdraw the window regulator handle from the shaft.
3 Remove the arm rest (two screws) (photo).
4 Unscrew the single screw retaining the front corner panel and remove the panel (photo).
5 Extract the single screw and withdraw the dished plate from behind the door remote control lever (photo).
6 Insert a flat blade at the bottom edge of the door and prise the trim panel from the door. Now insert the fingers and working round the edge of the door release all the panel clips and lift the panel away (photo).
7 Carefully peel off the waterproof sheet from the door.
8 Refitting is a reversal of removal but use new trim panel clips where required and install the regulator handle with the glass fully raised.

14 Door glass, lock and latch - removal and refitting

1 Remove the interior trim panel as described in the preceding Section.
2 Using a screwdriver, prise out the moulding and weatherstrip from the glass slot in the door frame.
3 Temporarily refit the window regulator handle and wind the glass

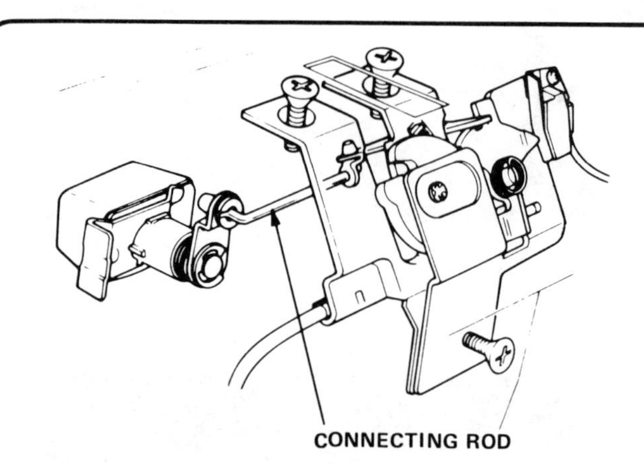

Fig. 12.7 The tailgate latch (Sec. 11)

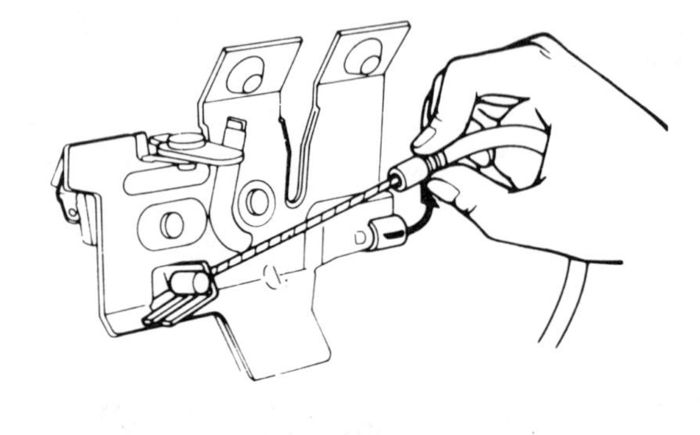

Fig. 12.9 Disconnect the cable from the latch (Sec. 12)

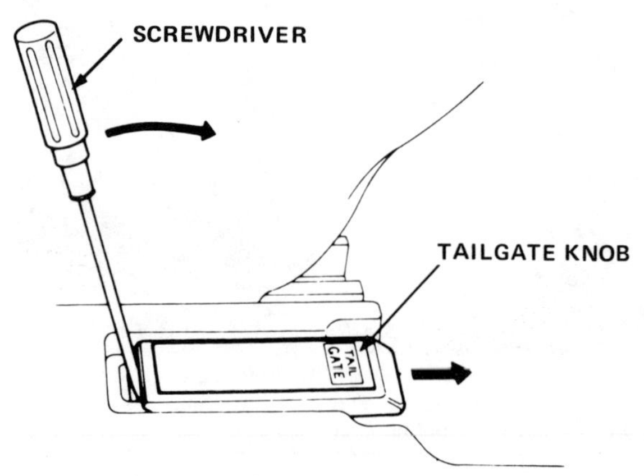

Fig. 12.8 Method of removing the tailgate release knob (Sec. 12)

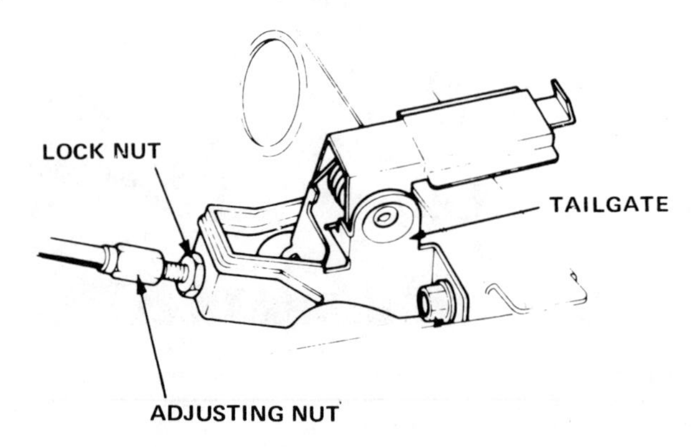

Fig. 12.10 Tailgate release and adjustment nut for the cable (Sec. 12)

DOOR MOULDING
PLAIN WASHER
LOCK WASHER
UPPER HINGE
OUTER DOOR SEAL
CLIP
*Pry up to release clips
release clips.
LOWER HINGE
INSIDE HANDLE CASE
DOOR SWITCH PLUG
SELF-TAPPING SCREW
INSIDE HANDLE CASE
CLIP
SEAL
ESCUTCHEON PLATE
CLIP
INNER DOOR SEAL
LINING
REGULATOR HANDLE
Loosen hinge bolts and adjust in or out until door is flush with body
SELF-TAPPING SCREW 6 x 16
DOOR HOLE VALVE
DOOR HANDLE
INSIDE HANDLE SCREW FASTENER

Fig. 12.11 The door and trim components (Sec. 13)

13.1 Remove the regulator handle and retaining clip

13.3 Remove the armrest

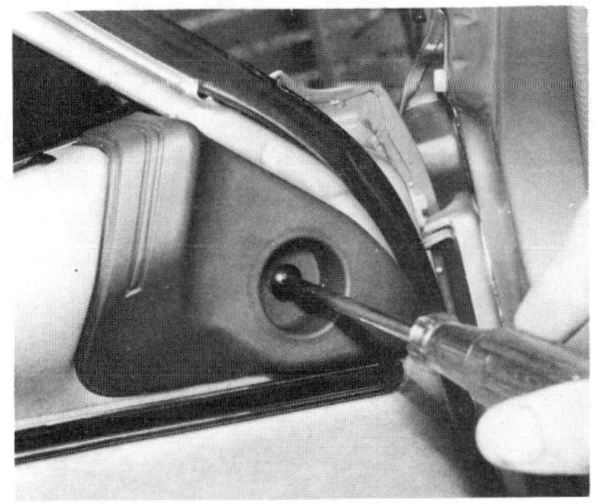

13.4 Remove the front corner panel

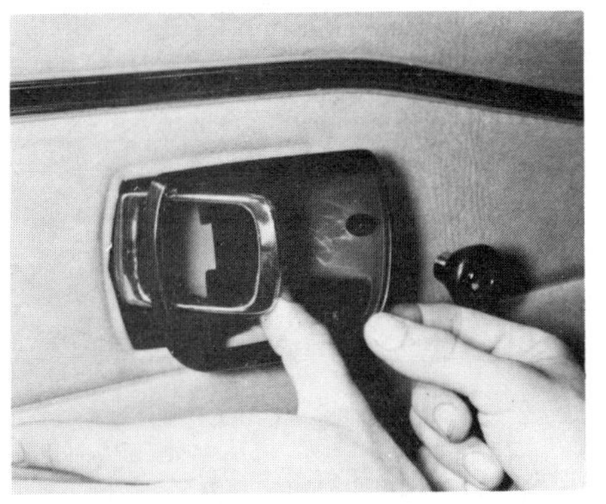

13.5 Withdraw the dished plate

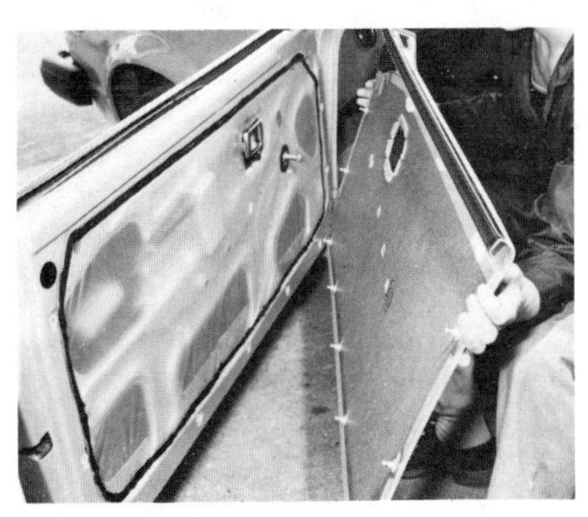

13.6 Remove the panel

to a position where the regulator channel to glass retainer channel securing bolts can be removed through the inner door panel (photo).
4 Remove the six bolts retaining the window regulator mechanism and withdraw the mechanism.
5 Remove the glass guide channel.
6 Disconnect the connecting rods to the exterior door handle, and the lock cylinder. Prise the lock cylinder retaining spring free and remove the lock. Unscrew the retaining nuts and remove the exterior handle. Do not alter the position of the connecting rod to exterior handle adjustable connector. Temporarily tape it to secure in position.
7 Unbolt and remove the lock remote control handle and lock mechanism from the door cavity, and disconnect the cable and connecting rod to the latch (photo).
8 To remove the latch unscrew and remove the three retaining screws (photo).

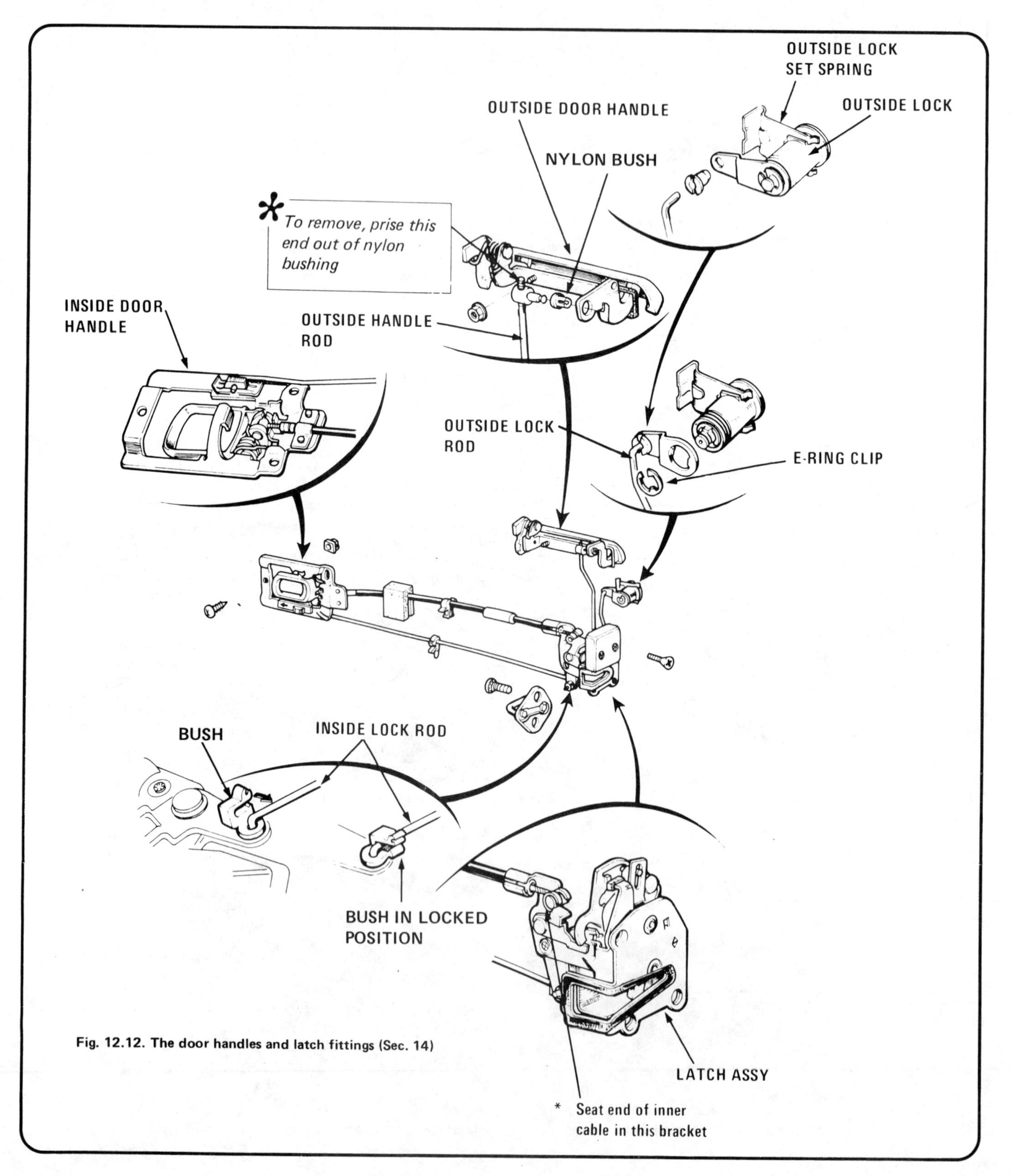

Fig. 12.12. The door handles and latch fittings (Sec. 14)

14.3 The regulator channel to glass channel retaining bolt

14.7 The remote control handle

14.8 The door latch retaining screws

9 Do not attempt to repair a worn or damaged window regulator, door lock or latch unit, but obtain a new one.
10 If the window is renewed, position it in the channel in the same location as the old one. The distance between the end of the glass at the rear and the retaining channel end must be 2.36 in (60 mm).
11 Refitting is a reversal of removal, but it may be necessary to adjust the glass guide channel to allow the glass to move up and down without binding. Apply a light lubrication to the respective handle to lock and latch connections, and check the correct operation of these components prior to refitting the inner door trim panel.

15 Doors - removal, refitting and adjustment

1 The door hinge plates are bolted to the body pillars.
2 To remove a door, open it wide and support it on a jack placed under its bottom edge. Use a rag or a piece of rubber to protect the door edge.
3 Mark the position of the hinge plates on the body pillars to facilitate refitting.
4 Unscrew and remove the bolts from the body pillars and lift the door from the body. Retain any shims which may be located under the hinge plates.
5 Refitting is a reversal of removal.
6 Any adjustment required to set the door evenly within the door frame can be carried out by releasing the hinge bolts. If the door is not flush with the adjacent body panels, loosen the hinge plate bolts on the door itself and move the door as necessary.
7 Smooth and positive closure of the door can be obtained by releasing the screws on the lock striker and moving it in whichever direction is required.

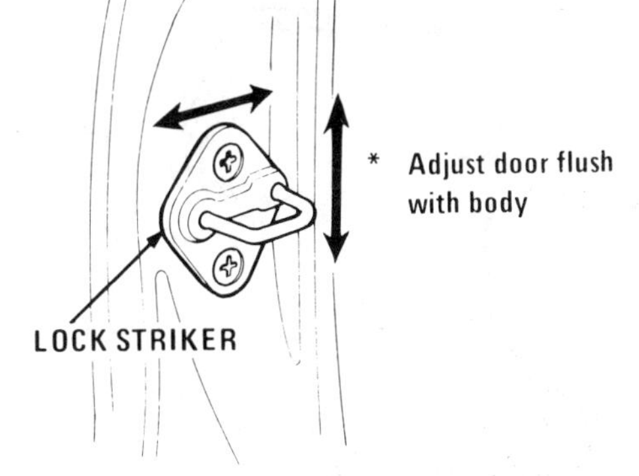

Fig. 12.13 The striker plate and adjustment (Sec. 15)

16 Windscreen/rear window glass - removal and refitting

1 The windscreen and rear window glass are held in rubber mouldings which are 'locked' by the trim moulding on the outer side of the rubber surround. Always wear gloves for protection when removing or installing the windscreen.

Removal

2 Begin by carefully extracting the bright trim moulding from the windscreen seal. The ends of the trim can be exposed by moving the moulding joint covers to one side.
3 Once the trim has been removed, enlist the help of at least one person, then with one person inside the car and one outside, very carefully push the windscreen outwards from its aperture beginning at either top corner of the screen.
4 The rubber moulding around the screen will flex sufficiently to allow the screen to move outwards once the trim has been removed.

Refitting

5 Check that the rubber moulding is in good condition, and that no cracks or surface deterioration can be found.
6 Fit the rubber moulding around the screen, and then insert a length of string or cord into the major slot on the periphery of the seal. Pass it totally around the seal, and let it emerge with about 5 inches (127 mm) of overlap and 8 inches (203 mm) hanging near one of the bottom corners.
7 Position the glass and seal into the window aperture from the outside with the string hanging into the car interior. Again enlist the help of at least one person and press the screen into the aperture.
8 Press the screen at the point where the strings emerge from the rubber moulding, then pull the strings to bring the lip of the moulding around the edge of the window aperture. Continue to apply pressure to the screen near to the moving parts of the string which are being pulled slowly and smoothly from the seal.
9 Once the string has been pulled out of the seal, check that the seal is properly fitted on both sides of the window aperture.
10 Now that the rubber seal and screen glass are in place, 'lock' the seal by pressing the bright trim moulding into the outside of the seal. Lubricate the seal with soap solution to ease the insertion of the trim. A special tool, which can be improvised is necessary to lift the seal rubber lips over each side of the bright trim.

17 Rear quarter window - removal and refitting

1 Open the window and unscrew the quarter lock retaining screw.
2 Carefully remove the cover and then unscrew the quarter lock retaining screw. Support the window and remove the hinge cover and then the window.
3 The hinge and lock can be removed by unclipping the 'E' clip, using a screwdriver to prise it free.
4 If the moulding and seal are to be removed, unscrew the quarter moulding retaining screw, and then withdraw the quarter moulding followed by the seal (Figs.12.14 and 12.15).

18 Heater unit - removal and refitting

1 Removal of the heater unit necessitates draining the cooling system as described in Chapter 2 or alternatively, disconnecting the inlet and outlet hoses and plugging them. With the latter method

Fig. 12.14 The rear quarter window cover and screw (Sec. 17)

Fig. 12.15 The quarter window seal and moulding (Sec. 17)

Loosen band and pull off hose

* Coolant will flow out when hose is pulled off

Fig. 12.16 The heater unit inlet and outlet hose connections (Sec. 18)

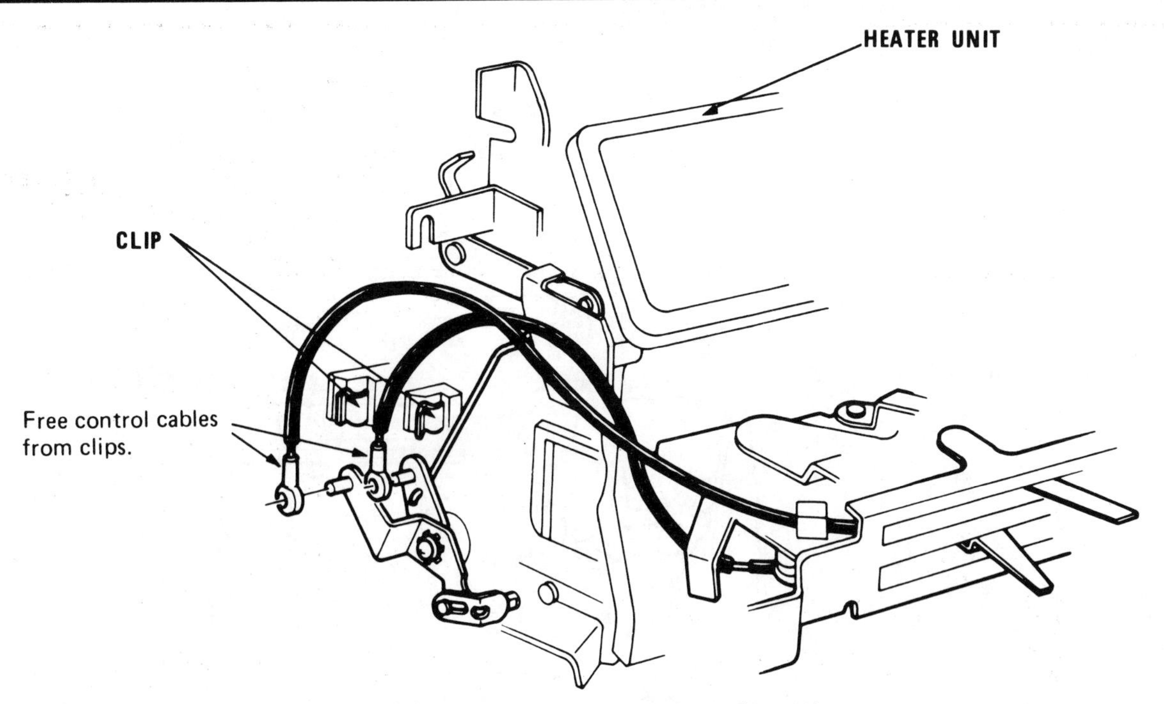

Fig. 12.17. The heater unit control cables (Sec. 18)

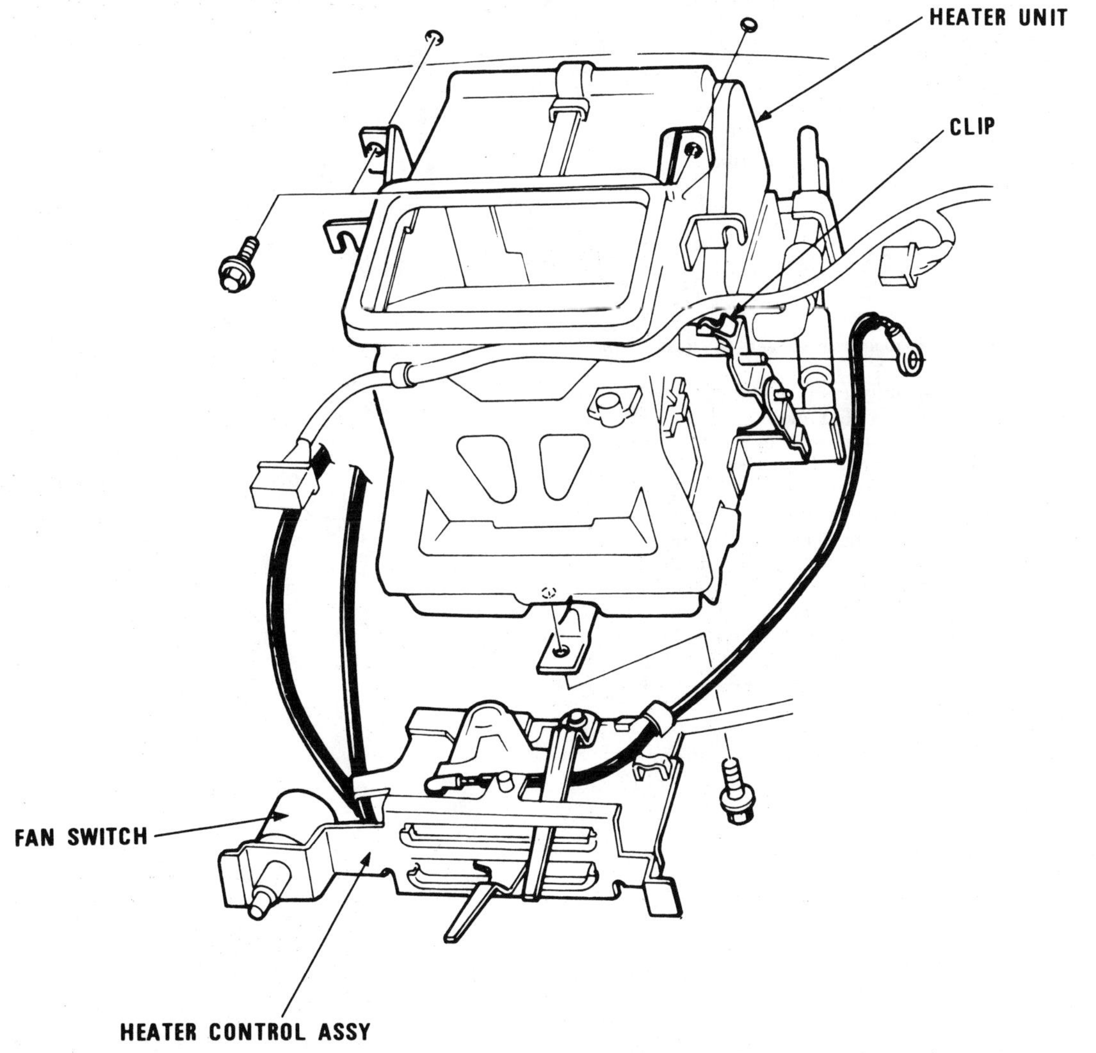

Fig. 12.18 The heater unit retaining bolt positions and the control valve cable (Sec. 18)

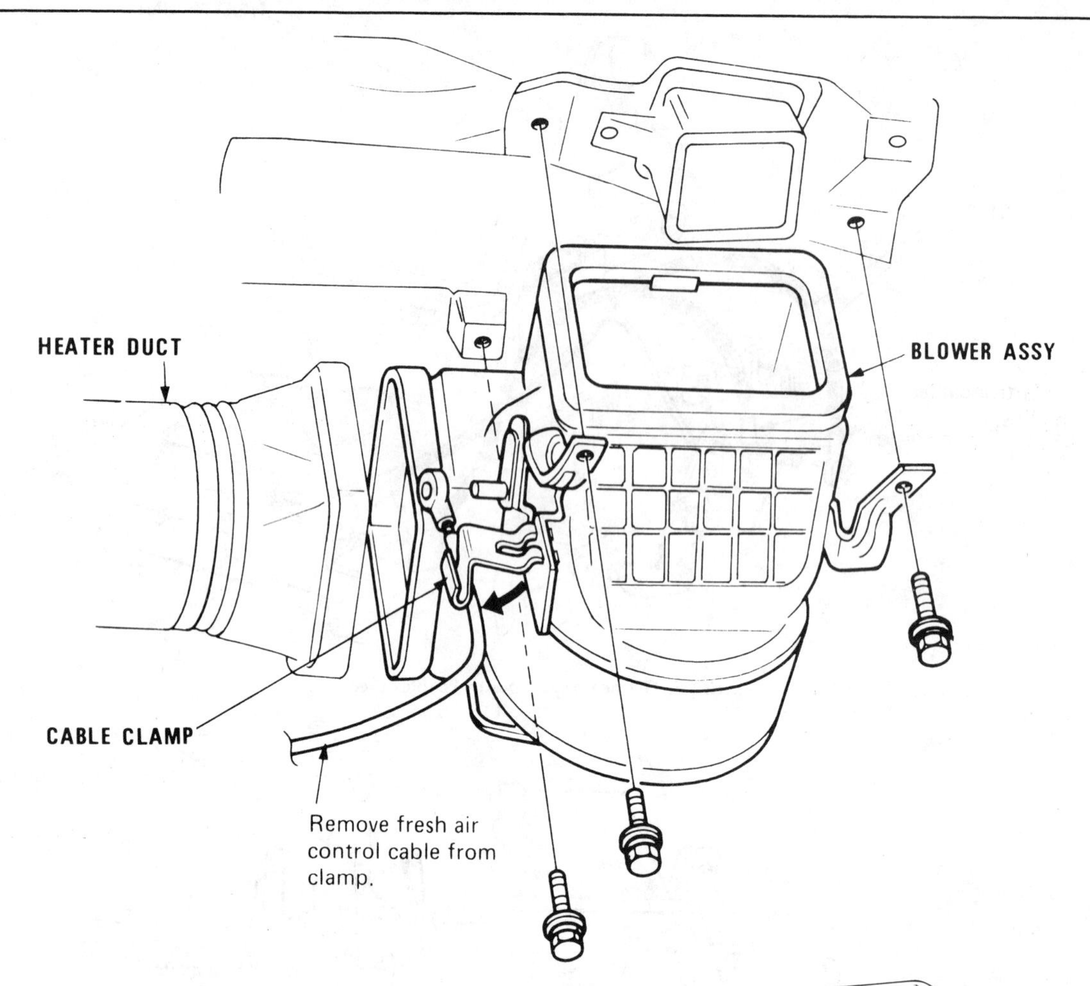

Fig. 12.19. The blower unit (Sec. 19)

ensure that the coolant is cool.

2 In either case, it is advisable to place rags beneath the heater unit to soak up any spillage of coolant during removal.

3 Having disconnected the inlet and outlet hoses, carefully remove the facia panel as described in Chapter 10, Section 28.

4 Unscrew and remove the heater unit attachment nut from the engine compartment side. Prise the control cables from the retaining clips, Fig. 12.17.

5 Unscrew and remove the right and left-hand upper retaining bolts and separate the valve control cable from its retaining clip (Fig. 12.18).

6 Unscrew the lower retaining bolts and carefully remove the unit.

7 Refitting is a reversal of removal but ensure that the respective hoses are correctly located, and the operating cables function correctly. Bleed any air from the cooling system and check for signs of leakage.

19 Heater blower unit - removal and refitting

1 Remove the glovebox from the facia panel, then disconnect the fresh air cable from the cable clamp on the blower unit, Fig. 12.19.

2 Unscrew and remove the three unit retaining bolts and carefully remove the blower unit.

3 To dismantle the blower for inspection and/or renewal of parts, prise the retaining clips free.

4 Refitting is a reversal of removal.

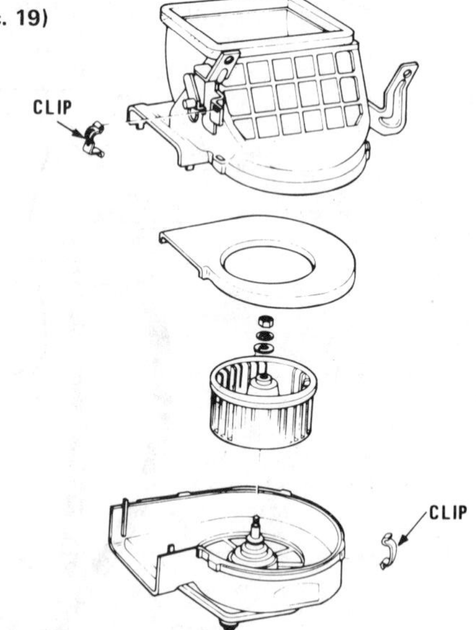

Fig. 12.20 The blower components, accessible on removal of the retaining clips (Sec. 19)

Chapter 13 Supplement: Revisions and information on later models

Contents

1 Introduction

This Supplement covers modifications to vehicles built during production years 1978 to 1984.

The mechanical changes have been minor in character, but major alterations in body styling occurred in January 1982 (photo).

In order to use the Supplement to best advantage, it is suggested that it is consulted before the main Chapters of the Manual. This will ensure that any relevant information can be collated and absorbed in the original procedures described in Chapters 1 to 12 to enable any work to be carried out correctly.

Hatchback (1983 model)

Engine compartment

1 *Suspension strut upper mounting*
2 *Ignition coil*
3 *Bonnet latch*
4 *Windscreen wiper motor*
5 *Master cylinder*
6 *Carburettor*
7 *Fusible link*
8 *Washer reservoir support*
9 *Washer fluid reservoir*
10 *Oil filler cap*
11 *Timing belt cover*
12 *Battery*
13 *Distributor*
14 *Radiator cooling fan*
15 *Alternator*
16 *Coolant expansion tank*
17 *Radiator cap*

Front end viewed from underneath

1 *Radius rod*
2 *Track control arm*
3 *Tie-rod end balljoint*
4 *Engine sump pan*
5 *Engine oil drain plug*
6 *Driveshaft*
7 *Steering rack housing*
8 *Anti-roll bar*
9 *Exhaust pipe*
10 *Centre beam*
11 *Flexible mounting*
12 *Transmission*
13 *Clutch release arm*
14 *Brake caliper*

Rear end, viewed from underneath

1	*Silencer*	3	*Radius rod*	5	*Towing eye*	7	*Fuel tank*
2	*Suspension lower arm*	4	*Anti-roll bar*	6	*Brake load-sensing valve*	8	*Fuel tank drain plug*

2 Specifications

The Specifications listed here are revised or supplementary to the main Specifications given at the beginning of each Chapter.

Engine (October 1978 on)

Displacement	1602 cc (97.76 cu. in)
Bore	3.03 in (77.0 mm)
Stroke	3.39 in (86.0 mm)
Performance (output)	80 bhp at 5000 rev/min (DIN) (59 kW at 5000 rev/min)
Maximum torque	93 lbf ft at 3500 rev/min (126.5 Nm at 3500 rev/min)

Cylinder block

Bore diameter	3.031 to 3.032 in (77.00 to 77.02 mm)
Wear limit	3.033 in (77.05 mm)
Rebore limit	0.010 in (0.25 mm)

Pistons

Skirt outside diameter	3.0299 to 3.0311 in (76.960 to 76.990 mm)
Piston clearance in bore	0.0004 to 0.0023 in (0.01 to 0.06 mm)
Wear limit	0.004 in (0.10 mm)
Compression ring end gap	0.006 to 0.014 in (0.15 to 0.35 mm)

Camshaft

Cam lobe height (exhaust)	1.554 to 1.564 in (39.471 to 39.726 mm)

Valves

Valve stem outside diameter:	
Inlet	0.2748 to 0.2751 in (6.98 to 6.99 mm)
Exhaust	0.2732 to 0.2736 in (6.94 to 6.95 mm)
Stem to guide clearance:	
Inlet	0.0008 to 0.0020 in (0.02 to 0.05 mm)
Wear limit	0.004 in (0.10 mm)
Exhaust	0.0024 to 0.0035 in (0.06 to 0.09 mm)
Wear limit	0.006 in (0.15 mm)
Valve seat width:	
Inlet	0.063 to 0.073 in (1.60 to 1.85 mm)
Exhaust	0.055 to 0.065 in (1.40 to 1.65 mm)
Valve spring free length (inner spring):	
Nippon type:	
Inlet	1.67 in (42.4 mm)
Exhaust	1.94 in (49.2 mm)
Chuo type:	
Inlet	1.67 in (42.4 mm)
Exhaust	1.99 in (50.6 mm)
Valve spring free length (outer spring):	
Nippon type:	
Inlet	1.66 in (42.16 mm)
Exhaust	2.01 in (51.05 mm)
Chuo type:	
Inlet	1.66 in (42.16 mm)
Exhaust	2.03 in (51.56 mm)
Valve guide inside diameter	0.276 to 0.277 in (7.01 to 7.03 mm)

Valve clearances (cold)

Inlet	0.0048 to 0.0068 in (0.12 to 0.17 mm)
Exhaust	0.0098 to 0.0118 in (0.25 to 0.30 mm)

Valve timing	**To 1980**	**1981 on**
Inlet opens	10° ATDC	10° ATDC
Inlet closes	40° ABDC	30° ABDC
Exhaust opens	40° BBDC	30° BBDC
Exhaust closes	10° BTDC	10° BTDC

Lubrication system

Oil pump

Clearance (inner to outer rotor)	0.006 to 0.008 in (0.15 to 0.20 mm)
Clearance (outer rotor to pump body)	0.004 to 0.008 in (0.10 to 0.20 mm)
Rotor end face clearance	0.001 to 0.006 in (0.025 to 0.15 mm)
Oil capacity (with filter renewal)	3.1 Imp qt (3.5 litre)

Cooling system

Coolant capacity (including expansion tank)	5.1 Imp qt (5.8 litre)

Fuel system

Fuel tank capacity	13.2 Imp gal (60.0 litre)

Carburettors

Type	Keihin 20/26 downdraught twin-choke
Venturi diameters:	
Primary	0.787 in (20 mm)
Secondary	1.027 in (26 mm)
Idle speed (Headlamps on, radiator fan off):	
Manual (5-speed)	700 to 800 rev/min (in neutral)
Automatic (2-speed)	650 to 750 rev/min (in gear)
CO percentage	3% maximum
Fast idle speed	1400 to 2000 rev/min
Fuel type	91 RON (2-star)

Type	Keihin 22/28 downdraught twin choke
Venturi diameters:	
Primary	0.866 in (22.0 mm)
Secondary	1.102 in (28.0 mm)
Idle speed (Headlamps off, radiator fan off):	
Manual (5-speed)	700 to 800 rev/min (in neutral)
Automatic (3-speed)	650 to 750 rev/min (in gear)
CO percentage	3% maximum
Fast idle speed	1500 to 2500 rev/min
Fuel type	91 RON (2-star)

Ignition system

Timing (at idle):

2-speed automatic	6° BTDC
3-speed automatic to 1980	4° BTDC
3-speed automatic 1981 on	3° to 7° BTDC
5-speed manual to 1980	4° BTDC
5-speed manual 1981 on	3° to 7° BTDC

Spark plugs

	NGK	Denso	Champion
To 1981	BPR-5ES	W16 EXR-U	RN-10Y
1981 on	BR-5EY	W16 EXR-U	RN-11YC
High speed	BPR-6ES	W20 EXR-U	RN-8Y

Electrode gap:	
NGK	0.031 to 0.035 in (0.8 to 0.9 mm)
Denso, Champion	0.028 to 0.031 in (0.7 to 0.8 mm)

Clutch

Release arm (tip) free play	0.20 to 0.25 in (5.1 to 6.4 mm)
Pedal free play	0.39 to 1.18 in (10.0 to 30.0 mm)
Pedal (released) height above floor	7.0 in (177.8 mm)
Pedal (clutch disengagement) height above floor	1.26 in (32.0 mm)

Manual transmission

Type	Five forward speeds and reverse

Ratios	**To 1981**	**1981 on**
1st	3.181 to 1	3.181 to 1
2nd	1.842 to 1	1.944 to 1
3rd	1.200 to 1	1.250 to 1
4th	0.896 to 1	0.896 to 1
5th	0.718 to 1	0.741 to 1
Reverse	3.000 to 1	3.000 to 1

Tolerances

5th/reverse shift shaft pin to reverse shift fork clearance	0.002 to 0.014 in (0.05 to 0.35 mm)
Wear limit	0.02 in (0.5 mm)
Reverse shift fork slot width	0.278 to 0.285 in (7.06 to 7.24 mm)
Reverse shift fork to gear clearance	0.008 to 0.04 in (0.2 to 1.0 mm)
Wear limit	0.07 in (1.78 mm)
Reverse shift fork finger gap	0.46 to 0.48 in (11.68 to 12.19 mm)

Mainshaft clearances

Synchroniser baulk ring to gear clearance	0.033 to 0.043 in (0.84 to 1.09 mm)
Wear limit	0.016 in (0.4 mm)
Shift fork to synchro-ring groove clearance	0.014 to 0.026 in (0.35 to 0.65 mm)

Synchro-ring groove width (new)	0.266 to 0.270 in (6.75 to 6.85 mm)
3rd/4th shift shaft to shift guide clearance	0.008 to 0.02 in (0.2 to 0.5 mm)
Wear limit	0.03 in (0.8 mm)
Width of shift guide notch (new)	0.469 to 0.472 in (11.9 to 12.0 mm)
3rd gear shoulder to 2nd gear shoulder clearance	0.0012 to 0.0071 in (0.03 to 0.18 mm)
Wear limit	0.012 to (0.3 mm)
3rd gear thickness	1.158 to 1.160 in (29.42 to 29.47 mm)
Wear limit	1.15 in (29.2 mm)
4th gear shoulder to spacer collar clearance	0.0012 to 0.0071 in (0.03 to 0.18 mm)
Wear limit	0.012 in (0.3 mm)
4th gear thickness	1.158 to 1.160 in (29.42 to 29.47 mm)
Wear limit	1.15 in (29.2 mm)
5th gear shoulder to spacer collar clearance	0.001 to 0.005 in (0.03 to 0.13 mm)
Wear limit	0.01 in (0.25 mm)
5th gear thickness	1.06 to 1.062 in (26.92 to 26.97 mm)
Wear limit	1.055 in (26.8 mm)

Countershaft clearances

1st gear shoulder to thrust washer clearance	0.001 to 0.003 in (0.03 to 0.08 mm)
Thrust washer thicknesses:	
A	0.119 to 0.120 in (3.02 to 3.04 mm)
B	0.118 to 0.119 in (3.00 to 3.02 mm)
C	0.117 to 0.118 in (2.98 to 3.00 mm)
D	0.116 to 0.117 in (2.95 to 2.98 mm)
2nd gear shoulder to 3rd gear shoulder clearance	0.0012 to 0.004 in (0.03 to 0.1 mm)
Wear limit	0.007 in (0.18 mm)
2nd gear thickness	1.200 to 1.198 in (30.48 to 30.43 mm)

Shift arm holder and selector mechanism clearances

Shift arm holder (collar to shim) clearance	0.0004 to 0.008 in (0.01 to 0.2 mm)
Shim thicknesses:	
A	0.031 in (0.8 mm)
B	0.039 in (1.0 mm)
C	0.047 in (1.2 mm)
D	0.055 in (1.4 mm)
E	0.063 in (1.6 mm)
Shift arm to guide clearance	0.004 to 0.012 in (0.1 to 0.3 mm)
Wear limit	0.024 in (0.6 mm)
Shift guide slot width	0.311 to 0.315 in (7.9 to 8.0 mm)
Selector arm to interlock clearance	0.002 to 0.01 in (0.05 to 0.25 mm)
Wear limit	0.03 in (0.76 mm)
Selector arm finger gap	0.396 to 0.4 in (10.05 to 10.15 mm)
Shift arm to shift rod guide clearance	0.002 to 0.01 in (0.05 to 0.25 mm)
Wear limit	0.03 in (0.76 mm)
Shift rod guide slot width	0.46 to 0.47 in (11.68 to 12.0 mm)
Selector arm to shift rod guide clearance	0.002 to 0.01 in (0.05 to 0.25 mm)
Wear limit	0.02 in (0.5 mm)
Selector arm tab width	0.469 to 0.472 in (11.9 to 12.0 mm)

Gearbox oil capacity

From dry	4.4 pint (2.5 litre)
At oil change	4.2 pint (2.4 litre)

Torque wrench settings

	lbf ft	kgf m
Clutch housing to transmission	20	2.7
Oil filler plug	35	4.7
Cover bolts	9	1.2
Shift rod guide lock bolt	25	3.4
Gear selector mounting bolts	10	1.3
Reverse lamp switch	18	2.4
Detent ball plugs	16	2.1
Mainshaft nut	65	8.8
Countershaft nut	65	8.8
Shift arm holder bolts	9	1.2

Hondamatic transmission

Type	Three forward speeds and reverse

Ratios

1st (L)	2.047 : 1
2nd (*)	1.370 : 1
3rd (OD)	0.969 : 1
Reverse (R)	1.954 : 1

Positions N (neutral) and P (parking) are provided

Transmission fluid capacity

From dry	8.6 Imp pt (4.9 litre)
At fluid change	4.4 Imp pt (2.5 litre)

Settings and tolerances

Pump gear endfloat	0.001 to 0.002 in (0.03 to 0.05 mm)
Wear limit	0.003 in (0.08 mm)
Pump gear to valve body clearance:	
Drive gear	0.0039 to 0.0055 in (0.10 to 0.14 mm)
Driven gear	0.002 to 0.004 in (0.05 to 0.10 mm)
Wear limit	0.006 in (0.15 mm)
Servo valve return spring free length	1.24 in (31.5 mm)
Minimum length	1.10 in (28.0 mm)
Mainshaft thrust washer to needle bearing clearance	0.003 to 0.006 in (0.07 to 0.15 mm)

Selective splined washer thicknesses:

A	0.116 to 0.118 in (2.95 to 3.00 mm)
B	0.119 to 0.120 in (3.02 to 3.05 mm)
C	0.121 to 0.122 in (3.07 to 3.10 mm)
D	0.123 to 0.124 in (3.12 to 3.15 mm)
E	0.125 to 0.126 in (3.17 to 3.20 mm)
F	0.127 to 0.128 in (3.22 to 3.25 mm)
H	0.129 to 0.130 in (3.27 to 3.30 mm)
I	0.131 to 0.132 in (3.32 to 3.35 mm)
J	0.133 to 0.134 in (3.37 to 3.40 mm)

Countershaft reverse gear hub to drivegear clearance	0.003 to 0.006 in (0.07 to 0.15 mm)
Countershaft OD gear to thrust washer clearance	0.003 to 0.006 in (0.07 to 0.15 mm)

Countershaft drivegear thrust washer selective thicknesses:

A	0.089 to 0.091 in (2.26 to 2.31 mm)
B	0.091 to 0.093 in (2.31 to 2.36 mm)
C	0.093 to 0.094 in (2.36 to 2.39 mm)
D	0.095 to 0.096 in (2.42 to 2.45 mm)
E	0.097 to 0.098 in (2.46 to 2.49 mm)
F	0.099 to 0.100 in (2.52 to 2.55 mm)
G	0.101 to 0.102 in (2.57 to 2.60 mm)

Countershaft OD gear splined washer selective thicknesses:

A	0.116 to 0.118 in (2.95 to 3.00mm)
B	0.119 to 0.120 in (3.02 to 3.05 mm)
C	0.121 to 0.122 in (3.07 to 3.10 mm)
D	0.123 to 0.124 in (3.12 to 3.15 mm)
E	0.125 to 0.126 in (3.17 to 3.20 mm)
F	0.127 to 0.128 in (3.22 to 3.25 mm)
H	0.129 to 0.130 in (3.27 to 3.30 mm)
I	0.131 to 0.132 in (3.32 to 3.35 mm)
J	0.133 to 0.134 in (3.37 to 3.40 mm)
Clutch endplate-to-top disc clearance	0.016 to 0.028 in (0.4 to 0.7 mm)

Clutch endplate selective thicknesses:
Plate marking

1	0.091 in (2.3 mm)
2	0.102 in (2.6 mm)
3	0.114 in (2.9 mm)
4	0.126 in (3.2 mm)
5	0.138 in (3.5 mm)
11	0.085 in (2.15 mm)
12	0.096 in (2.44 mm)
13	0.108 in (2.75 mm)
14	0.120 in (3.05 mm)
15	0.132 in (3.35 mm)
16	0.144 in (3.65 mm)

Torque wrench settings

	lbf ft	kgf m
Torque converter to pump bolts	9	1.2
Driveplate bolts	9	1.2
Damper bracket bolts	16	2.2
Starter/side mounting bolt	33	4.5
Radius rod nut	32	4.4
Radius rod bolt	40	5.5
Torque rod bracket bolts	28	3.9
Oil cooler hose banjo bolt	7	1.0
Mainshaft locknut	69	9.5
Countershaft locknut	69	9.5

Speedometer driven gear holder bolt	7	1.0
Shift control cable retainer bolt	20	2.7
Shift arm bolt	9	1.2
Valve body bolts	9	1.2
Servo bolts	9	1.2
Transmission housing to torque converter housing bolts:		
10.0 mm	33	4.5
8.0 mm	20	2.7
Parking pawl stop bolt	10	1.4
Idler shaft holder bolts	9	1.2
End cover bolts	9	1.2

Braking system

Disc type ... Ventilated

Disc diameter ... 7.5 in (190.0 mm)

Disc thickness ... 0.47 in (12.0 mm)

Minimum regrind thickness ... 0.39 in (10.0 mm)

Drum internal diameter ... 7.87 in (200.0 mm)

Maximum internal diameter ... 7.91 in (201.0 mm)

Torque wrench settings	**lbf ft**	**kgf m**
Caliper guide bolts	20	2.7
Hose banjo bolts	25	3.5
Pipeline unions	12	1.6

Electrical system

Battery ... 45 Ah

Alternator ... 60 Ah

Starter motor ... 0.8 kW

Bulbs	**Wattage**
Headlamps	40/60
Front parking lamps	5
Front direction indicator lamps	21
Rear direction indicator lamps	21
Stop/tail lamps	21/5
Reversing lamps	21
Rear fog warning lamps	21
Rear numberplate lamps	5
Interior lamp	8
Warning and indicator lamps	1.2
Fuse box lamps	5
Glove box lamp	3.4
Instrument panel lamps	1.2
Heater control illumination	1.2
Heated rear window indicator lamp	1.2

Suspension and steering

Front wheel alignment

1978 to 1979

Camber	0° 40′
Castor	1° 20′
Toe-in	0.04 in (1.0 mm)

1980 on

Camber	0°
Castor	1° 25′
Toe	0°

Rear wheel alignment

Camber:	
1978 to 1979	0° 10′
1980 on	0°
Toe	0°

Power steering

Overall ratio	16.3 to 1
Number of turns, lock-to-lock	3.07
Power steering fluid capacity	0.70 Imp qt (0.80 litre)

Tyres

Size	165 SR 13

Tyre pressures

Front	24 lbf/in² (1.65 bar)
Rear	24 lbf/in² (1.65 bar)

Torque wrench settings	**lbf ft**	**kgf m**
Rear suspension		
Strut upper mounting nuts	16	2.2
Piston rod nut	23	3.2
Strut pinch-bolt	40	5.5
Rear toe cam plate bolt	47	6.5
Anti-roll bar clamp bolt	16	2.2
Power-assisted steering gear		
Rack and pinion housing mounting bolts	16	2.2
Shift rod torque arm bolt	9	1.1
Exhaust flange nuts	36	5.0
Centre beam bolts	16	2.2
Tie-rod balljoint nuts	32	4.3
Shift rod clevis bolt	16	2.2
Fluid line union nuts:		
Inner lines	16	2.2
Outer lines	27	3.7
Pump pivot bolt	36	5.0
Pump adjusting bolt	18	2.4

Bodywork

Dimensions

Overall length:	
Hatchback	165.3 in (4198 mm)
Saloon	173.2 in (4399 mm)
Overall width	65.0 in (1650 mm)
Overall height:	
Hatchback	53.3 in (1355 mm)
Saloon	54.1 in (1375 mm)
Wheelbase	96.5 in (2450 mm)
Track (front)	56.3 in (1430 mm)
Track (rear)	55.9 in (1420 mm)
Ground clearance	6.7 in (170 mm)
Kerb weight* - standard models:	
Hatchback	2051 lb (930 kg)
Saloon	2085 lb (945 kg)
** With power steering add 29 lb (13 kg)*	
Kerb weight - Executive models:	
Hatchback	2105 lb (955 kg)
Saloon	2150 lb (975 kg)
Maximum towing weight	2072 lb (941 kg)

Torque wrench settings	**lbf ft**	**kgf m**
Safety belt anchor bolts	23	3.2
Bumper mounting bolts	16	2.2
Compressor mounting nuts	31	4.3
Air conditioner pipeline or hose unions:		
3/8 in (9.53 mm) diameter hose or pipe	12	1.6
1/2 in (12.7 mm) diameter hose or pipe	18	2.4
5/8 in (15.88 mm) diameter hose or pipe	25	3.4

3 Engine

Modifications

1 As from October 1978, the engine capacity has been increased slightly to 1602 cc by increasing the bore and reducing the stroke (see Specifications).

2 Coincident with this, the combustion chamber has been redesigned in wedge form. In addition the inlet and exhaust valves have been enlarged and the manifold modified.

3 Improved engine mountings are also fitted.

Engine/transmission - removal and refitting

4 On the models covered by this Supplement, it is recommended that the bumper apron and the radiator grille (Section 13A) are removed before removal of the engine/transmission.

5 On vehicles equipped with power steering, remove the speed sensor complete with hoses. Do not disconnect the hoses from the speed sensor or there will be a loss of fluid.

6 Remove the power steering pump drivebelt. Then unbolt the pump and move it aside. Do not disconnect the hoses.

7 On vehicles (Executive) equipped with air conditioning, it is possible to remove the compressor drivebelt, unbolt the compressor and move it aside without discharging the system. The flexibility of the connecting hoses is sufficient to permit the necessary movement.

8 On vehicles having the three-speed Hondamatic transmission, the speed selector control cable should be disconnected from the transmission by unbolting the cable holder. Disconnect the oil cooler hoses and plug them.

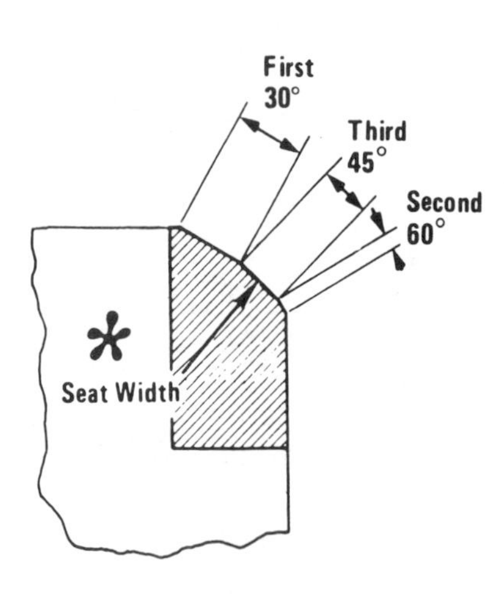

Fig. 13.1 Modified valve seat cutting angles (October 1978 on)

3.9B Engine mounting - rear

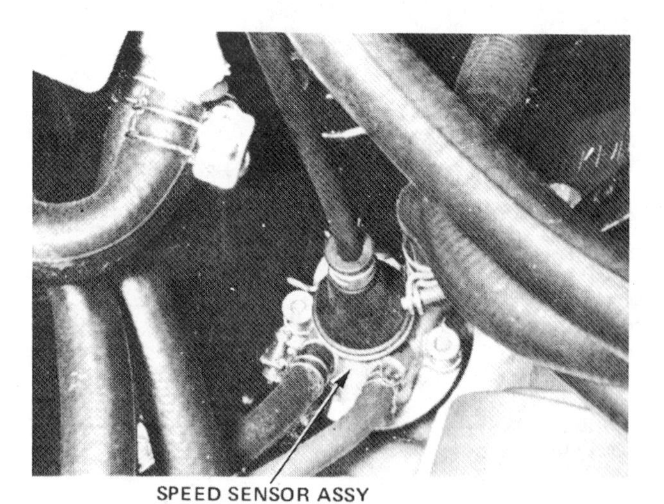

Fig. 13.2 Speed sensor and hoses (power steering)

3.9C Engine mounting - centre beam

3.9A Engine mounting - front. Damper arrowed

9 The engine/transmission mountings have been redesigned as shown in Fig. 13.3. Once the engine is in position, the mounting bolts must be tightened to the specified torque in alphabetical order (photos).

A	*14 lbf ft*	*2.0 kgf m*
B	*21 lbf ft*	*2.9 kgf m*
C	*28 lbf ft*	*3.9 kgf m*
D	*54 lbf ft*	*7.5 kgf m*
E	*54 lbf ft*	*7.5 kgf m*
F	*29 lbf ft*	*4.0 kgf m*

Valve clearances - adjustment

10 Remove the rocker cover.

11 Apply a socket wrench to the crankshaft pulley bolt and turn it in an anti-clockwise direction to set No. 1 piston at TDC. This can be established by removing No. 1 spark plug and feeling the compression being generated when the finger is placed over the plug hole.

12 The indentation on the edge of the timing belt cover should be at its highest point with the two sprocket rim grooves parallel with the upper face of the cylinder head and the word UP on the sprocket spoke visible. An additional check can be made if the distributor cap is removed when the contact end of the rotor should be pointing to No. 1 contact in the distributor cap (if fitted).

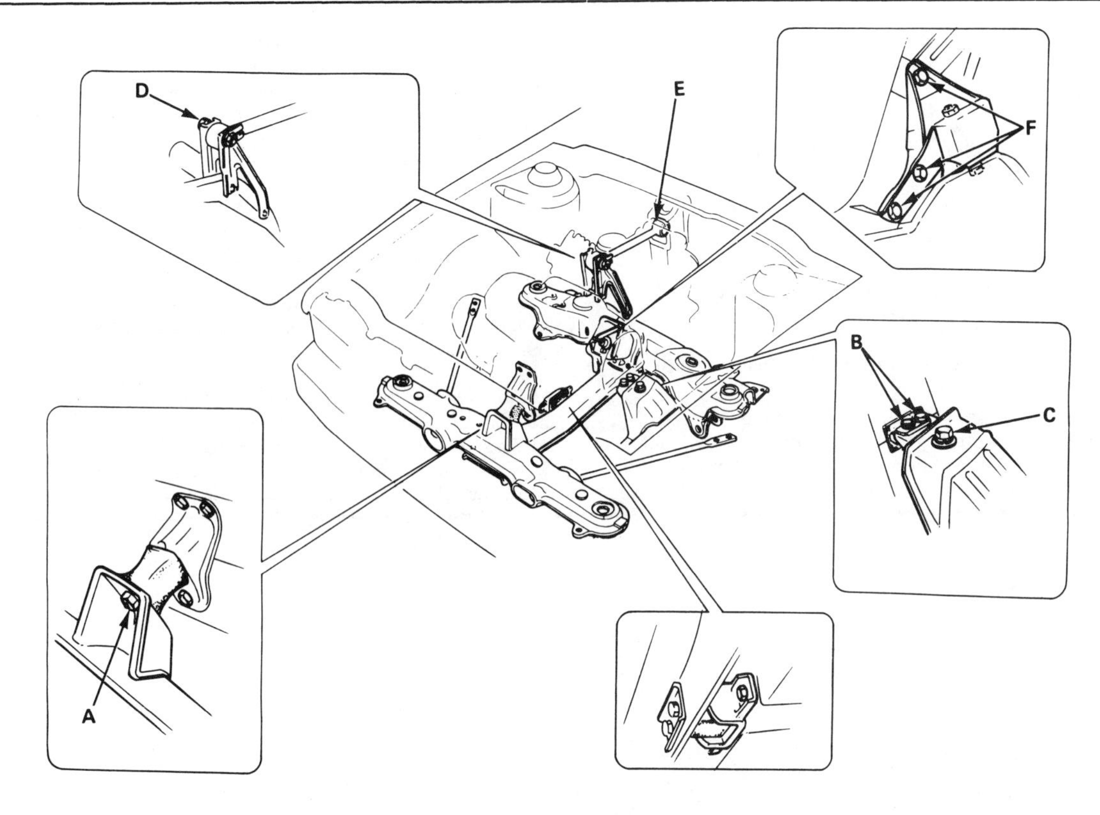

Fig. 13.3 Modified engine/transmission mountings

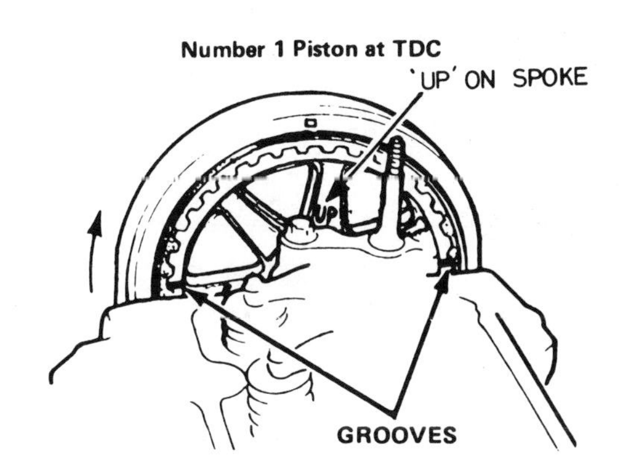

Fig. 13.4 Camshaft sprocket marks with No 1 piston at TDC

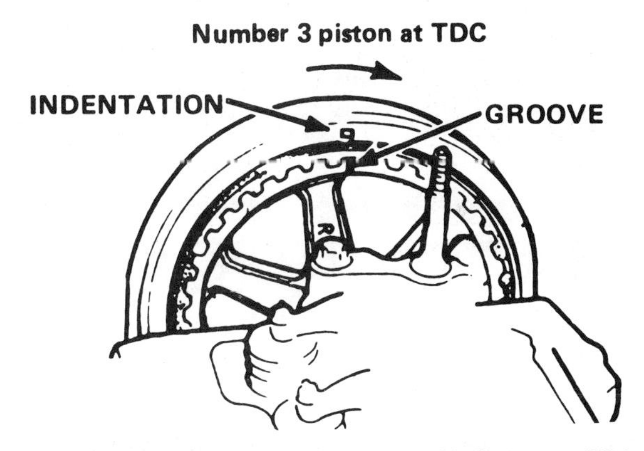

Fig. 13.5 Camshaft sprocket marks with No 3 piston at TDC

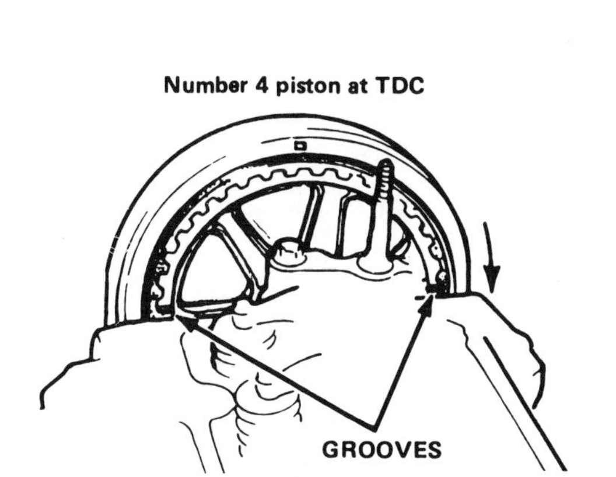

Fig. 13.6 Camshaft sprocket marks with No 4 piston at TDC

13 Check both valves on No. 1 cylinder. Remember that the inlet and exhaust valve clearances are different. Numbering from the camshaft sprocket end of the cylinder head, the valves are:

Inlet	*2 - 4 - 5 - 7*
Exhaust	*1 - 3 - 6 - 8*

14 Insert the appropriate feeler blade between the end of the valve stem and the ball end of the rocker arm adjuster screw when it should be a stiff sliding fit. If adjustment is required, release the locknut and turn the adjuster screw.

15 When the clearance is correct, tighten the locknut without altering the position of the adjuster screw. Recheck the clearance.

16 Turn the crankshaft through 180° (half a turn) in an anti-clockwise direction until the groove on the sprocket rim is in alignment with the indentation on the belt cover. The word UP on the sprocket spoke should not be visible and the distributor rotor should be pointing to No. 3 spark plug lead contact in the distributor cap (if fitted).

17 Adjust the valve on this cylinder.

18 Turn the crankshaft through another 180° to bring No. 4 piston

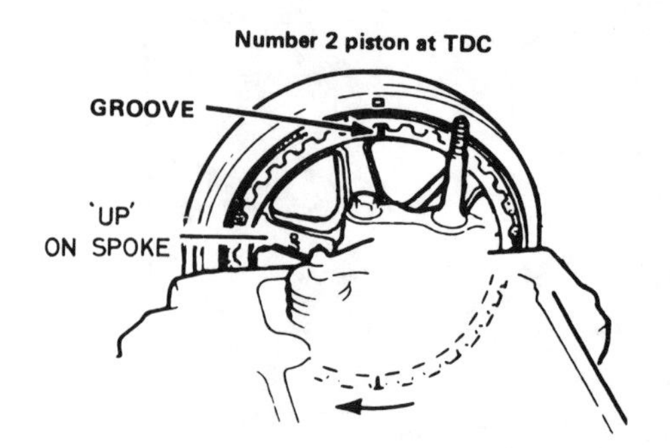

Fig. 13.7 Camshaft sprocket marks with No 2 piston at TDC

to TDC. Both sprocket grooves will be parallel with the top face of the cylinder head, but the word UP on the sprocket spoke will not be visible. Check that the distributor rotor is pointing at No. 4 spark plug lead contact in the distributor cap (if fitted).

19 Adjust the valves on this cylinder.

20 Turn the crankshaft through another 180° to bring No. 2 piston to TDC. One groove on the sprocket should be in alignment with the indentation in the belt cover and the word UP on the sprocket spoke should be visible. Check that the distributor rotor is pointing at No. 2 spark plug lead contact in the distributor cap (if fitted).

Oil pump (Hondamatic transmission)

21 The oil pump fitted to vehicles equipped with automatic transmission differs from that fitted to models with manual transmission.

22 An additional rotor is incorporated in the auto type oil pump to pressurise engine oil to the oil cooler which is located at the side of the radiator.

Oil cooler (Hondamatic transmission)

23 The oil cooler mentioned in the preceding paragraph is bolted to the side of the cooling system radiator.

24 To drain the cooler before removal, disconnect the hoses and allow the oil to run out into a suitable container.

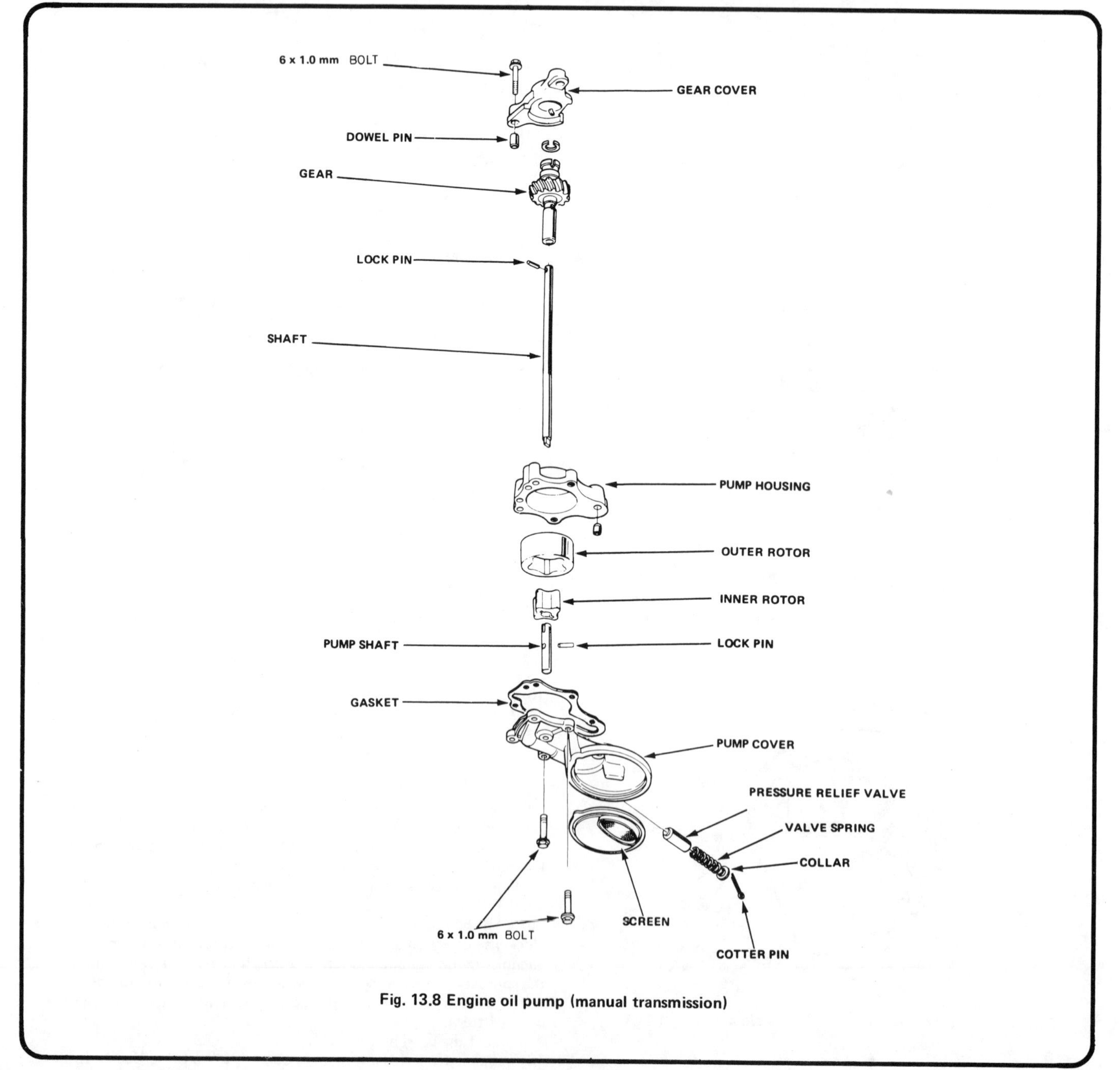

Fig. 13.8 Engine oil pump (manual transmission)

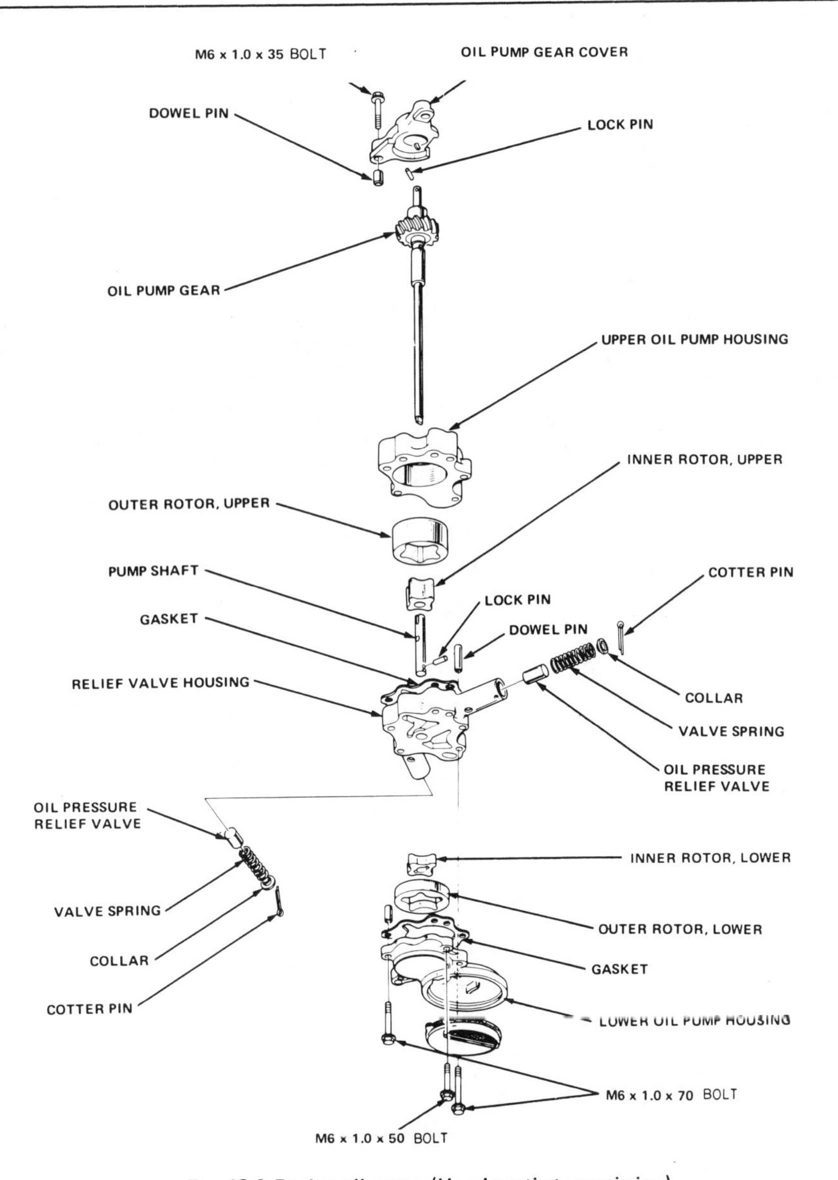

Fig. 13.9 Engine oil pump (Hondamatic transmission)

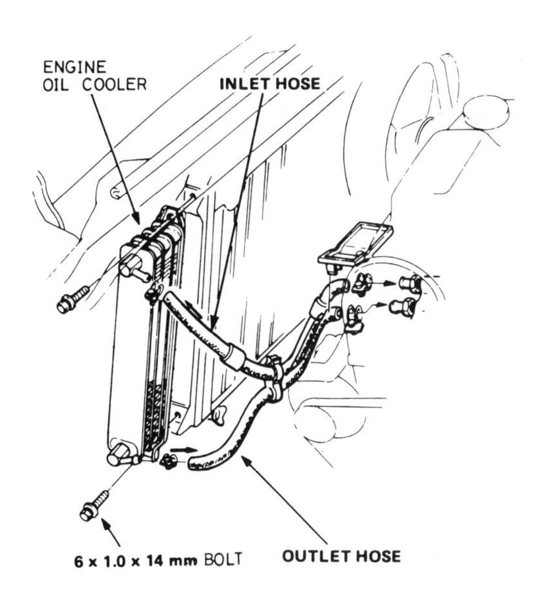

Fig. 13.10 Engine oil cooler (Hondamatic transmission)

Cylinder head - removal, engine in vehicle

25 On vehicles with power steering, remove the pump adjustment bolt and lift off the drivebelt. Detach the pump inlet hose and the fluid return hose and plug them to avoid contamination. Remove the pump mounting bolt and lift the pump from its bracket. Tie the pump to the right side of the engine compartment with strong wire so it will be out of the way.

26 On vehicles with air conditioning, remove the A/C drivebelt cover, then loosen the belt adjusting nut and remove the drivebelt. Remove the A/C compressor mounting bolts and loosen the bolt in the hose bracket at the radiator. **Note:** *Do not disconnect any high pressure hoses unless the system has been properly discharged.* The compressor can be lifted out and wired up out of the way without discharging the system or disconnecting any hoses. Unbolt and remove the A/C compressor bracket.

27 After reinstalling the power steering pump and hoses check the fluid level, and fill it if necessary. Start the engine and run it at fast idle speed. While the engine is running, turn the steering wheel from lock-to-lock several times to bleed the air from the system. Check the fluid level again and fill it if necessary.

Engine - modified components

28 As already mentioned, certain components of the later engines have been modified. The accompanying illustrations should be consulted when working on these models.

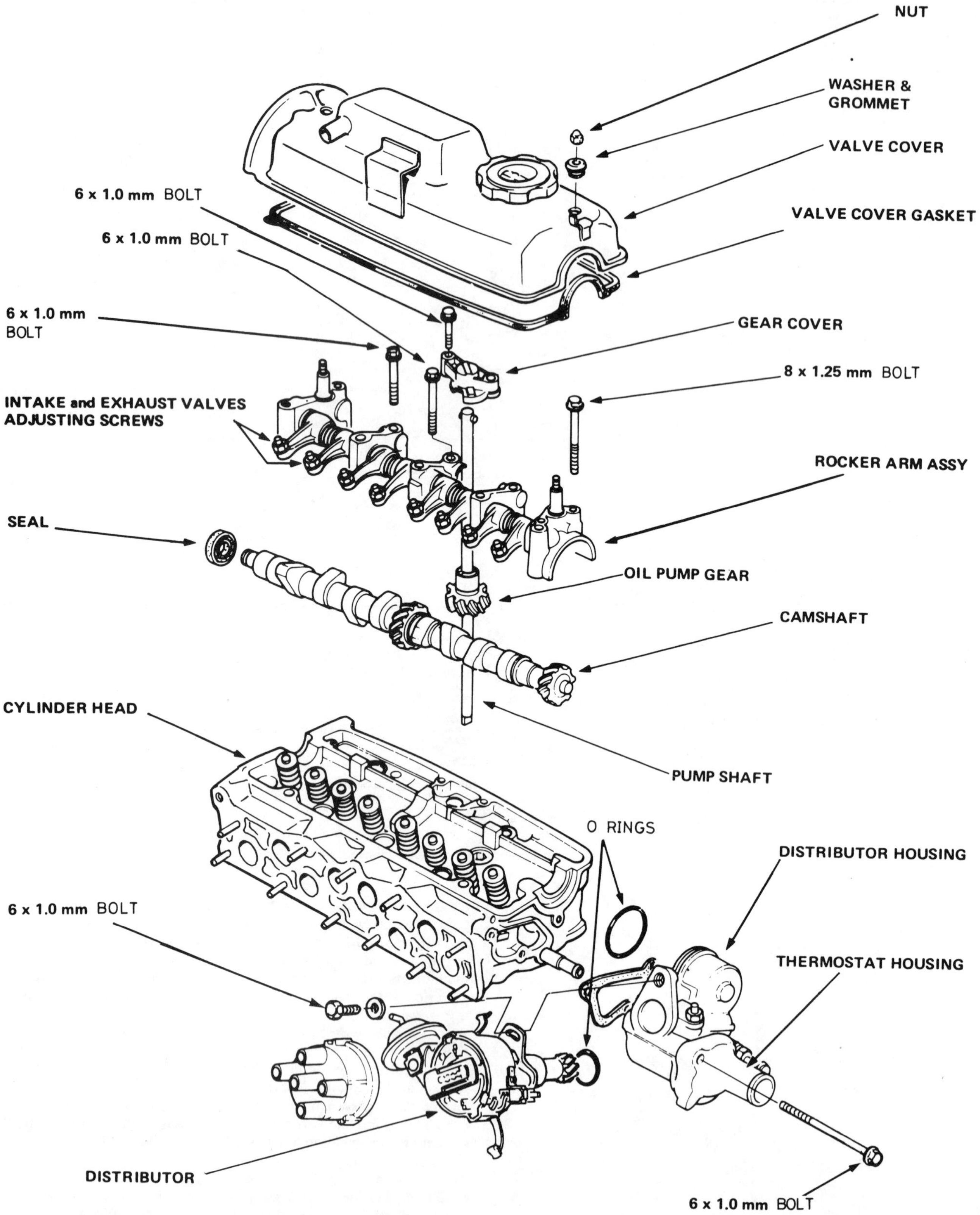

NUT

WASHER & GROMMET

VALVE COVER

VALVE COVER GASKET

6 x 1.0 mm BOLT

6 x 1.0 mm BOLT

6 x 1.0 mm BOLT

GEAR COVER

8 x 1.25 mm BOLT

INTAKE and EXHAUST VALVES ADJUSTING SCREWS

ROCKER ARM ASSY

SEAL

OIL PUMP GEAR

CAMSHAFT

CYLINDER HEAD

PUMP SHAFT

O RINGS

DISTRIBUTOR HOUSING

6 x 1.0 mm BOLT

THERMOSTAT HOUSING

DISTRIBUTOR

6 x 1.0 mm BOLT

Fig. 13.11 Cylinder head

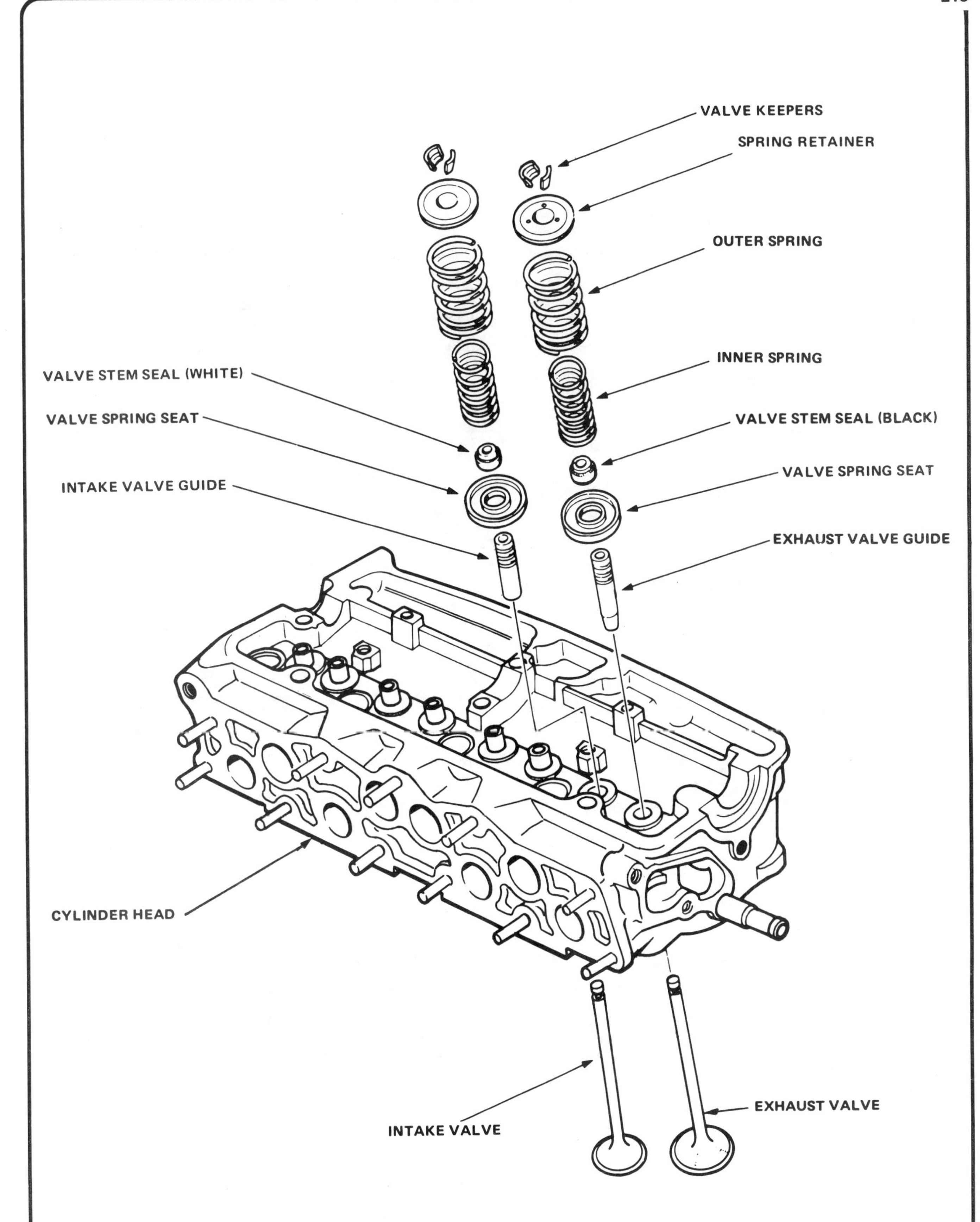

Fig. 13.12 Valve details

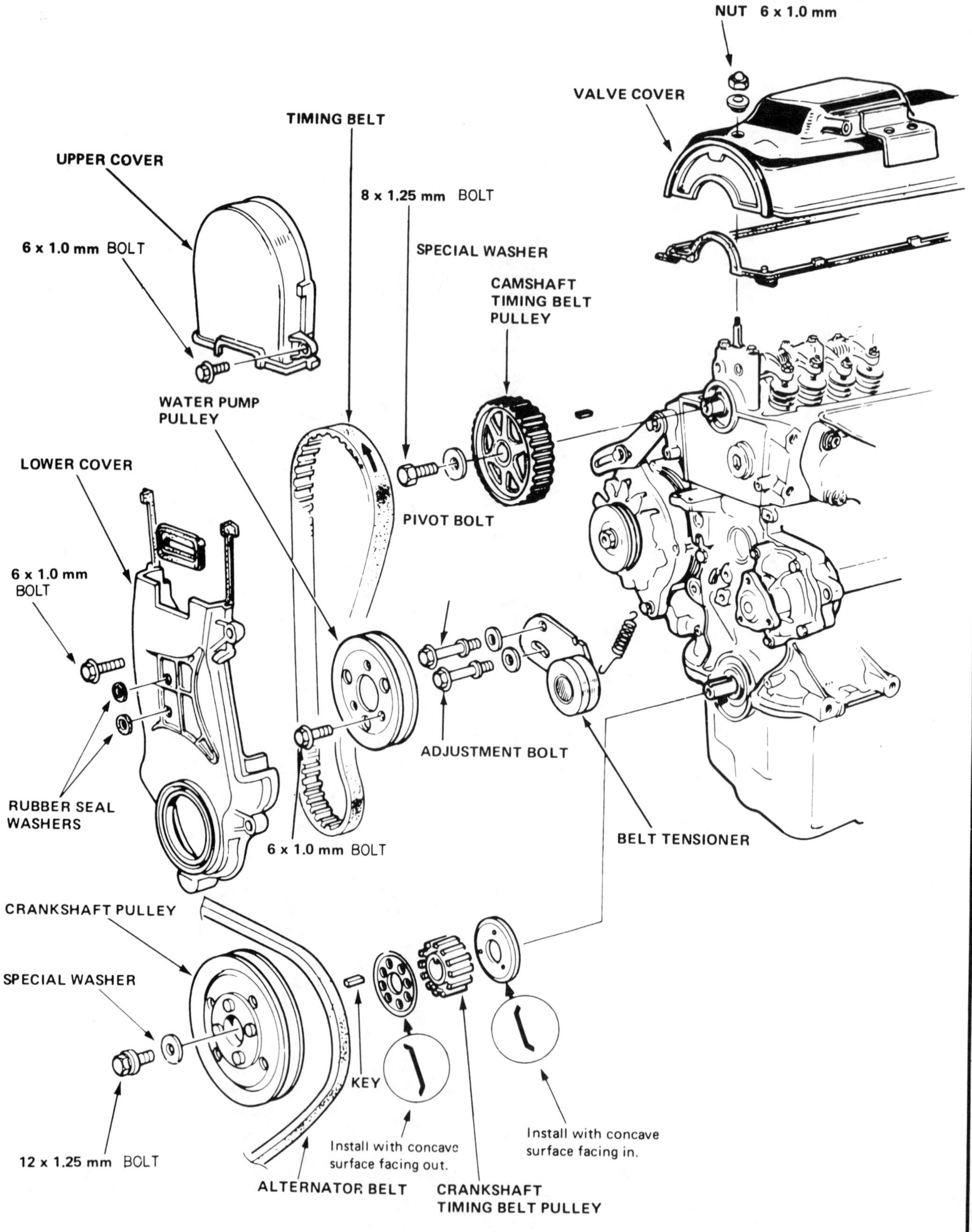

NUT 6 x 1.0 mm
VALVE COVER
TIMING BELT
UPPER COVER
8 x 1.25 mm BOLT
6 x 1.0 mm BOLT
SPECIAL WASHER
CAMSHAFT TIMING BELT PULLEY
WATER PUMP PULLEY
LOWER COVER
PIVOT BOLT
6 x 1.0 mm BOLT
ADJUSTMENT BOLT
RUBBER SEAL WASHERS
BELT TENSIONER
6 x 1.0 mm BOLT
CRANKSHAFT PULLEY
SPECIAL WASHER
KEY
Install with concave surface facing in.
Install with concave surface facing out.
12 x 1.25 mm BOLT
ALTERNATOR BELT
CRANKSHAFT TIMING BELT PULLEY

Fig. 13.13 Timing belt components

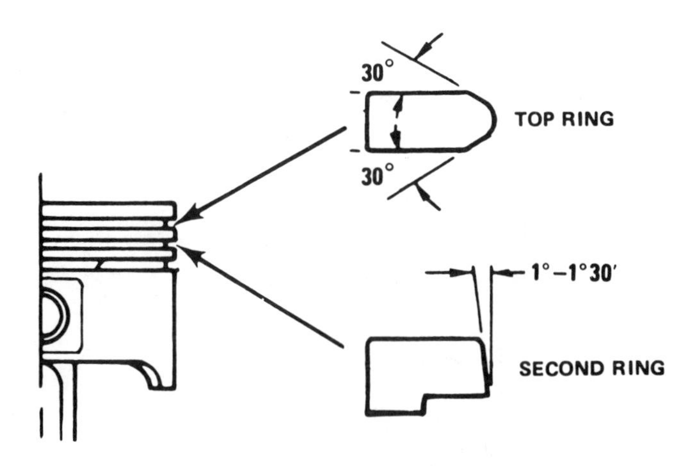

Fig. 13.14 Piston ring identification

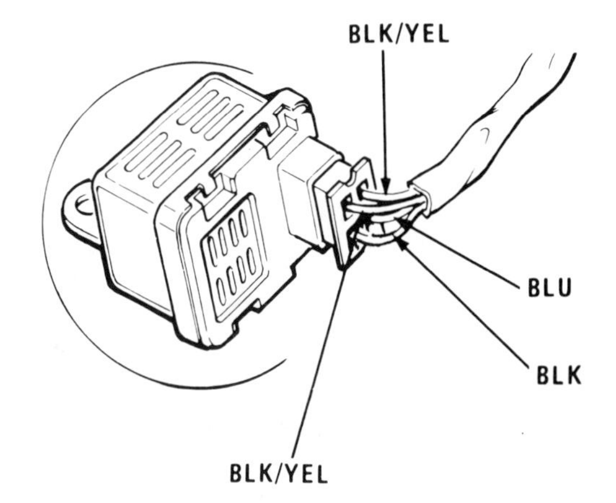

Fig. 13.15 Fuel pump relay leads

4 Fuel system

Fuel tank capacity

1 The fuel tank capacity has been increased on post 1982 models.

Fuel tank - removal

2 A protective shield is fitted to the fuel tank and this must be unbolted and removed before attempting to withdraw the fuel tank.

Fuel pump cut-off relay

3 The colour coding of the leads to the fuel pump relay connector plug has been changed as shown.

Fuel filter

4 The fixing of the fuel filter has been redesigned.
5 Before attempting to disconnect the filter, clamp the inlet and outlet fuel hoses to prevent loss of fuel. Self-locking grips are useful for this purpose.
6 Depress the filter locking tab and pull the filter up out of its mounting bracket.
7 After releasing the hose clips, pull the hoses from the filter using a twisting action.

Low fuel level sensor and warning lamp

8 A thermistor type sensor is located on the end of the fuel pick-up pipe within the fuel tank.
9 If two gallons (ten litres) or less fuel are in the fuel tank the low fuel level warning lamp should come on. A fault is most likely due to a blown bulb in the instrument panel. If the bulb is satisfactory, check the wiring connections at the sender unit, if these are in order then the sender unit must be removed, as described in Chapter 3, and renewed.

Carburettor (1977 to 1981)

Float level checking and adjustment

10 With the top of the carburettor held so that the float hangs vertically downwards, measure the distance from the underside of the cover gasket to the lower edge of the float at its mid point. This dimension should be between 1.39 and 1.47 in (35.4 and 37.4 mm).
11 With the carburettor float set correctly, measure the clearance between the float needle and the float. This clearance should be between 0 and 0.04 in (0 and 1.0 mm). If the clearance is outside these limits, turn the adjusting screw until the correct dimension is achieved and then apply sealant to the top of the adjusting screw to lock it.

Accelerator pump stroke adjustment

12 The stroke of the accelerator pump is determined by the distance which the operating lever can travel before being stopped by coming in contact with the lug on the carburettor air intake.

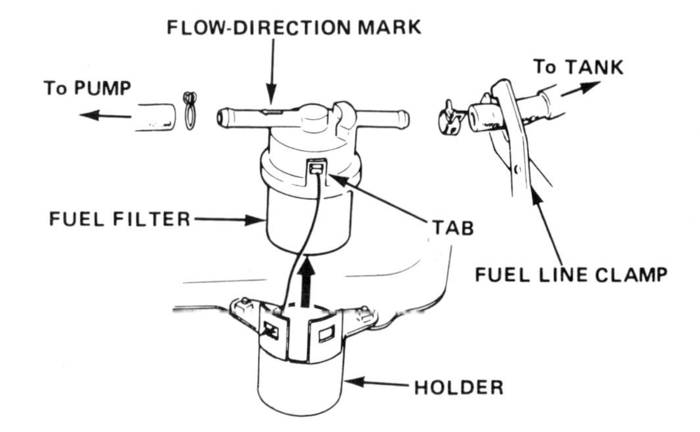

Fig. 13.16 Later type fuel filter

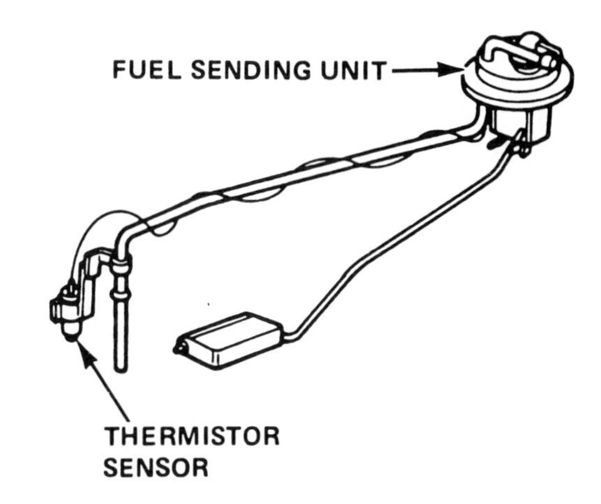

Fig. 13.17 Fuel level sender unit and low level thermistor

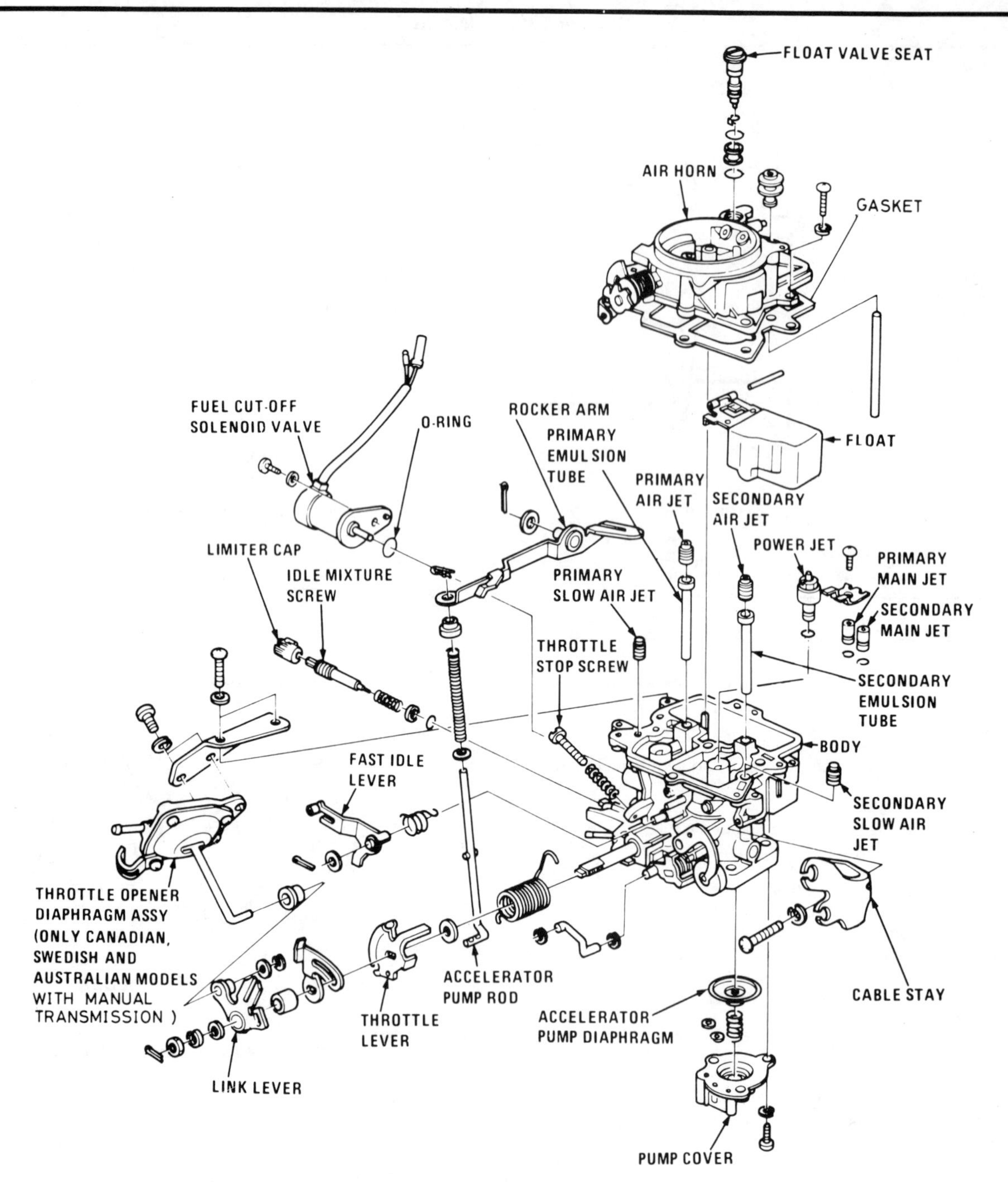

Fig. 13.18 Exploded view of later type carburettor

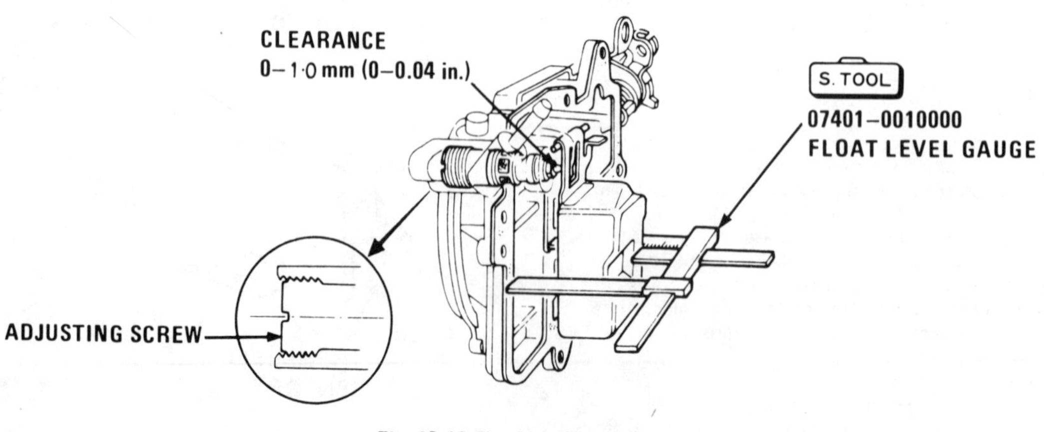

Fig. 13.19 Checking float setting

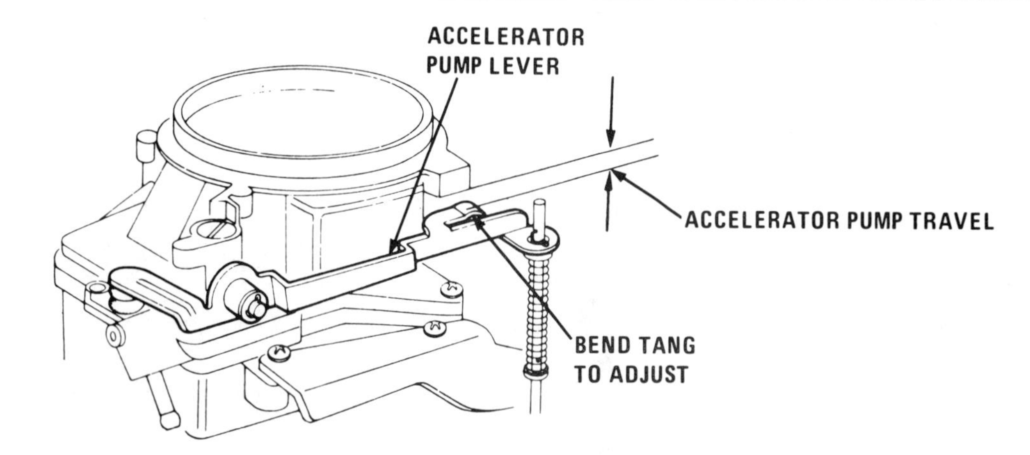

Fig. 13.20 Accelerator pump adjustment

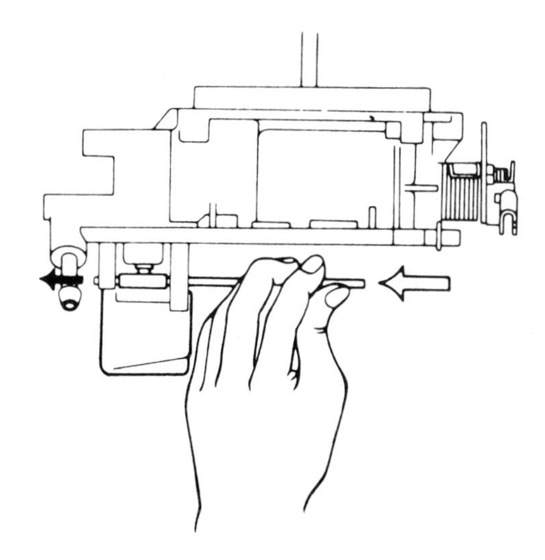

Fig. 13.21 Driving out float pivot pin

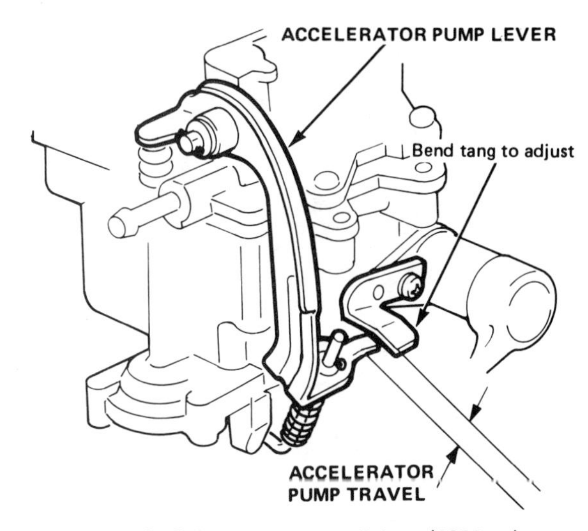

Fig. 13.23 Accelerator pump linkage (1982 on)

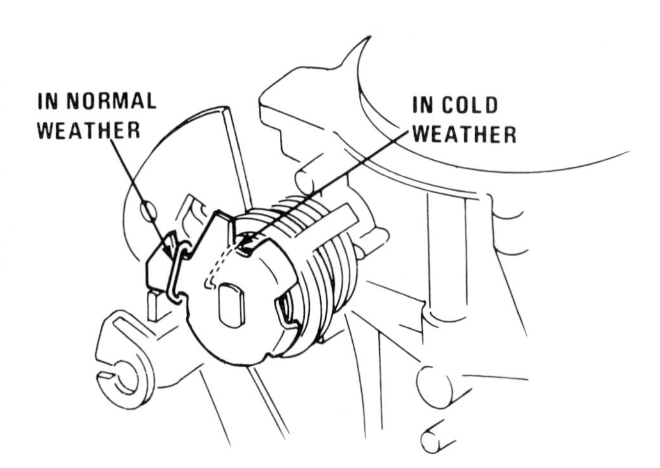

Fig. 13.22 Choke relief valve spring

13 The correct pump stroke is 0.532 in (13.5 mm) and the tang on the operating lever (Fig. 13.20) should be bent so that the correct stroke is achieved.

Carburettor float removal

14 The fulcrum pin of the float is a press fit in the two support lugs and must be tapped out, using a very thin pin punch.

15 To remove the pin, tap it from the end which is in the longer of the two support lugs (Fig. 13.21).

16 When refitting the pin, insert it into the shorter support lug first and tap it home. Take care not to tap the support lug because these are very brittle and could break off.

Choke relief valve adjustment

17 If the car is difficult to start when the weather is very cold, or if it is impossible to drive the car with the choke operated, the tension on the choke valve should be increased.

18 To increase the spring tension, unhook the end of the spring from the lug on the end of the choke shaft, and hook the spring end round the next lug in a clockwise direction (Fig. 13.22).

Carburettor (1982 on)

Accelerator pump linkage

19 This carburettor differs slightly from the earlier model by having a modified accelerator pump linkage.

20 The pump lever should travel between 0.73 and 0.77 in (18.5 and 19.5 mm) when measured between the stop on the carburettor body and the tang on the throttle lever. If adjustment is required, bend the tang.

Idle speed and mixture adjustment

21 Ideally, an exhaust gas analyser should be used for this work, but using the alternative idle-drop method should prove satisfactory.

22 The mixture screw is sealed with a plug and this should not be removed unless the idle cannot be set satisfactorily using only the idle speed screw.

23 Have the engine at normal operating temperature with the valve clearances and ignition settings correct.

24 Make sure that the headlamps and radiator cooling fan are off.

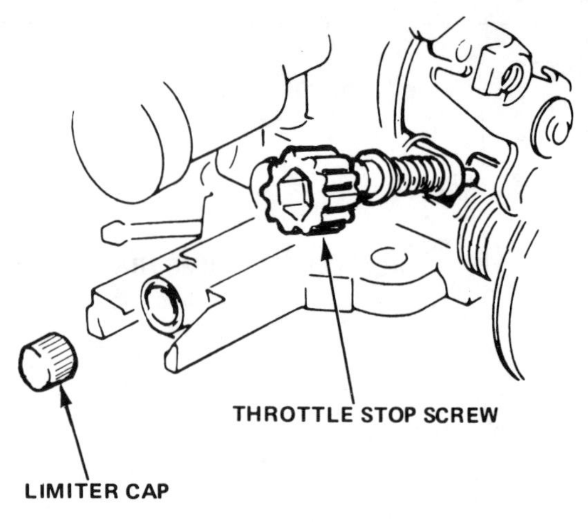

Fig. 13.24 Throttle speed screw (1982 on)

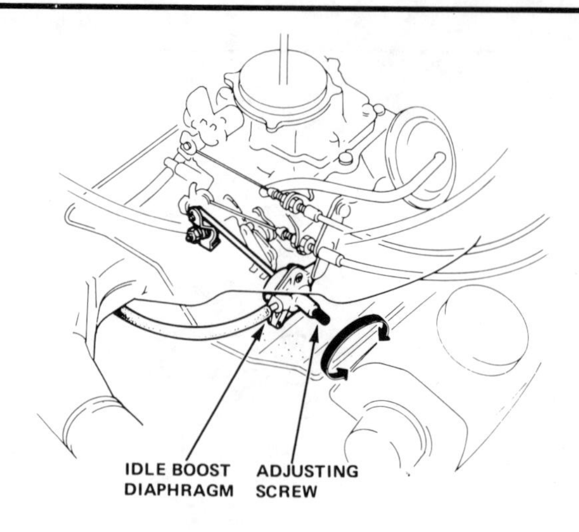

Fig. 13.25 Idle boost device

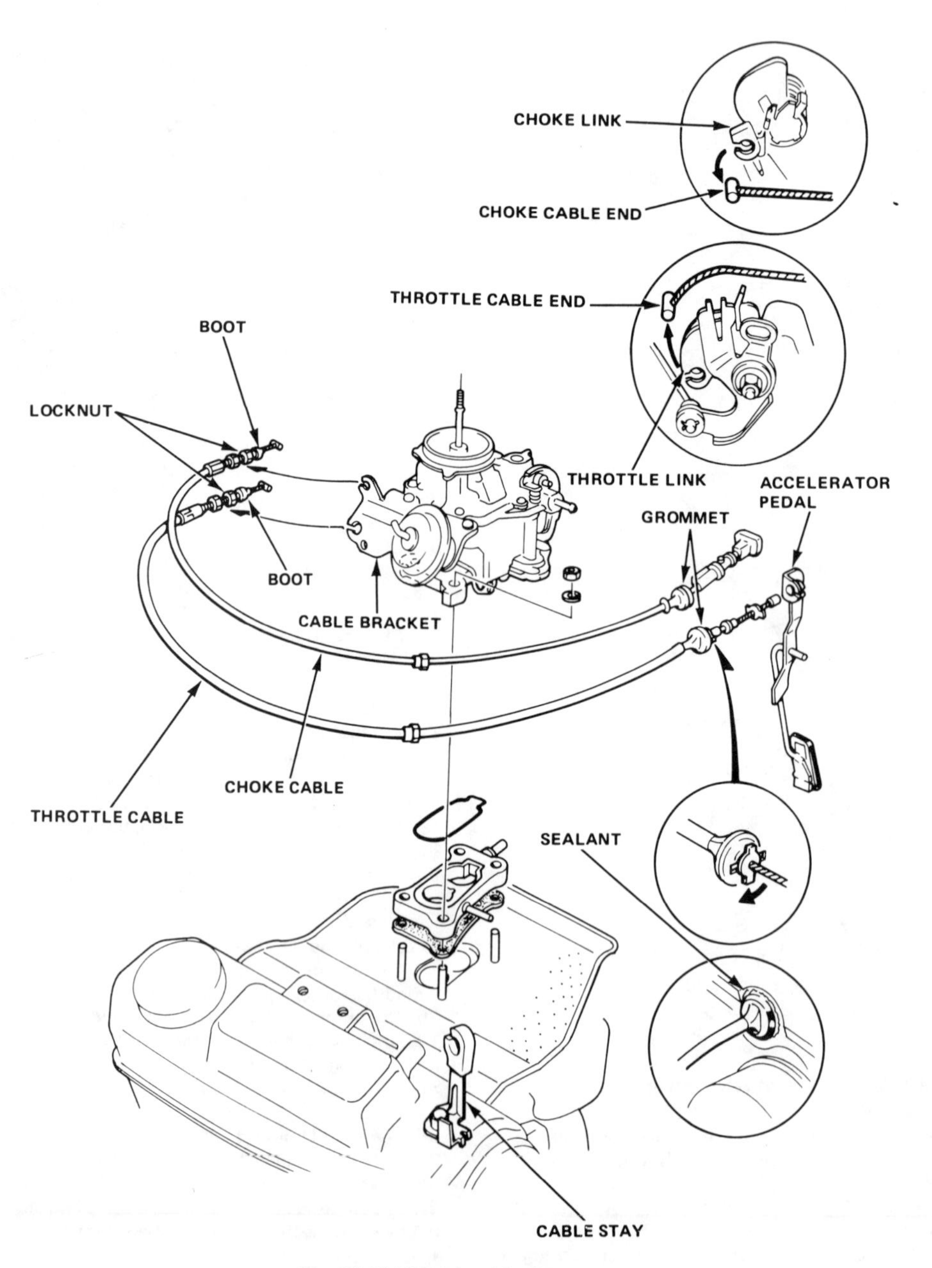

Fig. 13.26 Throttle and choke cables

CO meter method

25 With the engine idling, insert the probe of the analyser into the exhaust tailpipe by at least 16.0 in (40.0 cm).
26 Adjust the idle speed to achieve the specified level according to type of transmission fitted.
27 Check the CO reading on the meter carefully following the meter manufacturer's instructions. If it is outside the specified level, adjust the mixture screw.

Idle drop method

28 Adjust the idle speed to specification and then turn the mixture screw to obtain the highest idle speed. Readjust the idle speed to within the specified range according to type of transmission.
29 Now turn the mixture screw clockwise until the idle speed drops as follows:

Manual transmission	*by 60 rev/min*
Automatic transmission	*by 30 rev/min*

30 Readjust idle speed to specification.
31 On vehicles equipped with air conditioning, switch it on when the idle speed should still be within specified range. If it is not, remove the rubber cap from the idle boost diaphragm and turn the screw now exposed as required.

Accelerator cable - removal, refitting and adjustment

32 At the carburettor, push back the rubber dust excluder and release the cable locknut.
33 Pull the cable conduit back until the inner cable can be slid from the throttle link.
34 Unhook the cable from the accelerator pedal.
35 Release the cable from the stay on the rocker cover.
36 Twist the cable grommet on the engine compartment rear bulkhead through 90° and withdraw the cable into the engine compartment.
37 Refit by reversing the removal operations and then adjust in the following way.
38 By means of the locknuts at the carburettor end of the cable, adjust the cable tension to give a deflection (slackness) of between 0.16 and 0.40 in (4.0 to 10.0 mm).
39 With the accelerator fully depressed, check that the throttle valves are in the fully open position. With the accelerator pedal fully released, check that the throttle lever is in contact with the idle speed screw.

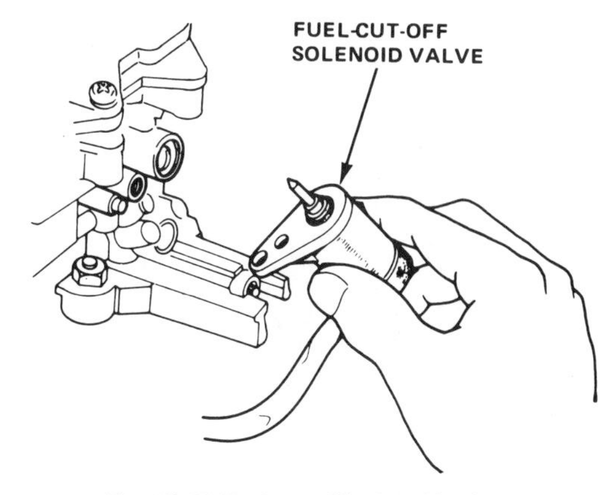

Fig. 13.27 Fuel cut-off solenoid valve

Choke cable - removal, refitting and adjustment

40 Disconnect the choke cable from the carburettor in a similar way to that described for the accelerator cable. On some models, the choke cable is connected at the carburettor end by a clevis pin.
41 Disconnect the leads from the choke warning switch at the control knob just behind the facia panel.
42 Unscrew the choke control knob bezel nut and release the choke cable bulkhead grommet.
43 Withdraw the cable assembly into the vehicle interior.
44 Refitting is a reversal of removal but use the cable locknuts at the carburettor to give a cable deflection (slackness) of between 0.20 and 0.24 in (5.0 to 6.0 mm).
45 Check the fully open and fully closed positions of the choke valve plate.

Fuel cut-off solenoid valve

46 The purpose of this valve which is fitted to the carburettor is to prevent run-on after the ignition is switched off. This is achieved by the valve needle cutting off fuel flow to the idle circuit.
47 A faulty valve can cause running-on and rough or erratic idling.
48 Operation of the valve can be checked by unbolting it from the carburettor and turning the ignition switch on and off.

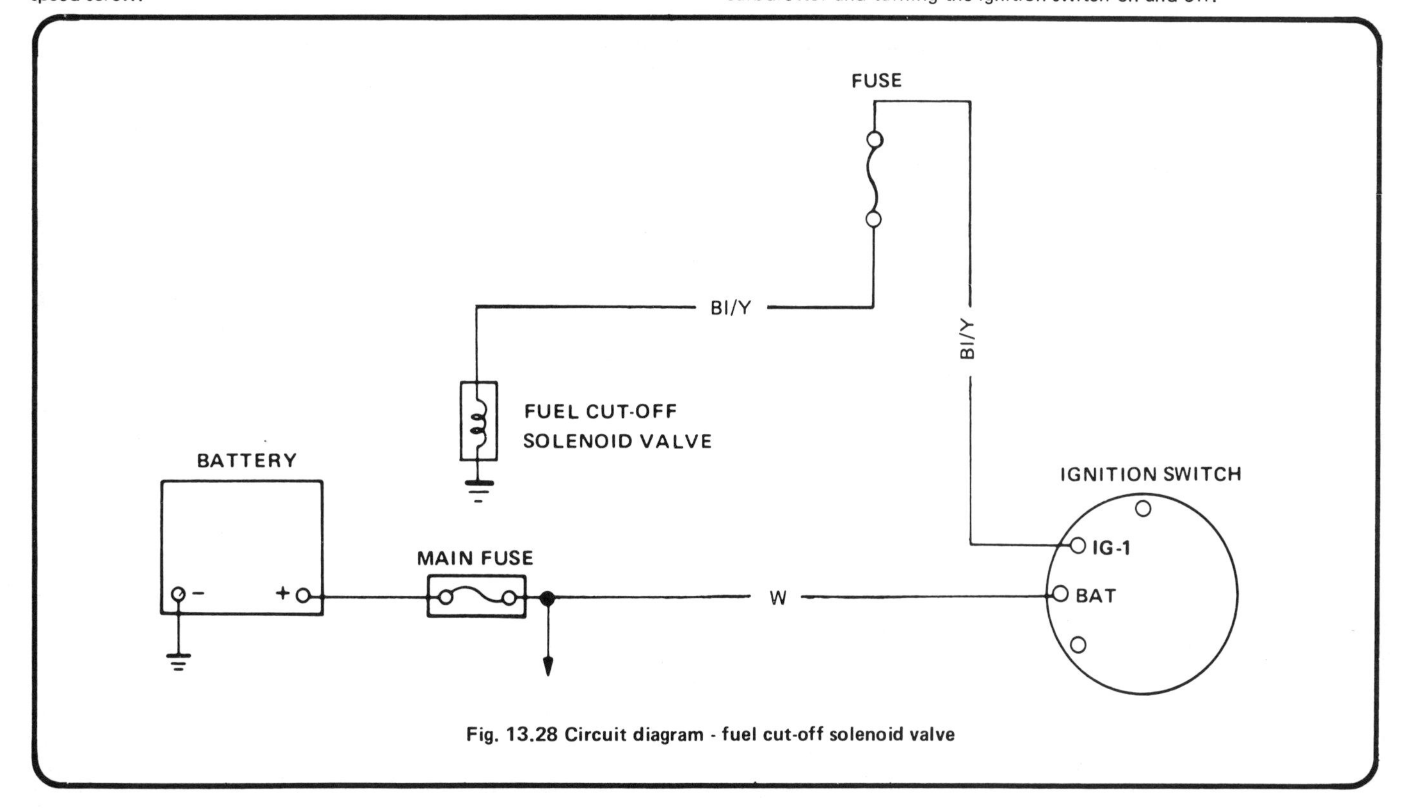

Fig. 13.28 Circuit diagram - fuel cut-off solenoid valve

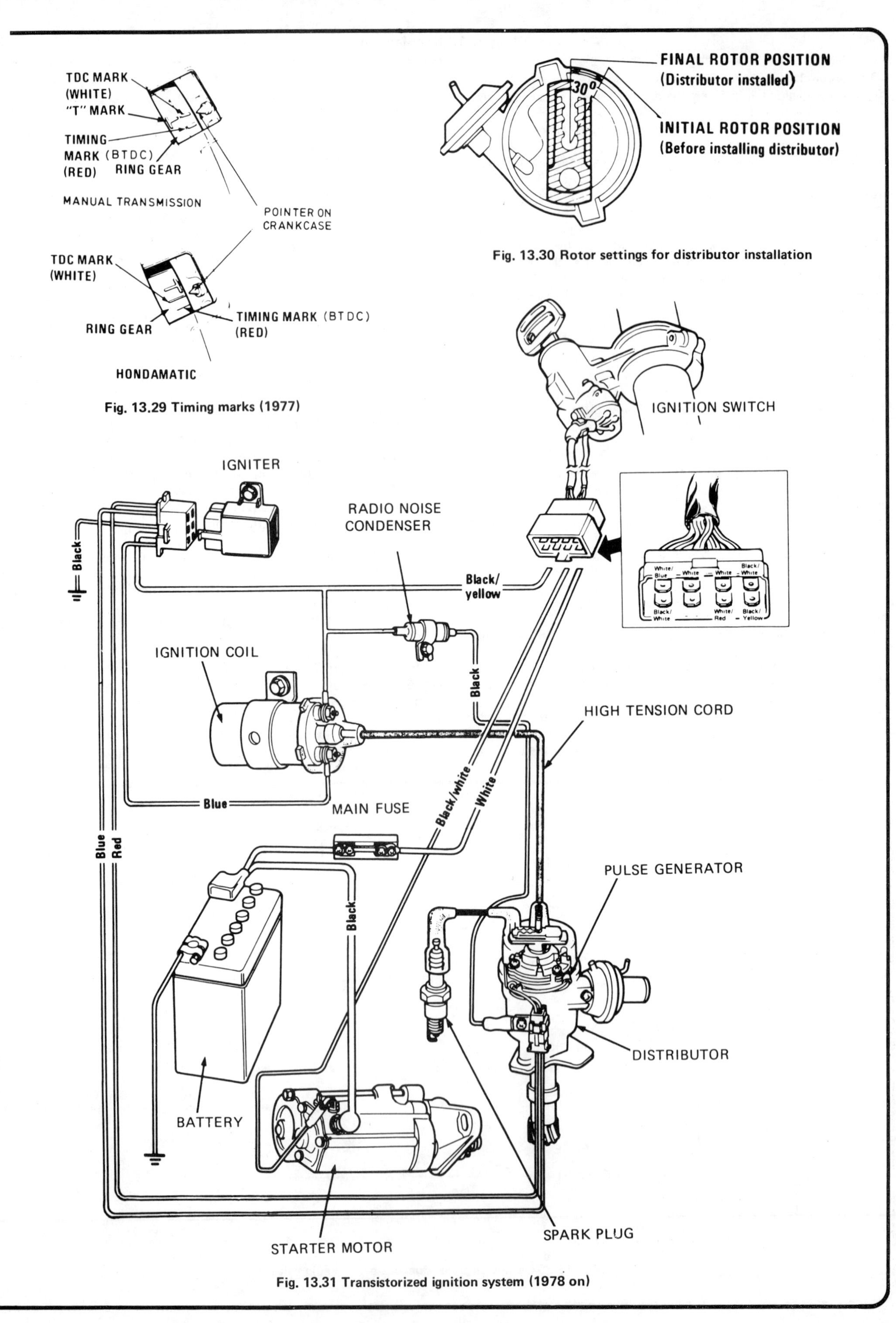

Fig. 13.29 Timing marks (1977)

Fig. 13.30 Rotor settings for distributor installation

Fig. 13.31 Transistorized ignition system (1978 on)

5 Ignition system

Distributor (1977) - removal and refitting

1 To remove the distributor, take off the cap and lay it to one side. There is no need to disconnect the coil or spark plug HT leads.
2 Disconnect the vacuum tube and the LT lead from the distributor.
3 Unscrew the distributor clamp plate bolt and withdraw the distributor from the engine.
4 To install the distributor, bring No. 1 piston (nearest crankshaft pulley) to top dead centre. The piston can be proved to be rising on the compression stroke if No. 1 spark plug is removed and a finger held over the plug hole. Check that the appropriate TDC mark on the flywheel ring gear is opposite the pointer according to the transmission type with which the car is equipped.
5 Hold the distributor over its recess in the engine so that the hole in the clamp plate is aligned with the bolt hole.
6 Turn the rotor arm to the *Initial* position as shown in the diagram.
7 Push the distributor into position making sure that its O-ring is correctly located and the distributor shaft gears mesh. The rotor will turn to take up its *Final* position.
8 Using a stroboscope as described in Chapter 4, Section 8, set the timing and then tighten the distributor clamp bolt. Fit the distributor cap, LT lead and vacuum pipe.
9 Re-check the timing using a stroboscope when the engine is warm.

Transistorized ignition (October 1978 on) - description

10 Cars produced after this date are equipped with a fully transistorized ignition system.
11 The circuit incorporates an igniter and a pulse generator.
12 An ignition coil is retained, but the mechanical breaker points are no longer required.
13 The system improves starting and virtually eliminates the need for periodical maintenance.

Distributor (transistorized ignition) - removal and refitting

14 Disconnect the high tension leads from the spark plugs.
15 Disconnect the vacuum pipes from the vacuum advance unit.
16 Disconnect the condenser wire from the distributor.
17 Disconnect the igniter leads by separating the coupling plug on the side of the distributor body.
18 Unscrew and remove the clamp bolt, and withdraw the distributor from the engine.
19 To install the distributor, first set No. 1 piston to TDC (flywheel marks in alignment).
20 Turn the distributor rotor until the marks, on the distributor body and the pinion gear, are in alignment.
21 Hold the distributor over its recess so that the anchor plate hole is centrally positioned over the bolt hole. Then insert the distributor complete with its sealing O-ring.
22 Tighten the anchor plate bolt just more than finger tight.
23 Fit the distributor cap. The mark on the cap should be in alignment with the contact end of the rotor arm (positioned at TDC).
24 Connect the leads and vacuum pipes.
25 Start the engine and bring it to normal operating temperature. Connect a stroboscope in accordance with the manufacturer's instructions.

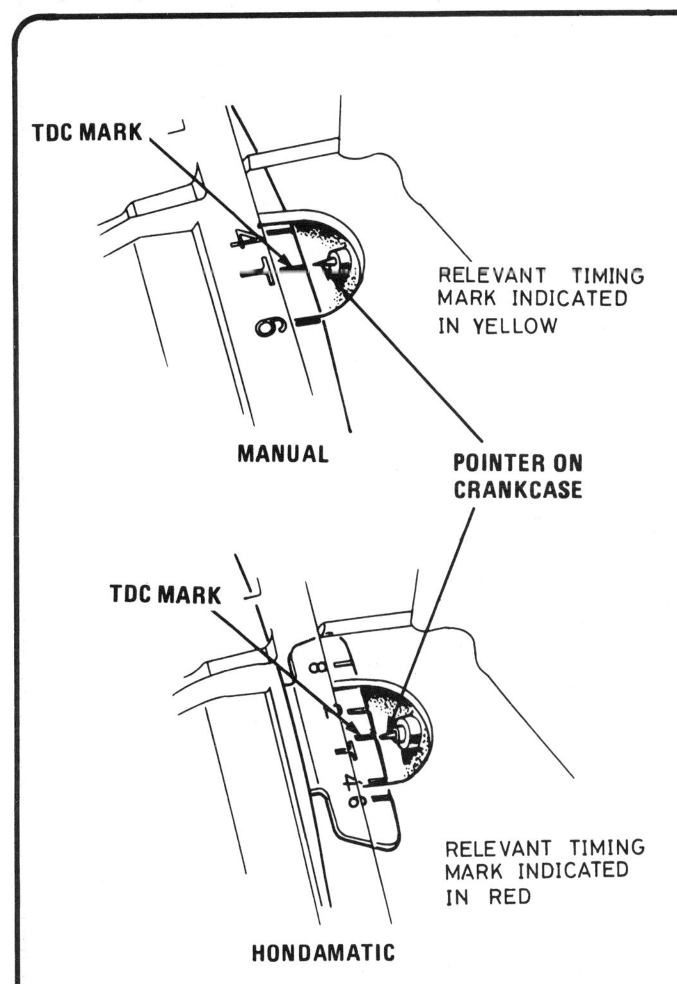

Fig. 13.32 Timing marks (1978 on)

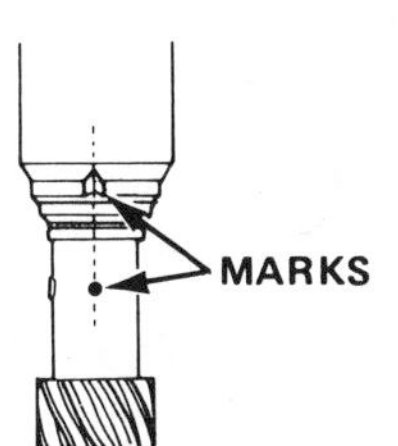

Fig. 13.33 Distributor pinion/body alignment marks (Toyodenso)

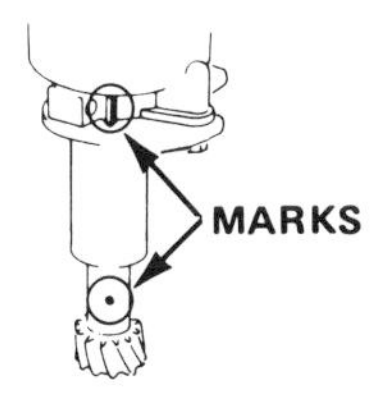

Fig. 13.34 Distributor pinion/body alignment marks (Hitachi)

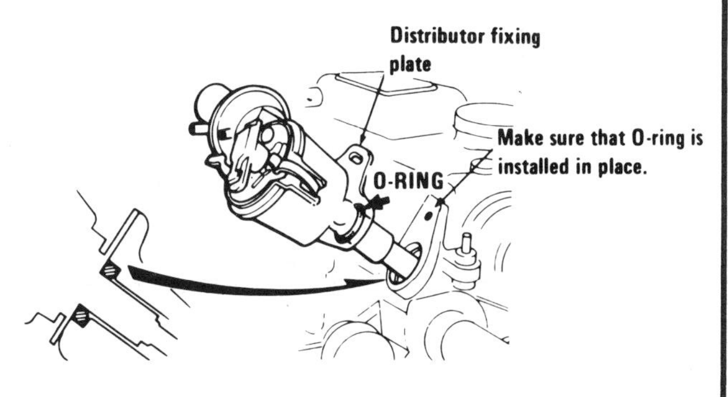

Fig. 13.35 Distributor clamp plate and O-ring

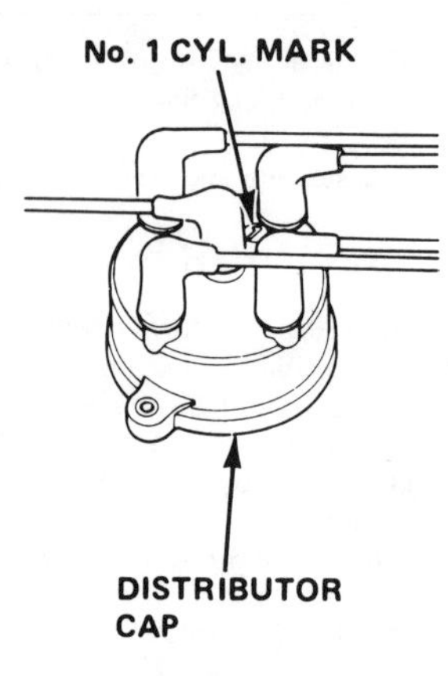

Fig. 13.36 No. 1 cylinder rotor alignment mark (Toyodenso distributor cap)

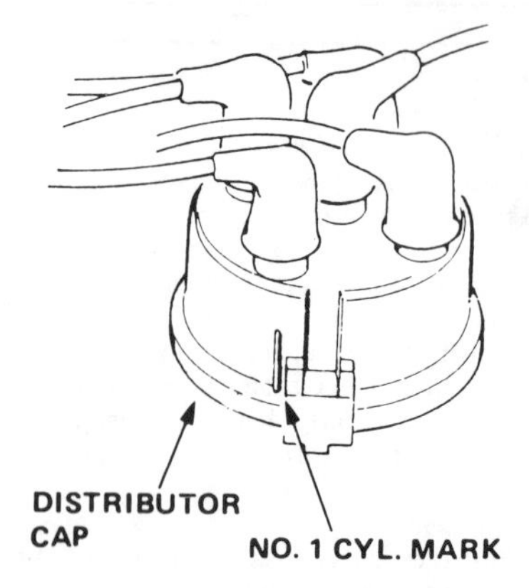

Fig. 13.37 No 1 cylinder rotor alignment mark (Hitachi distributor cap)

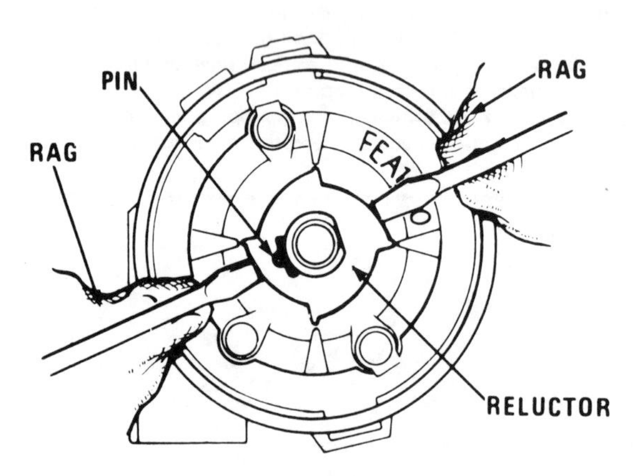

Fig. 13.38 Removing reluctor

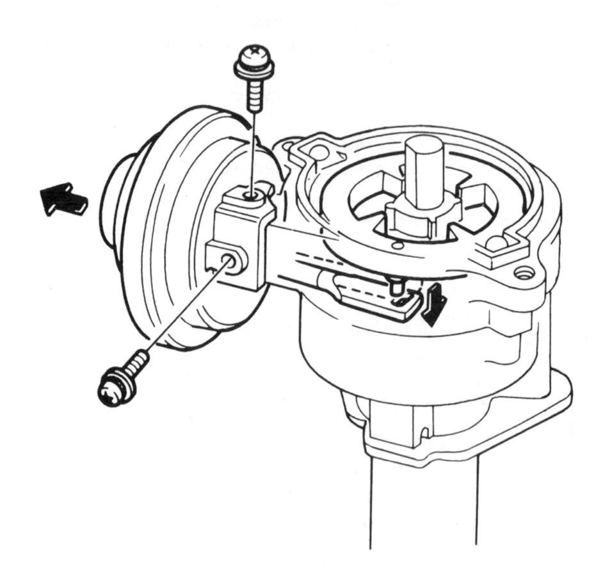

Fig. 13.39 Removing distributor vacuum unit

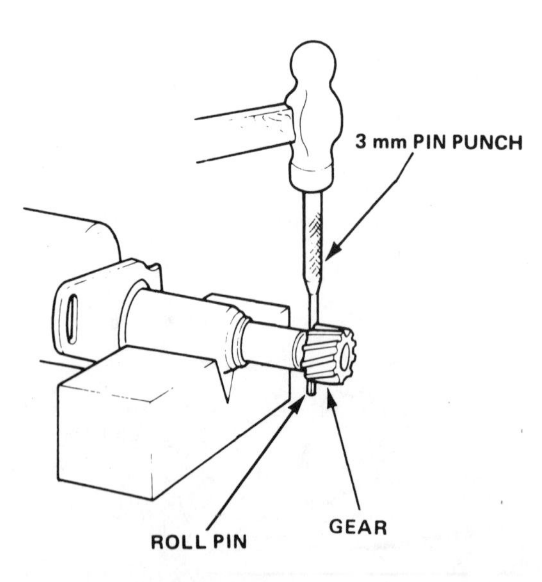

Fig. 13.40 Removing distributor gear pin

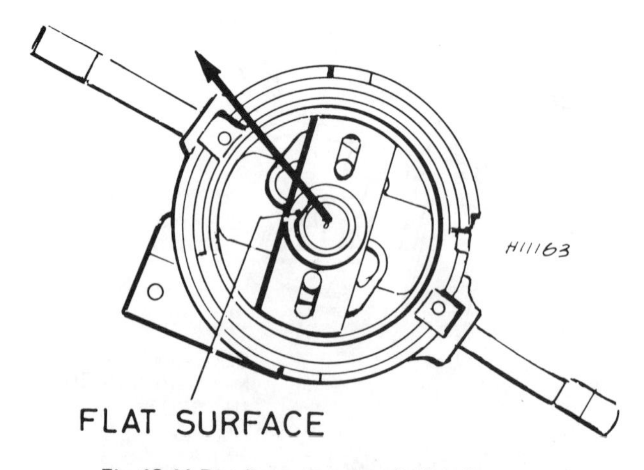

Fig. 13.41 Distributor gear installation diagram with shaft flat as indicated (up to 1981 and later Hitachi)

26 With the engine idling, point the light at the flywheel timing marks and turn the distributor slightly one way or the other to align the timing mark with the pointer at the flywheel or driveplate. The ignition timing will then be as specified at idling speed.

Distributor (transistorized ignition) - overhaul

27 The operations are similar to those described for mechanical breaker distributors in Chapter 4, but observe the following:
28 Using two screwdrivers as levers, prise up the reluctor and remove it.
29 Remove the vacuum unit by extracting the securing screws and depressing the diaphragm connecting link as the unit is withdrawn.
30 If necessary, drive out the pin and remove the pinion gear.
31 When reassembling the distributor, fit the pinion gear in the following way:

Distributors up to 1981 and later Hitachi type
32 Align the marks on the pinion gear and the distributor body and drive in the connecting pin. With the marks still in alignment, fit the rotor shaft so that the flat is towards the vacuum unit.

Toyodenso distributors
33 Align the pinion gear and body marks, drive in the pin and fit the rotor shaft so that the flat is as shown, Fig. 13.42.
34 Fit the baseplate. On Hitachi distributors, align the baseplate notch as shown in Fig. 13.43 before tightening the fixing screws.
35 Check that the upper plate moves freely. If the vacuum unit arm pin rotates past the end of the slot in the lower plate, correct the situation by rotating the plate past its limit in the opposite direction.
36 Fit the reluctor and then drive in the roll pin so that its seam is furthest from the shaft.
37 On all distributors except Toyodenso type, check that the air gaps are equal. If they are not, release the three fixing screws and move the stator as necessary. Retighten the screws.

Spark plugs and leads - removal and refitting

38 Before removing a spark plug, brush or vacuum clean dirt and grit from around the plug body to prevent it dropping into the cylinder when the plug is unscrewed.
39 Grip the rubber connecting sleeve, not the lead, when disconnecting the HT lead from the spark plug.
40 Use a box spanner or socket to unscrew the spark plug; keep the

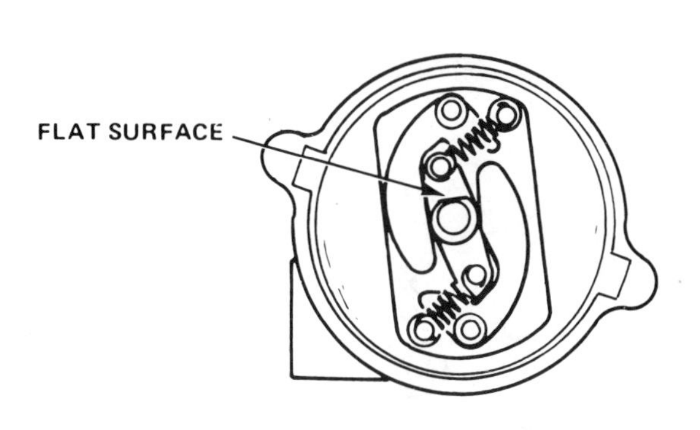

Fig. 13.42 Distributor gear installation with shaft flat as indicated (Toyodenso)

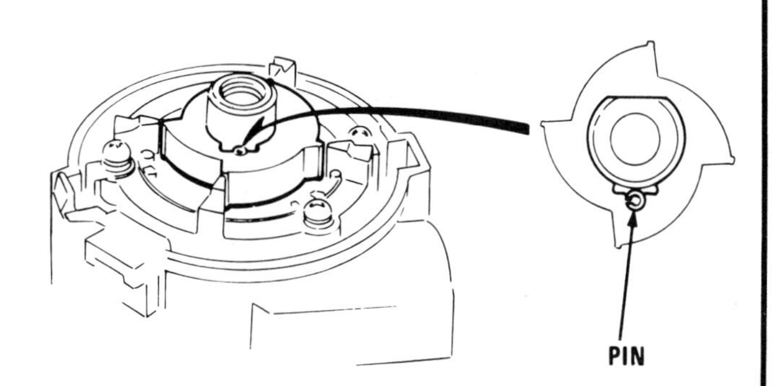

Fig. 13.44 Reluctor roll pin

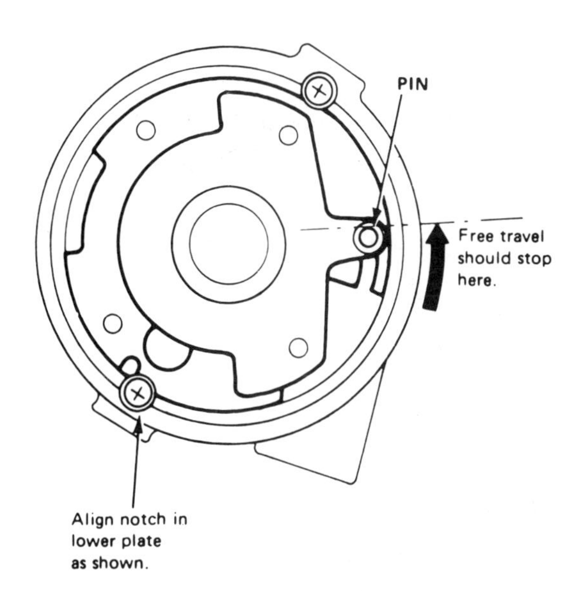

Fig. 13.43 Breaker plate fitting diagram

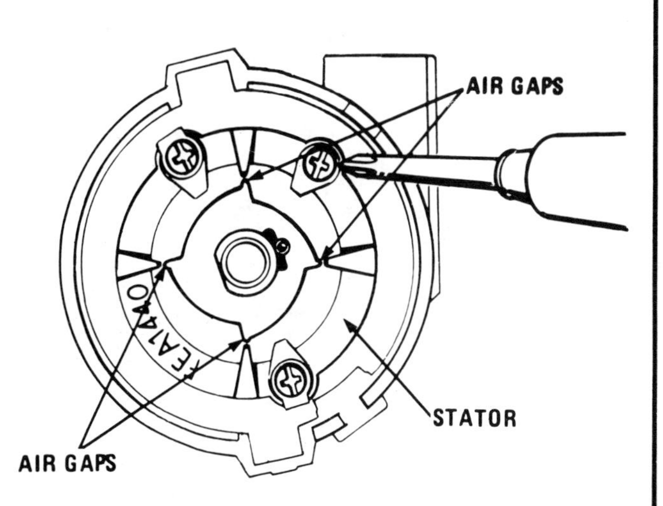

Fig. 13.45 Reluctor to stator equal air gaps

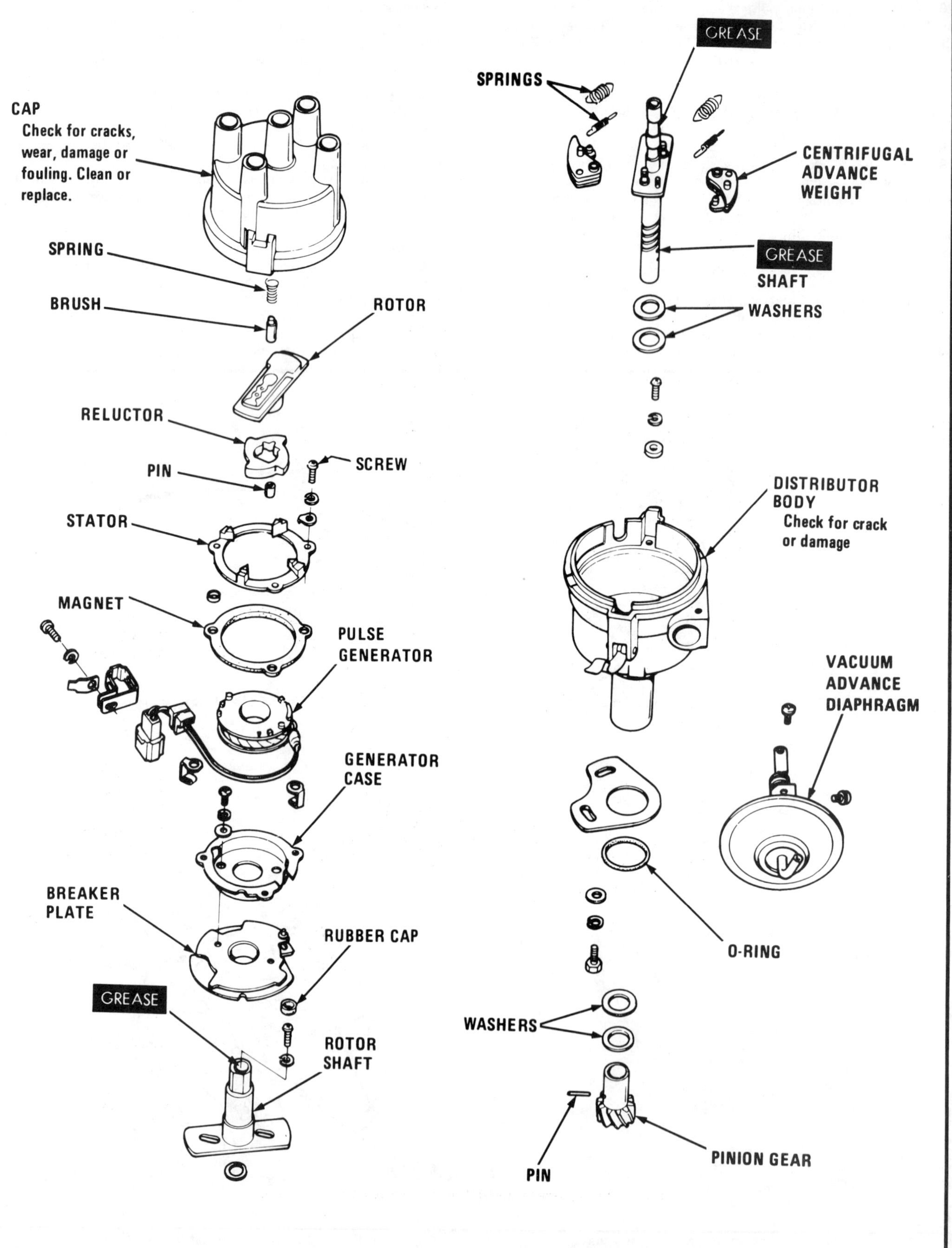

Fig. 13.46 Exploded view of distributor (1978 to 1980)

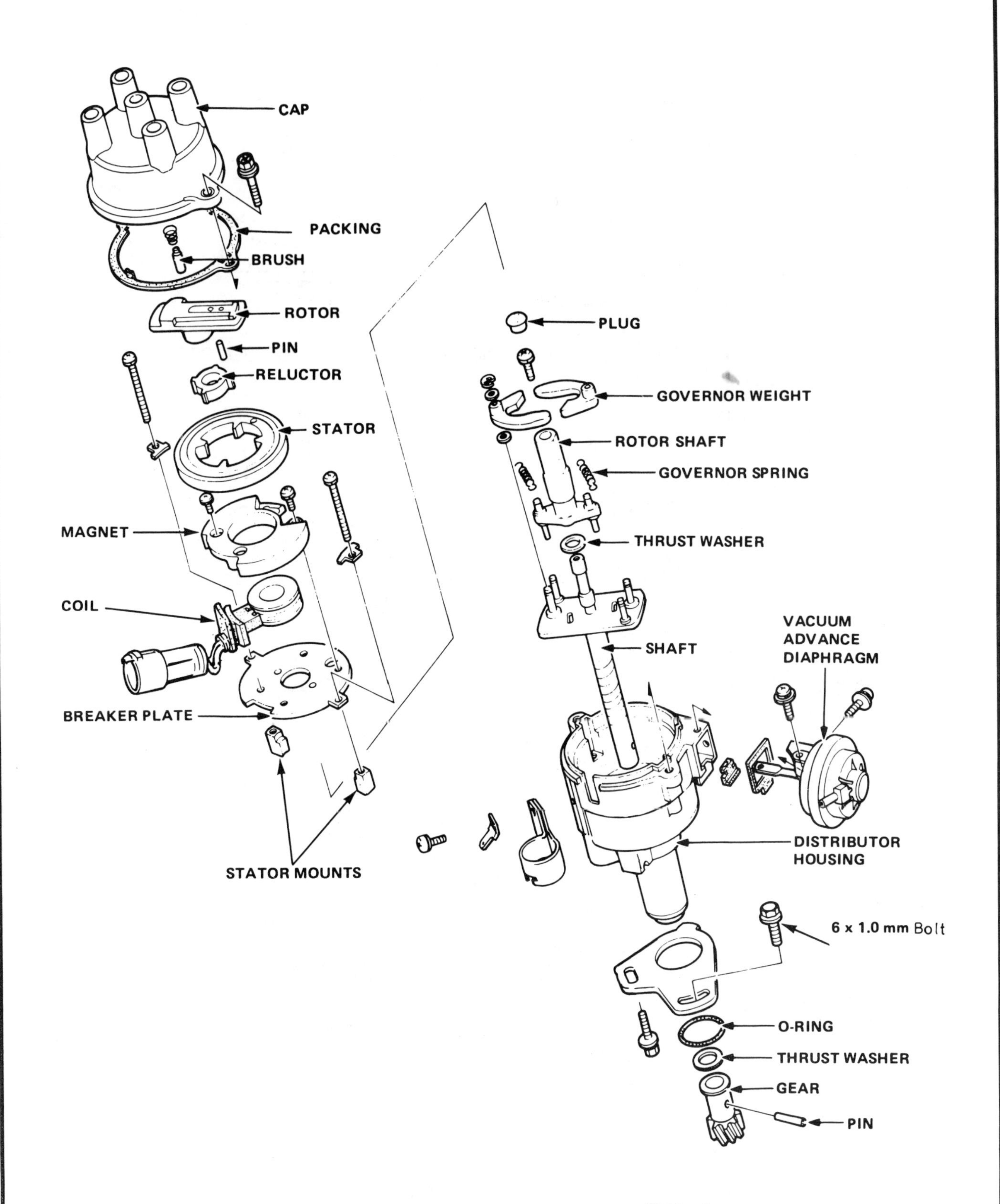

Fig. 13.47 Exploded view of Toyodenso distributor (1981 on)

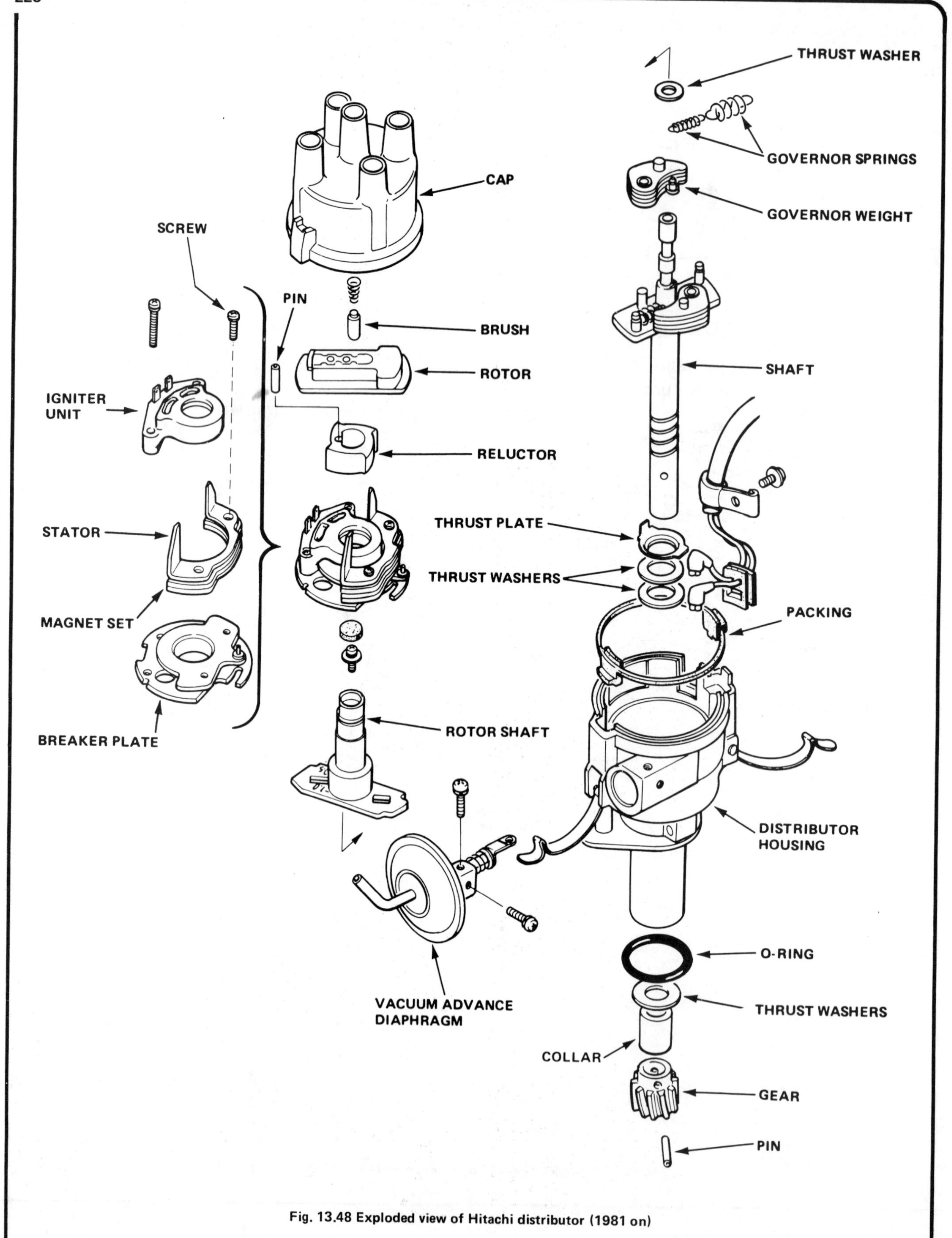

Fig. 13.48 Exploded view of Hitachi distributor (1981 on)

tool straight, otherwise the ceramic part of the plug could fracture.
41 If machine cleaning is not available, satisfactory results can be obtained using a wire brush, but avoid brushing the centre insulator because conductance paths may be created. Clean between the body and the centre insulator carefully.
42 If the centre electrode has rounded off, it is time to renew the plugs.
43 Set the gap to the specified clearance, apply a smear of grease to the plug threads and screw them into clean seats finger tight (photo).

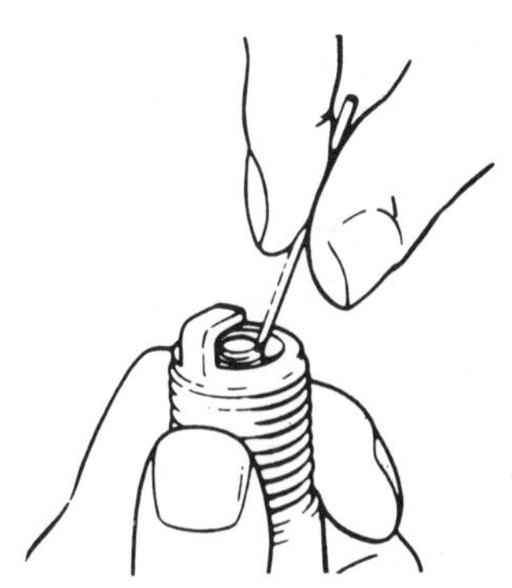

Fig. 13.49 Cleaning spark plug between body and centre electrode

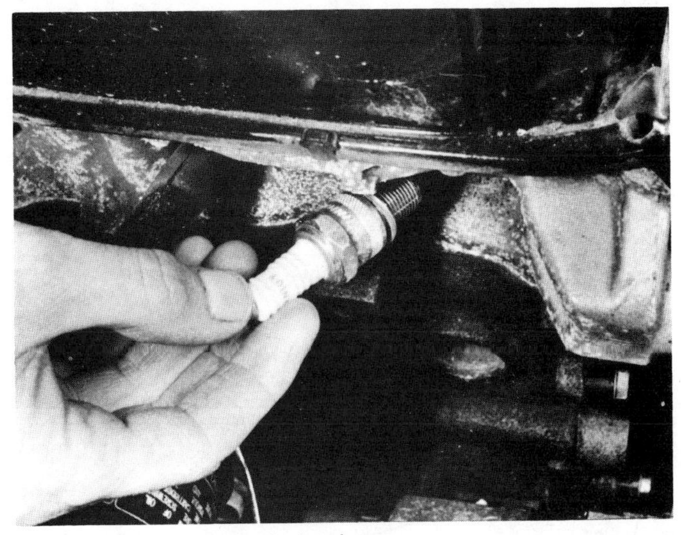

5.43 Screwing in spark plug by hand

5.44 Tightening spark plug

44 Tighten to 17 lbf ft (2.3 kgf m). If a torque wrench is not available, do not overtighten, but just seat them lightly otherwise the threads in the light alloy cylinder head may be damaged (photo).
45 Check that the HT leads in the distributor cap sockets are secure and free from corrosion then reconnect the leads in the correct sequence.
46 The ignition coil is mounted on the engine compartment rear bulkhead and has a waterproof cover to protect the terminals and HT cable socket (photo).

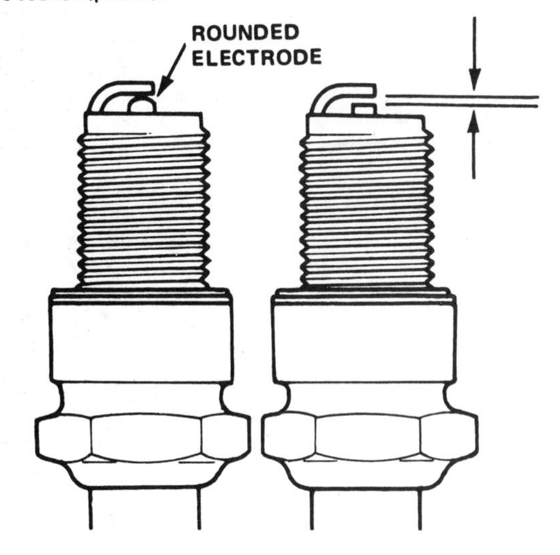

Fig. 13.50 Spark plug centre electrode conditions

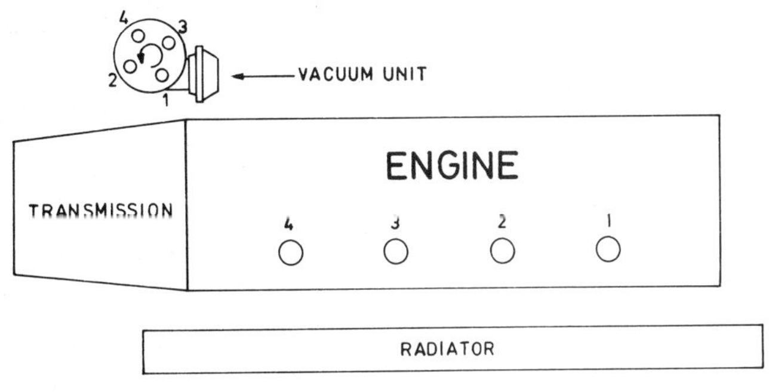

Fig. 13.51 Spark plug lead connecting diagram

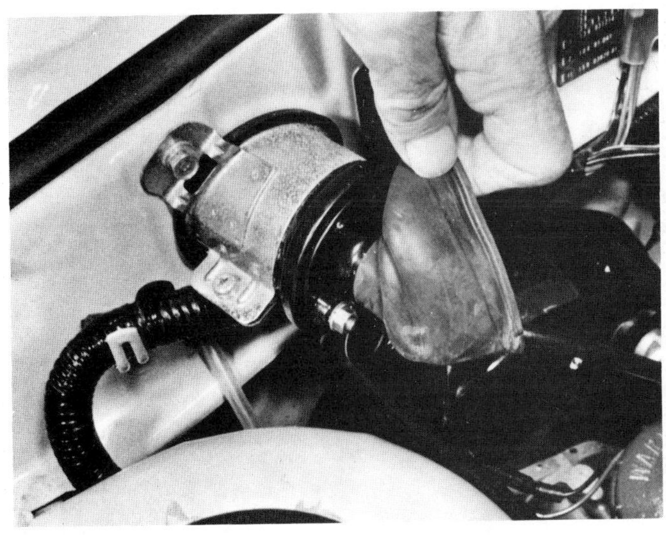

5.46 Ignition coil and protective cover

6 Clutch

Cable actuation

1 In 1982, actuation of the clutch was changed from hydraulic to cable.

2 A modified form of release lever and fork are used in conjunction with the cable system.

Clutch - adjustment

3 Check the free play at the end of the release arm. If it is outside the specified tolerance, turn the knurled adjuster at the cable bracket on the clutch housing. If the release arm play is correct then the pedal free play should be as specified (photo).

Clutch cable - removal and refitting

4 Slacken the cable adjuster at the clutch housing bracket.

5 Working inside the vehicle, extract the three screws and take off the facia lower panel complete with the fuse box finisher plate. Withdraw the panel and at the same time disconnect the fuse lamp plug.

6 Remove the insulating pad from the forward underside of the facia panel. This is held by one press plug and a metal tab.

7 Extract one screw and one press plug and take off the right-hand heater duct.

8 With the top of the clutch pedal arm now exposed, unhook the pedal return spring and then unhook the clutch cable end fitting from the pedal arm.

9 Disconnect the cable from the release lever within the engine

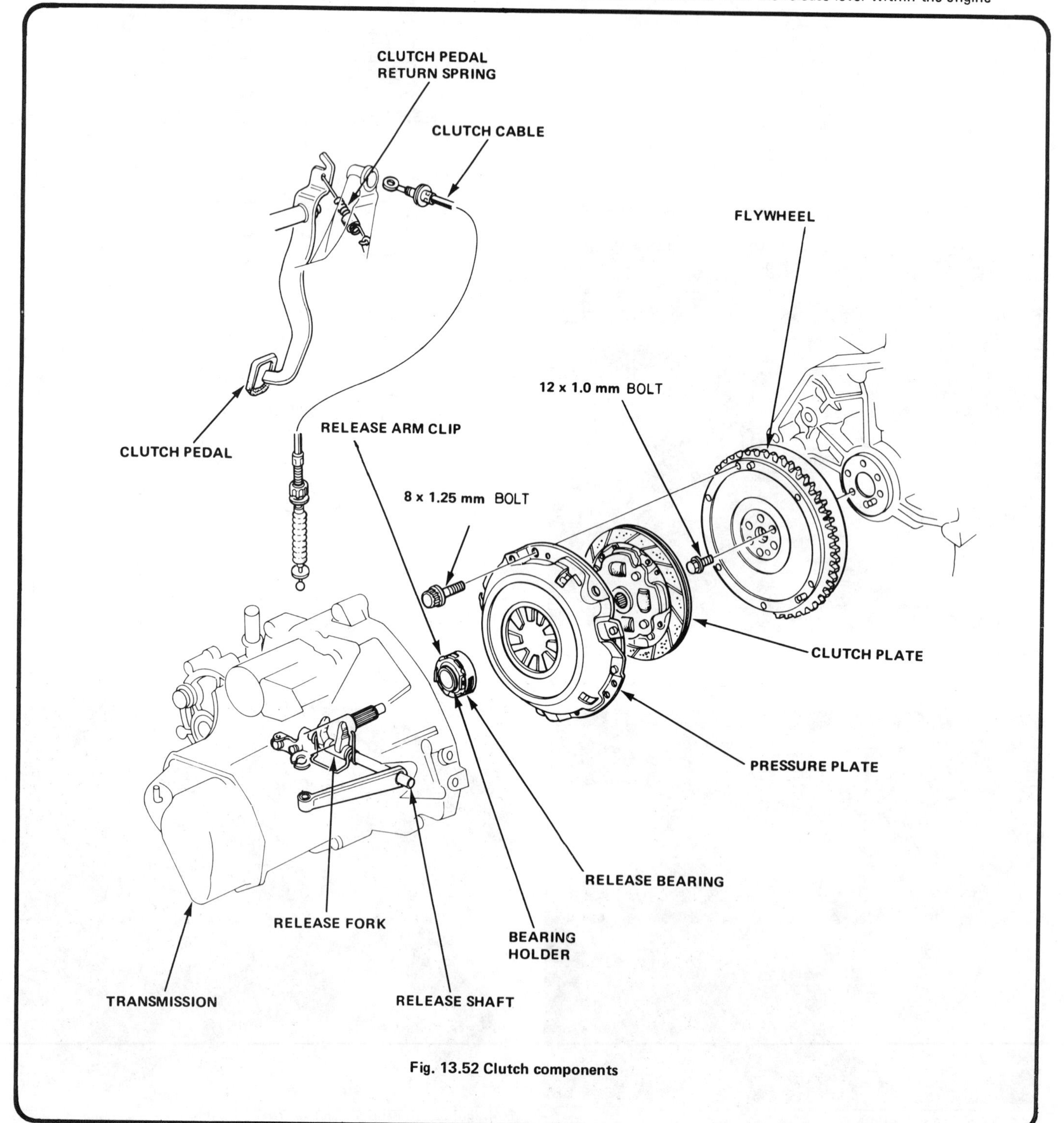

Fig. 13.52 Clutch components

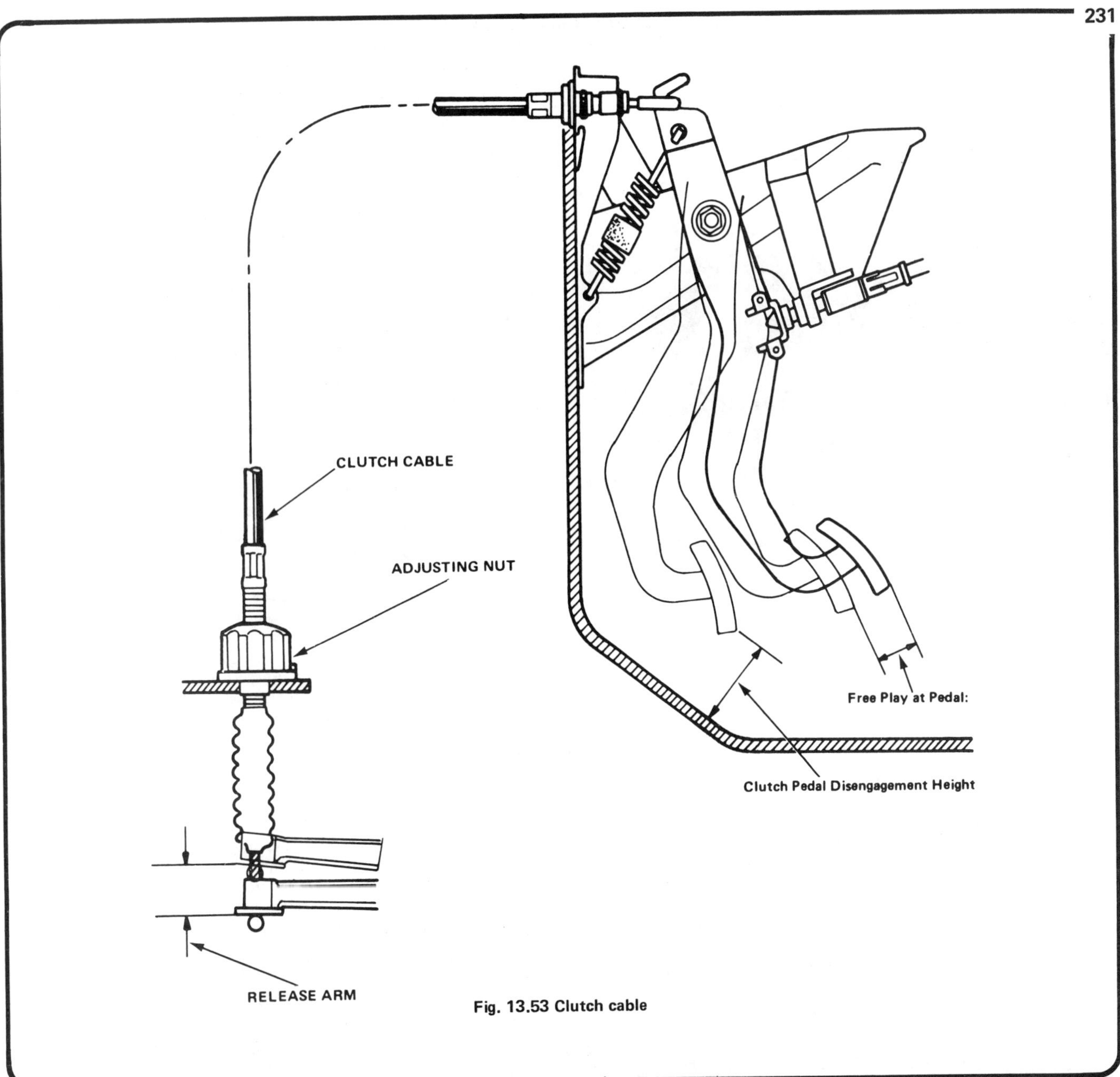

Fig. 13.53 Clutch cable

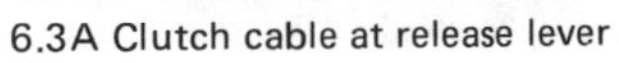

6.3A Clutch cable at release lever

6.3B Clutch cable adjuster

Fig. 13.54 Clutch release arm bolt

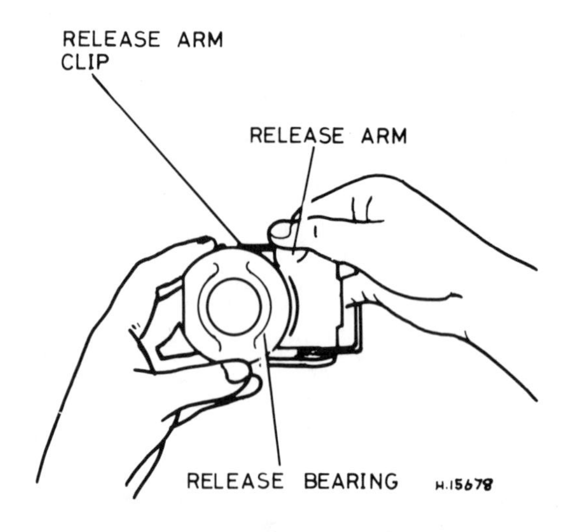

Fig. 13.55 Release bearing and spring clips

compartment and withdraw the complete cable assembly through the bulkhead into the engine compartment.
10 Refitting is a reversal of removal, but adjust the pedal free movement as described earlier.

Clutch release components

11 To remove the clutch release bearing on cable actuated clutches, unscrew and remove the release arm bolt, pull out the pivot shaft and withdraw the arm with bearing.
12 Release the spring clip and separate the bearing from the arm.
13 If the bearing is noisy when spun with the fingers, it must be renewed. The bearing is of grease-sealed type and must not be washed in solvent.
14 Fit the bearing to the arm, engage the spring in the bearing holes. Apply a little molybdenum disulphide grease to the friction surfaces of the arm and shaft.
15 Use a new lockplate and bolt the arm to the shaft.
16 Check the assembly for smooth operation.

7 Manual transmission

Manual transmission (October 1978 on) - description

1 The five-speed manual transmission fitted after October 1978 is of different design compared with earlier models and the following procedures must be followed when working on the transmission.
2 The gear ratios have been modified.

Lubricant - topping up and renewal

3 At the intervals specified in Routine Maintenance, remove the oil filler/level plug.
4 If necessary, add oil of specified grade until it just runs from the plug hole. Refit the plug.
5 At the specified intervals, remove the oil filler/level plug and the drain plug. Catch the oil in a suitable container. It is recommended that the oil is drained hot after a run.
6 Fit the drain plug using a new washer and then add oil of the specified grade until it just begins to run out of the filler/level hole. Fit the filler plug.

Gearchange control linkage

7 Components of the gearchange linkage vary in detail from those shown in Chapter 6, but the information given in Section 6 of that Chapter will otherwise apply.

Manual transmission - removal and refitting

8 If the vehicle is equipped with power steering, disconnect the speedometer drive cable and the sensor unit and tie them up out of the way. Disconnection of flexible hoses is unnecessary.
9 The removal and refitting operations are as described in Chapter 6 except that reference to detachment of the clutch slave cylinder will not apply as the clutch is actuated by cable.
10 Slacken the cable adjuster completely and then disconnect the cable from the release arm.

Manual transmission - overhaul

Dismantling

11 Clean the exterior of the gearbox using paraffin and a stiff brush or by using a water soluble solvent. Remove the clutch release mechanism.
12 Unbolt and remove the end cover from the transmission.
13 Relieve the staking on the mainshaft and countershaft nuts.
14 At this point, check the clearance between the spacer collar and the shoulder on the 5th gear and record it.
15 Shift the transmission into reverse gear by moving the selector rod.
16 The input shaft must now be held stationary so that the mainshaft and countershaft nuts can be unscrewed. To do this, either fit the special tool (07923–6890100) or if the clutch driven plate is to be renewed, fit this on to the input shaft splines and use the plate as an anchor by passing a bar or rod through it.
17 Unscrew the locknuts using a 30 mm socket, noting that they have left-hand threads.
18 Drive out the roll pin which holds the 5th gear shift fork to the shift shaft.
19 Pull off mainshaft 5th gear, the shift fork and synchro assembly.
20 Pull off the countershaft 5th gear.
21 Unscrew and remove the three detent plugs and extract the springs and balls.
22 Unscrew and remove the reversing lamp switch.
23 Unscrew and remove the thirteen bolts which hold the transmission casing to the clutch housing.
24 Tap off the transmission casing using a soft-faced mallet.
25 Shift the transmission into neutral and then withdraw the shift guide shaft.
26 Withdraw the reverse/idler shaft and gear.
27 Grip the 3rd/4th and 1st/2nd shift shafts and pull them upwards to engage 4th and 2nd gears.
28 Remove the 5th/reverse shift shaft by pulling it upwards while the reverse shift fork is lifted.
29 Tilt the interlock and shift guide and remove them.
30 Withdraw the mainshaft and countershaft geartrains as an assembly together with 1st/2nd and 3rd/4th shift shafts.
31 Unscrew the three fixing bolts and remove the gear selector assembly.
32 Remove the differential and crownwheel assembly from the

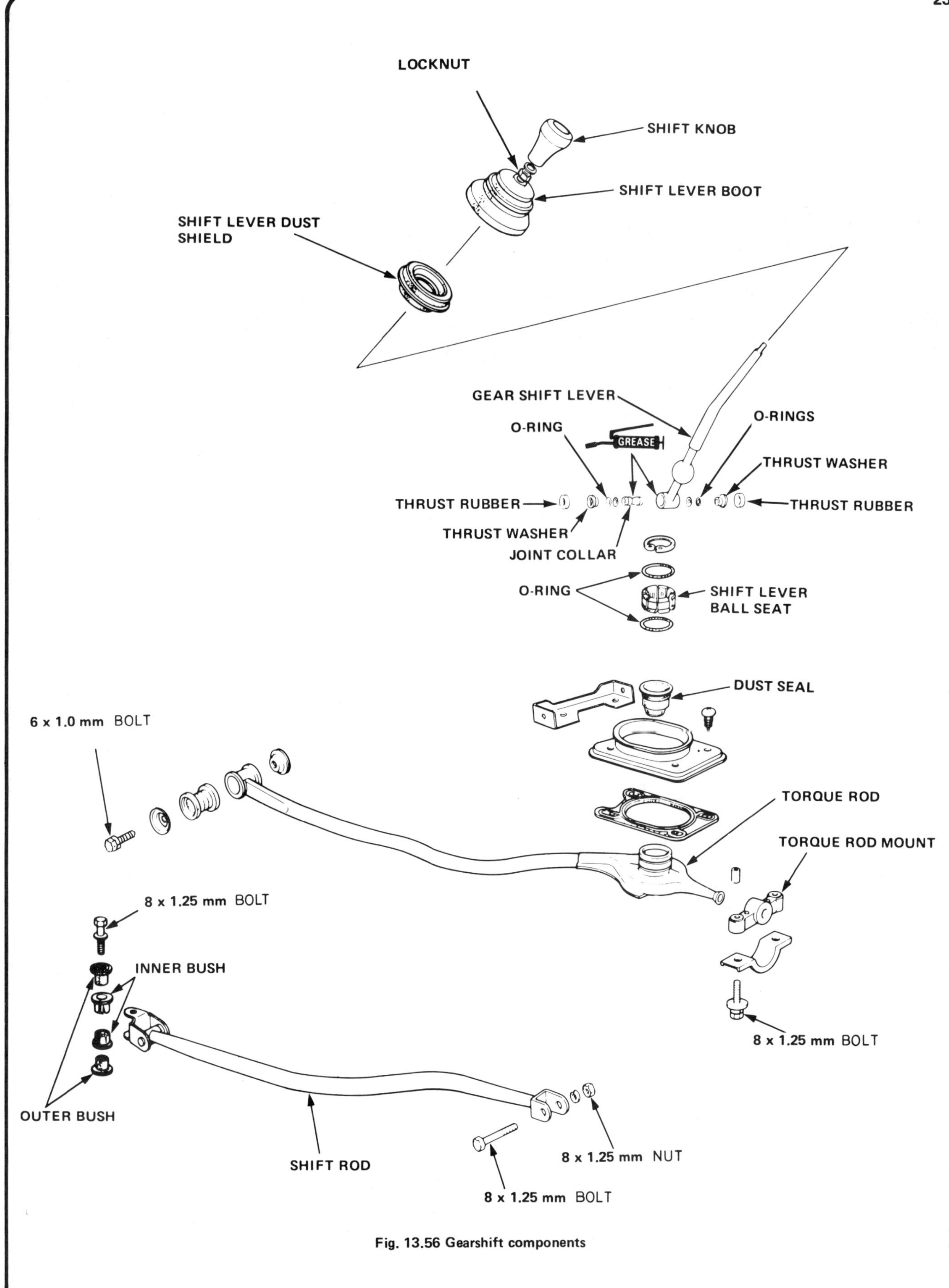
LOCKNUT
SHIFT KNOB
SHIFT LEVER BOOT
SHIFT LEVER DUST SHIELD
GEAR SHIFT LEVER
O-RING
GREASE
O-RINGS
THRUST WASHER
THRUST RUBBER
THRUST RUBBER
THRUST WASHER
JOINT COLLAR
O-RING
SHIFT LEVER BALL SEAT
DUST SEAL
6 x 1.0 mm BOLT
TORQUE ROD
TORQUE ROD MOUNT
8 x 1.25 mm BOLT
INNER BUSH
8 x 1.25 mm BOLT
OUTER BUSH
SHIFT ROD
8 x 1.25 mm NUT
8 x 1.25 mm BOLT

Fig. 13.56 Gearshift components

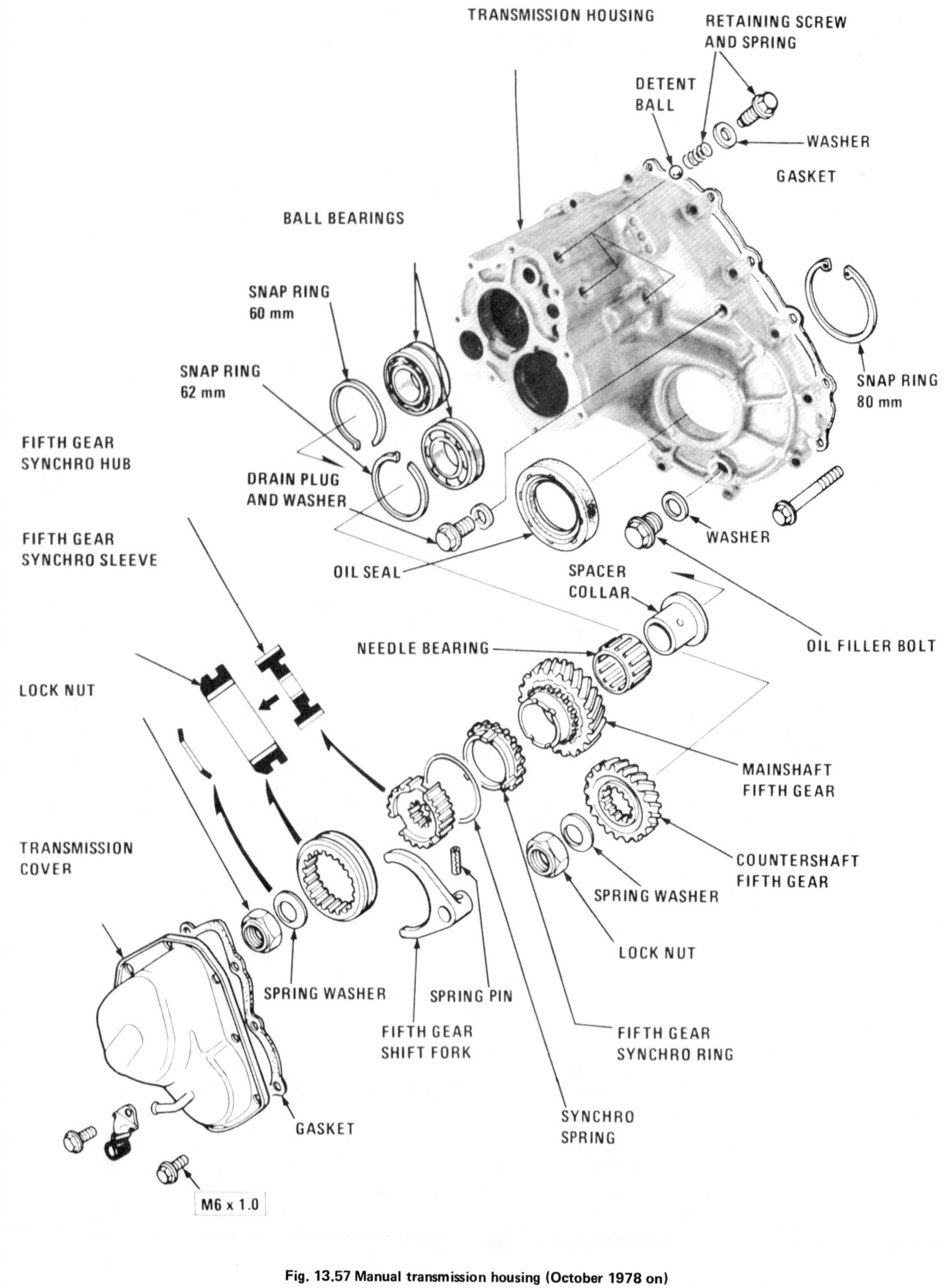

TRANSMISSION HOUSING
RETAINING SCREW AND SPRING
DETENT BALL
WASHER
GASKET
BALL BEARINGS
SNAP RING 60 mm
SNAP RING 62 mm
SNAP RING 80 mm
FIFTH GEAR SYNCHRO HUB
DRAIN PLUG AND WASHER
FIFTH GEAR SYNCHRO SLEEVE
OIL SEAL
WASHER
SPACER COLLAR
OIL FILLER BOLT
NEEDLE BEARING
LOCK NUT
MAINSHAFT FIFTH GEAR
TRANSMISSION COVER
COUNTERSHAFT FIFTH GEAR
SPRING WASHER
LOCK NUT
SPRING WASHER
SPRING PIN
FIFTH GEAR SHIFT FORK
FIFTH GEAR SYNCHRO RING
GASKET
SYNCHRO SPRING
M6 x 1.0

Fig. 13.57 Manual transmission housing (October 1978 on)

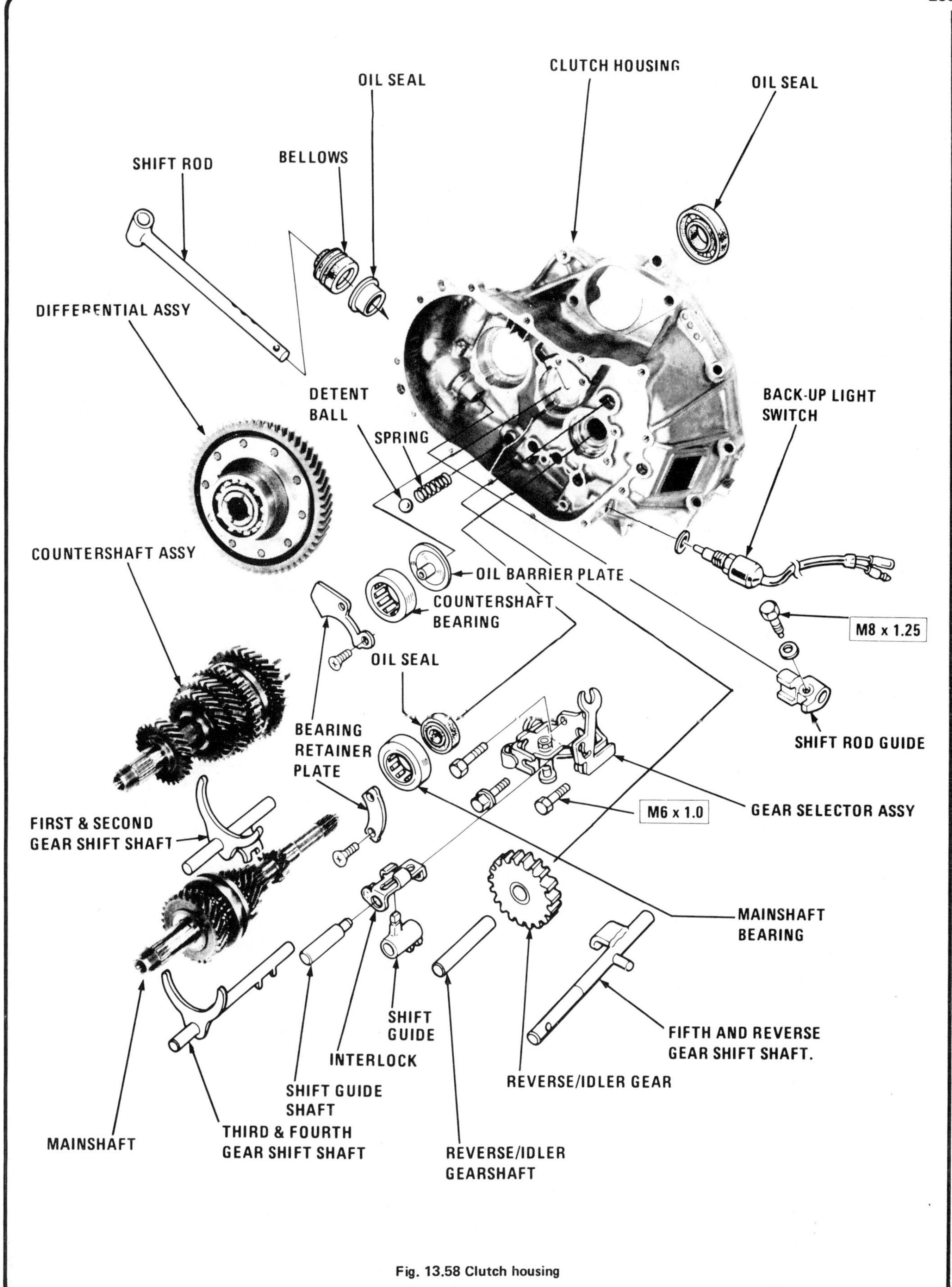
OIL SEAL
CLUTCH HOUSING
OIL SEAL
SHIFT ROD
BELLOWS
DIFFERENTIAL ASSY
DETENT
BALL
SPRING
BACK-UP LIGHT
SWITCH
COUNTERSHAFT ASSY
OIL BARRIER PLATE
COUNTERSHAFT
BEARING
M8 x 1.25
OIL SEAL
BEARING
RETAINER
PLATE
SHIFT ROD GUIDE
GEAR SELECTOR ASSY
M6 x 1.0
FIRST & SECOND
GEAR SHIFT SHAFT
MAINSHAFT
BEARING
SHIFT
GUIDE
FIFTH AND REVERSE
GEAR SHIFT SHAFT.
INTERLOCK
REVERSE/IDLER GEAR
SHIFT GUIDE
SHAFT
MAINSHAFT
THIRD & FOURTH
GEAR SHIFT SHAFT
REVERSE/IDLER
GEARSHAFT

Fig. 13.58 Clutch housing

Fig. 13.59 Relieving shaft locknut staking

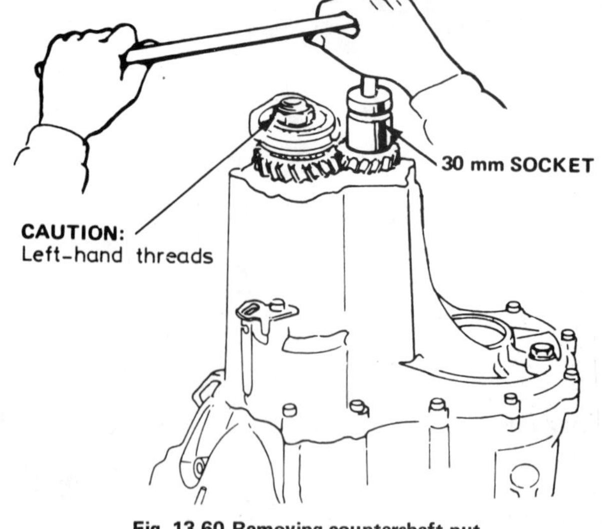

Fig. 13.60 Removing countershaft nut

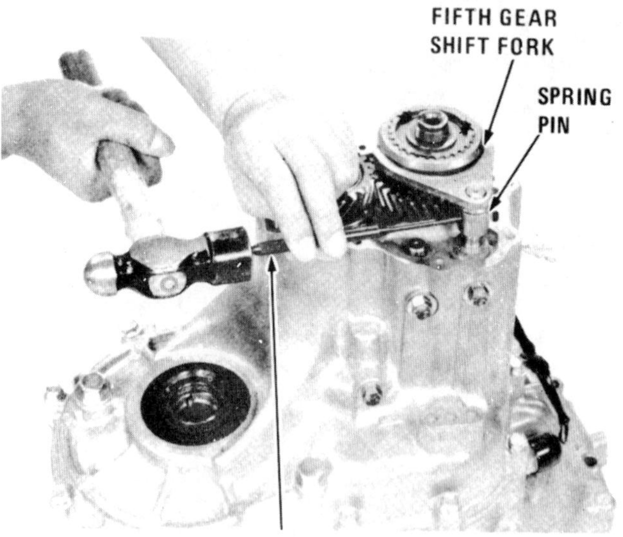

Fig. 13.61 Removing 5th gear shift fork roll pin

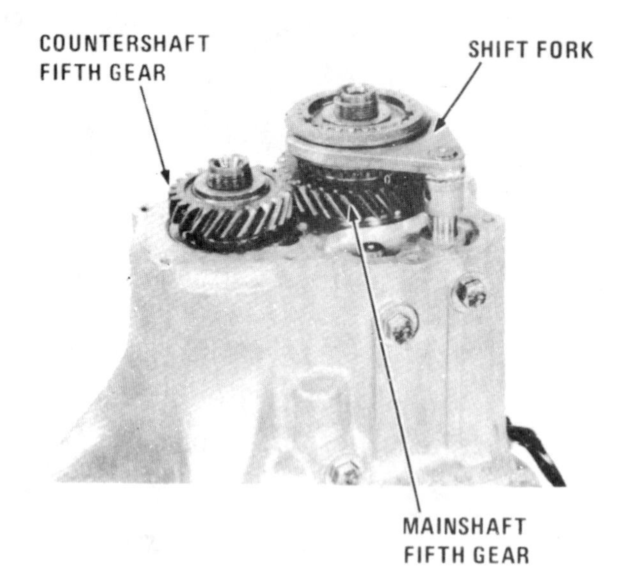

Fig. 13.62 5th gears and shift fork

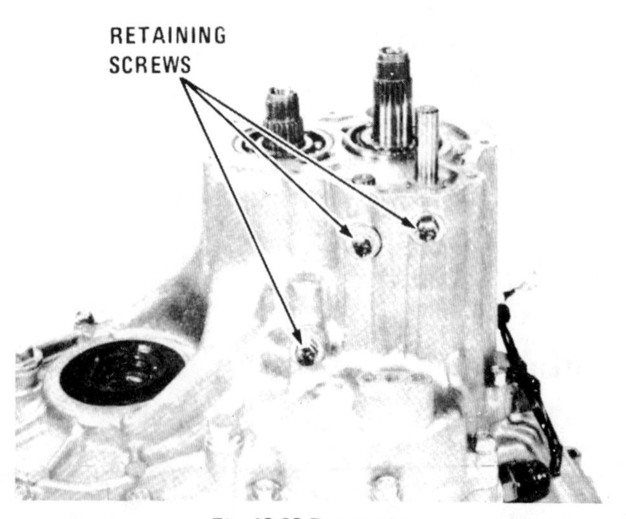

Fig. 13.63 Detent plugs

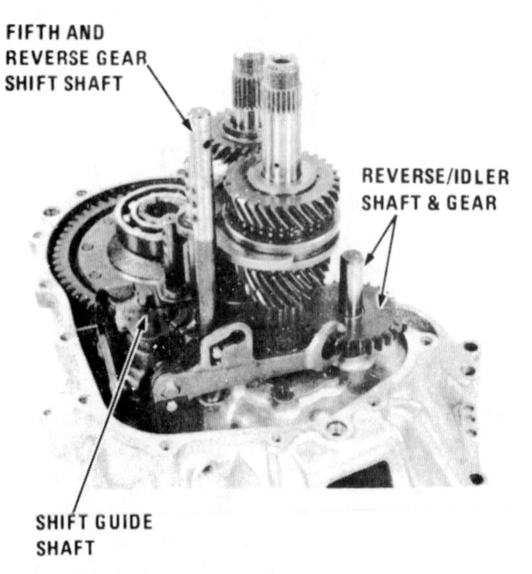

Fig. 13.64 5th/reverse gears and shafts

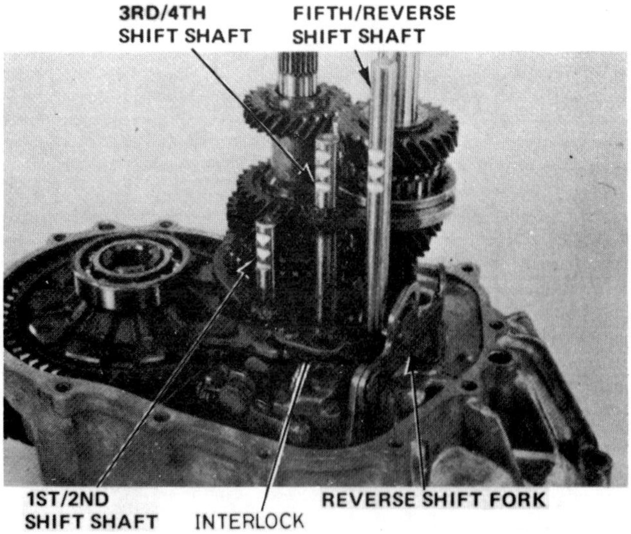

3RD/4TH SHIFT SHAFT
FIFTH/REVERSE SHIFT SHAFT
1ST/2ND SHIFT SHAFT
INTERLOCK
REVERSE SHIFT FORK

Fig. 13.65 Shift components

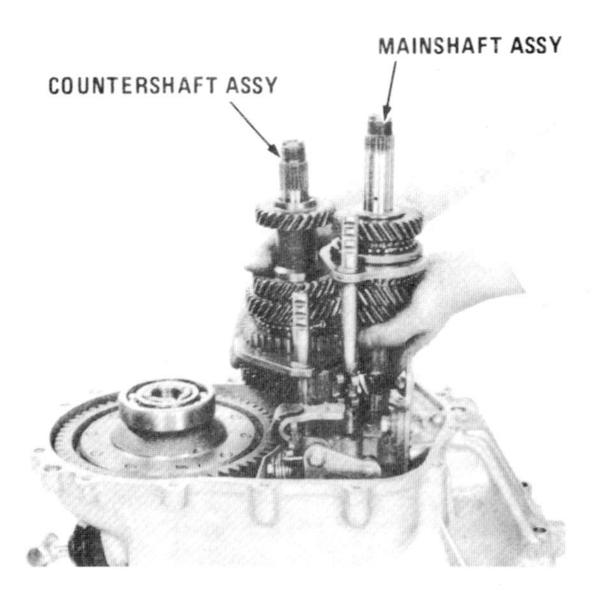

Fig. 13.66 Removing geartrains

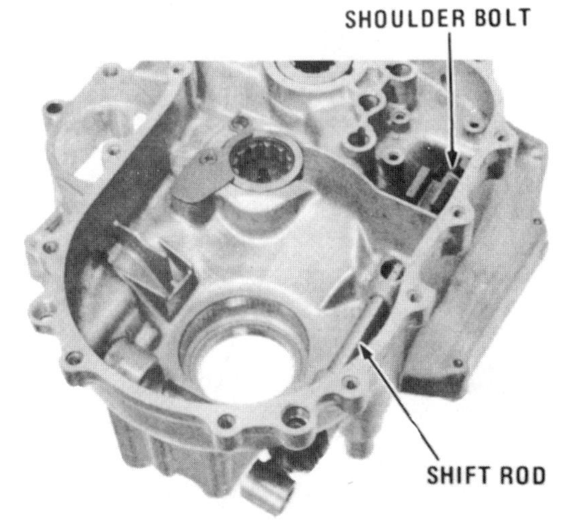

Fig. 13.67 Shift rod and shouldered bolt

transmission casing by tapping the differential carrier bearings free with a piece of tubing.

33 Remove the gearchange rod after extracting the shouldered bolt, but cover the casing with a cloth to prevent the detent ball, which is located under the rod, from flying out.

Inspection and repair

34 With the transmission dismantled, examine each component for wear and damage.

35 Renew oil seals as a matter of routine.

36 The clutch housing bearings can be renewed once their retainer plates have been withdrawn. An impact screwdriver will be required to unscrew the retainer plate screws. Support the transmission casing webs when installing a new bearing and re-stake the retainer plate screws.

37 Before the transmission casing bearings can be pressed out, the retaining circlips must be expanded with a pair of circlip pliers.

38 Dismantle the mainshaft and countershaft, keeping the parts in order and noting that the needle bearings for 3rd, 4th and 5th gears are identical.

39 The synchro units must be inspected and checked for wear. If there has been a history of noisy gearchanging or if the synchromesh could be easily 'beaten' then it is recommended that a new synchro assembly is fitted. Check the baulk ring teeth for wear and the gear cone surface for wear. Press the baulk ring on to the gear cone at the same time twisting it until it stops. This should be after the ring has turned through between 10° and 20°. Now measure the clearance between the ring and the gear. This should not be less than the specified limit otherwise renew the ring and gear if necessary.

40 Check the shift fork to synchro sleeve groove clearances using a feeler blade. This should not exceed the specified limit otherwise renew the shift fork or the sleeve or both after comparison with new components.

41 Check the shift shaft to reverse shift fork clearance.

42 Check the reverse idler to reverse shift fork clearance.

43 Check the 5th/reverse shift shaft to shift guide clearance. If any clearances exceed the specified limit, renew the components.

Reassembly

44 Commence reassembly by fitting the components to the mainshaft in the order shown in Fig. 13.75. The assembly must include the bearings which will have been withdrawn from the transmission housing and 5th gear components.

45 Assemble the countershaft after reference to Fig. 13.76.

46 Install the mainshaft and countershaft assemblies simultaneously into the clutch housing. Shift the transmission into gear and prevent the input shaft from rotating by one of the methods described in Paragraph 16.

47 Tighten the shaft locknuts (left-hand thread) to the specified torque.

48 Remove the geartrains from the clutch housing and measure the following clearances:

Mainshaft

49 3rd gear shoulder to 2nd gear shoulder 0.0012 to 0.0071 in (0.03 to 0.18 mm). If not as specified renew 3rd gear. If gear is satisfactory renew synchro hub.

50 4th gear shoulder to spacer collar 0.0012 to 0.007 in (0.03 to 0.18 mm). If the clearance is not as specified measure the thickness of 4th gear. If this is less than 1.15 in (29.3 mm) it must be renewed. If gear is satisfactory renew synchro hub.

51 5th gear shoulder to spacer collar 0.0012 to 0.004 in (0.03 to 0.1 mm). If the clearance is not as specified measure the thickness of 5th gear. If this measures less than 1.055 in (26.8 mm) it must be renewed.

Countershaft

52 1st gear shoulder to 1st gear thrust washer 0.0012 to 0.003 in (0.03 to 0.08 mm), otherwise renew the thrust washer from one of the four different thicknesses available.

53 3rd gear shoulder to 2nd gear shoulder 0.0012 to 0.004 in (0.03 to 0.1 mm). If the clearance is not as specified, measure the thickness of 2nd gear which should not be less than 1.192 in (30.3 mm) otherwise renew it.

54 The aforegoing clearances should be checked and recorded in sequence on each geartrain. But any new spacers, gears or thrust

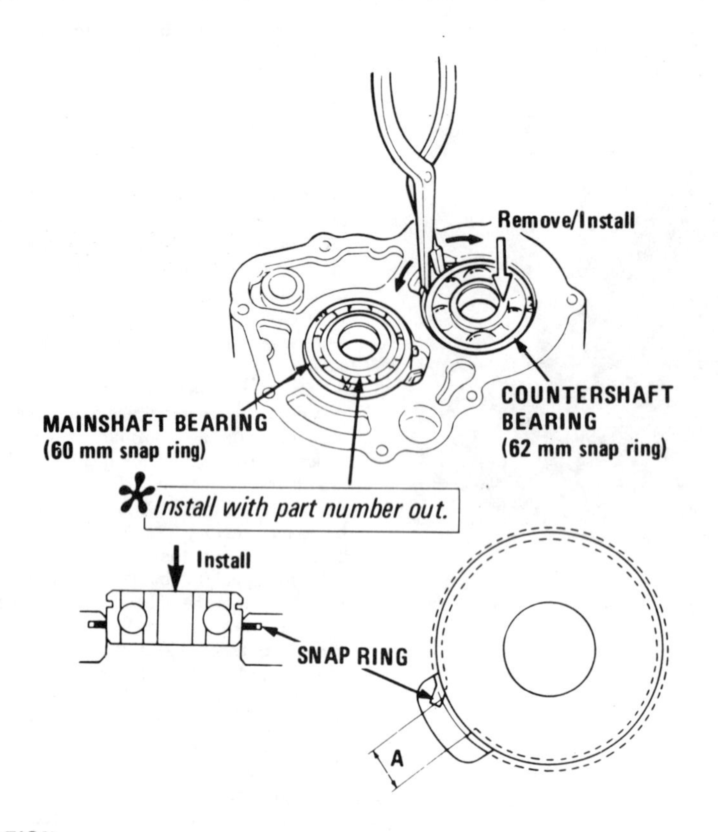

SNAP RING INSTALLATION

	Ring end gap A (As installed)	Ring end gap A (As expanded by bearing)
MAINSHAFT BEARING	10.1–14.6 mm (0.398–0.575 in.)	17.9–23.2 mm (0.705–0.913 in.)
COUNTERSHAFT BEARING	9.5–14.0 mm (0.374–0.551 in.)	17.7–23.0 mm (0.697–0.906 in.)

Fig. 13.68 Transmission housing bearings and circlips

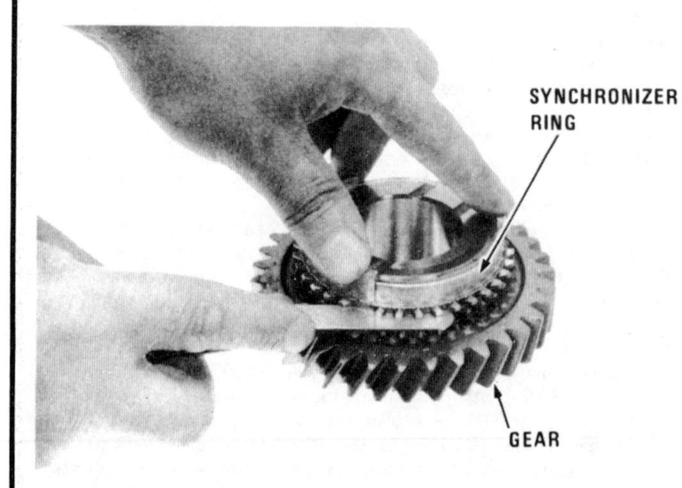

Fig. 13.69 Checking synchro baulk ring for wear

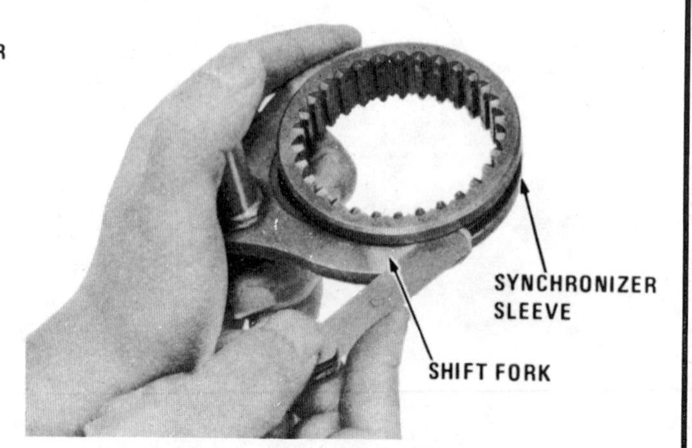

Fig. 13.70 Checking synchro ring groove to fork clearance

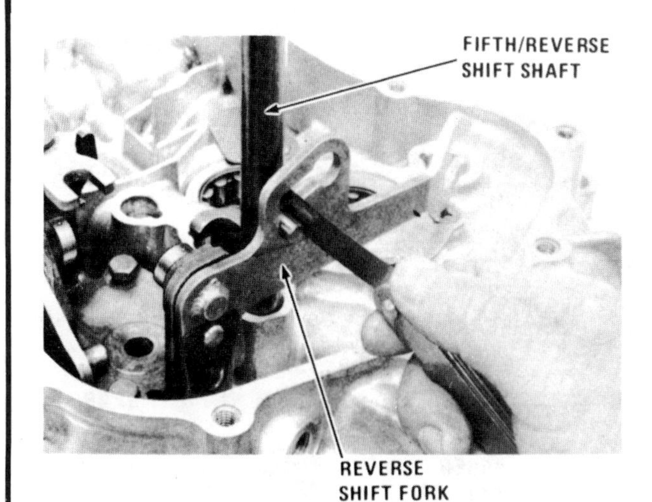

Fig. 13.71 Checking shift shaft to reverse shift fork clearance

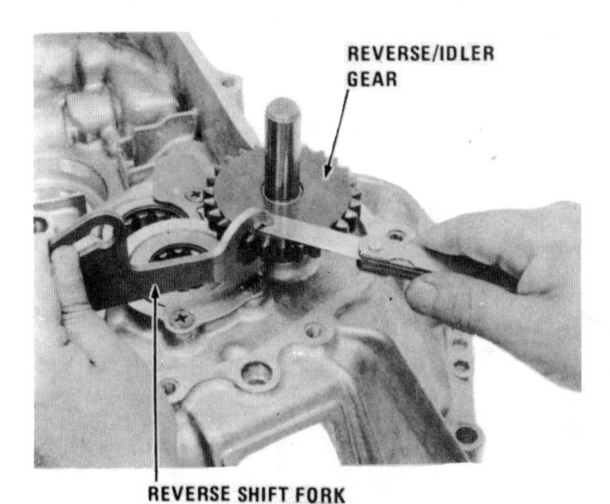

Fig. 13.72 Checking reverse idler gear to shift fork clearance

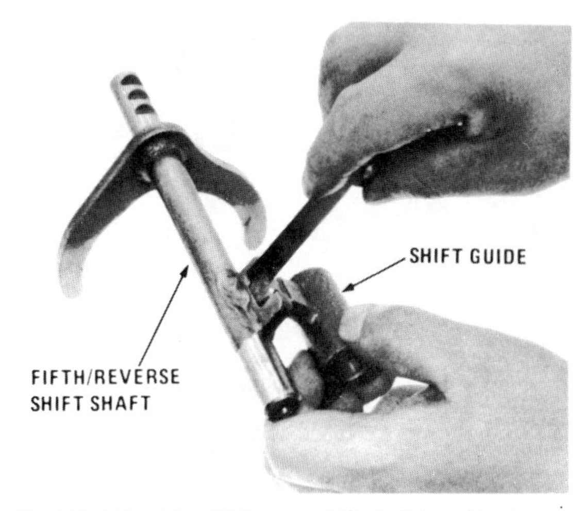

Fig. 13.73 Checking 5th/reverse shift shaft to guide clearance

Each synchronizer sleeve and its associated synchronizer hub have three sets of higher teeth (120 degrees apart) that must be matched when assembled.

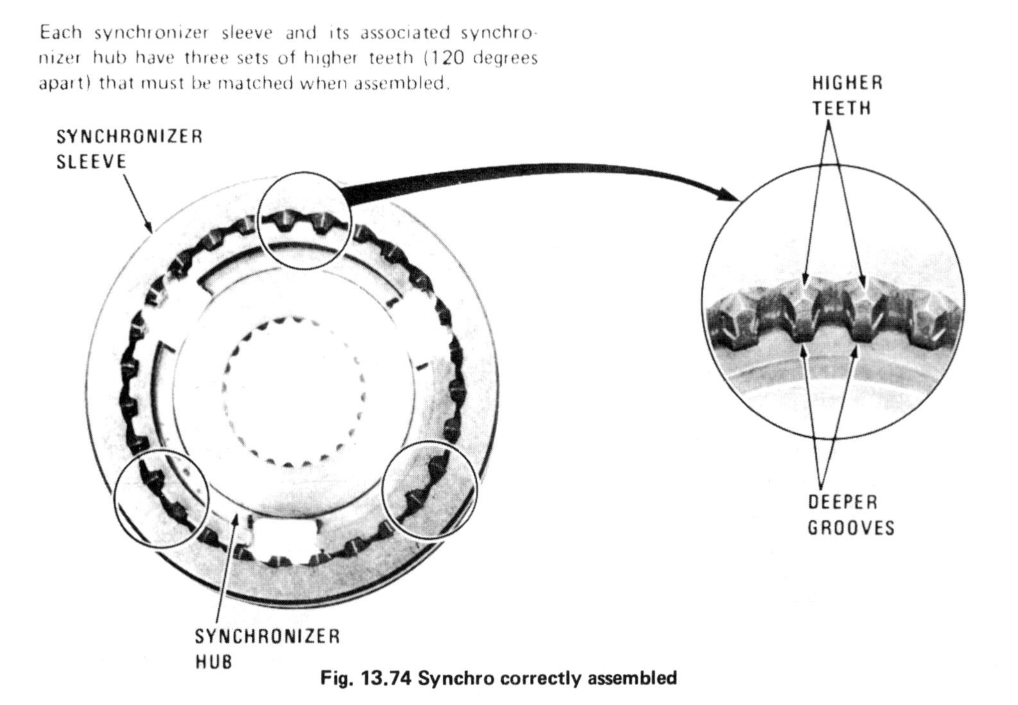

Fig. 13.74 Synchro correctly assembled

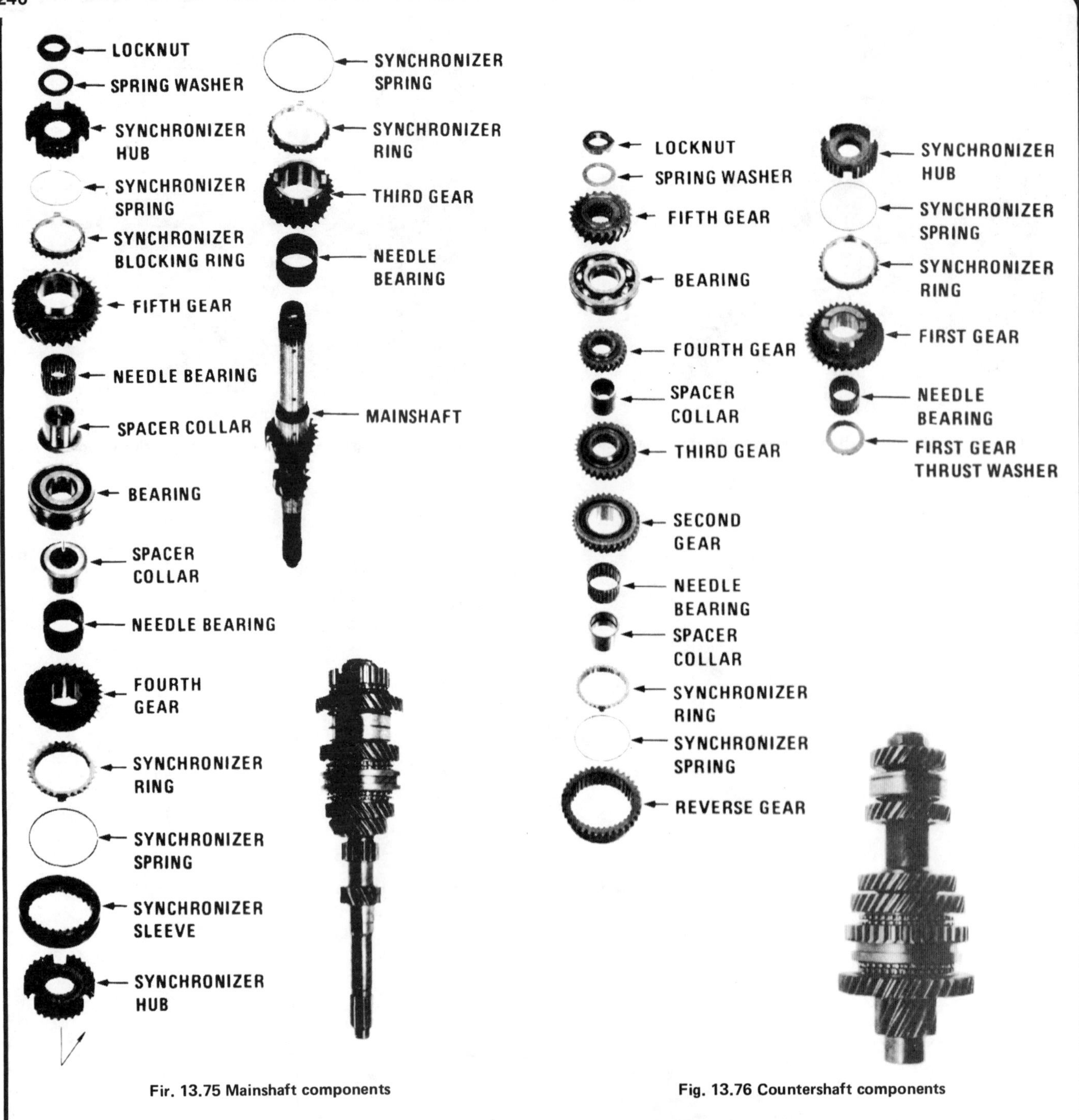

Fir. 13.75 Mainshaft components

Fig. 13.76 Countershaft components

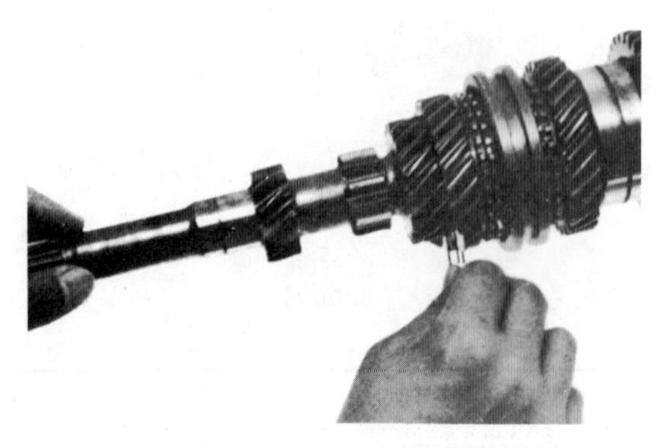

Fig. 13.77 Measuring 3rd gear clearance

Fig. 13.78 Measuring 4th gear clearance

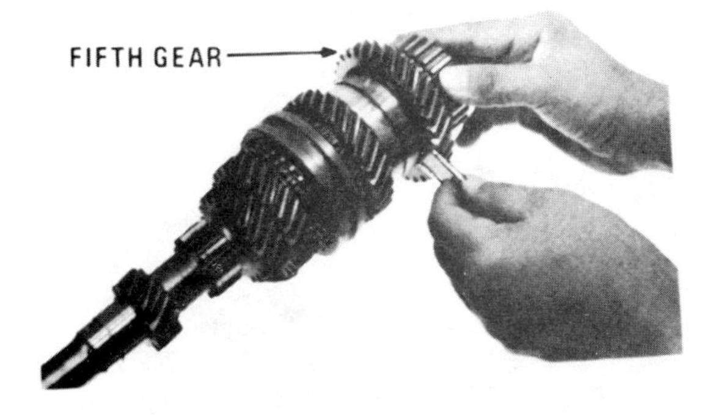

Fig. 13.79 Measuring 5th gear clearance

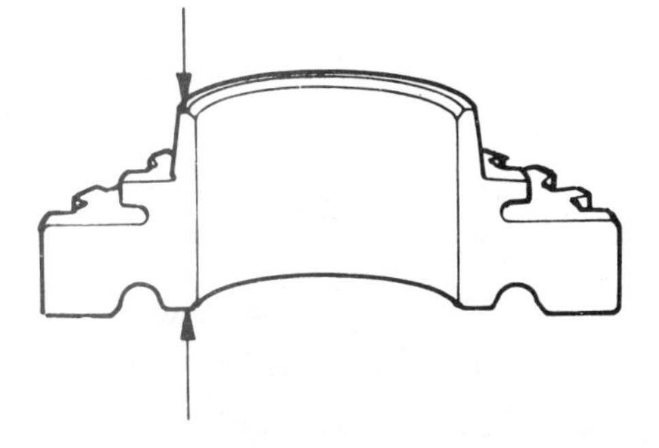

Fig. 13.80 Gear thickness measuring points

Fig. 13.81 Measuring 1st gear to thrust washer clearance

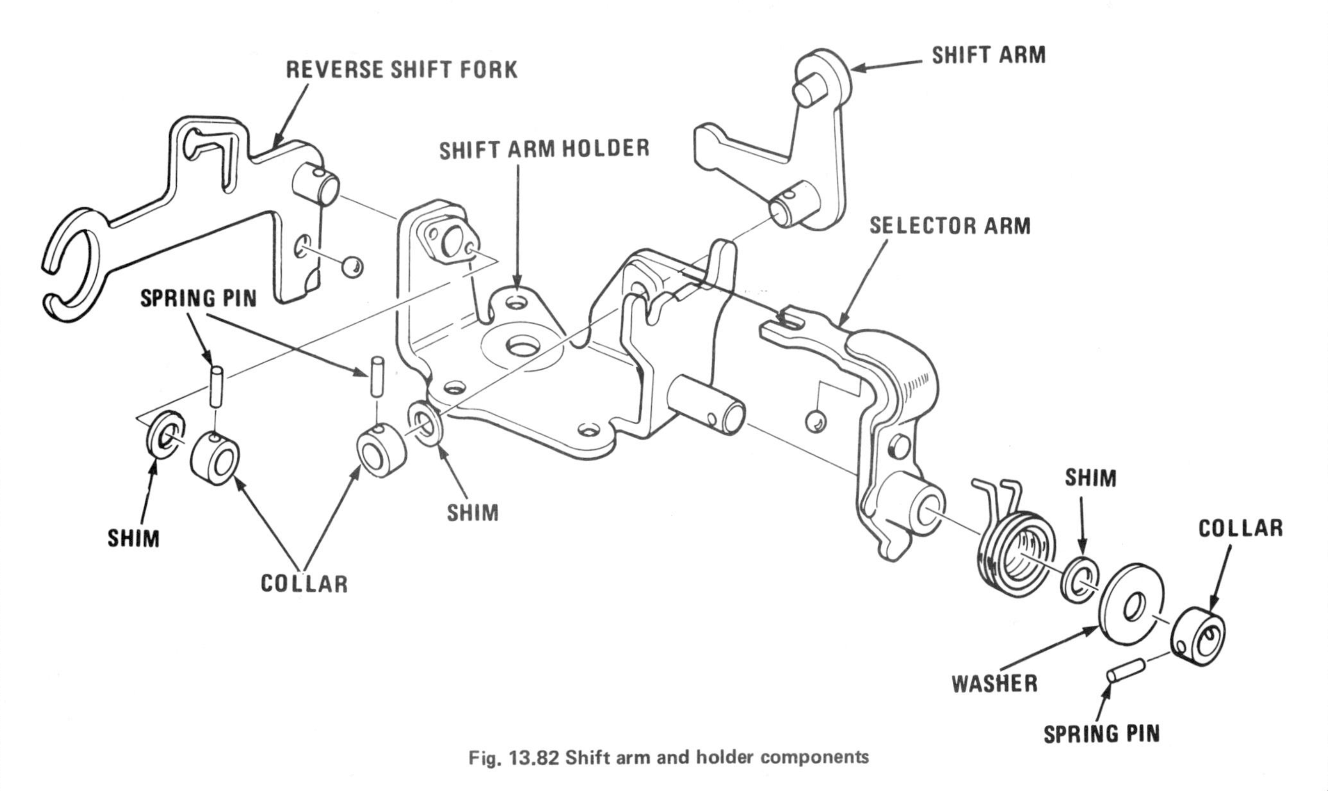

Fig. 13.82 Shift arm and holder components

Fig. 13.83 Measuring shift arm holder to shim clearance

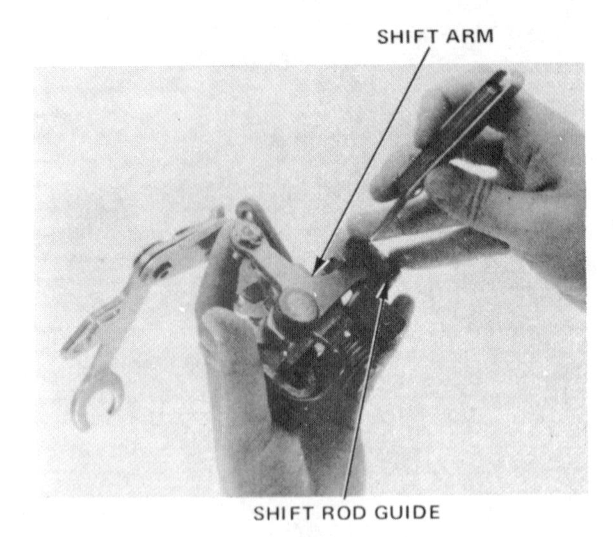

Fig. 13.86 Meassuring shift arm to shift rod guide clearance

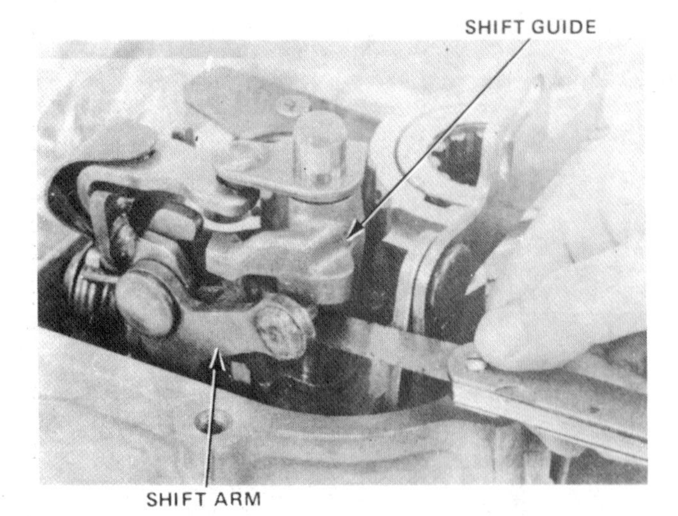

Fig. 13.84 Measuring shift arm to guide clearance

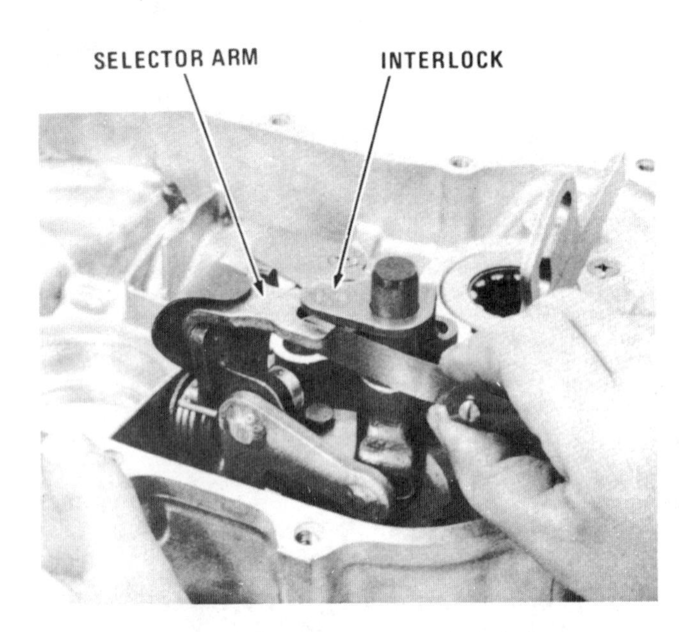

Fig. 13.87 Measuring selector arm to interlock clearance

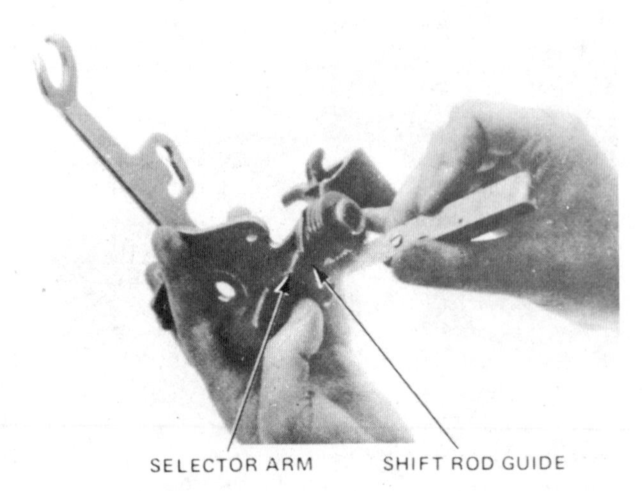

Fig. 13.85 Measuring selector arm to shift rod guide clearance

washers should not be substituted until all the clearances have been measured. Once the new components have been fitted to the shafts again check all the clearances in conjunction with the tolerances given in this Section or listed in the Specifications Section at the front of this Chapter.

55 Once the correct clearances have been established, remove the shaft bearings and 5th gear components. Install the bearings in the transmission casing.

Gear selector mechanism

56 The next operation during preliminary reassembly is to check for wear in the components of the gearchange and selector assemblies.

57 Using a feeler blade, measure the clearance between the shift arm holder and each shim. If the clearance is outside the permitted tolerance (0.0004 to 0.008 in – 0.01 to 0.2 mm) then renew the shims, from the five thicknesses available, to bring the gap into specified tolerance.

58 Measure the clearance between the shift arm and the shift guide. This should not exceed 0.02 in (0.5 mm) otherwise renew the guide.

59 Check the clearance between the selector arm and the shift guide

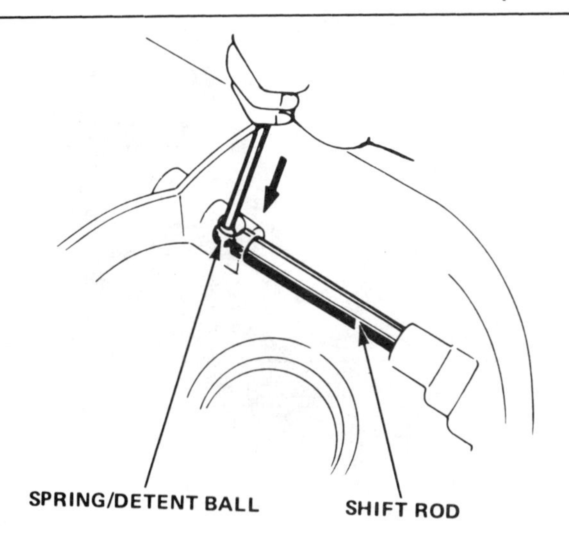

Fig. 13.88 Fitting shift rod detent ball

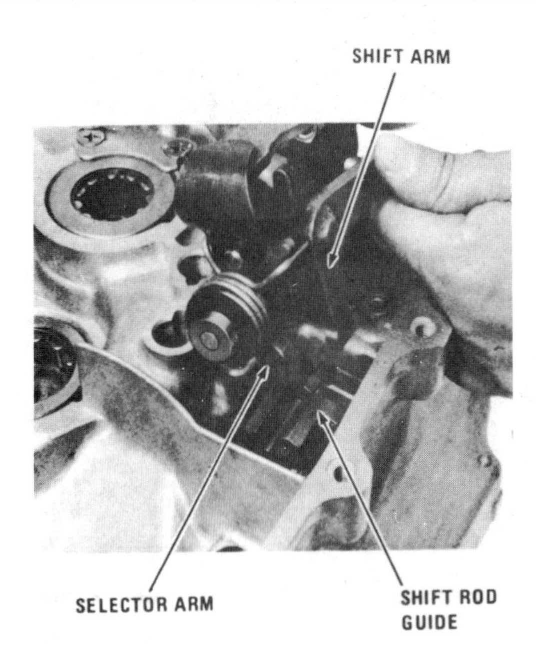

Fig. 13.90 Selector and shift arms engaged in guide cut-outs

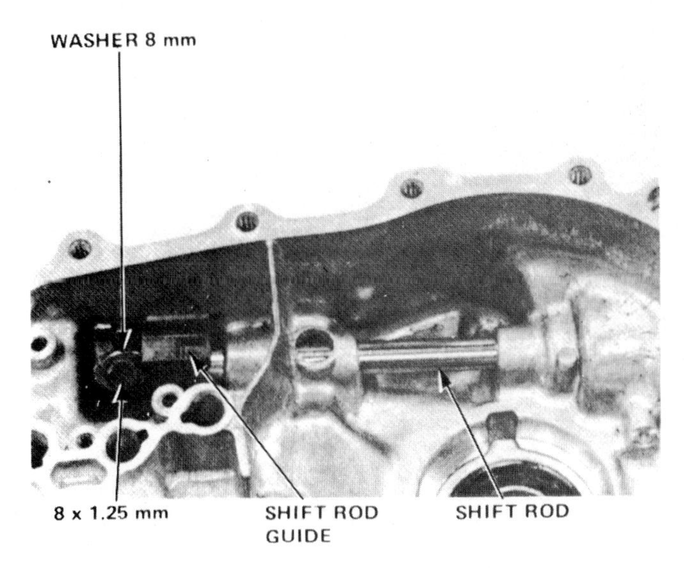

Fig. 13.89 Shift rod installed

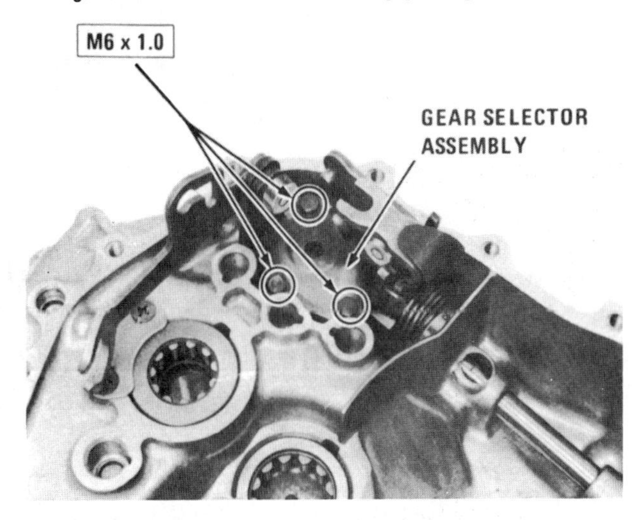

Fig. 13.91 Fitting gear selector assembly

which should not exceed 0.02 in (0.5 mm) otherwise renew the selector arm.

60 Check the clearance between the shift guide and the shift arm. This should not exceed 0.03 in (0.8 mm) otherwise renew the guide.

61 Check the selector arm to interlock clearance which should not exceed 0.03 in (0.8 mm) otherwise renew the arm.

62 Slip the bellows on to the shift rod.

63 Locate the detent ball and spring, then slide the rod into position whilst depressing the ball. Make sure that the notches on the gearshift rod face into the clutch housing. As the gearshift rod passes into position locate the shift rod guide on to it.

64 Engage the selector arm and the shift arm into the cut-outs in the shift rod guide.

65 Fit the complete gear selector assembly on to the clutch housing. Then insert and tighten the three mounting bolts to the specified torque.

66 Reassembly proper may now commence. Install the differential assembly into the clutch housing.

67 As an assembly, install the mainshaft, countershaft, 1st/2nd shift shaft, 3rd/4th shift shaft making sure that the synchro sleeves are located in 4th and 2nd gear positions to ease installation.

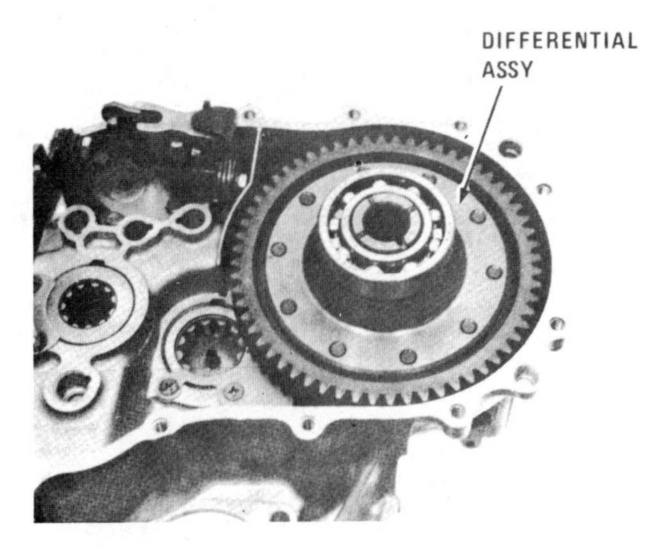

Fig. 13.92 Differential assembly

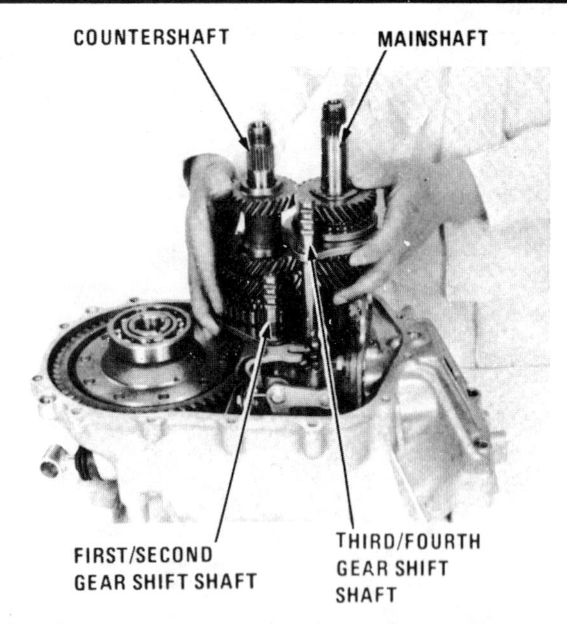

Fig. 13.93 Installing geartrains and shift shafts simultaneously

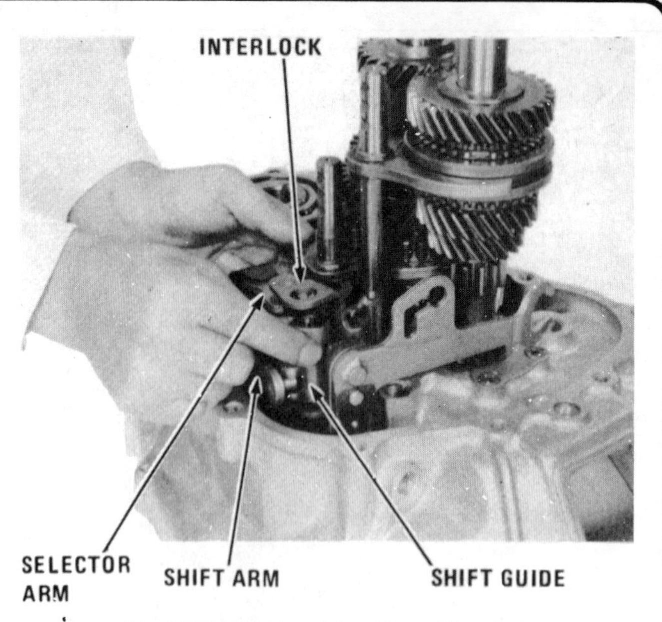

Fig. 13.94 Engaging shift guide and interlock

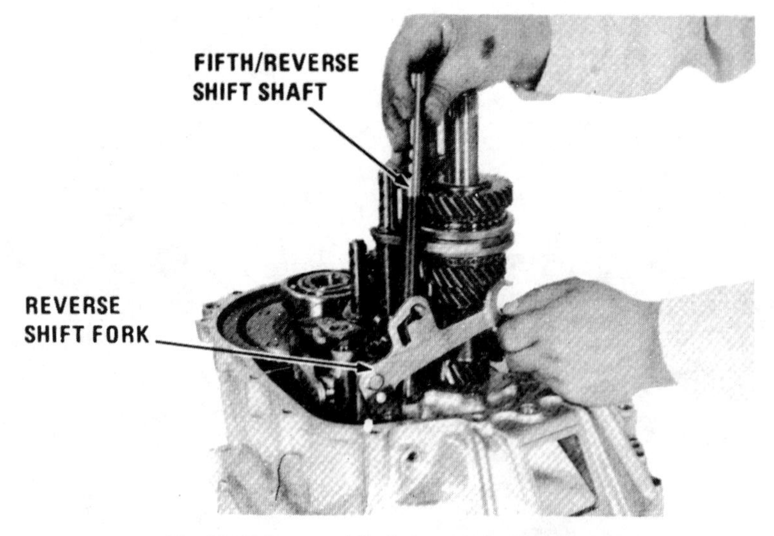

Fig. 13.95 Reverse shift fork to shaft engagement

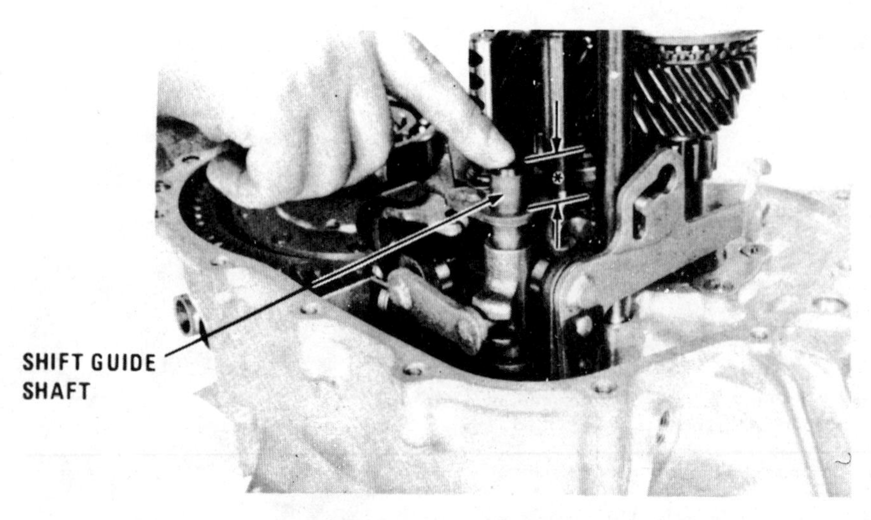

Fig. 13.96 Shift guide shaft setting

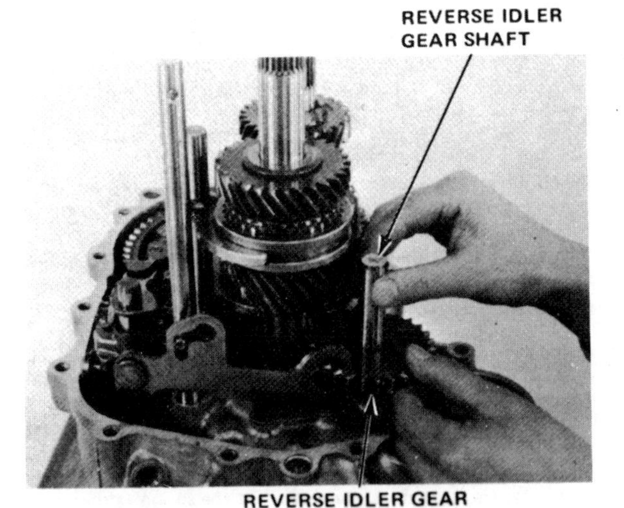

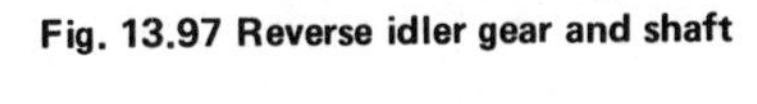

Fig. 13.97 Reverse idler gear and shaft

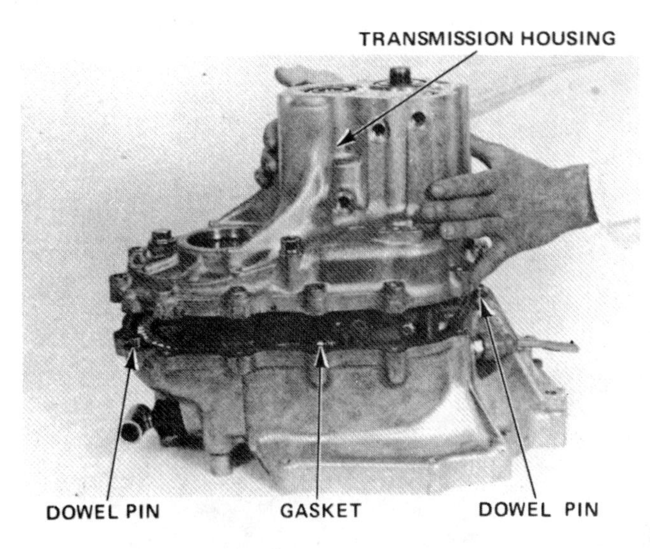

Fig. 13.98 Connecting housings

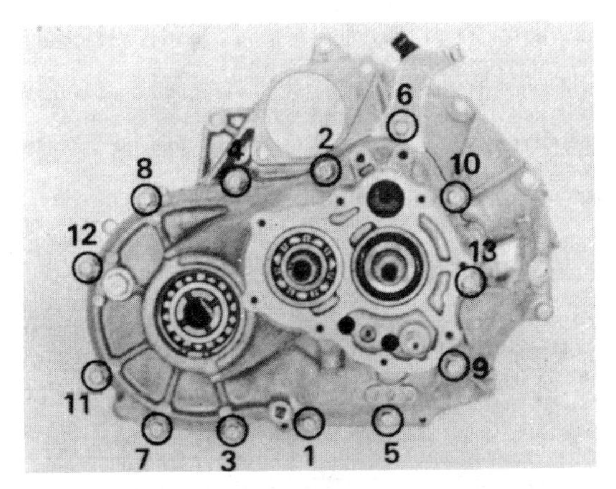

Fig. 13.99 Transmission housing bolt tightening sequence

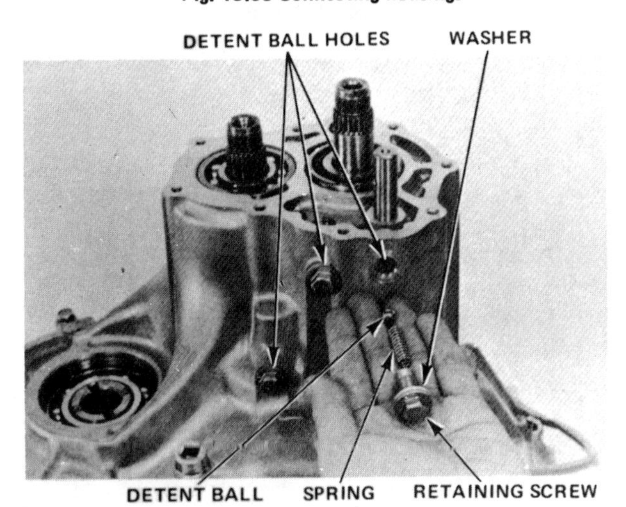

Fig. 13.100 Detent balls, springs and plugs

Fig. 13.101 5th gear spring washer on countershaft

Fig. 13.102 5th gear spring washer on mainshaft

Fig. 13.103 Shaft locknuts

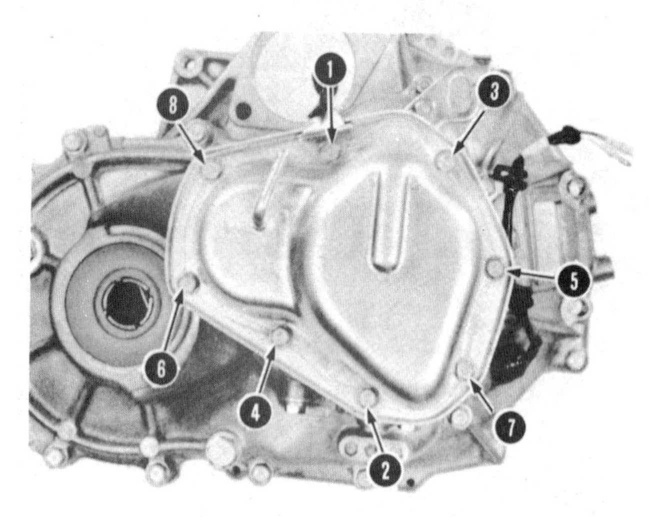

Fig. 13.104 End cover bolt tightening sequence

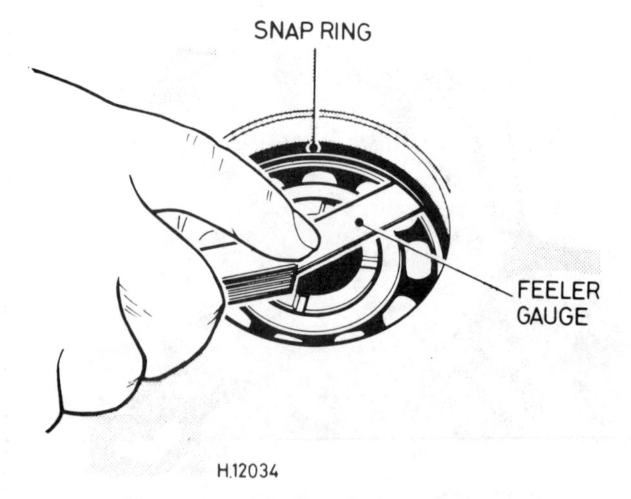

Fig. 13.105 Checking clutch housing bearing circlip clearance

68 Raise the mainshaft assembly slightly so that the interlock and the shift guide can be engaged.
69 Set the gearshift rod in neutral and then engage the interlock with the selector arm 1st/2nd gear shift shaft and 3rd/4th shift shaft. Engage the shift rod guide with the shift arm.
70 Fit 5th/reverse shift shaft and connect it with the reverse shift fork.
71 Install the shift guide shaft and check that it does not project (indicated in the diagram) by more than 0.5 in (12.5 mm), otherwise check for a fault in assembling.
72 Fit the reverse idler gear and shaft.
73 Screw the reversing lamp switch into position.
74 Fit a new gasket to the clutch housing flange and tap the dowel pins into position.
75 Lower the transmission housing on to the clutch housing aligning the shafts and making sure that the shift guide shaft engages in the blind hole in the transmission casing.
76 Tighten the bolts to the specified torque and in the sequence shown.
77 Insert the three detent balls, springs, screws and washers.
78 Fit 5th gear to the end of the countershaft so that the projecting side of the gear is towards the gear case. Fit the spring washer with its concave side towards 5th gear.
79 To the end of the mainshaft, fit the spacer collar, the needle bearing, 5th gear and the synchro assembly with the shift fork engaged in the groove in the synchro sleeve.
80 Fit the spring washer with the concave side towards the synchro hub.
81 Temporarily tighten the mainshaft and countershaft locknuts and drive in the roll pin to secure 5th gear shift fork.
82 Set the transmission in gear and hold the input shaft as previously explained, then tighten the shaft nuts to the specified torque. Loosen the nuts and tighten to the full torque setting once more. Then stake the nuts into the slots in the shafts.
83 Fit a new gasket to the flange on the transmission housing, install the cover then insert and tighten the bolts to the specified torque and in the sequence shown.
84 Fit the circlip into the recess in the bearing housing in the clutch housing and using feeler blades check the clearance between the circlip and the outer face of the bearing. This should not exceed 0.006 in (0.15 mm) otherwise change the circlip for one of another thickness from the five sizes available.
85 Fit the oil seal so that the part number is visible to you.
86 Fit the oil seal to the clutch housing in a similar way.

8 Hondamatic transmission (1980 on)

PART A - GENERAL INFORMATION, REMOVAL AND REFITTING

1 At the end of 1979, the Hondamatic transmission was changed from a two-speed to a three-speed type.
2 Control mechanisms have been incorporated within the transmission so that, with D selected, gear changing is automatically carried out to suit road speed and engine loading. With 2 selected, no upshift into 3rd (top) gear will occur; this position is therefore useful when engine braking is required.
3 This type of transmission is unusual, at least when compared with 'conventional' automatics, in that they use the same system of gearing as their manual counterpart instead of epicyclic (planetary) gearboxes. For the experienced home mechanic this is an advantage in so far as the transmissions are only slightly more difficult to overhaul than a similar manual gearbox. Some special tools will be required, however, and cleanliness is of the utmost importance - a very small particle of grit in the wrong place can create havoc in the hydraulic control system. Anyone contemplating overhaul should first ascertain that spare parts are available, then compare the likely rebuild cost with the price of an exchange transmission. A transmission oil cooler is located at the base of the radiator.

Fluid - topping up and renewal

4 Have the transmission fluid hot after the vehicle has come in from a run. Let the engine idle.
5 Switch off the engine and immediately unscrew the dipstick, withdraw it and wipe it clean on a non-fluffy rag. Re-insert the dipstick - do not screw it in - withdraw it for the second time and read off the

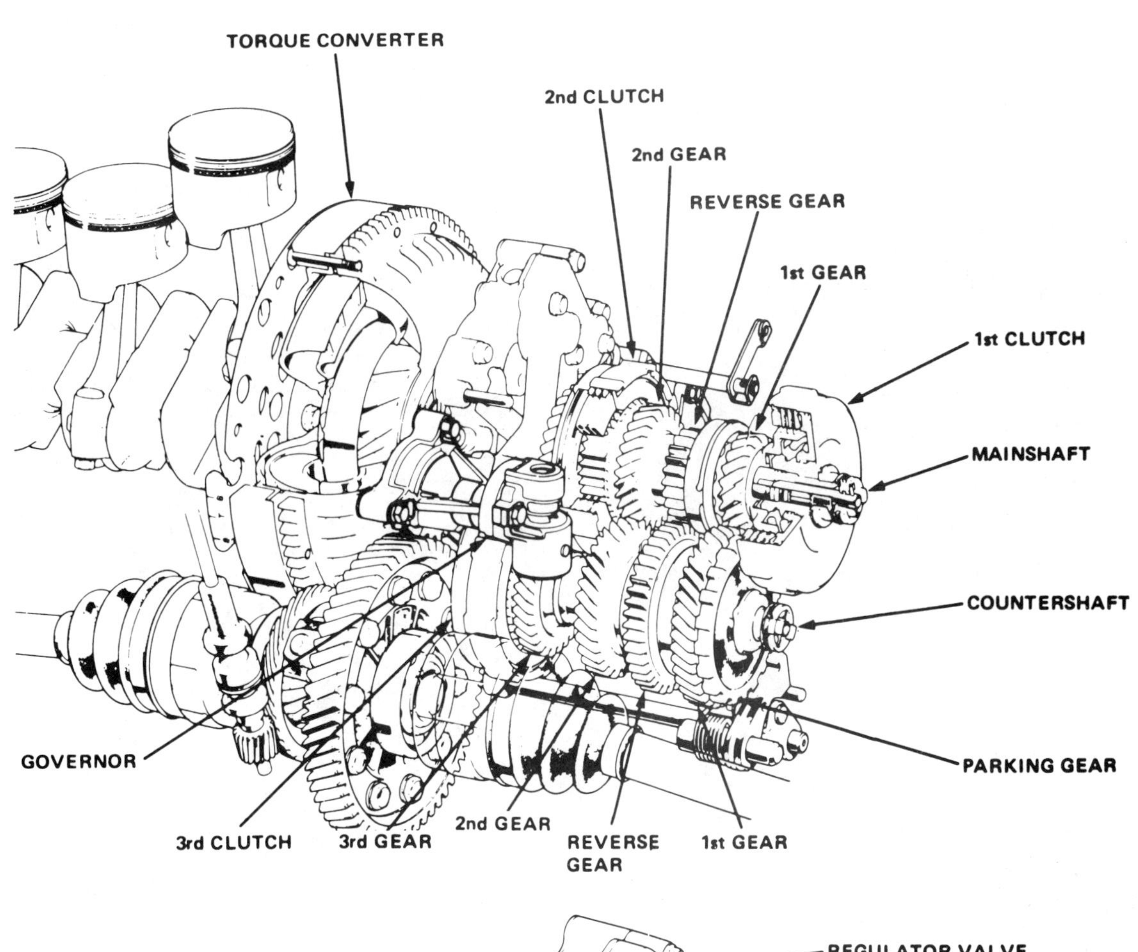

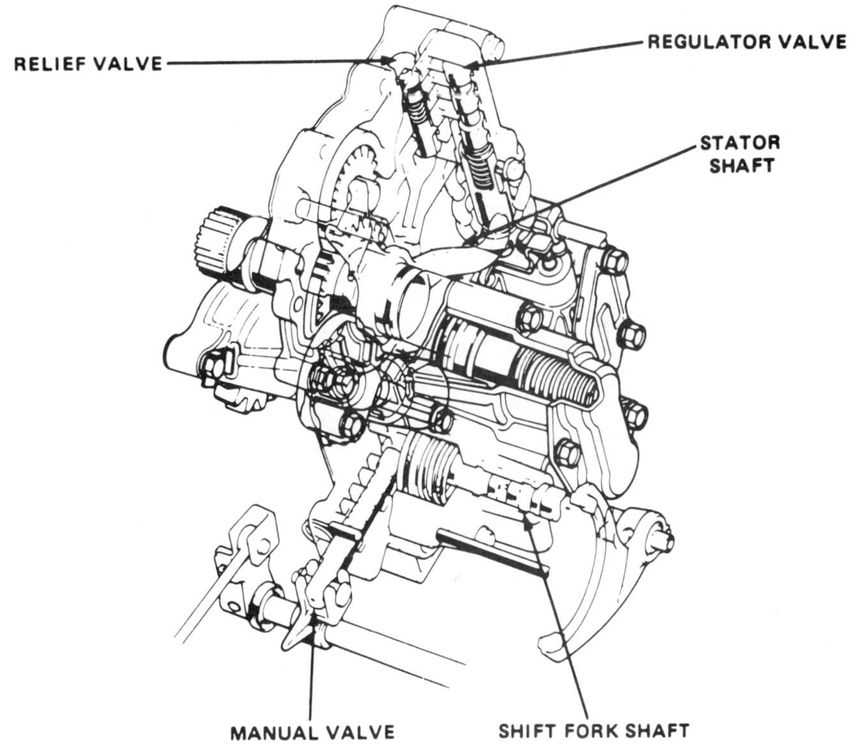

Fig. 13.106 Cutaway view of 3-speed Hondamatic transmission

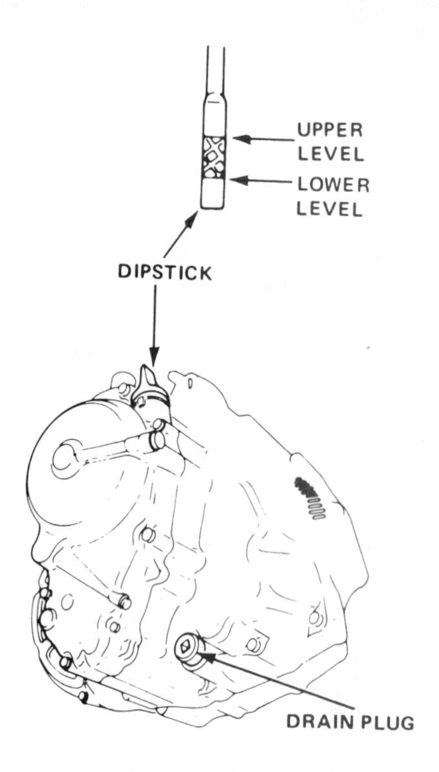

Fig. 13.107 Hondamatic dipstick and drain plug

fluid level. Add specified fluid if necessary to bring the fluid to the upper level mark.
6 Screw the dipstick into place.
7 The transmission fluid should be renewed at the specified intervals by unscrewing the drain plug and allowing it to run into a container. It is recommended that the fluid is hot when draining. Caution is required owing to the very high temperatures of automatic transmission fluid.
8 Refill through the dipstick hole.

Automatic transmission - removal and refitting

9 The transmission can be removed independently of the engine, leaving the latter in position in the car. Obviously if any major work is required to the engine at the same time, it will be easier to remove the engine/transmission and then separate them, as described in Chapter 1.
10 To remove the transmission on its own, first disconnect the negative lead from the battery terminal and then disconnect the earth strap from the transmission casing.
11 Release the steering lock and move the gear selector to the Neutral (N) position.
12 Disconnect the leads from the starter motor and solenoid, the coolant temperature sender and the distributor.
13 Disconnect the transmission fluid cooler hoses and tie them up next to the radiator. Plug the exposed connections to prevent the entry of dirt.
14 Loosen the front wheel nuts, then jack up and securely support the front of the vehicle. Chock the rear wheels.
15 Drain the transmission fluid into a suitable container.
16 Remove the retaining clip and withdraw the speedometer cable.
17 Do not remove the holder because the speedometer gear could fall into the transmission.
18 If the vehicle is equipped with power-assisted steering, remove the speedometer complete with speed sensor and hoses.
19 Take the weight of the engine on a hoist, and remove the two transmission upper mounting bolts and the side mounting bolt.
20 Remove the subframe centre beam.
21 Remove the pinch-bolt from the balljoint on the right-hand track control arm. Use a copper hammer to disconnect the balljoint from the stub axle carrier.
22 Remove the right-hand radius rod.
23 Disconnect the anti-roll bar from the right-hand track control arm.
24 Turn the right-hand steering knuckle outwards as far as it will go, then lever against the inboard CV joint to free the driveshaft from its housing. Do not pull on the outboard joint or hub or the inboard joint may separate.
25 Remove the remaining starter bolt and remove the starter motor down through the chassis.
26 Remove the damper bracket located in front of the torque converter cover plate.
27 Remove the torque converter cover plate.
28 Working inside the vehicle, remove the centre console and the shift indicator.

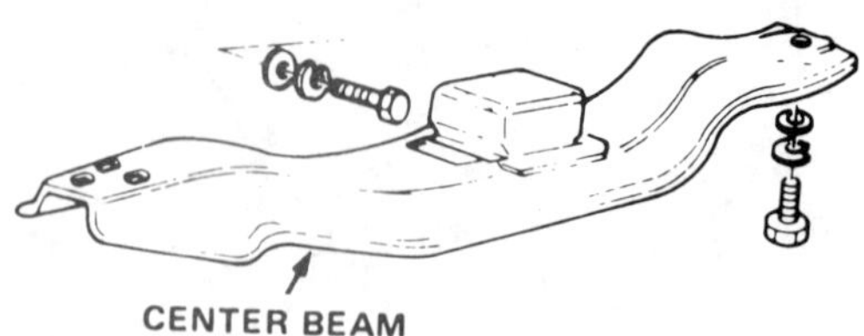

Fig. 13.108 Subframe centre beam

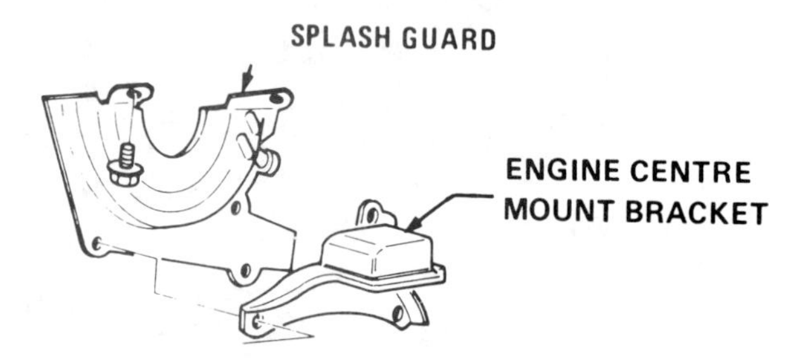

Fig. 13.109 Cover plate and damper

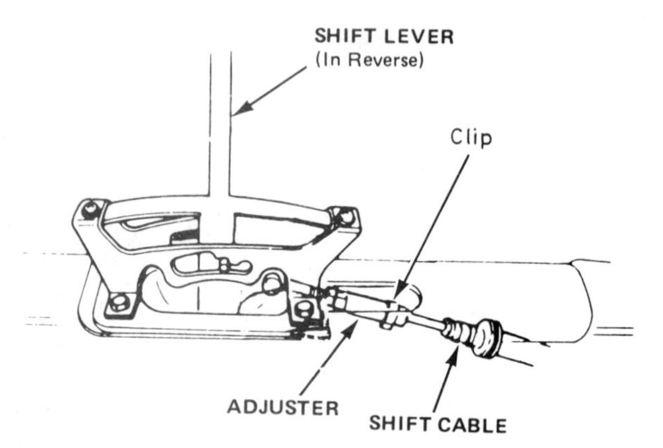

Fig. 13.110 Shift control

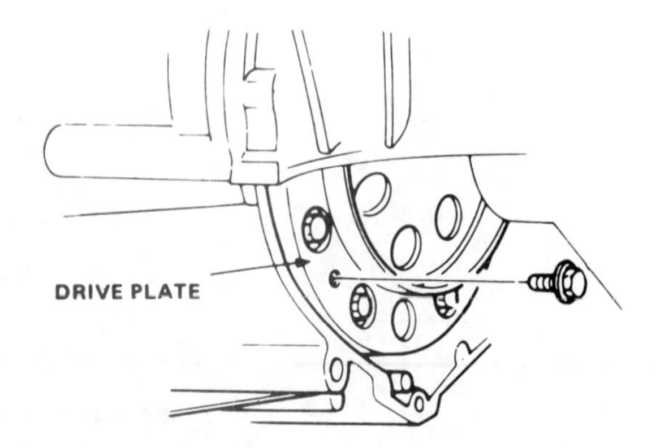

Fig. 13.111 Driveplate to converter bolts (not recessed)

29 Remove the lockpin from the adjuster and shift cable.
30 Remove both bolts and pull the shift cable from the housing.
31 Unbolt the torque converter from the driveplate. Rotate the crankshaft to gain access to all eight bolts. *Do not remove the sixteen (recessed) bolts which hold the ring gear to the torque converter.*
32 Remove the three rear mounting bolts from the transmission housing. Remove the mounting.
33 Remove the transmission lower mounting bolt.
34 Pull the transmission from the engine until it clears the dowel pins. Make sure that the torque converter remains fully engaged within the housing.
35 Lever the left-hand driveshaft inboard joint out of the transmission until its snap-ring is released.
36 Withdraw the transmission and lower it to the floor. Take care to support the driveshaft.
37 Refitting is a reversal of removal, but observe the following points:

(a) Tighten the torque converter-to-driveplate bolts in diagonal sequence, first to half the specified torque and then to the specified torque.

(b) Use new circlips on the driveshafts and be sure that they are correctly engaged in their recesses in the differential.

(c) Refill the transmission with the specified quantity of fluid. start the engine and cycle the transmission through the gears a few times. Check the fluid level when normal engine operating temperature is reached.

(d) Check the control cable(s) and adjust if required.

PART B - DISMANTLING INTO MAJOR ASSEMBLIES, INSPECTION AND OVERHAUL OF SUB ASSEMBLIES

1 Withdraw the torque converter from its housing.
2 Remove the dipstick, then remove the bolts from the end cover and remove the cover. Remove the gasket, O-rings and dowel pins (if fitted).
3 Shift the transmission into Park and lock the mainshaft using Honda Tool 07923-6890201 or equivalent.
4 Relieve the locktabs or staking, as applicable, securing the mainshaft locknut. Remove the locknut - early models require a 16 mm peg spanner, later models require a 22 mm socket. It should be noted that

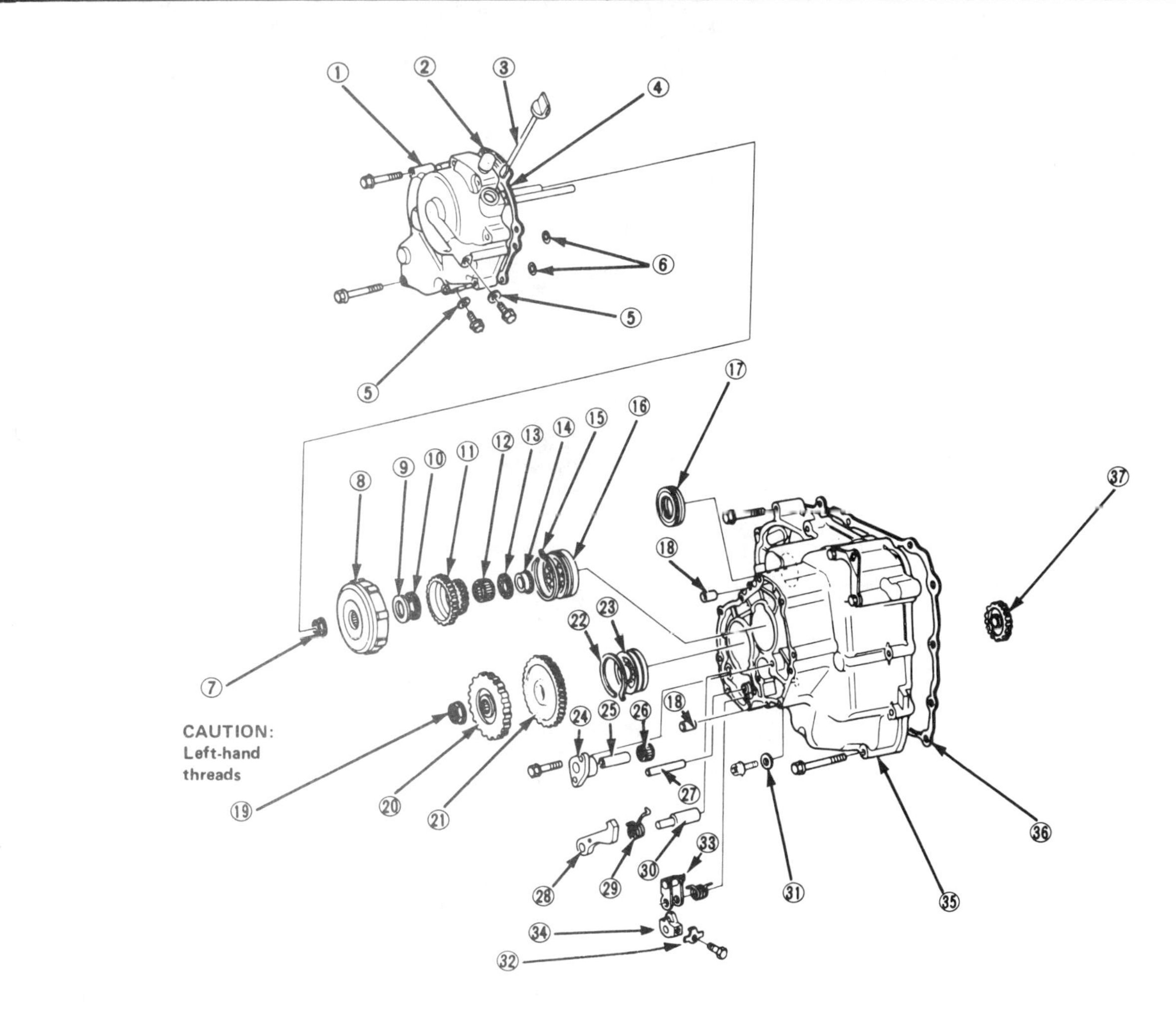

Fig. 13.112 Transmission housing components

1	*End cover*	11	*Low gear*	21	*Countershaft low gear*	31	*Drain plug washer*
2	*Breather*	12	*Needle bearing*	22	*Circlip*	32	*Lockplate*
3	*Dipstick*	13	*Needle thrust bearing*	23	*Countershaft bearing*	33	*Parking pawl lever*
4	*Gasket*	14	*Inner race*	24	*Idler shaft holder*	34	*Parking pawl stop*
5	*Washer*	15	*Circlip*	25	*Reverse idler shaft*	35	*Transmission housing*
6	*O-ring*	16	*Mainshaft bearing*	26	*Needle bearing*	36	*Gasket*
7	*Locknut*	17	*Differential oil seal*	27	*Stop pin*	37	*Reverse idler gear*
8	*Low clutch*	18	*Dowel pin*	28	*Parking pawl*		
9	*Thrust washer*	19	*Locknut*	29	*Parking pawl spring*		
10	*Needle thrust bearing*	20	*Parking gear*	30	*Parking pawl shaft*		

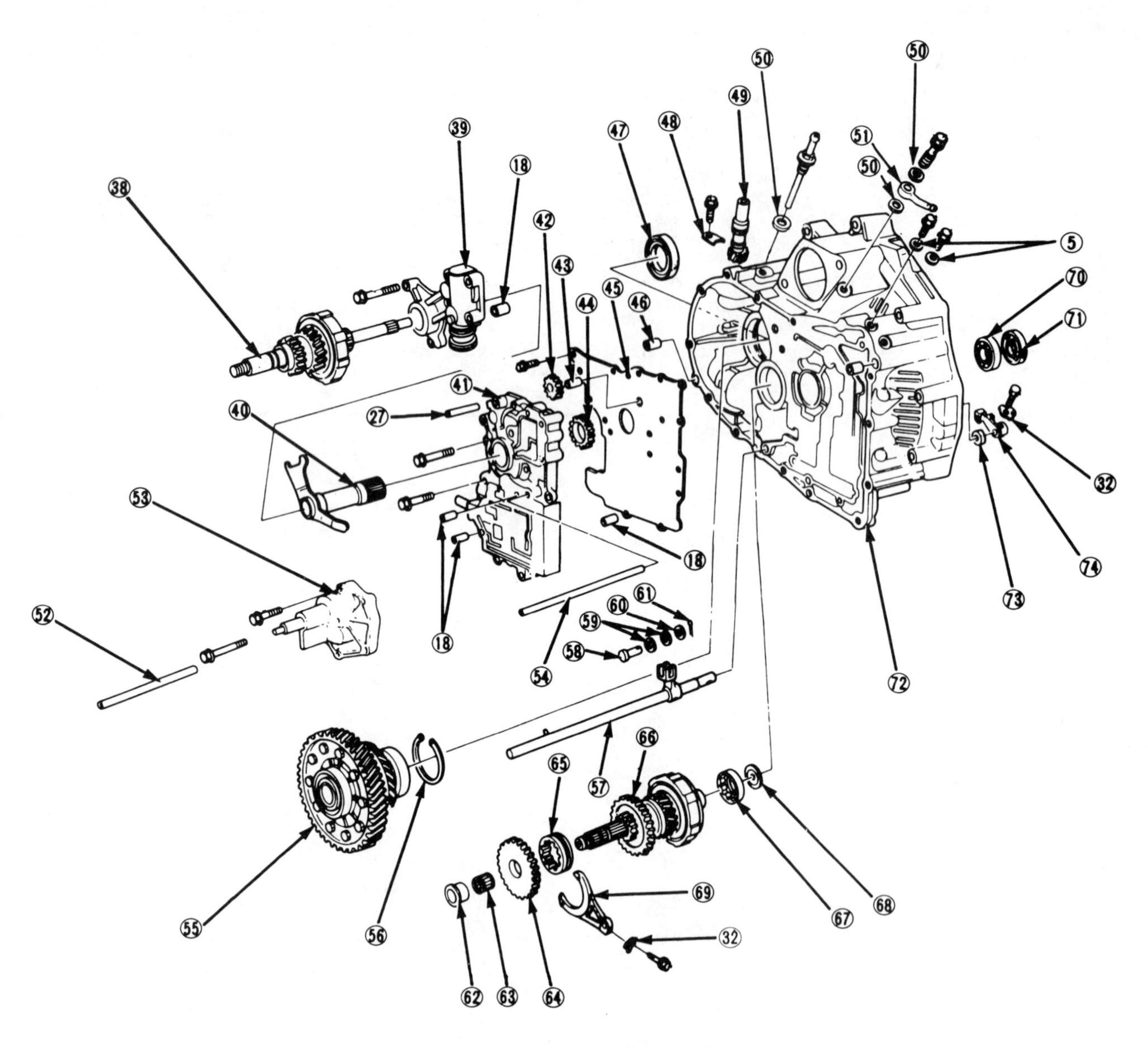

Fig. 13.113 Torque converter housing components

38	*Mainshaft*	48	*Speedometer gear set plate*	58	*Manual valve pin*	68	*Oil barrier plate*
39	*Regulator*	49	*Speedometer drivegear*	59	*Manual valve spacer*	69	*Reverse shift fork*
40	*Stator shaft*	50	*Washer*	60	*Washer*	70	*Mainshaft bearing*
41	*Valve body*	51	*Banjo union*	61	*Cotter pin*	71	*Mainshaft oil seal*
42	*Pump driven gear*	52	*OD clutch pipe*	62	*Inner race*	72	*Torque converter housing*
43	*Pump shaft*	53	*Servo*	63	*Needle bearing*	73	*Shift shaft oil seal*
44	*Pump drivegear*	54	*Low clutch pipe*	64	*Countershaft reverse gear*	74	*Shift arm*
45	*Separator plate*	55	*Differential*	65	*Reverse selector sleeve*		
46	*Dowel pin*	56	*Circlip*	66	*Countershaft assembly*		
47	*Differential oil seal*	57	*Shift arm shaft*	67	*Countershaft bearing*		

See also the key for Fig. 13.112

on later models, *the locknut has a left hand thread.* With the locknut removed, remove the low (1st) clutch from the end of the mainshaft.

5 Remove 1st gear and associated thrust washers, bearings, spacers, etc., from the mainshaft.

6 Relieve the staking on the countershaft locknut and remove the locknut (30.0 mm).

7 Remove the parking pawl and associated components, the parking gear and the countershaft low gear.

8 Move the control cable in or out until the pin on the shift arm shaft (control shaft) is positioned as shown in the accompanying illustration.

9 Remove any remaining spacers, collars, washers, etc., from the mainshaft and countershaft.

10 Unbolt and remove the idler shaft holder.

11 Remove the 14 bolts holding the transmission and torque converter housings together.

12 Separate the housings, ideally using a proper puller. In the absence of a puller, careful use of a soft-faced mallet may suffice to separate the housings, but it must be understood that damage may result from careless hammering.

13 Remove the gasket and any dowel pins.

14 Remove 1st and 3rd oil feed pipes.

15 From the countershaft, remove Reverse gear collar, needle roller bearing and Reverse gear itself.

16 Bend down the lockplate tab and remove the Reverse shift fork bolt. Remove the fork and selector sleeve together.

17 Lift the mainshaft and countershaft out of the housing together.

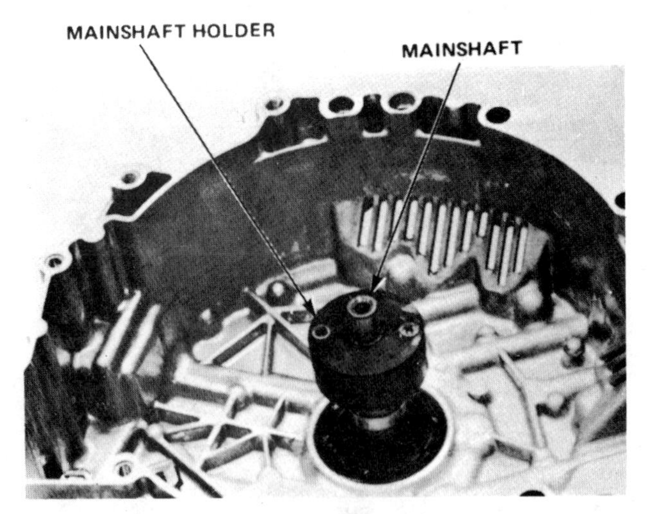

Fig. 13.114 Mainshaft locking tool

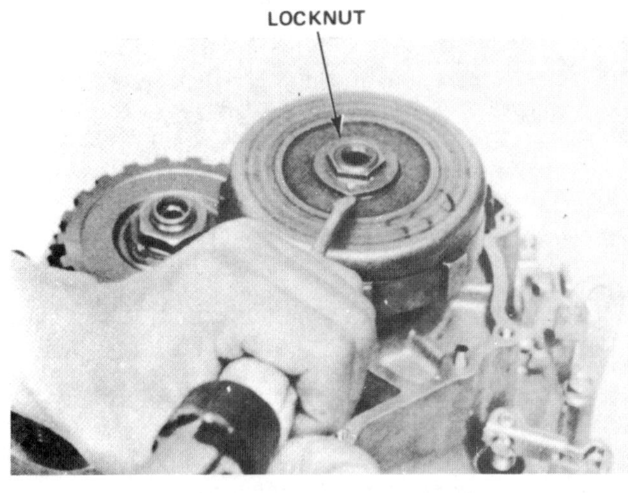

Fig. 13.115 Relieving locknut staking

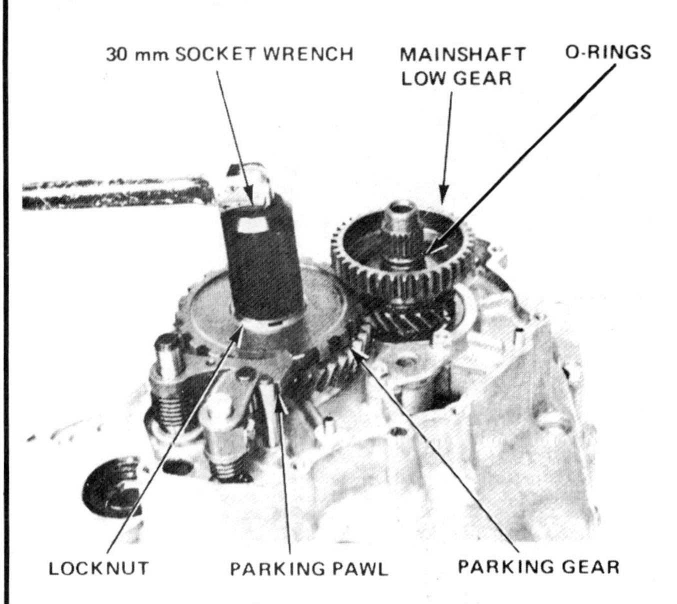

Fig. 13.116 Unscrewing shaft locknut

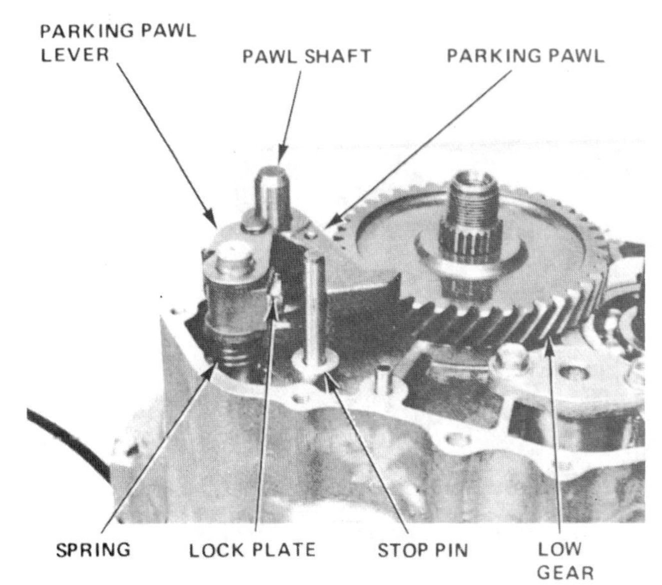

Fig. 13.117 Parking pawl components

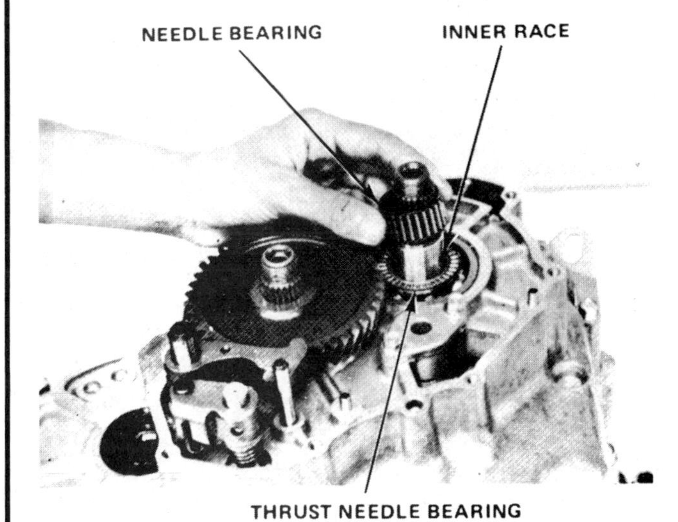

Fig. 13.118 Mainshaft needle bearings

Fig. 13.119 Shift arm shaft spring pin

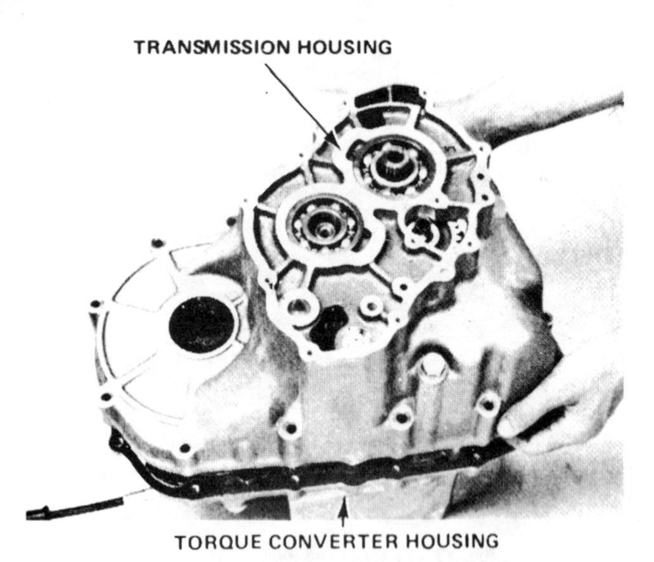

Fig. 13.120 Removing transmission housing

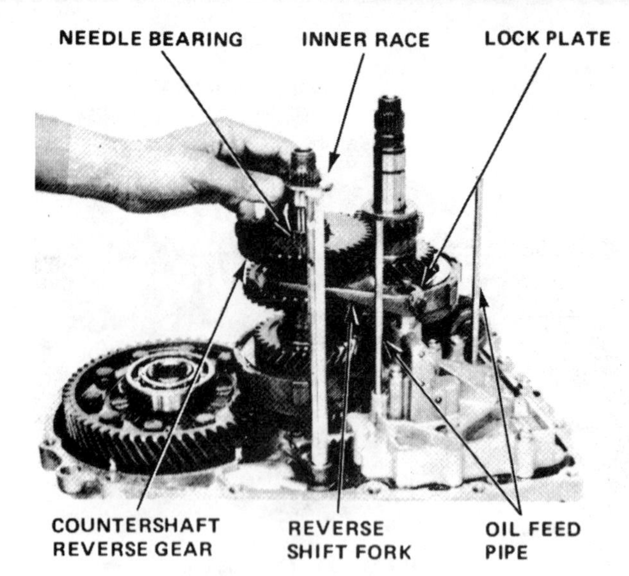

Fig. 13.121 Countershaft reverse gear

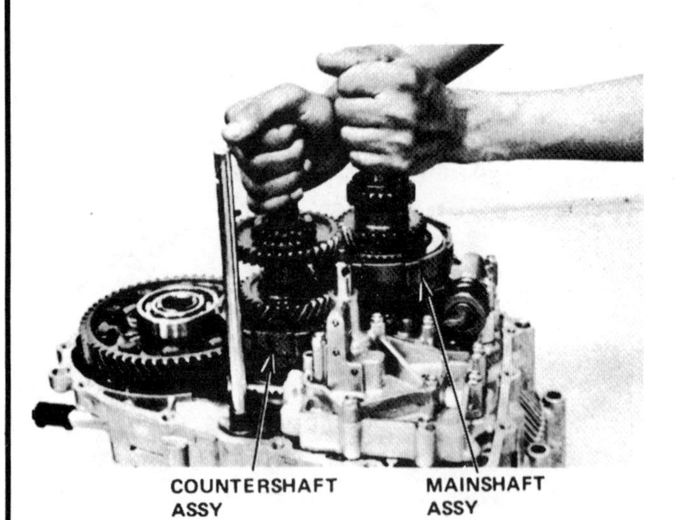

Fig. 13.122 Removing countershaft and mainshaft simultaneously

Fig. 13.123 Servo mounting bolts

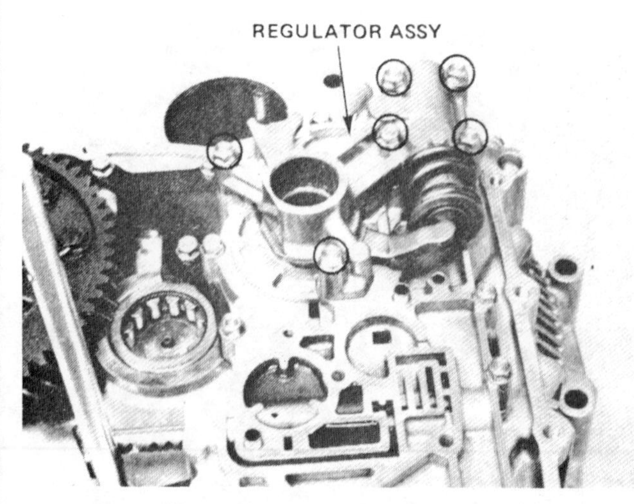

Fig. 13.124 Regulator mounting bolts

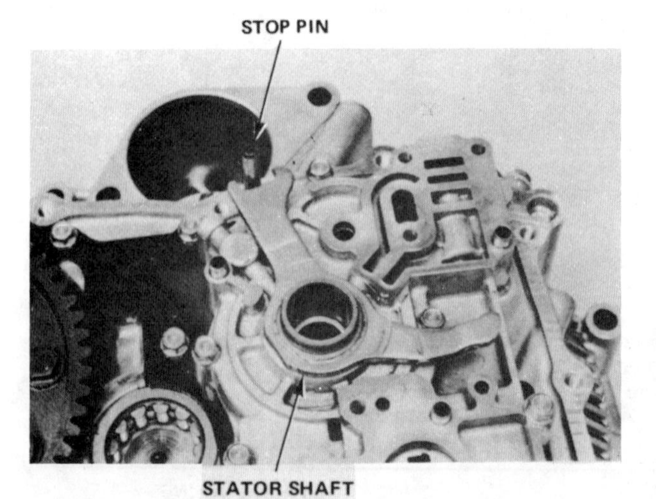

Fig. 13.125 Stator shaft and stop pin

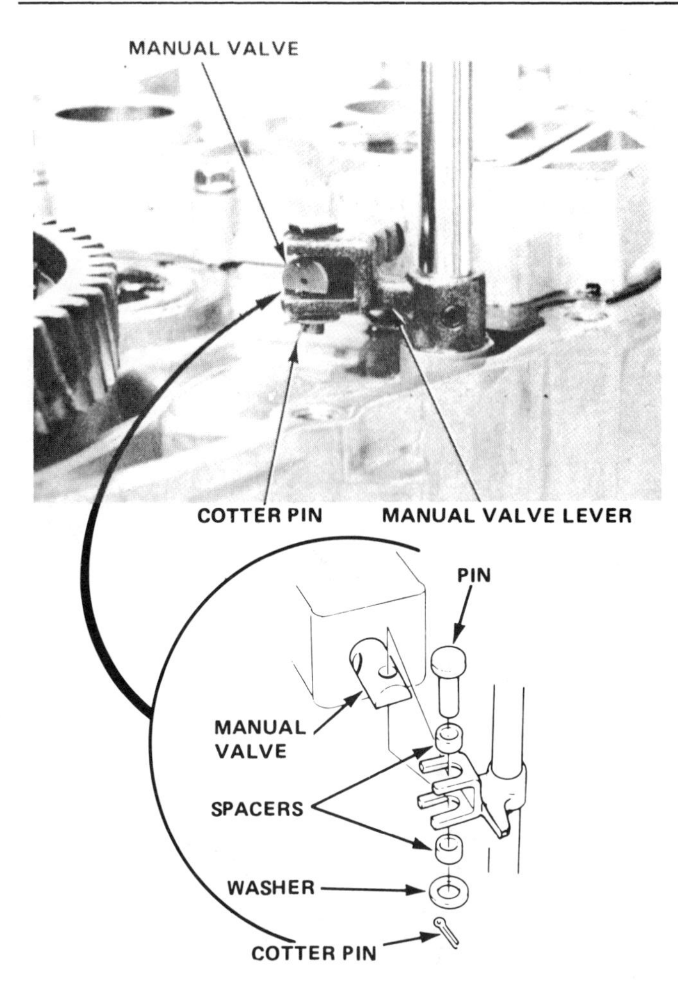

Fig. 13.126 Manual valve components

Fig. 13.127 Valve body

Fig. 13.128 Separator plate

18 Remove the servo assembly (6 bolts).
19 Remove the regulator valve assembly (6 bolts).
20 Remove the stator shaft stop pin, then remove the stator shaft arm and the dowel pins which hold the valve body to the torque converter housing.
21 Disconnect the manual valve from its lever.
22 Remove the four bolts which secure the valve body to the housing. Remove the valve body, being careful not to lose the torque converter check valve and spring.
23 Remove the oil pump gear and spring.
24 Remove the separator plate.
25 Remove the oil pick-up strainer. Obtain a new strainer for use on reassembly.
26 The transmission is now dismantled into major assemblies. The differential unit can be driven out if required - see Chapter 8. Removal and installation of the control shaft should be self-explanatory after reference to the relevant illustrations.

Major assemblies - inspection and overhaul

27 Clean all components thoroughly and dry with a lint-free rag - nylon rag is preferable. Replace all O-rings, gaskets, seals, etc., as a matter of course. Lubricate all components with clean automatic transmission fluid on reassembly.

Mainshaft

28 The mainshaft can be completely dismantled after extracting the snap-rings. Check the bearings for wear, the teeth of the gears and the splines of the shaft for wear or deformation. If the shaft is scored it must be renewed together with any other faulty components.
29 Install two new O-rings, followed by the 2nd/Drive clutch, the

Fig. 13.129 Oil pump strainer

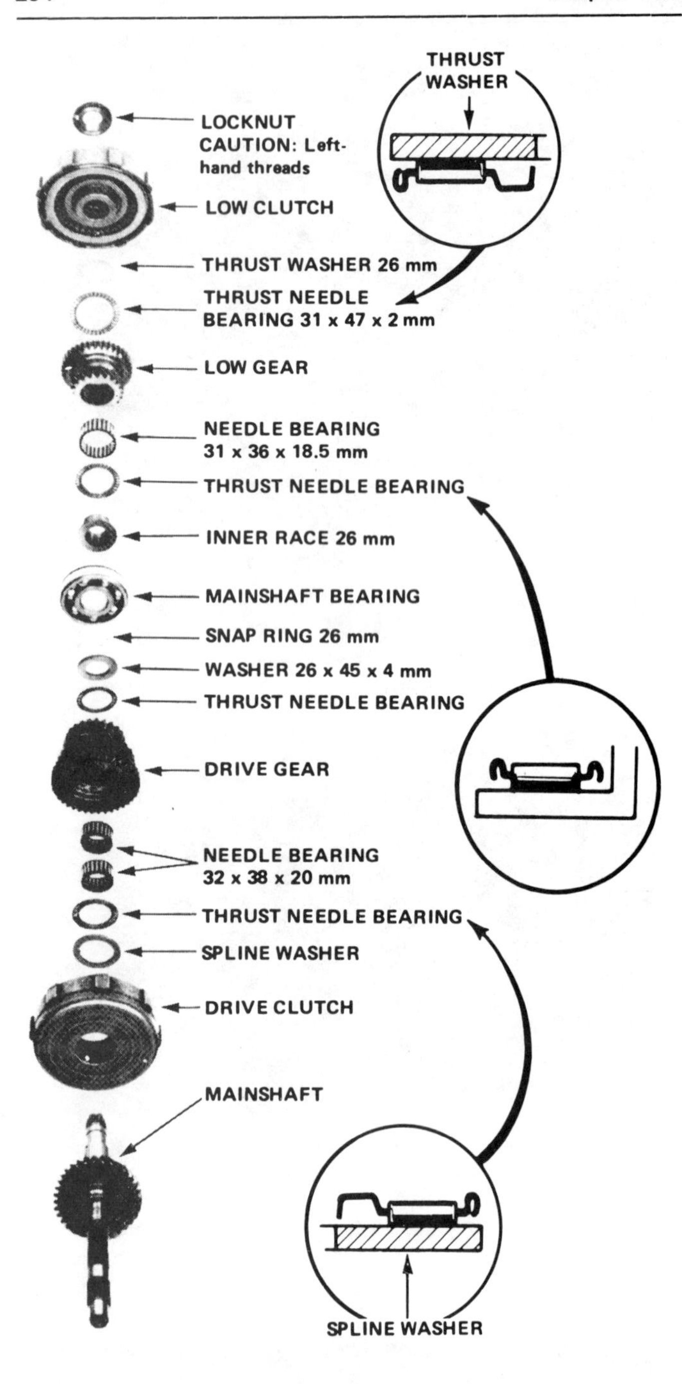

Fig. 13.130 Mainshaft components

splined thrust washer and the thrust bearing. Install 2nd/Drive gear and the two needle bearings, the second thrust bearing, thrust washer and circlip.

30 Continue reassembly by temporarily installing the transmission case bearing to the shaft, followed by the spacer collar, thrust washer or bearing. 1st (low) gear, thrust bearing and washer, 1st (low) clutch and locknut.

31 The locknut must now be tightened to 22 lbf ft (3.0 kgf m) so that the endfloat of the gears etc., may be checked and corrected if necessary. The best course of action is to reassemble the countershaft as described below, then mesh the two shafts and temporarily install them in the torque converter housing. With the mainshaft locking tool applied and the parking gear gripped firmly, the two locknuts can be tightened.

32 With the locknut tightened, check the clearance between the washer and the thrust needle bearing adjacent to 2nd gear. The clearance must be within the limits given in the Specifications. If necessary, measure the thickness of the 2nd clutch splined thrust washer and select one which gives the specified clearance. Thrust washers are available in nine thicknesses from 2.97 to 3.40 mm (0.116 to 0.134 in). Recheck the clearance after installing a new washer.

Fig. 13.131 Checking clearance between thrust washer and needle bearing adjacent to 2nd gear on mainshaft

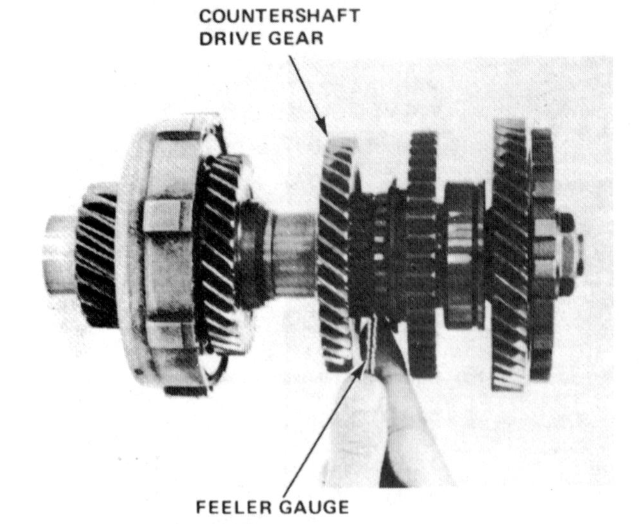

Fig. 13.132 Checking clearance between reverse selector hub and 2nd (drive) gear on countershaft

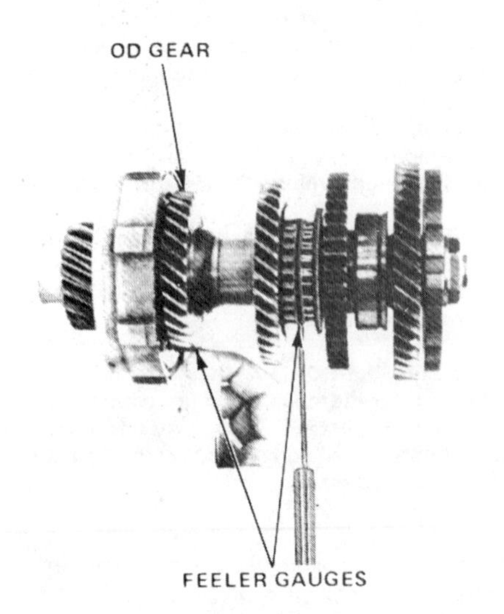

Fig. 13.133 Checking clearance between thrust washer and 3rd (OD) gear

Countershaft

33 Inspect the countershaft components for wear and damage and replace parts as necessary.

34 Reassemble the countershaft components, including the transmission case bearing and all components beyond it. Tighten the locknut to the specified torque as described in paragraph 31 then check the clearances as follows.

35 Measure the clearance between the shoulder of the Reverse selector hub and 2nd (Drive) gear. If it is outside the limits specified, the washer between 2nd and 3rd (OD) gears will have to be changed, but make the check below first.

36 With the feeler gauge used for the above check still in place –ie., with no play between 2nd gear and the selector hub - measure the clearance between the thrust washer and the shoulder of 3rd (OD) gear. If this is outside the specified limits, measure the thickness of the splined thrust washer and substitute one which will give the correct clearance.

37 Reassemble and recheck if new washers have to be installed.

Clutches

38 To dismantle the clutch, extract the snap-ring and lift away the endplate, discs and plates.

39 The clutch return coil spring must now be compressed with a suitable compressor (a long bolt with distance pieces will serve for this) so that the snap-ring, retainer and spring can be removed.

40 Place the clutch drum onto a soft surface and eject the clutch piston

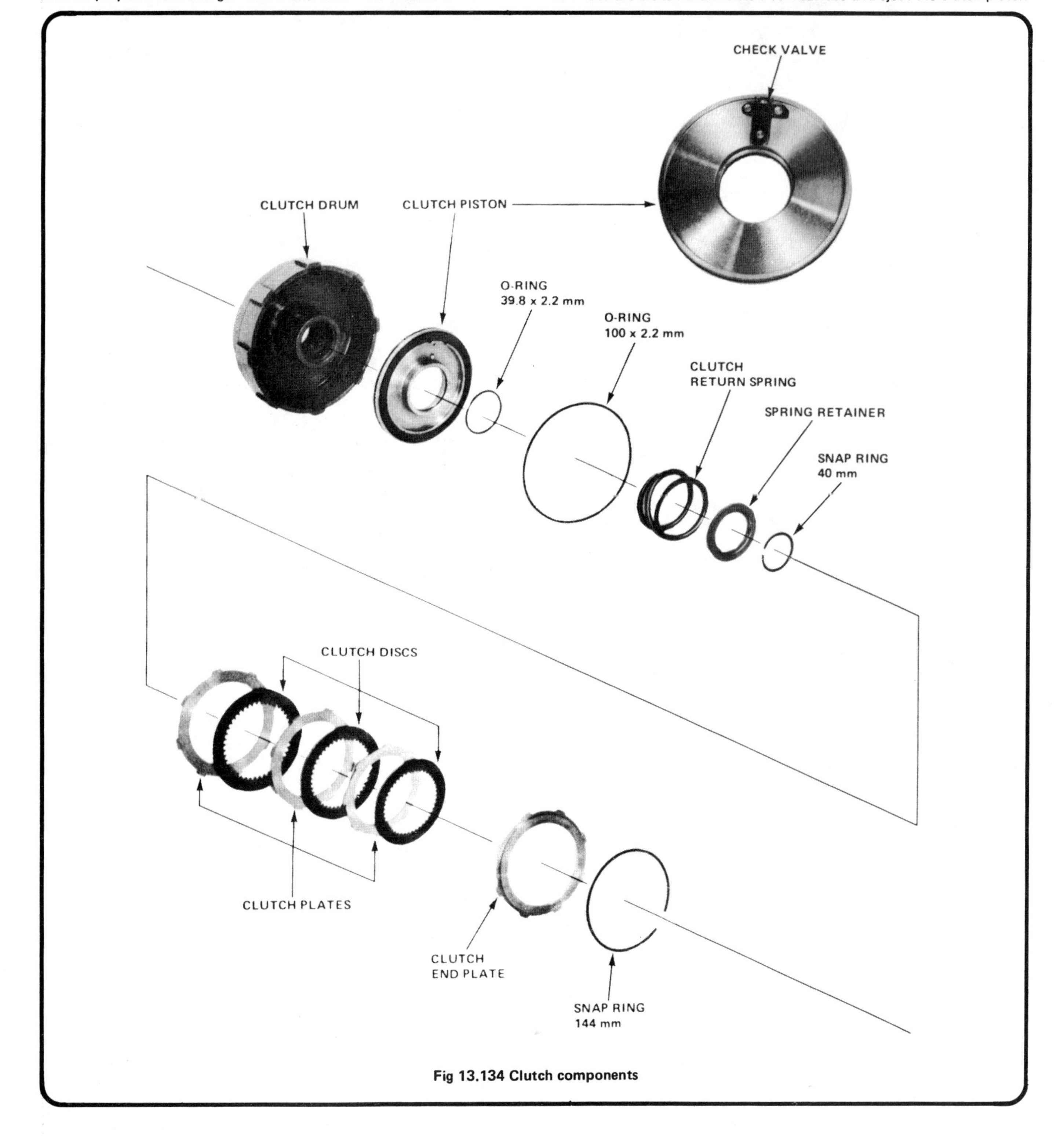

Fig 13.134 Clutch components

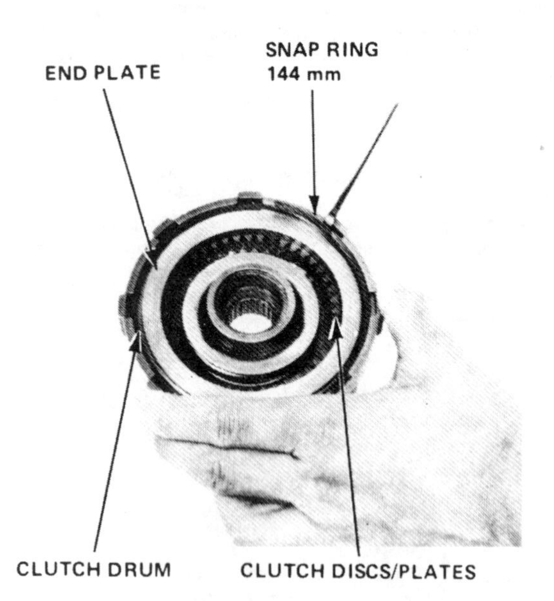

Fig. 13.135 Clutch drum

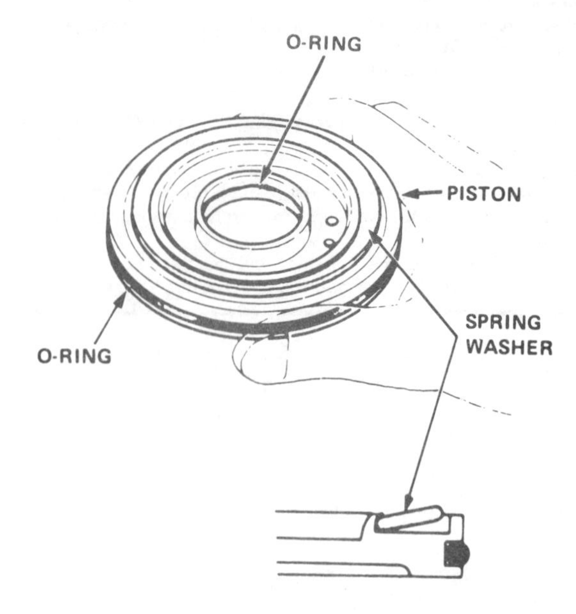

Fig. 13.136 Fitting cushion spring washer to clutch piston

by applying air from a tyre pump at one oil hole while blocking the other with a finger.
41 Clean all components and replace any which are worn or damaged.
42 Apply clean transmission fluid to all parts and then commence reassembly by installing two oil seal rings to the clutch drum.
43 Install a new O-ring on the clutch piston and then install the cushion spring as shown in the accompanying illustration.
44 Install a new O-ring on the clutch drum hub.
45 Press the piston into the clutch drum squarely using firm finger pressure.
46 Install the clutch spring and retainer, compress the spring and fit the snap-ring.
47 Install the clutch plates and discs alternately, having liberally applied transmission fluid to them. Make sure that the clutch endplate has its flat side against the clutch disc. Install the large securing snap-ring.
48 Using a feeler blade, measure the clearance between the last clutch disc and the endplate. This must be within the specified limits, if not, substitute an endplate of a different thickness. Eleven thicknesses are available.
49 The clutch can be checked for engagement by applying air pressure to an oilway in the drum hub. On removal of the air pressure the clutch should release.

Servo

50 Clean and inspect the components of the servo body and blow out the passages with air from a tyre pump.
51 Replace the O-ring seal on the valve as a matter of course. Replace the complete assembly if wear is evident. Check the spring free length against the Specifications and replace it with a new one if necessary.
52 When reassembling, make sure the return spring is properly seated. Pull the valve stem up fully and check that the groove in the stem is flush with, or higher than, the valve body. Dismantle and recheck if necessary.
53 If any worn parts are being renewed, they must carry the original part number. Remember to keep everything very clean and lubricate liberally with transmission fluid on reassembly.

Pressure regulator valve

54 Clean the body by blowing through with air from a tyre pump.
55 Renew any worn components.

Valve body

56 Inspect all components for wear and renew as necessary.
57 The valve body, pump drivegear and driven gear are supplied only as a matched set.
58 When reassembling the valve body, apply clean fluid to all components and then fit the manual valve with its flat face downwards followed by the detent rollers and spring.

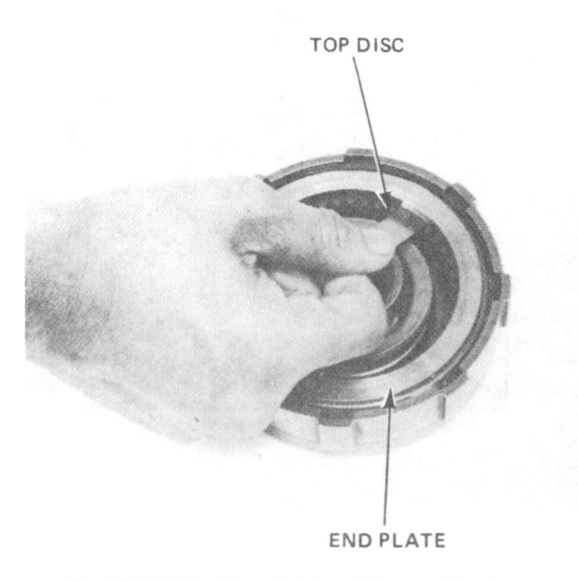

Fig. 13.137 Checking clutch endplate to disc clearance

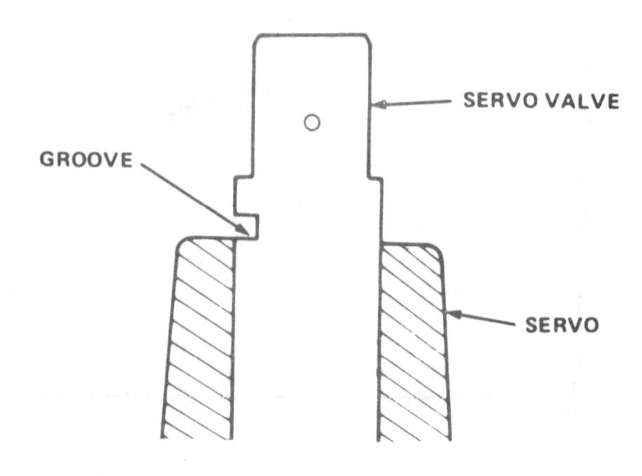

Fig. 13.138 Location of servo valve stem groove

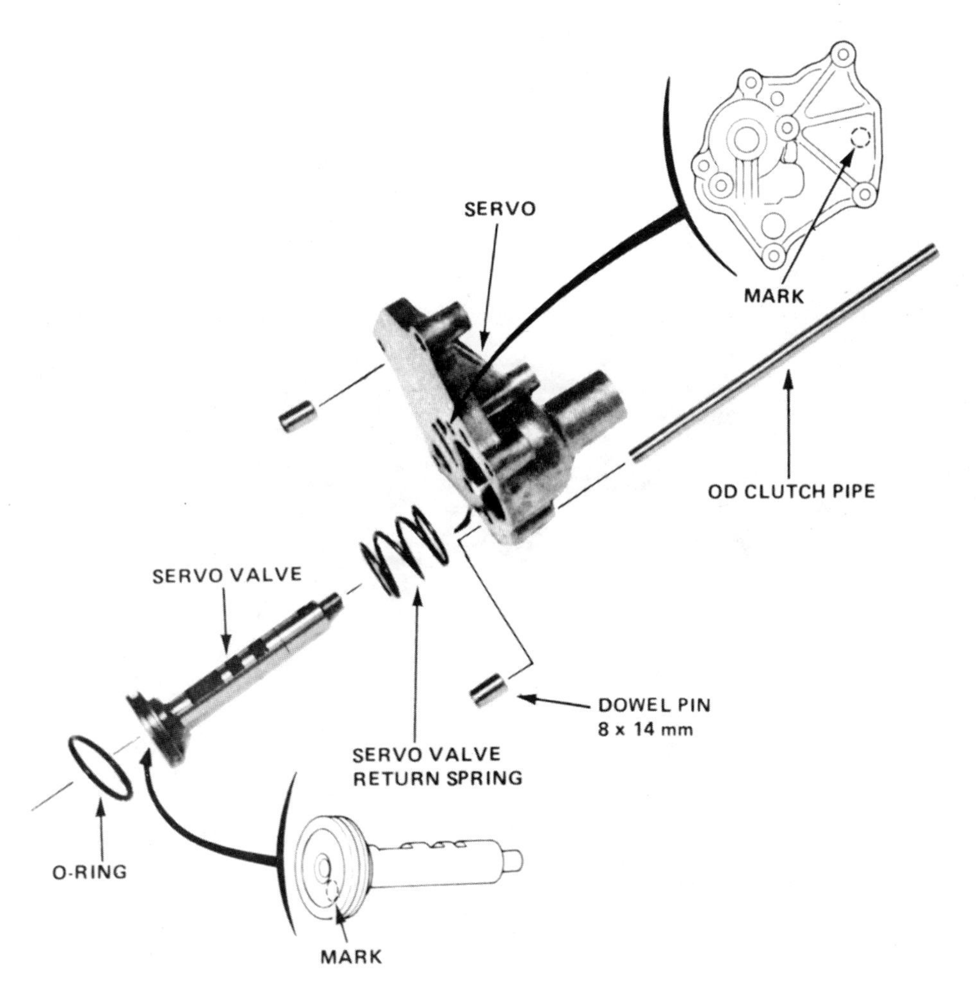

Fig. 13.139 Servo components

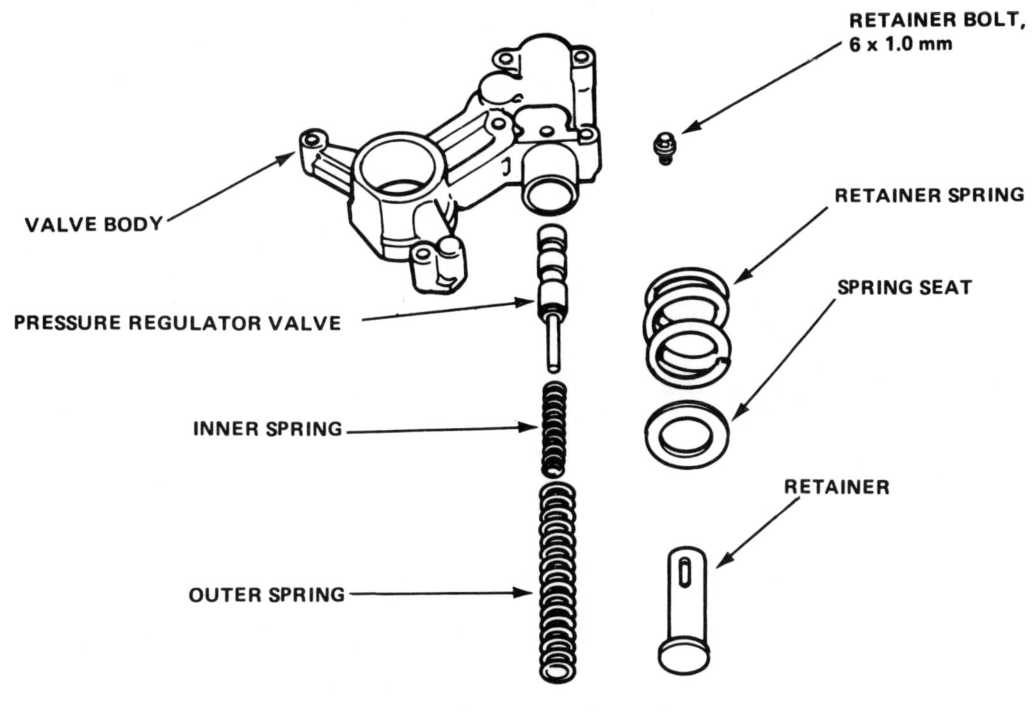

Fig. 13.140 Pressure regulator valve

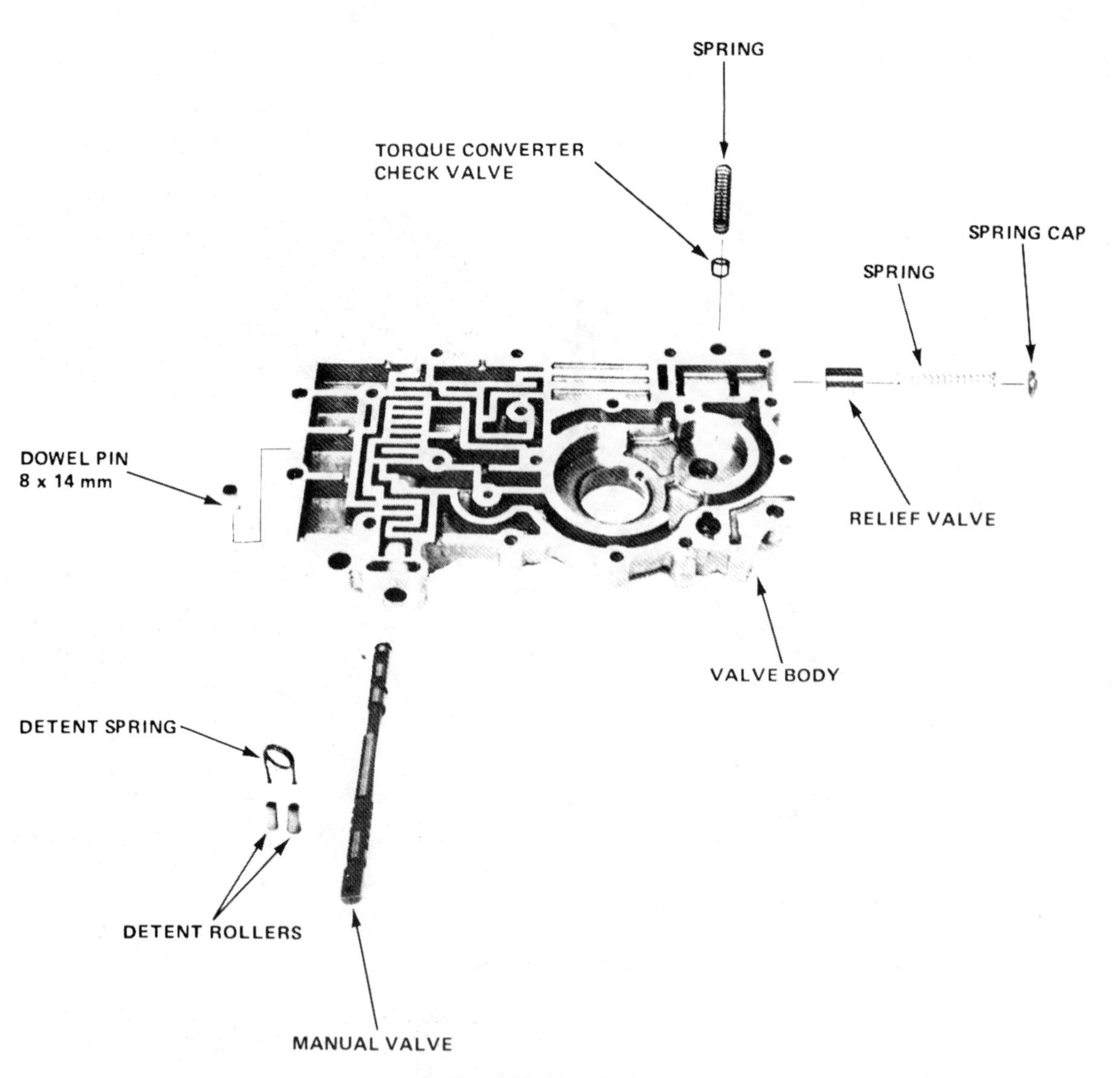

Fig. 13.141 Valve body

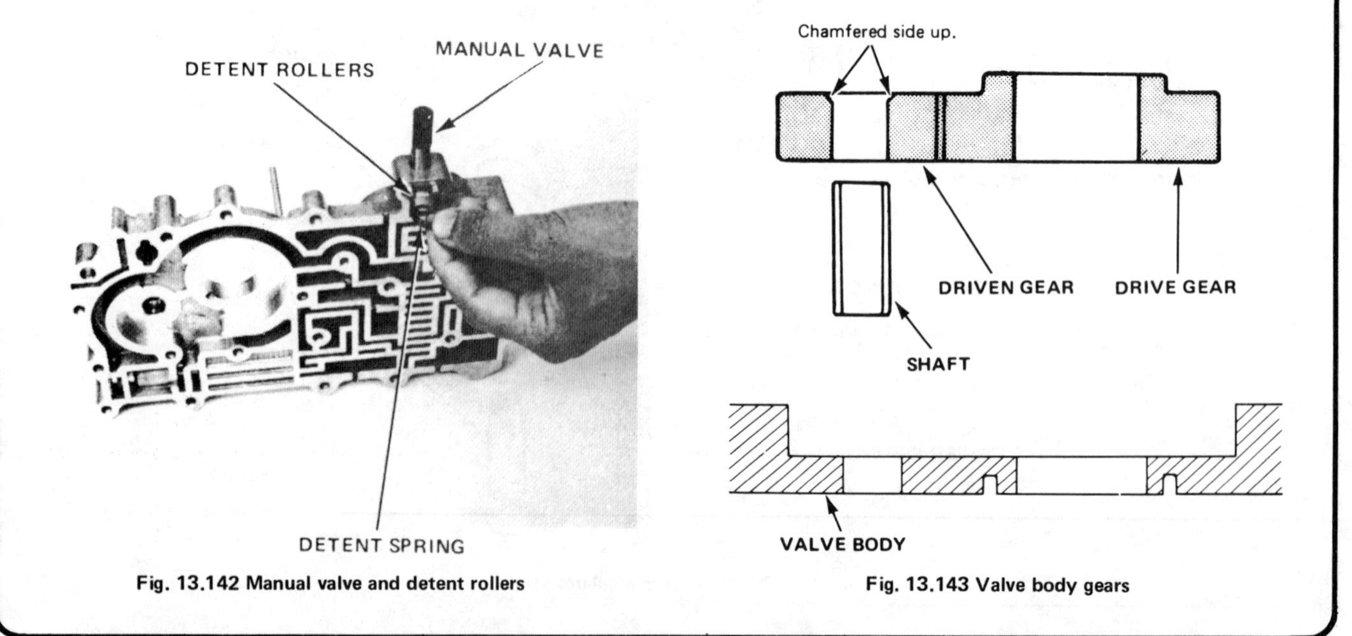

Fig. 13.142 Manual valve and detent rollers

Fig. 13.143 Valve body gears

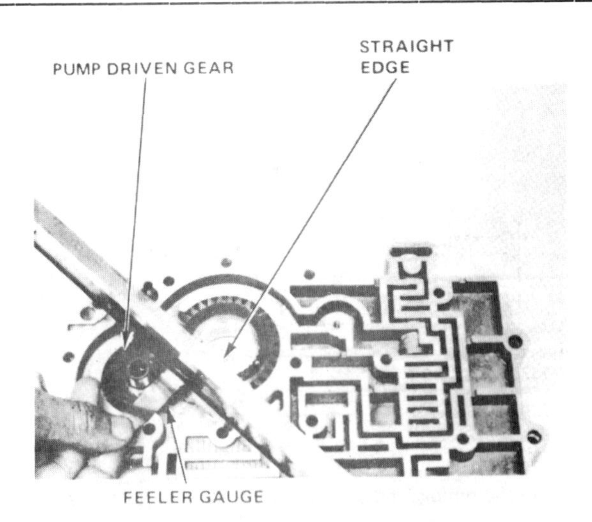

Fig. 13.144 Checking valve body gear endfloat

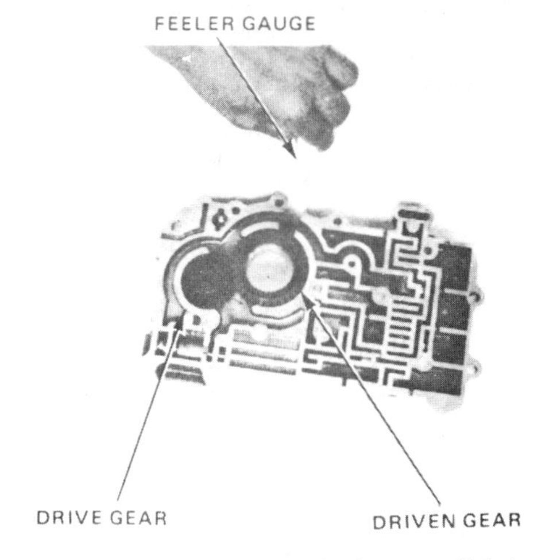

Fig. 13.145 Checking valve body gear radial clearance

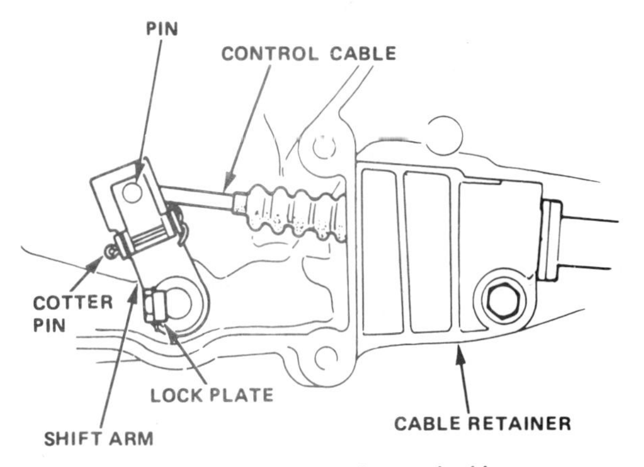

Fig. 13.146 Shift arm and control cable

59 Fit the gears in accordance with the diagram and then measure the end-float between the drivegear and the body surface. Use feeler blades and a straight-edge for this.

60 Measure the clearance between the gears and the body. If any measurements are outside the specified tolerance, renew the components.

Shift arm shaft

61 Remove the control cable retainer.

62 Pull out the cotter and clevis pins and disconnect the cable from the shift arm.

Fig. 13.147 Shift arm shaft

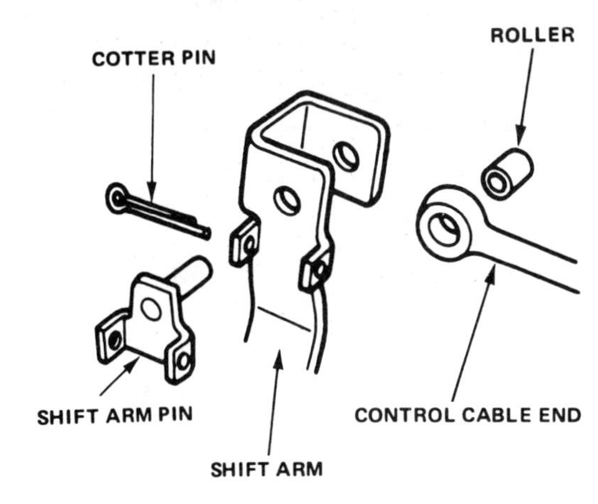

Fig. 13.148 Control cable connecting parts

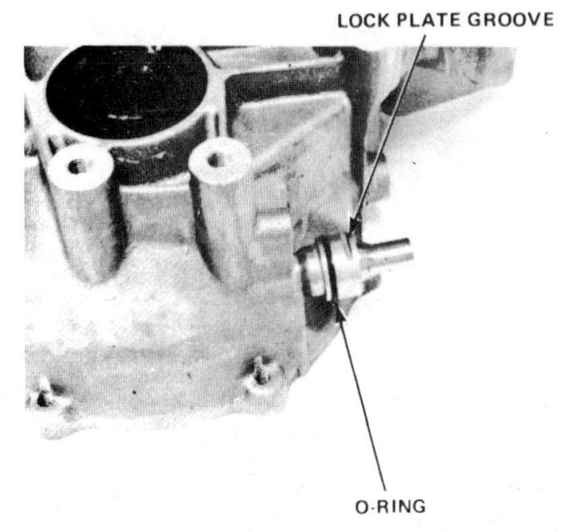

Fig. 13.149 Speedometer gear holder lockplate groove

63 Flatten the tab on the shift arm tab lock plate.

64 Remove the bolt and the shift arm.

65 Remove the shift arm shaft.

66 Reassembly is a reversal of dismantling, but use a new lockplate and tighten the cable retainer bolt to the specified torque.

Speedometer drivegear

67 The speedometer drivegear is held in place by a bolt and lockplate. The lockplate engages in a groove in the gear holder.

68 Always fit a new O-ring seal at reassembly.

Housing bearings and oil seals

69 The oil seals in the transmission housing should be replaced as a matter of routine at the time of major overhaul.

70 The bearings, if worn, can be replaced by expanding the bearing retaining circlips and pushing them out by hand. The differential must be removed before the countershaft bearing in the torque converter housing can be removed (refer to Chapter 8). If the differential side bearings or the transmission or torque converter housings are replaced, then the differential side clearance must be measured and if necessary, adjusted as described in Chapter 8. The Reverse idler shaft and its bearings are removed from the outside of the transmission housing while the Reverse idler gear is withdrawn into the interior.

71 When refitting the reverse idler gear, the countersunk side of the shaft-hole must be towards the torque converter.

End cover

72 To dismantle the end cover, extract the circlips, remove the oil feed pipes and O-rings.

73 When reassembling, fit new O-ring seals into the oil feed pipe flanges and make sure that as the pipes are pushed into position, their flange projections align with the notches in the end cover.

Torque converter

74 Scribe a line across the edge of the torque converter so that the cover and pump can be reassembled in their original relative positions.

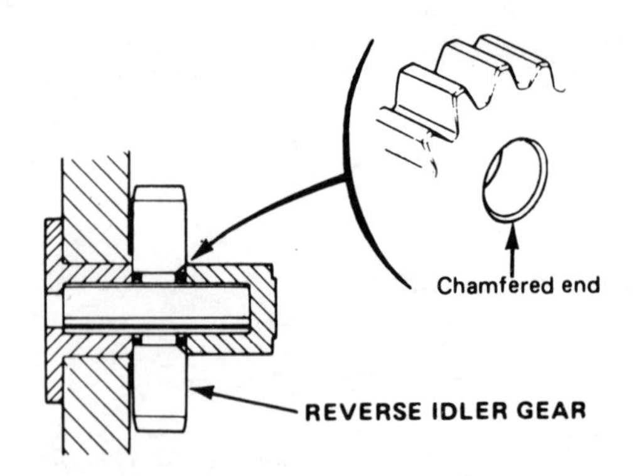

Fig. 13.150 Reverse idler gear

75 Unscrew and remove the connecting bolts and separate the components.

76 Check all components for wear, particularly the driveplate for cracks and the starter ring gear teeth. If the ring gear must be renewed, this is simple as it is bolted in place. Remember that the flat side of the ring is towards the torque converter cover.

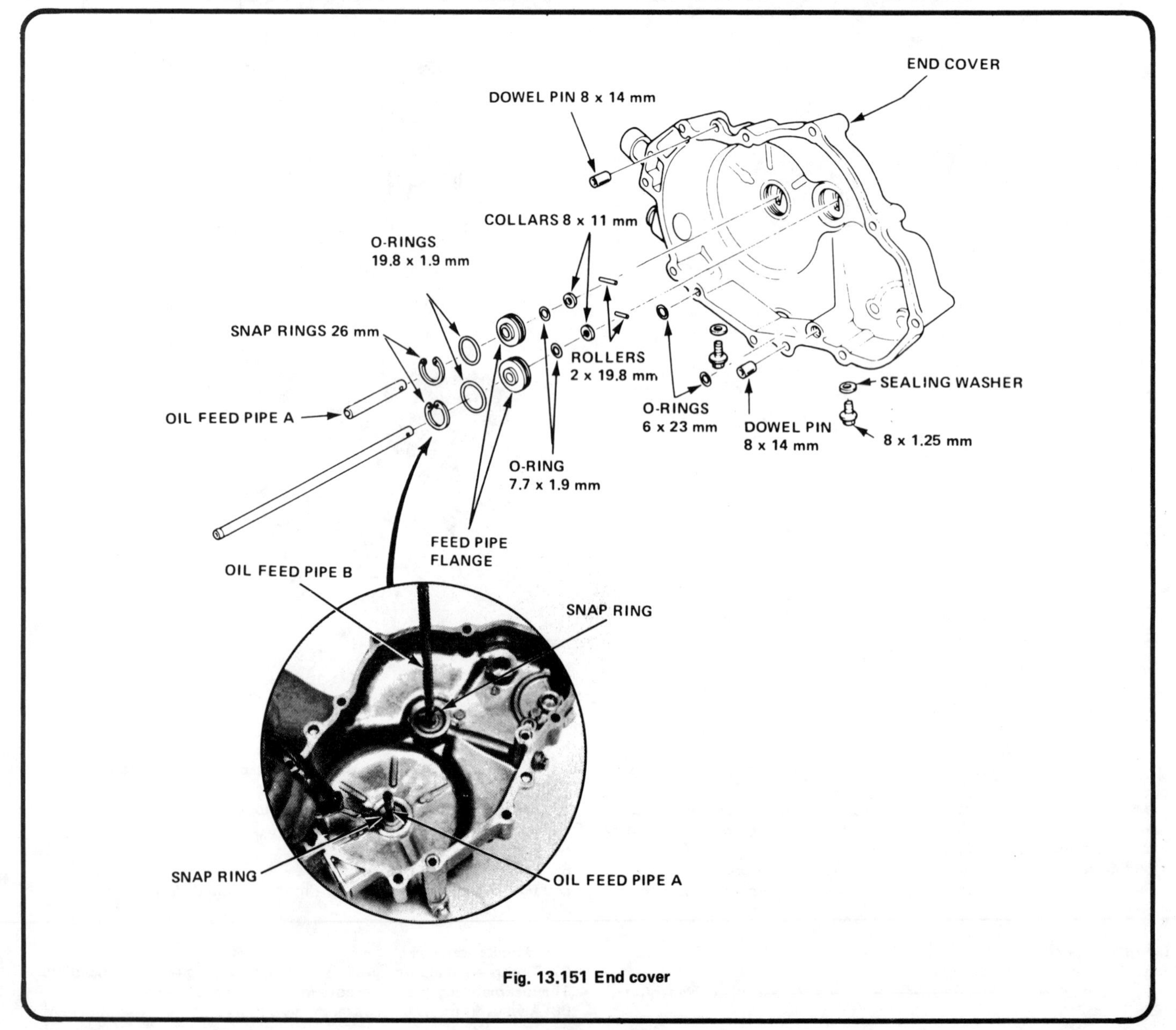

Fig. 13.151 End cover

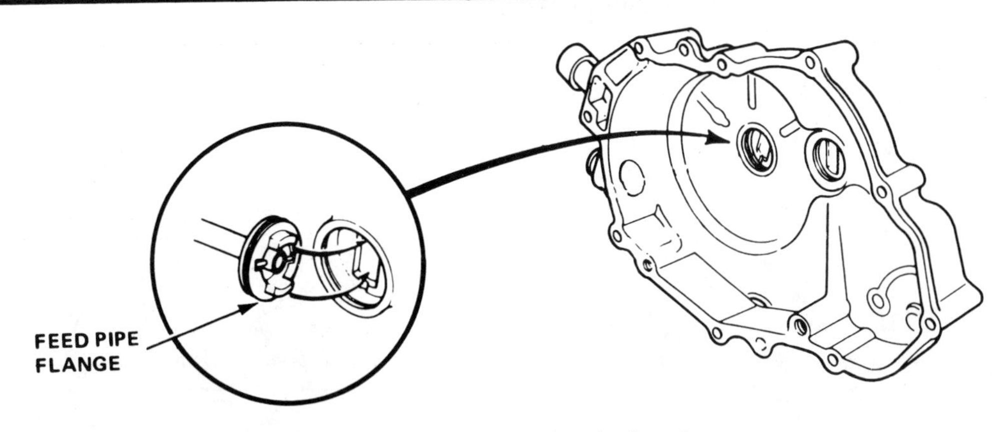

Fig. 13.152 Feed pipe flange location in end cover

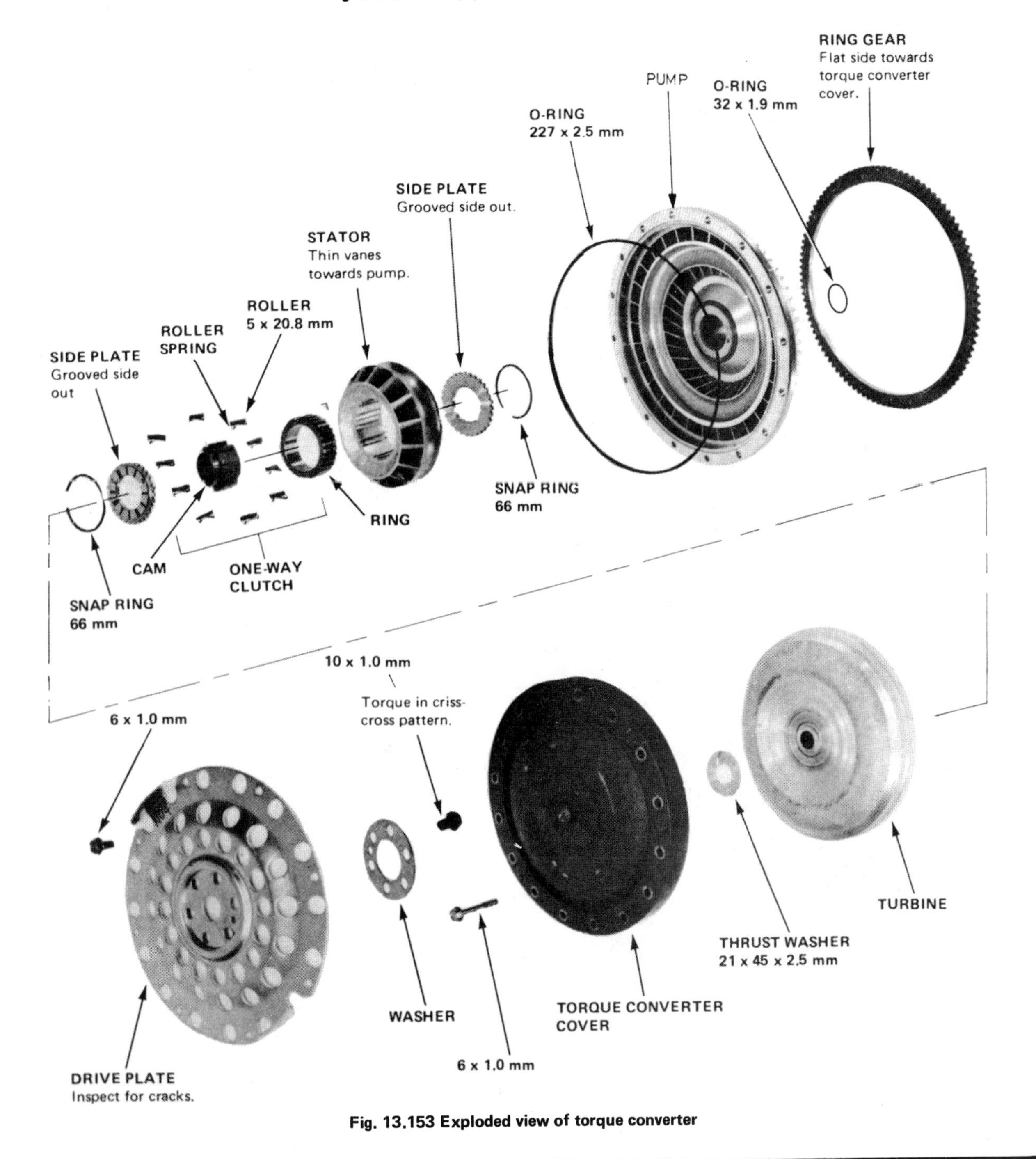

Fig. 13.153 Exploded view of torque converter

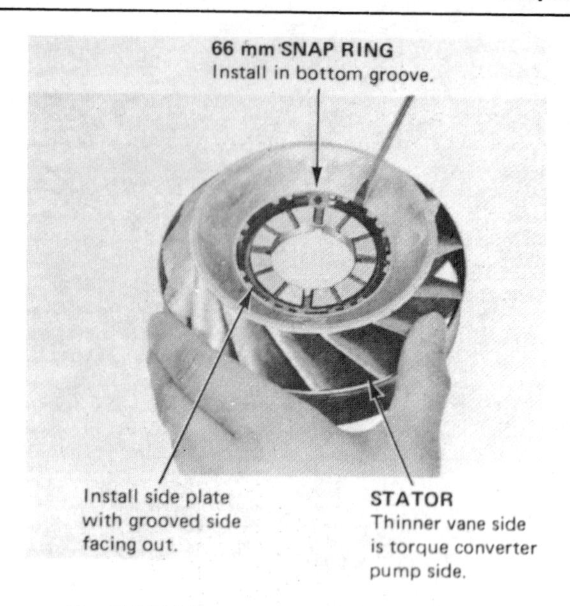

Fig. 13.154 First snap-ring and side plate in stator

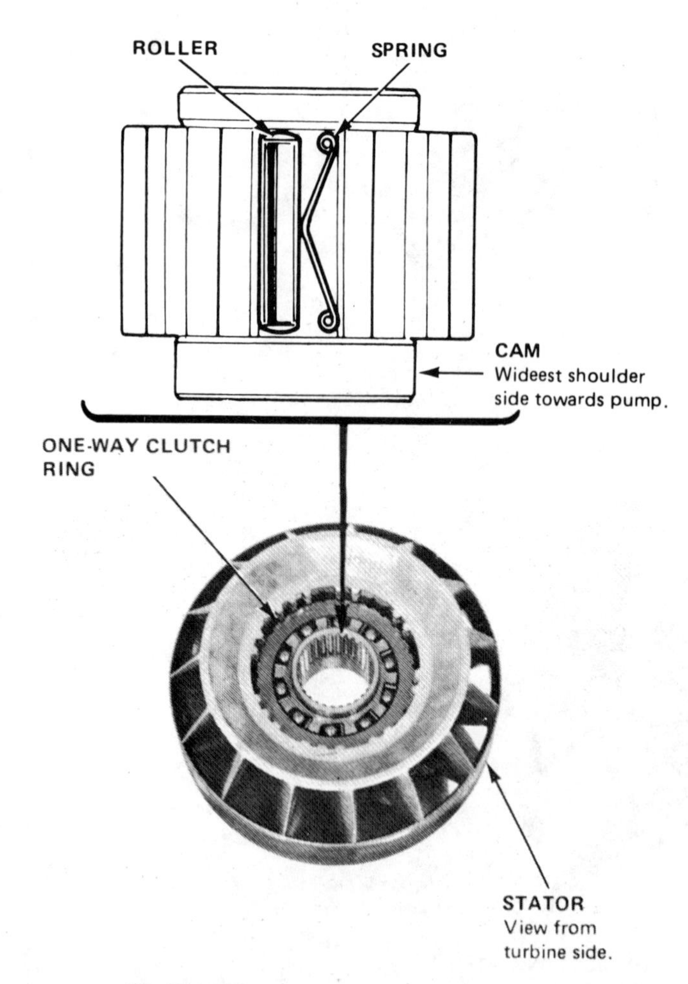

Fig. 13.155 One-way clutch ring and cam in stator

77 Commence reassembly of the torque converter by locating the first snap-ring and side plate (grooved side visible) in the stator.
78 Fit the one-way clutch ring and cam in the stator. Make sure that the widest shoulder on the cam is towards the pump.
79 Fit the clutch rollers and spring.

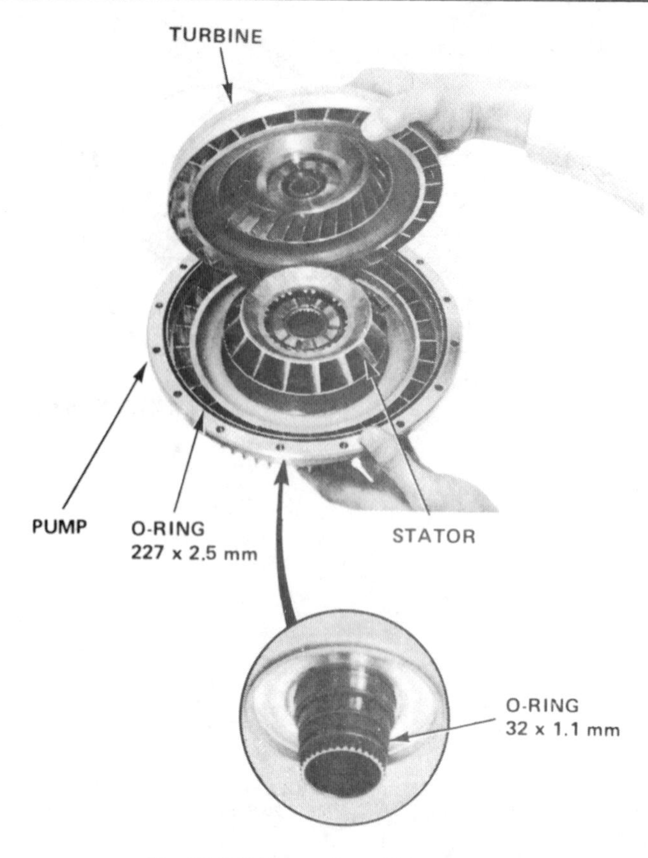

Fig. 13.156 Connecting turbine to stator

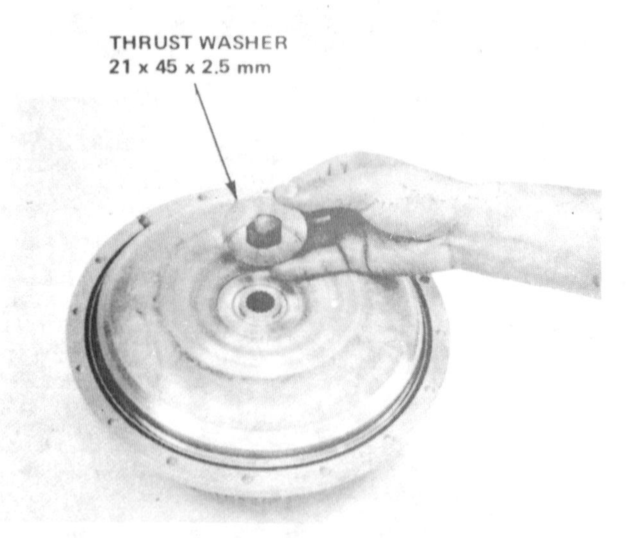

Fig. 13.157 Turbine thrust washer

80 Fit the second stator side plate (grooves visible) and the snap-ring.
81 Insert the stator shaft into the stator from the pump side and check the operation of the one-way clutch. It should only turn one way.
82 Thoroughly clean the O-ring grooves for both the large and small rings and fit new ones.
83 Locate the stator (thinner vanes towards pump) and then place the turbine on top of the pump.
84 Fit the thrust washer.
85 Fit the cover with the marks made at dismantling in alignment.
86 Fit the ring gear so that its flat side is towards the torque converter cover.
87 Tighten the connecting bolts in the sequence indicated.

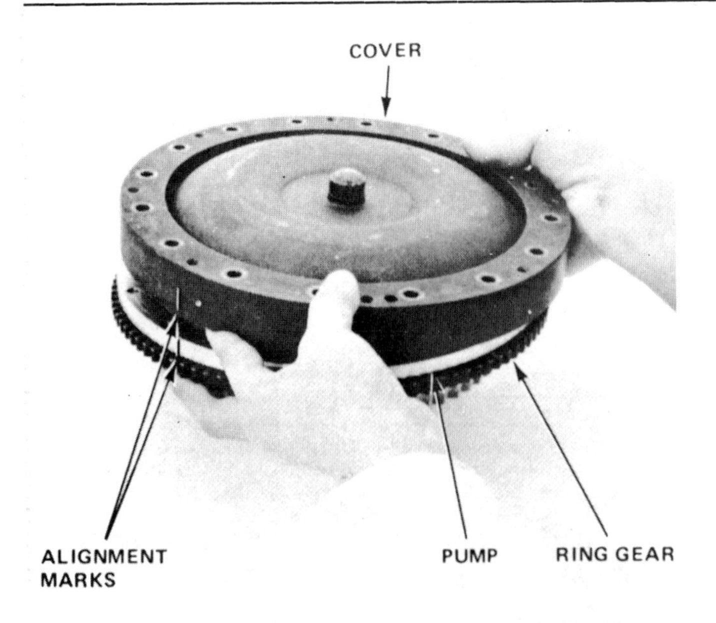

Fig. 13.158 Connecting pump and converter cover

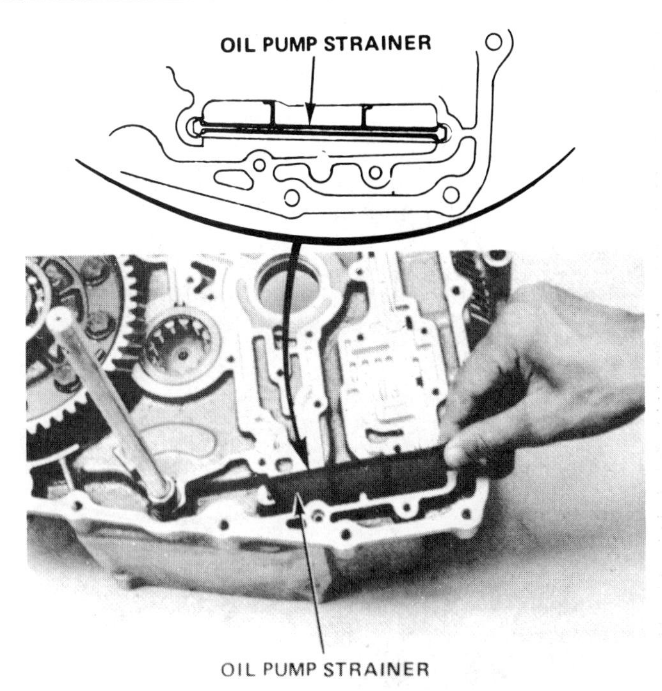

Fig. 13.160 Oil pump strainer

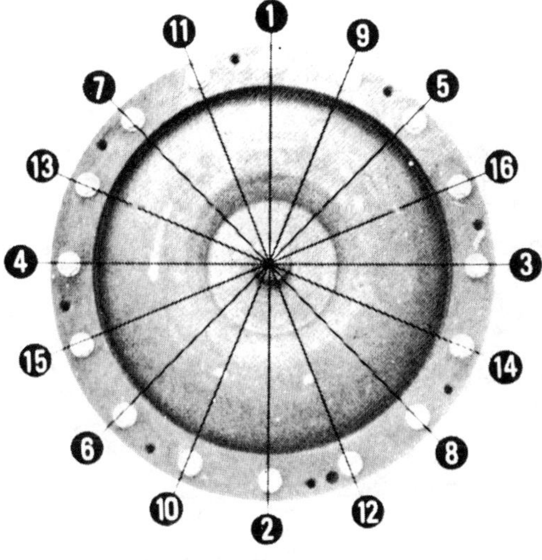

Fig. 13.159 Cover bolt tightening sequence

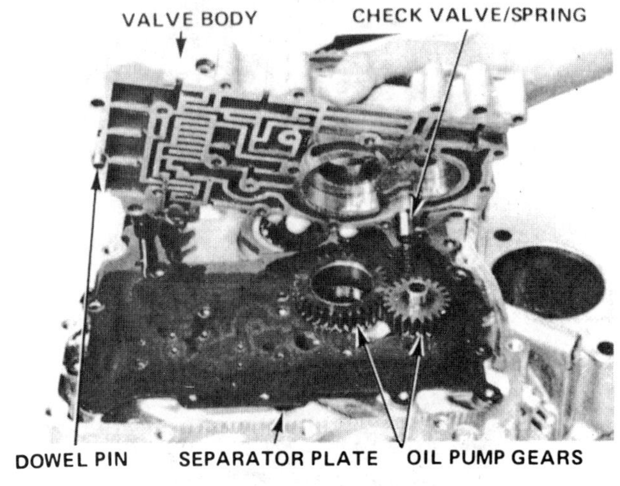

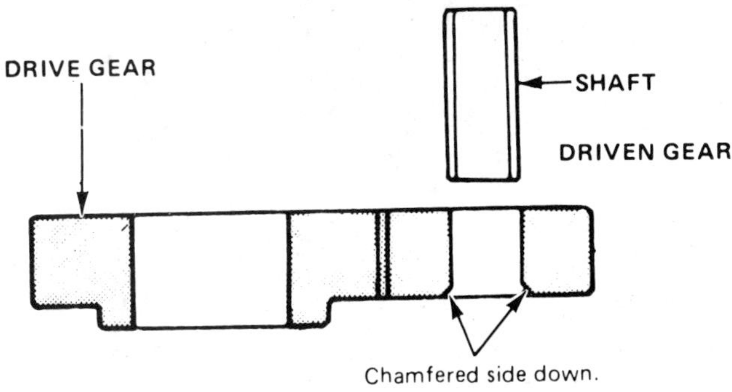

Fig. 13.161 Separator plate and oil pump gears

PART C - REASSEMBLY

1 Fit the differential assembly.
2 Install a new oil pump strainer, flanged side upwards.
3 Install the separator plate, the dowel pin, pump gears and shaft.
4 Install the check valve and spring to the valve body, then attach the valve body to the torque converter housing. Tighten the valve body securing bolts to the specified torque.
5 Locate a spacer on each side of the manual valve stem, attach the valve to the lever with the pivot pin and a new cotter pin.
6 Install the stator shaft (if removed), the shaft arm and stop pin. Install the two dowel pins in the valve body.
7 Install the regulator valve and tighten the securing bolts to the specified torque.
8 Install the servo, install the different length bolts in the correct location and tighten in the order shown in the accompanying illustration.

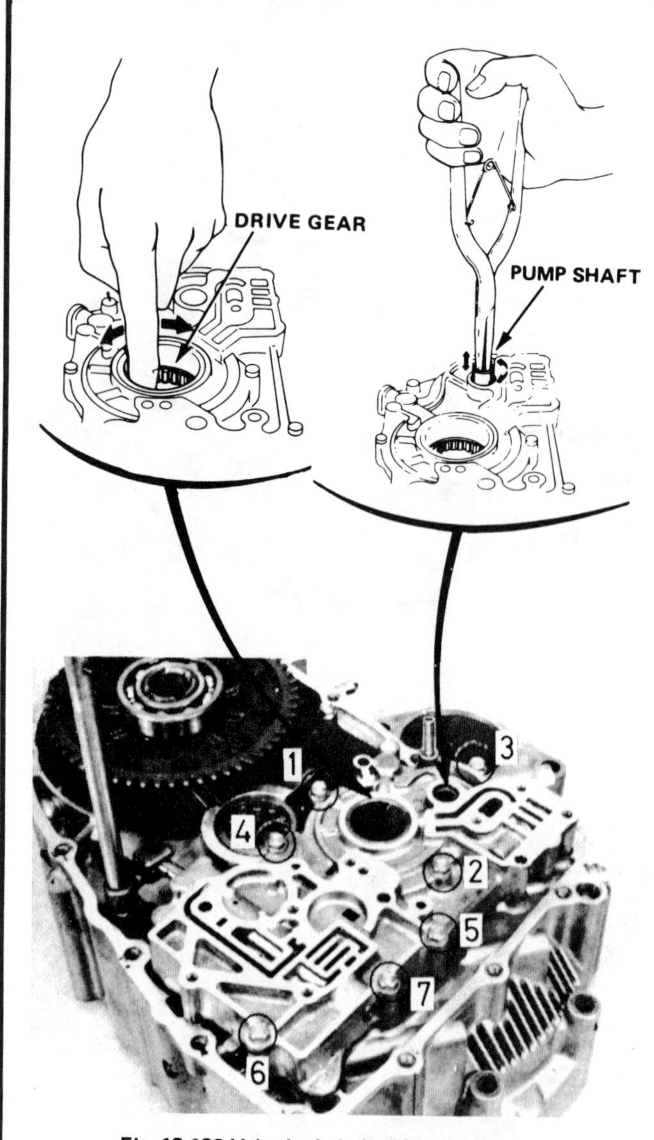

Fig. 13.162 Valve body bolt tightening sequence

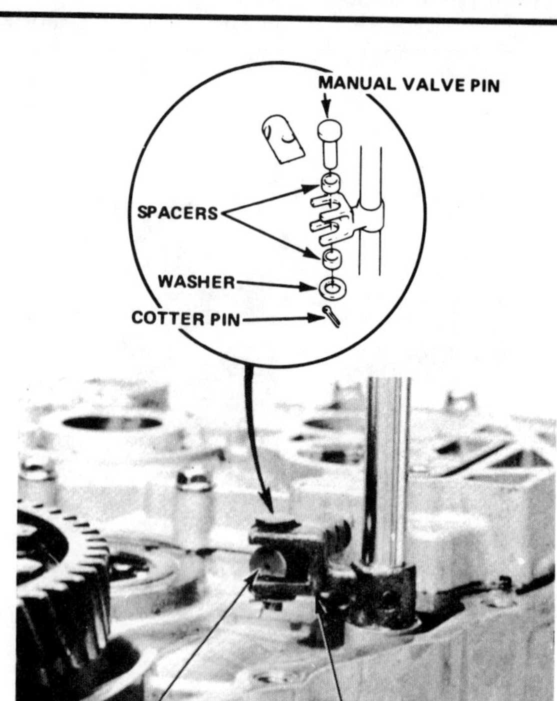

Fig. 13.163 Manual valve and lever

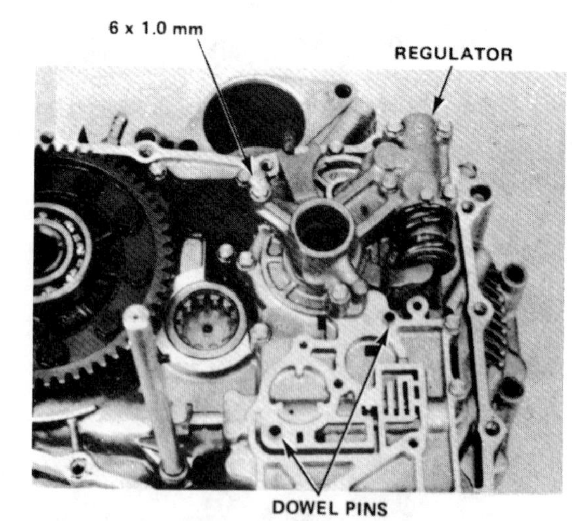

Fig. 13.165 Regulator fixing bolts

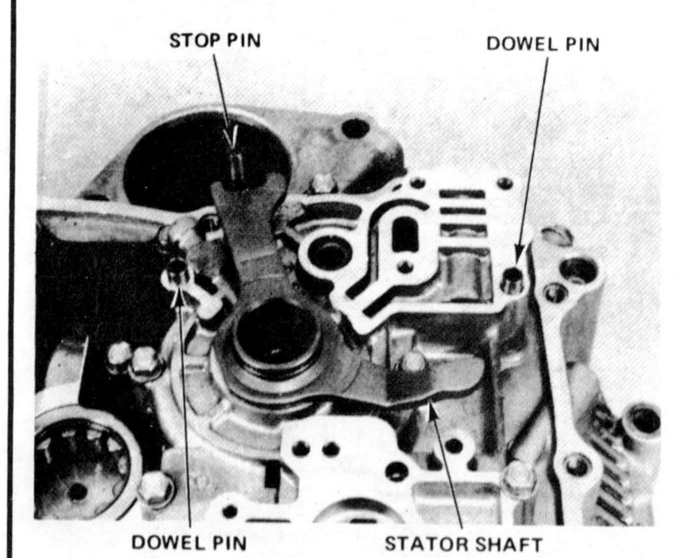

Fig. 13.164 Stator shaft and stop pin

Fig. 13.166 Servo fixing bolts

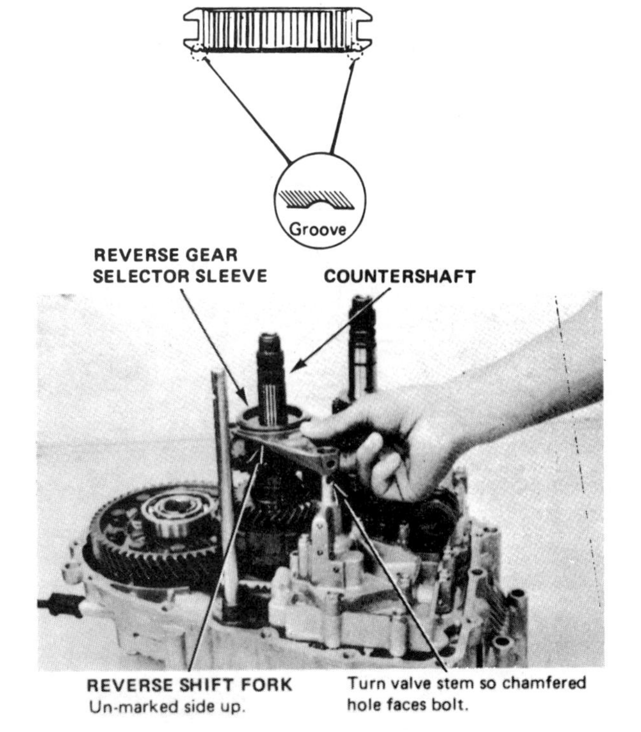

Fig. 13.167 Reverse gear selector sleeve and shift fork

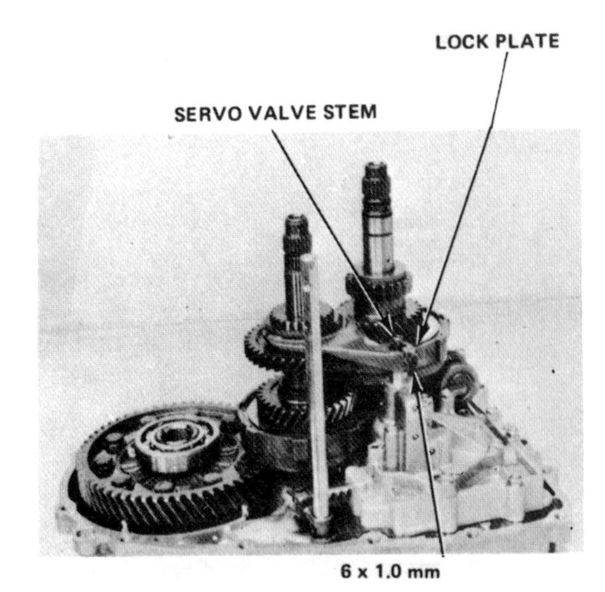

Fig. 13.168 Reverse shift fork lock plate

Fig. 13.169 Countershaft reverse gear and needle bearing

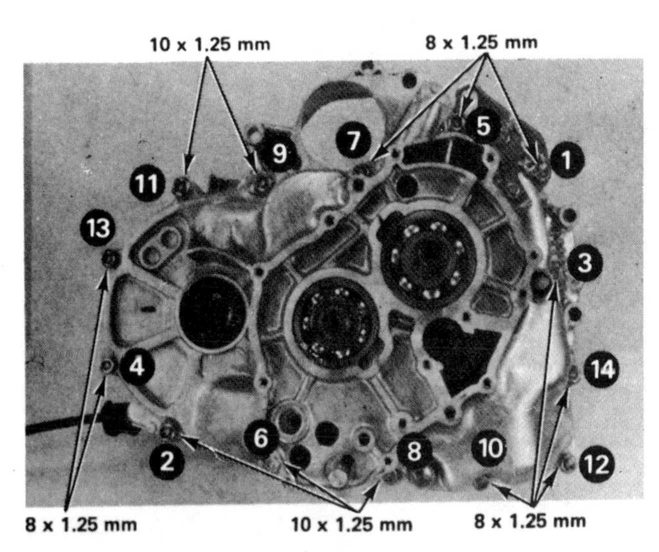

Fig. 13.170 Transmission housing bolt tightening sequence

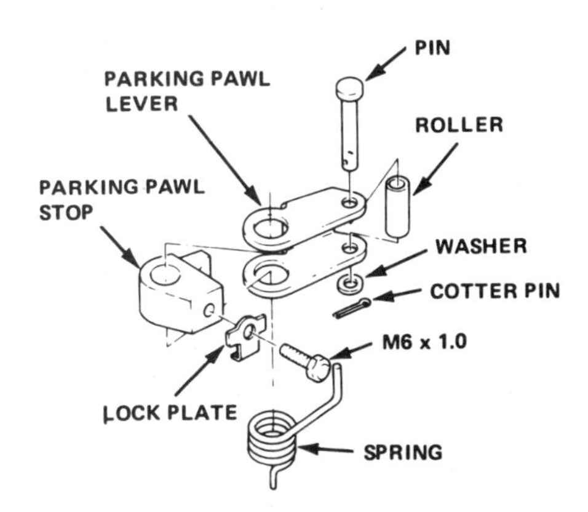

Fig. 13.171 Parking pawl lever components

Fig. 13.172 Countershaft low gear

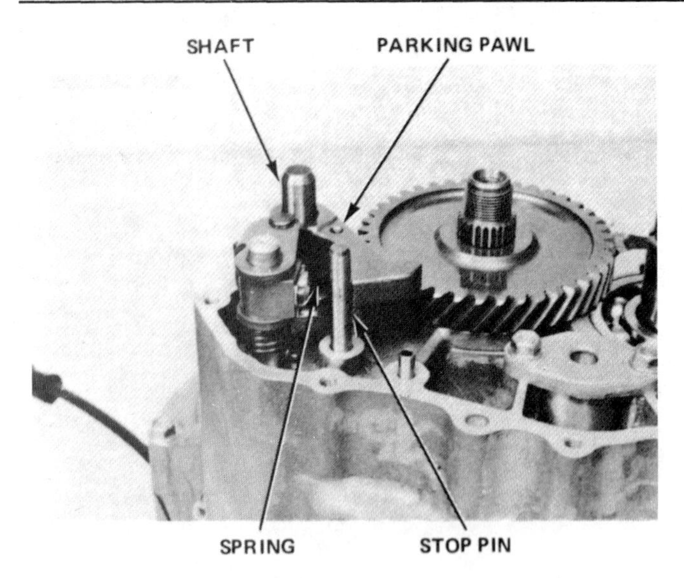

Fig. 13.173 Parking pawl installed

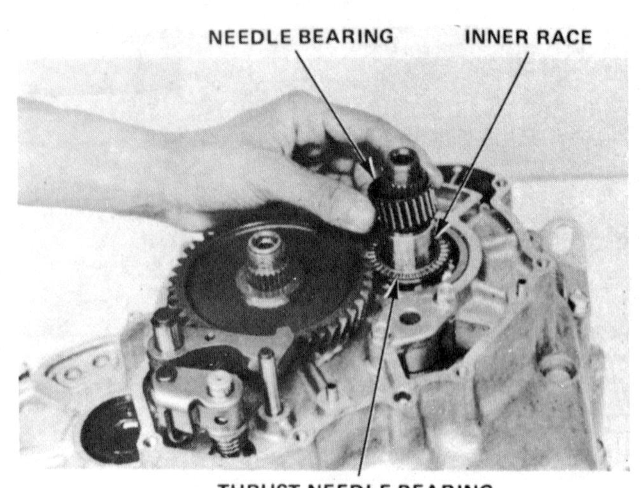

Fig. 13.174 Mainshaft needle bearing and inner race

9 Insert the enmeshed mainshaft and countershaft. If all is well they should go in fairly easily; in any event, do not attempt to hammer them into place, but remove and investigate if necessary.
10 Assemble the Reverse selector sleeve and shift fork, then attach them to the countershaft, grooved side down. Attach the fork to the servo valve stem, tighten the bolt and bend over the lockplate.
11 Install the countershaft Reverse gear, needle bearing and inner race.
12 Fit the oil feed pipes.
13 Install a new gasket and two dowel pins to the torque converter housing flange.
14 Connect the transmission housing to the torque converter housing. Make sure that the shafts, etc., line up, or the housings will not go on.
15 When the housings are correctly mated, tighten the bolts in diagonal sequence to the specified torque.
16 Install the parking pawl lever, spring and associated components on the shift shaft. Secure with the bolt and lockplate.
17 Fit countershaft 1st gear so that the side with the raised shoulder is towards the bearing.
18 Fit the idler shaft holder.
19 Install the parking pawl, shaft, spring and stop pin. Check that the spring forces the pawl away from the parking gear.

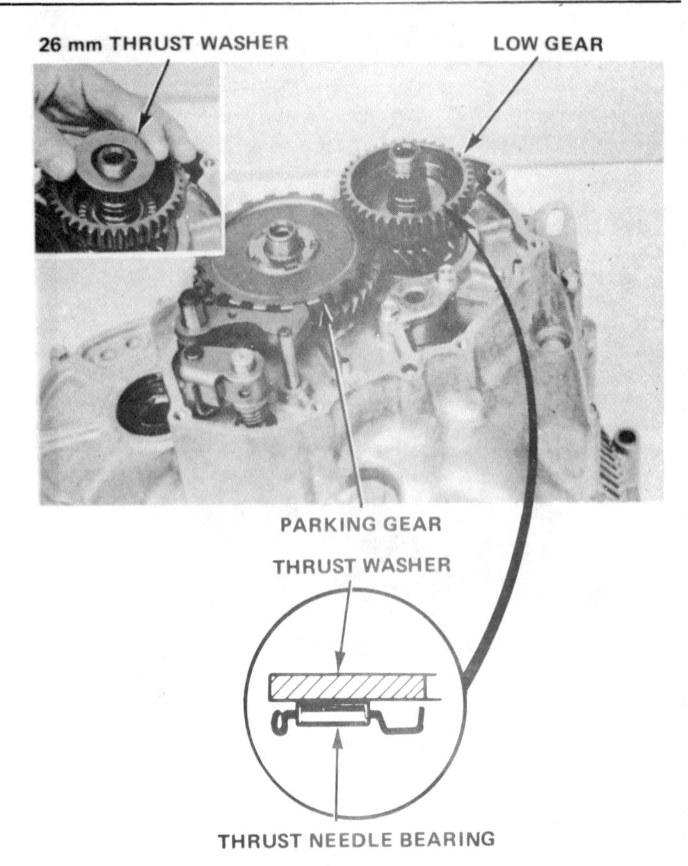

Fig. 13.175 Parking gear and low gear installed

Fig. 13.176 Mainshaft O-rings

20 Fit the mainshaft thrust needle bearing inner race and needle bearing.
21 Fit 1st gear and the parking gear as an assembly.
22 Fit the thrust needle bearing and the 26.0 mm thrust washer.
23 Fit the two new O-rings into the mainshaft grooves.
24 Select Park by pushing the control fully in.
25 Fit a new countershaft locknut and tighten to the specified torque. Stake the locknut into the slot in the parking gear.

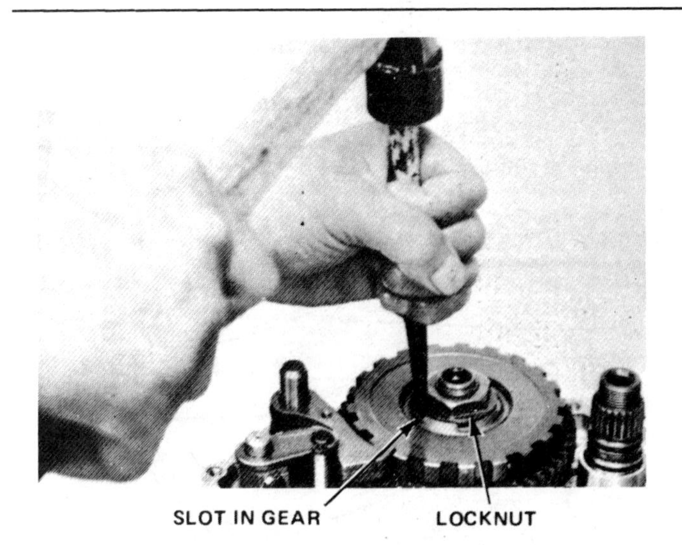

Fig. 13.177 Staking countershaft locknut

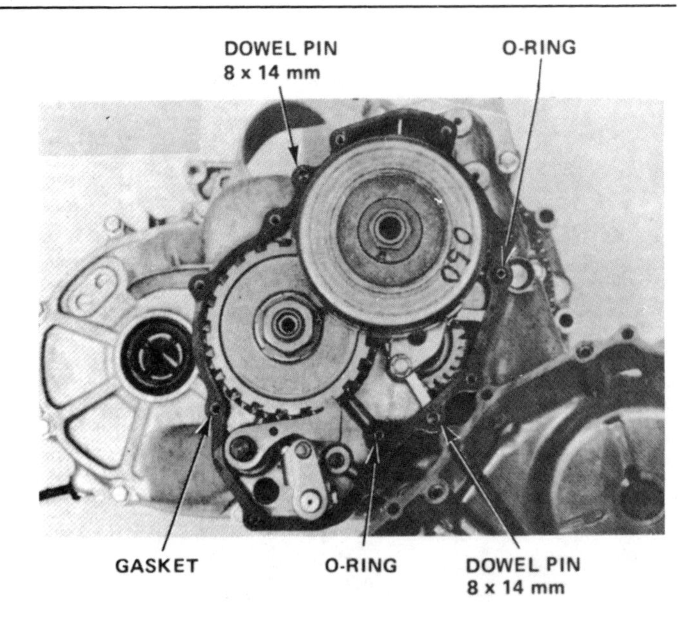

Fig. 13.180 Dowel pin and O-ring locations

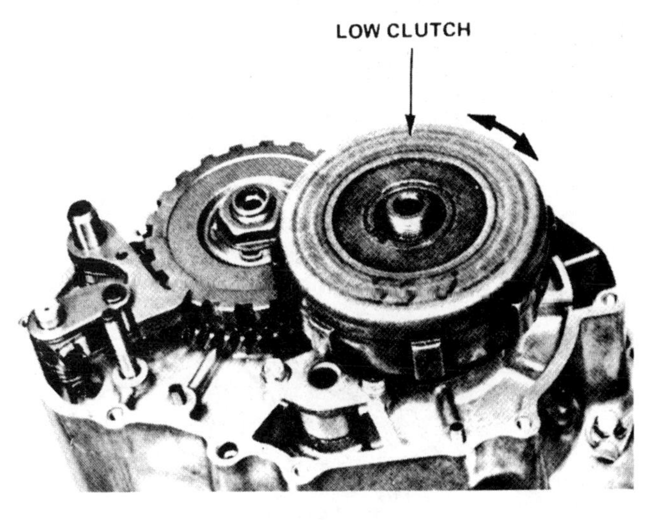

Fig. 13.178 Low clutch

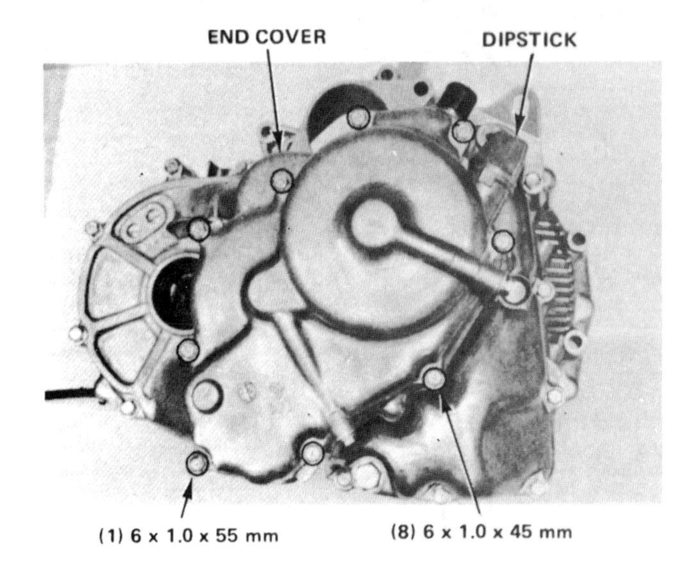

Fig. 13.181 End cover

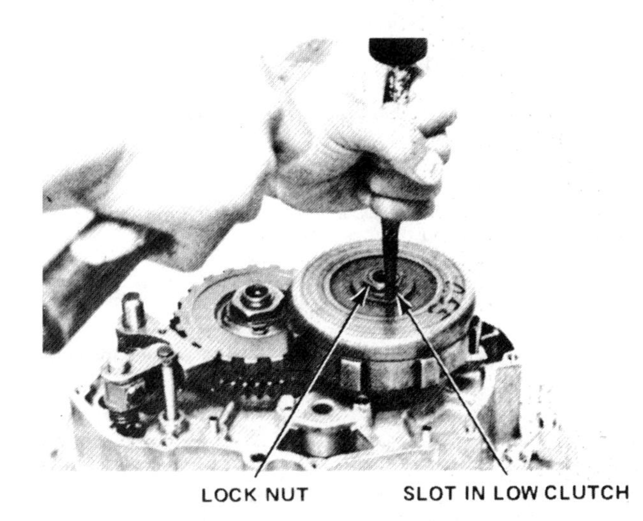

Fig. 13.179 Staking mainshaft locknut

26 Install low gear clutch and twist it until it is fully engaged.
27 Fit the mainshaft holder tool then screw on a new mainshaft locknut and tighten to the specified torque.
28 Check that the low clutch rotates freely without taking 1st gear with it.
29 Stake the locknut into the slot in the low clutch.
30 Fit the end cover dowel pins, two new O-rings and a new gasket and fit the end cover.
31 Tighten bolts to the specified torque.

PART D - CONTROLS AND SWITCHES - ADJUSTMENT

Control cable

1 Remove the centre console and select reverse gear.
2 Pull off the spring retaining clip from the end of the control cable.
3 Check that the holes in the control cable and the adjuster are in perfect alignment.

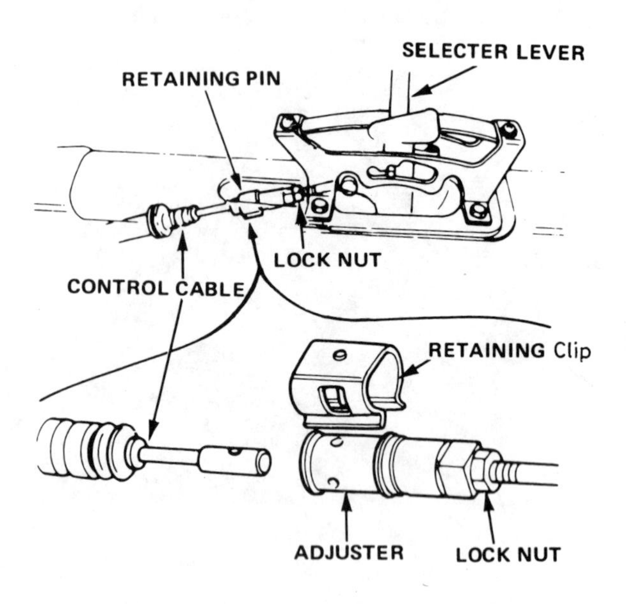

Fig. 13.182 Control cable connection to lever

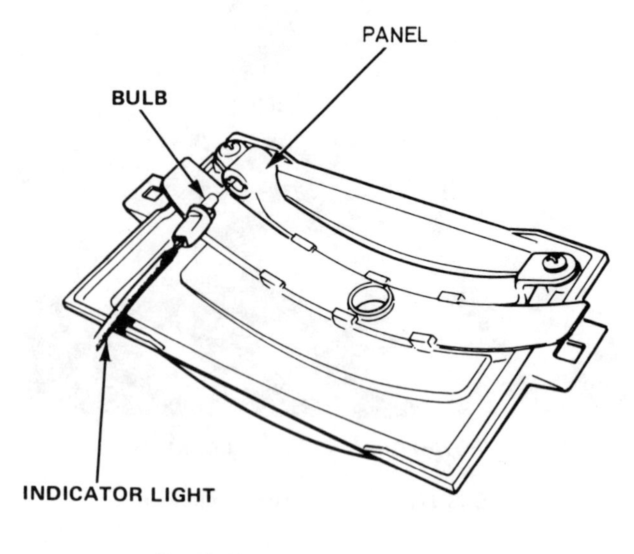

Fig. 13.184 Indicator panel and bulb

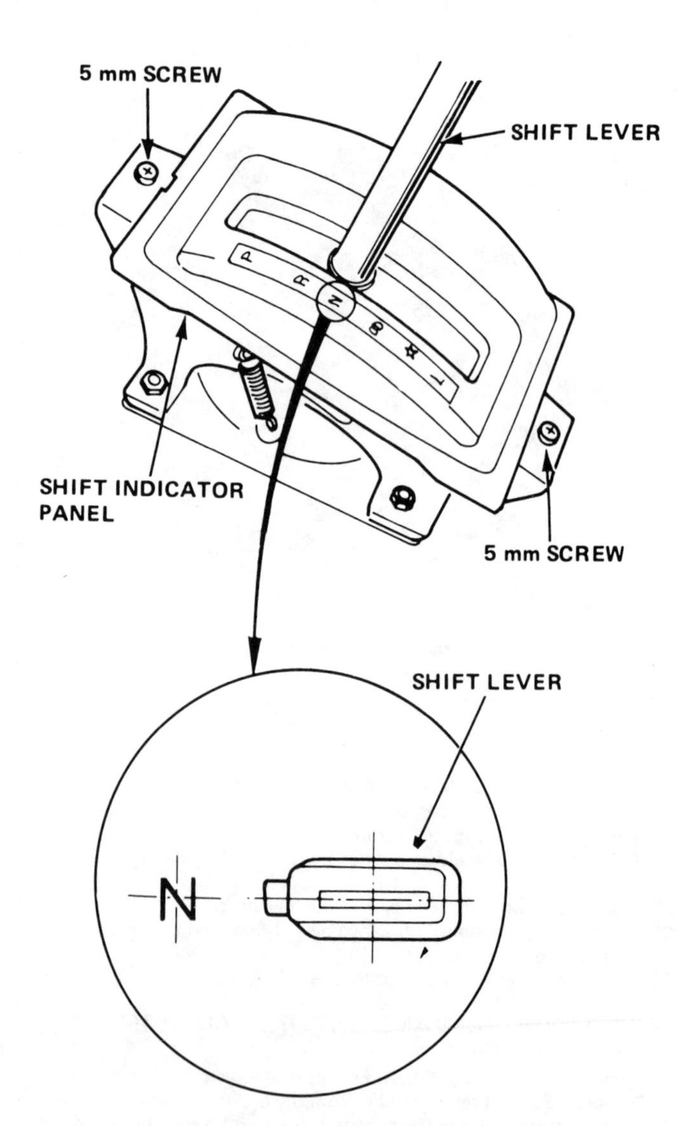

Fig. 13.183 Indicator panel fixing screws

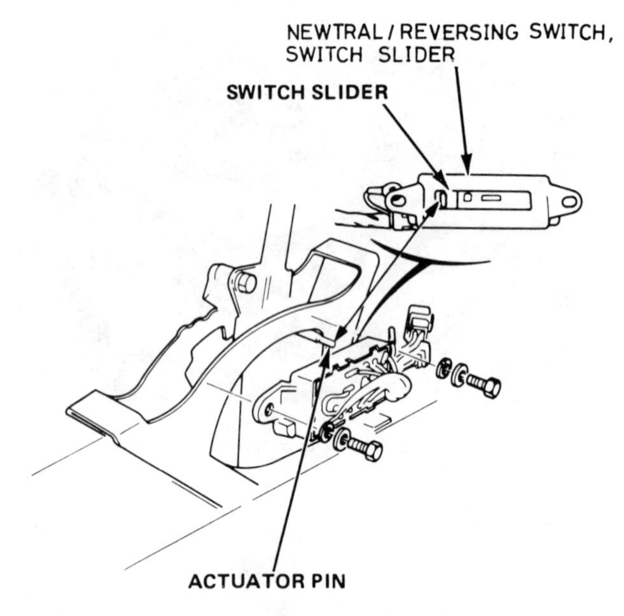

Fig. 13.185 Starter inhibitor and reversing lamp switch

4 If not, release the locknut and adjust as necessary. Note the two holes (90° apart) in the control cable end fitting to permit quarter-turn adjustments. Retighten the locknut and refit the clip.
5 Start the engine and check all gear positions

Shift indicator panel

6 Select each gear position and check that the indicator aligns with the panel symbol. If it does not, loosen the fixing screws and move the panel as necessary.

Starter inhibitor/reversing lamp switch

7 Remove the centre console and indicator panel. Loosen the switch fixing screws.
8 Select parking position and then move the switch slider to the parking position as shown.
9 Tighten the switch screws on completion.

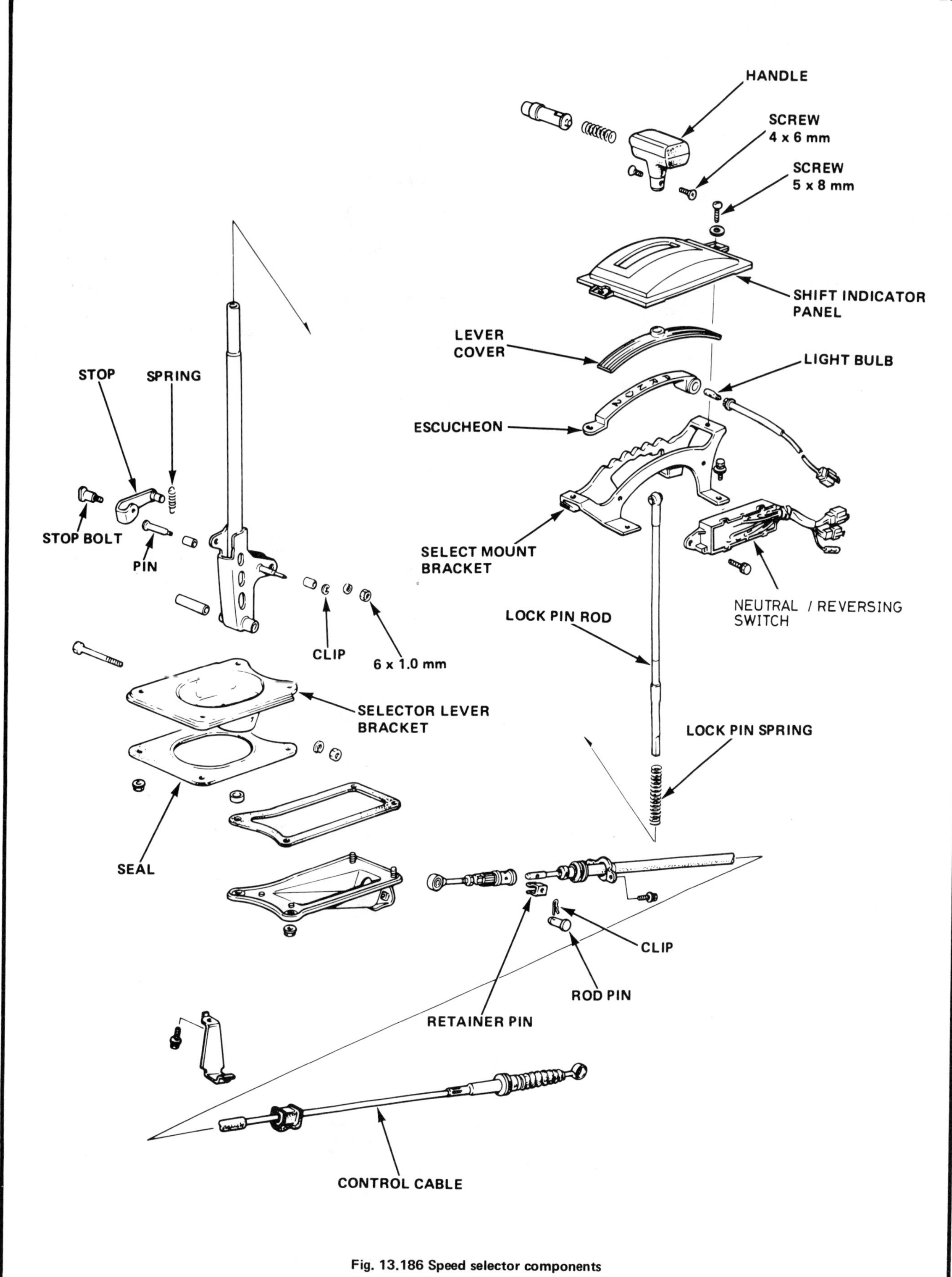

Fig. 13.186 Speed selector components

Fault diagnosis - automatic transmission

Note: *It cannot be over-emphasised that before deciding that the transmission has developed a serious internal fault due to failure of a component, the fluid level should be checked and the adjustment of the speed selector cable inspected.*

Symptom	Reason(s)
No drive in any gear	Incorrect fluid level Sheared driveplate Clogged pump filter
No drive in L but moves in * and OD	Broken mainshaft Seized servo shaft Seized reverse shaft
No drive in * but moves in L and OD	Broken control cable Defective low gear system
No drive in OD but moves in L and *	Sticking low clutch piston or broken O-ring Sticking low clutch check valve
No drive in R but moves in other gears	Broken low clutch feed pipe or O-ring Worn low clutch discs
Poor acceleration and slipping at start of engine speed increase	Defective drivegear system Sticking drive clutch piston or broken O-ring Sticking drive clutch check valve Broken drive clutch feed pipe Worn drive clutch discs Sticking OD clutch piston or broken O-ring Sticking OD clutch check valve Broken OD clutch feed pipe or O-ring Worn drive clutch discs sticking Sticking servo piston
Slip between L and *	Worn reverse selector spline Incorrect ignition settings Incorrect carburettor settings Poor engine compression
Slip between * and OD	Defective one-way clutch Sticking drive or OD clutch orifice

9 Driveshafts

Inboard joint - modification

1 As from October 1981 the inboard driveshaft joint is of spider type instead of the earlier ball and cage design.

2 The operations described in Chapter 8 will generally apply but observe the following:

(a) The rollers and their original grooves must be marked for correct reassembly.
(b) The spider is retained by an upper and a lower circlip.
(c) Do not alter the original positions of the rollers on the spider.
(d) Adjust the shaft overall lengths before fitting the bellows bands.

10 Braking system

Brake assemblies - modification

1 Both the front disc brakes and the rear drum brakes are of modified design. New procedures are described in this Section. The rear brakes are now of self-adjusting type.

2 A load sensing valve is located at the rear of the vehicle. Its purpose is to prevent rear wheel lock-up during heavy applications of the brake pedal by adjusting the brake pressure in accordance with the load being carried.

Disc pads - inspection and renewal

3 At the specified intervals, raise the front of the car and support securely on axle stands.

4 Remove the roadwheels.

5 Visually check the thickness of the friction material of the pads. If it is less than 0.063 in (1.6 mm) or if the thickness varies by more than

LEFT DRIVE SHAFT

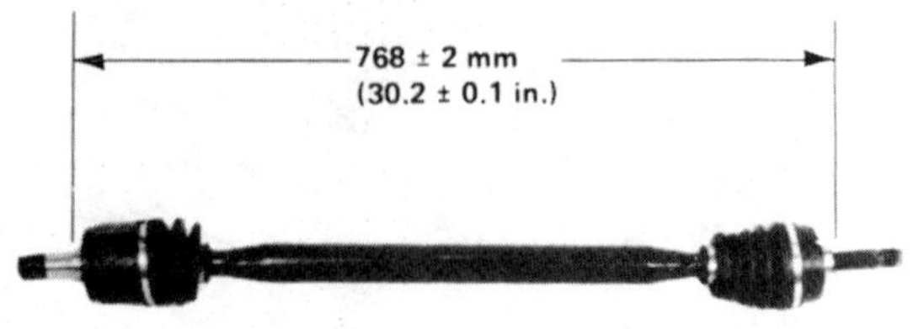

RIGHT DRIVE SHAFT

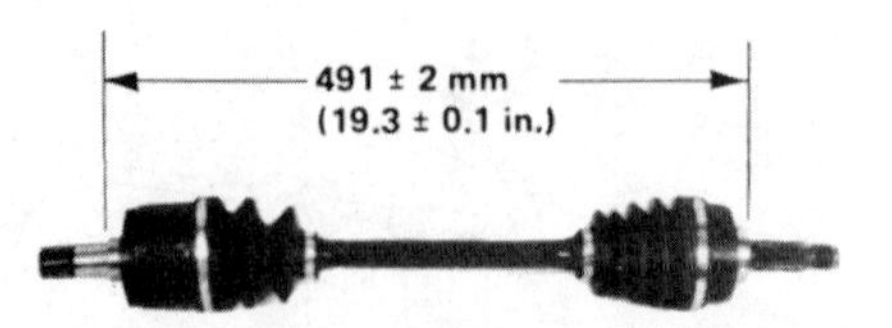

Fig. 13.187 Driveshaft/bellows setting diagram

0.08 in (2.0 mm) between the two pads on the same brake then the pads must be renewed in the following way (photo).

6 Unscrew and remove the lower guide bolt and release the caliper upper bolt. Swivel the caliper upwards off the pads (photo).

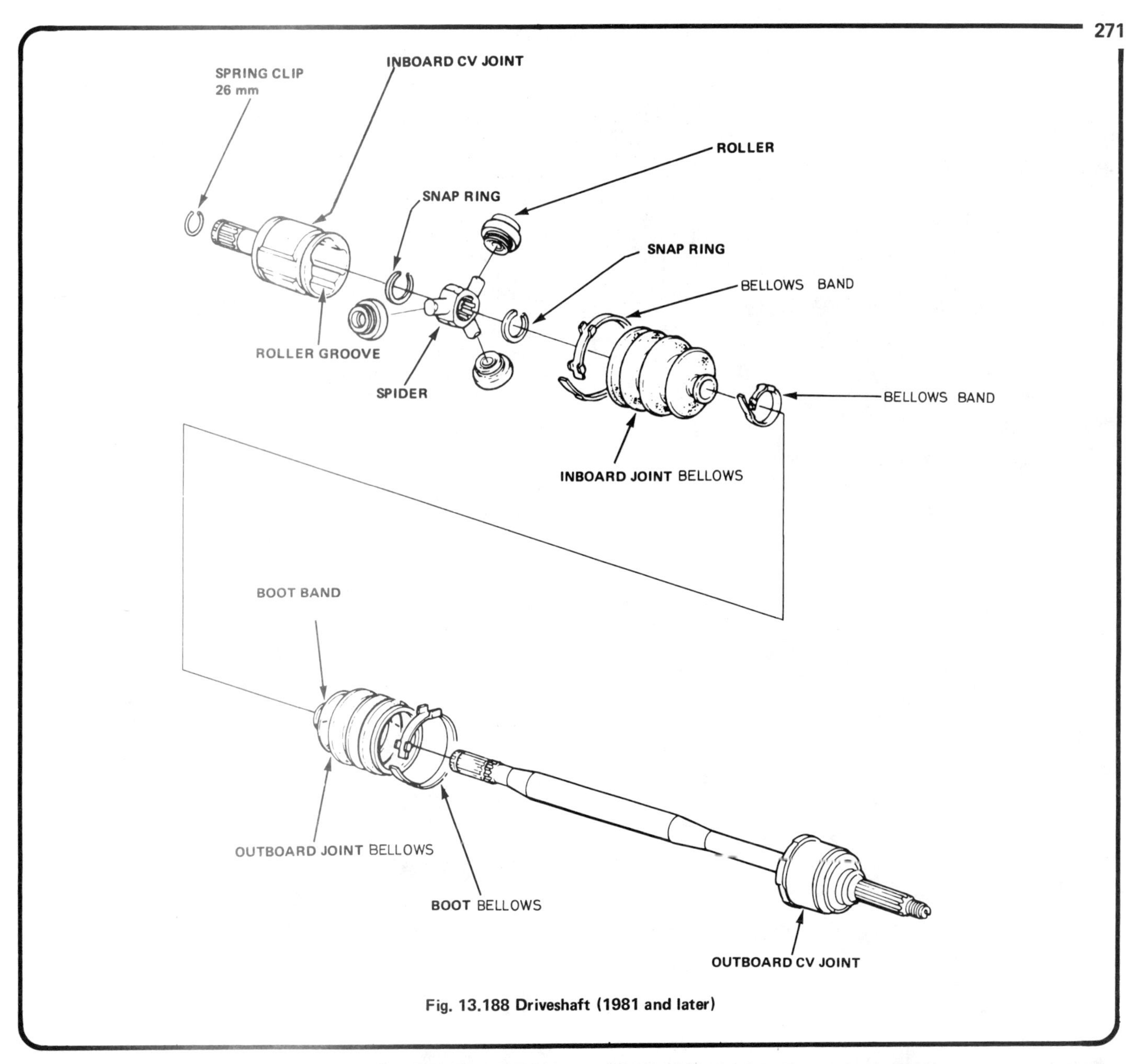

Fig. 13.188 Driveshaft (1981 and later)

10.5 Disc pads in position

10.6 Releasing caliper guide bolt

10.7A Removing outboard disc pad

7 Pull the pads out sideways and take off the anti-rattle springs and the outboard pad shim (photo).
8 Brush away all dirt and dust from the caliper mounting bracket taking care not to inhale the dust as it is injurious to health.
9 The caliper piston must now be depressed into its cylinder so that the new thicker pads can be accommodated when the caliper is refitted. Use a wide flat blade to do this and keep the piston square. As the piston is depressed, fluid from the hydraulic system will be expelled from the master cylinder reservoir unless some is syphoned out in anticipation. Alternatively, the caliper bleed screw can be unscrewed while the piston is being depressed, but make sure that a bleed tube is fitted to the screw and the end of the tube submerged in hydraulic fluid otherwise air may enter the system.
10 Apply a smear of high melting point grease to the backs of the new pads and refit them with their anti-rattle springs. Note that the outboard pad has the shim against its backplate.
11 Pivot the caliper into position and insert and tighten the guide bolt to the specified torque. Use thread locking fluid on the bolt threads (photo).
12 Repeat the operations on the opposite brake, refit the roadwheels, lower the car and apply the footbrake hard several times to position the pads against the disc.
13 Check the fluid level in the master cylinder reservoir and top up if necessary.

10.7B Removing inboard disc pad

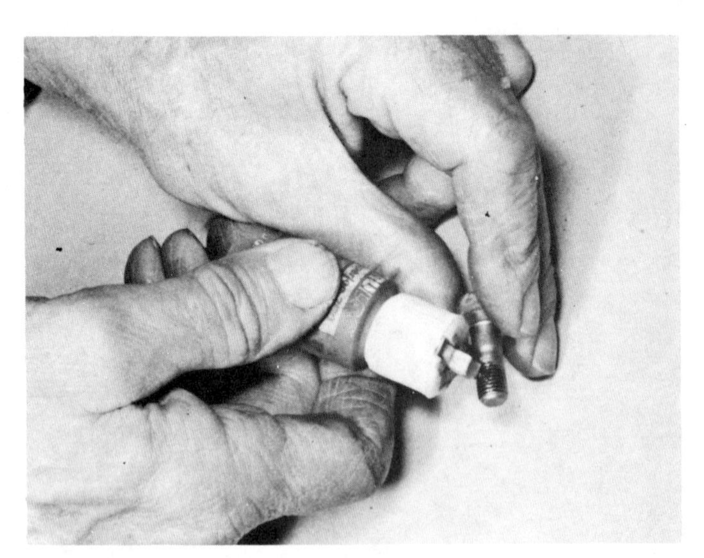
10.11 Applying thread locking fluid

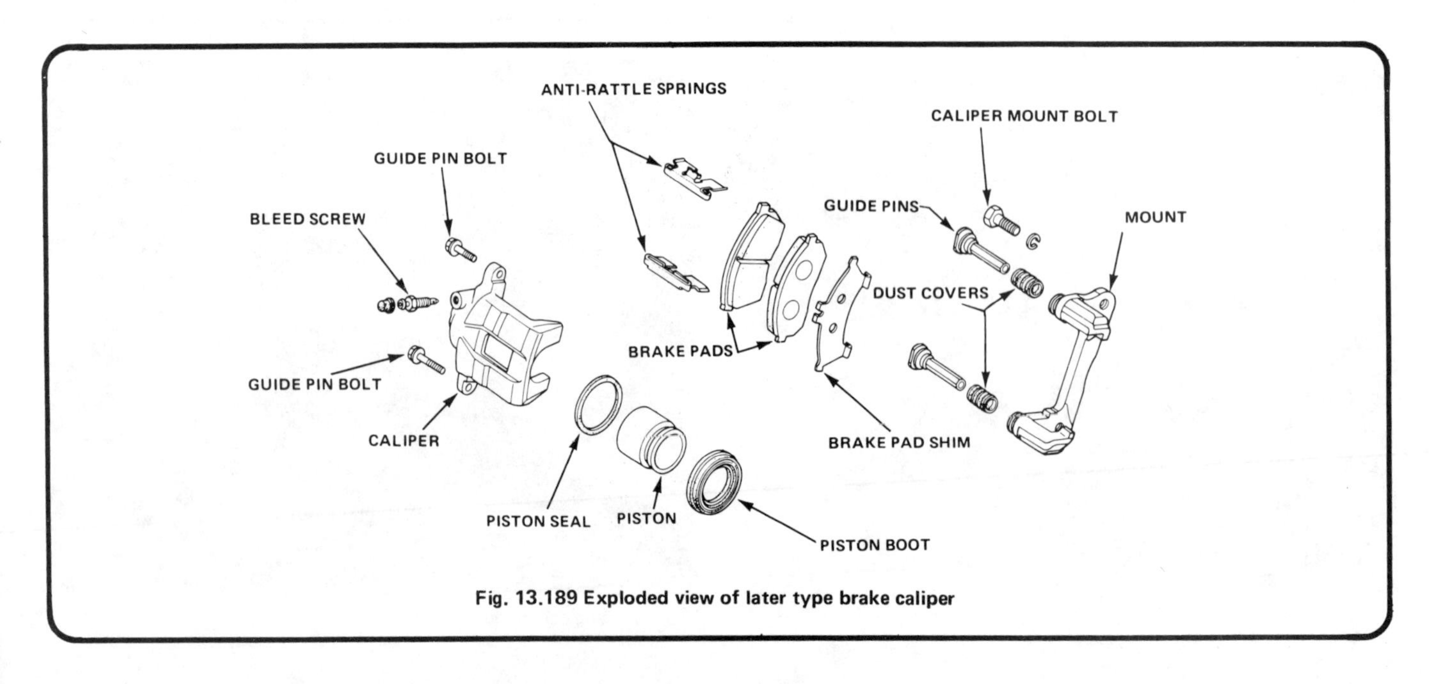

Fig. 13.189 Exploded view of later type brake caliper

Self-adjusting rear brakes - inspection and shoe renewal

14 Raise the rear of the car and remove the roadwheels. Check that the handbrake is fully released.

15 Lever off the grease cap.

16 Straighten the ends of the split pin, and remove it.

17 Take off the nut retainer and then unscrew and remove the nut and thrust washer.

18 Pull off the brake drum. If the drum is stuck tight, this may be due to the shoes being locked into grooves which have worn in the drums. In this event, prise out the plug from the brake backplate and insert a small screwdriver to release the tension of the self-adjuster lever and to rotate the adjuster star wheel until the shoes are free of the drum.

19 With the drum removed, check the thickness of the linings. If they are less than 0.079 in (2.0 mm) then the shoes should be renewed as a complete axle set. Do not attempt to re-line them yourself, this seldom seldom proves satisfactory (photo).

20 To remove the shoes, grip the shoe steady springs with a pair of pliers and turn through 90° to release them from their pins (photo).

21 Unhook the upper and lower shoe return springs (photos).

22 Release the handbrake cable from the lever on the trailing shoe (photo).

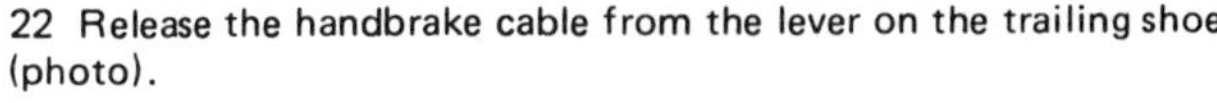

10.21A Shoe upper return spring

10.19 Right-hand rear brake assembly

10.21B Shoe lower return spring and handbrake cable

10.20 Shoe steady clip

10.22 Handbrake cable and shoe lever

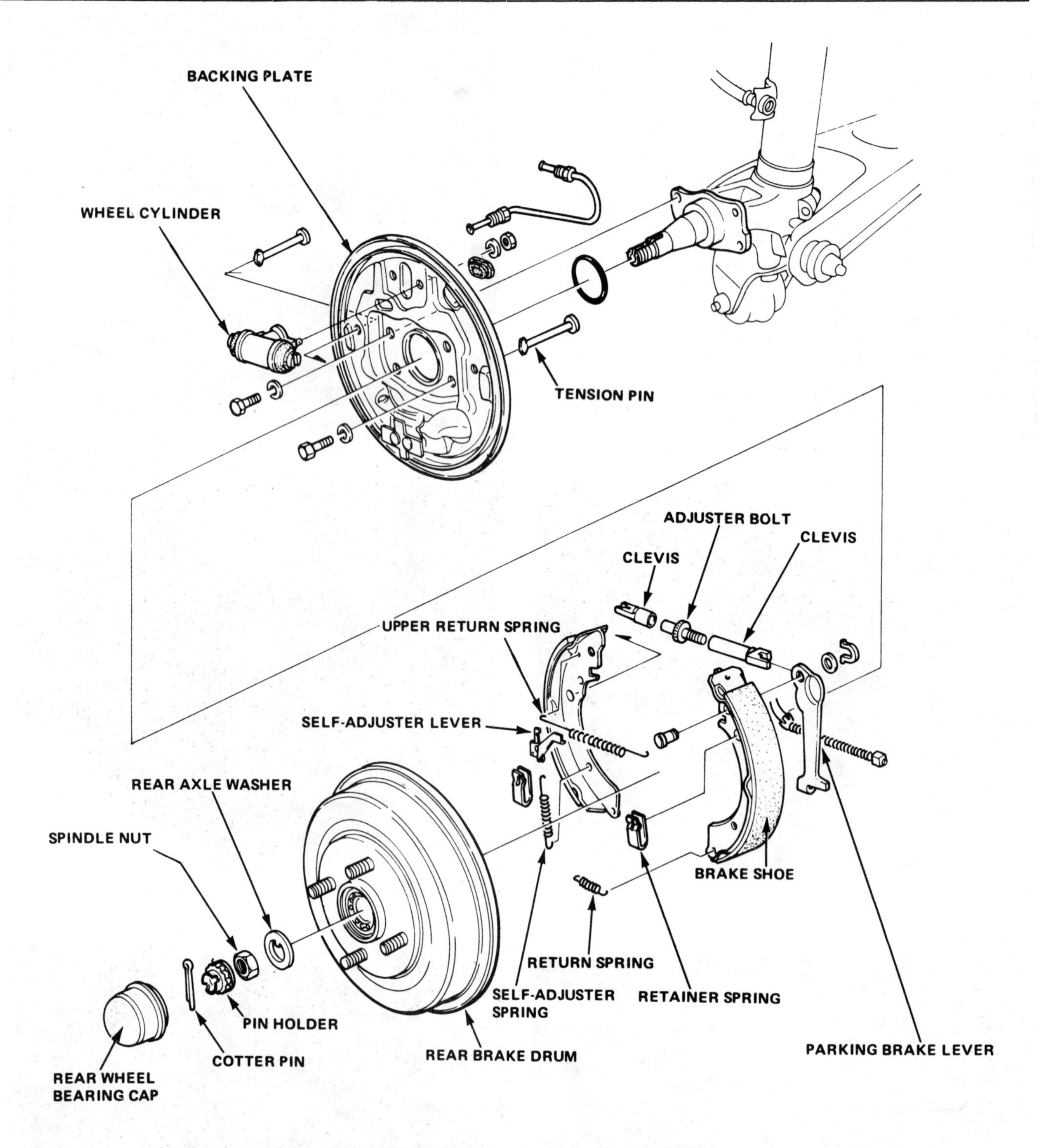

Fig. 13.190 Exploded view of self-adjusting drum brake

23 Remove the self-adjuster strut, lever and spring.
24 Take the shoes to the bench and set the new shoes out in the same relative position as the old ones were fitted to the backplate.
25 Prise off the circlip, remove the washer and pivot pin and transfer the handbrake lever to the new trailing shoe. The lever must lie behind the shoe when installed on the backplate (photo).
26 Apply a smear of grease to the projecting shoe rubbing points on the brake backplate and then offer up the trailing shoe and engage the handbrake cable with the shoe lever (photo).
27 Engage the upper return spring with the trailing shoe.
28 Clean and lightly grease the threads on the adjuster strut and then retract it fully.
29 Engage the self-adjuster strut with the leading shoe making sure that the self-adjuster lever is correctly located (photo).
30 Offer up the leading shoe with the self-adjuster and engage the end of the self-adjuster strut in the notch in the trailing shoe web. It is most important that the longer tine of the fork is towards you.
31 Connect the upper return spring to the leading shoe.
32 Connect the lower shoe return spring.
33 Pull the shoes carefully apart to expand them and slide them upwards to engage them in the wheel cylinder piston tappet slots and behind the lower anchor plate.
34 Connect the spring between the self-adjuster lever and the hole in the leading shoe web (photo).

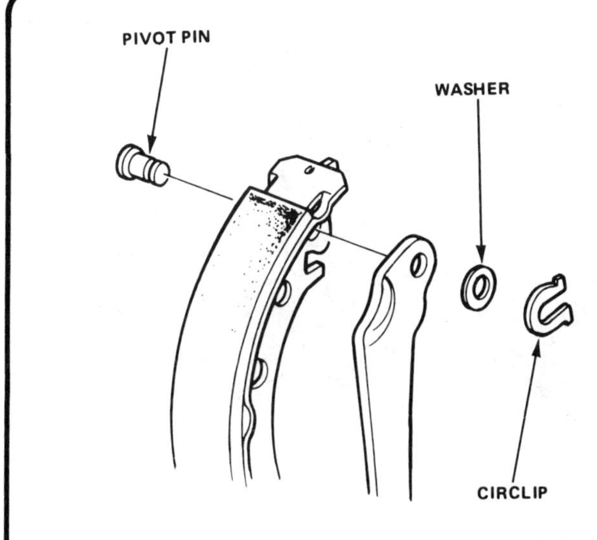

Fig. 13.191 Handbrake lever connection to shoe

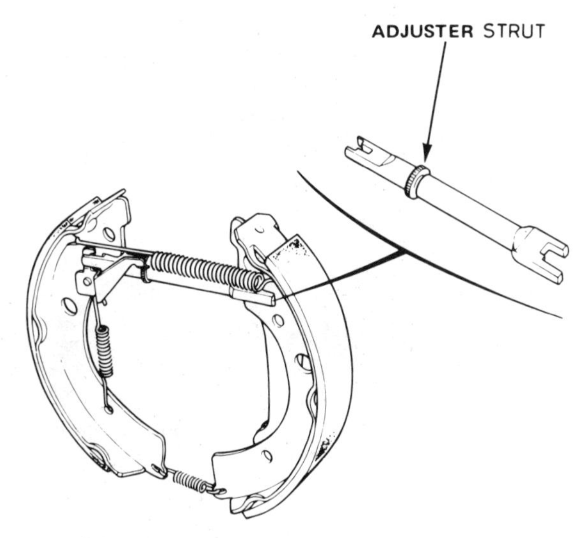

Fig. 13.192 Self-adjuster strut connection to trailing shoe

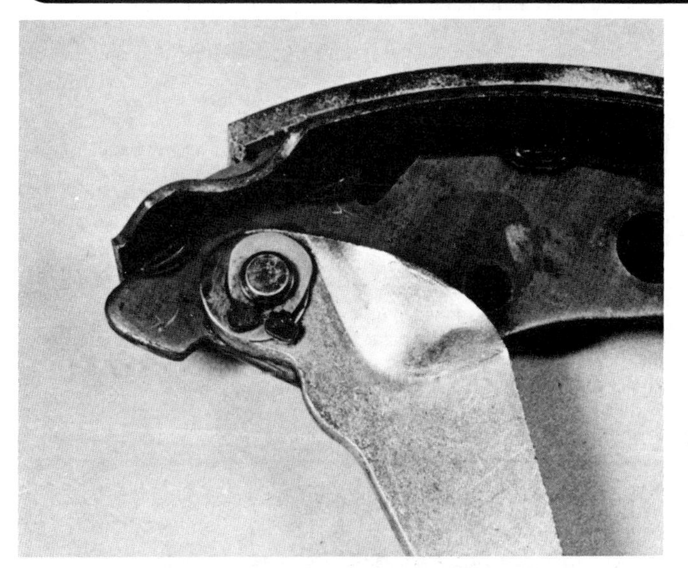

10.25 Shoe handbrake lever and circlip

10.26 Drum brake backplate

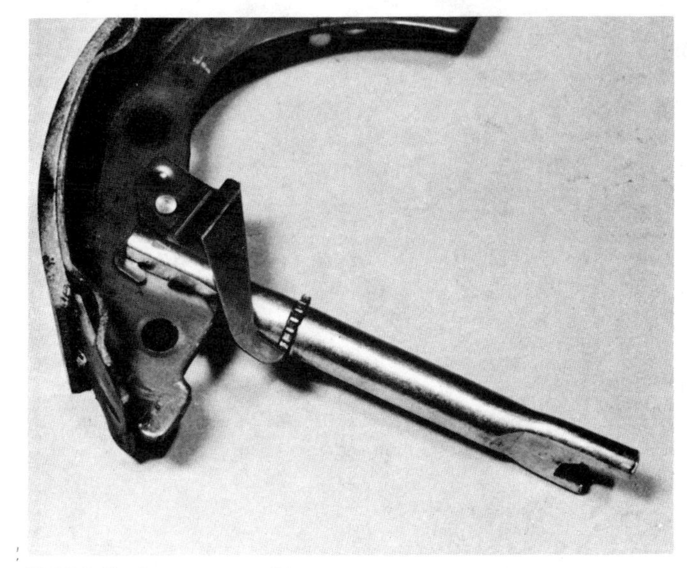

10.29 Self-adjuster strut and lever

10.34 Connecting self-adjuster lever spring

10.38A Rear hub outboard bearing

10.38B Rear hub thrust washer

10.38C Rear hub nut tightened

35 Fit the shoe steady pins and clips.
36 Rotate the adjuster star wheel to expand the shoes to the point where the drum will just slide over them. Check visually that the shoes are concentric with the brake backplate.
37 Before fitting the drum, check its interior condition. Deep scoring or grooving may be removed by refinishing, provided the internal diameter does not exceed the dimension moulded onto the drum, otherwise a new drum will be required.
38 Fit the drum outer bearing, thrust washer and screw on the nut. Tighten the nut to 20 lbf ft (2.7 kgf m) while turning the drum. Unscrew the nut and retighten finger tight only. All endfloat should now be eliminated otherwise suspect worn bearings (photo).
39 Fit the nut lock in such a position that its slots align with the split pin hole without altering the position of the nut.
40 Fit a new split pin, bend the ends around the nut retainer and tap on the grease cap (photo).
41 Repeat the operations on the opposite brake.
42 Refit the roadwheels and lower the car.
43 Apply the footbrake several times until the self-adjusters cease to 'click' indicating that the shoes are in close contact with the drums.

Handbrake - adjustment

44 Adjust the handbrake on cars with self-adjusting brakes in the following way.
45 Raise the rear wheels off the ground and check that the handbrake is fully released.
46 Prise the panel from the centre console to expose the cable equaliser.
47 Pull the handbrake lever on one notch and then turn the equaliser adjusting nut until the rear wheels just drag when turned.
48 Release the handbrake when the wheels should turn freely.
49 The handbrake should lock the rear wheels after being pulled over 4 to 8 notches.

Load sensing value - removal, refitting and adjustment

50 Place the car over an inspection pit or raise the rear end on ramps.
51 Disconnect the hydraulic pipes from the load sensing valve and quickly cap them to prevent loss of fluid (photo).
52 Disconnect the linkage between the valve and the rear anti-roll bar by unscrewing the locknuts.
53 Unbolt the valve and remove it.

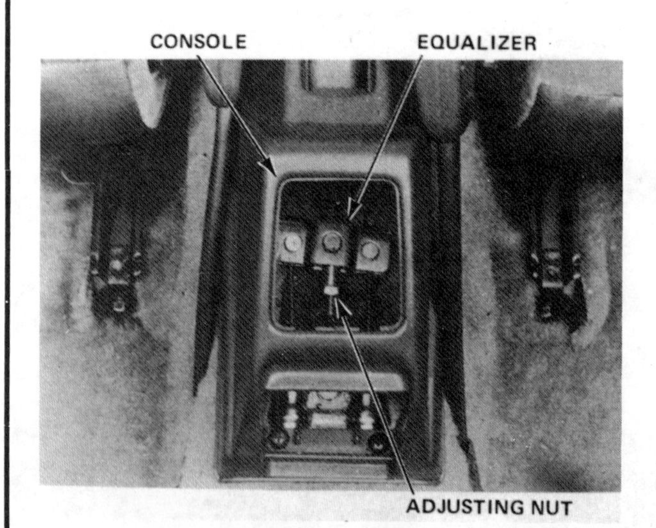

Fig. 13.193 Handbrake cable equaliser

10.40 Rear hub nut retainer, split pin and grease cap

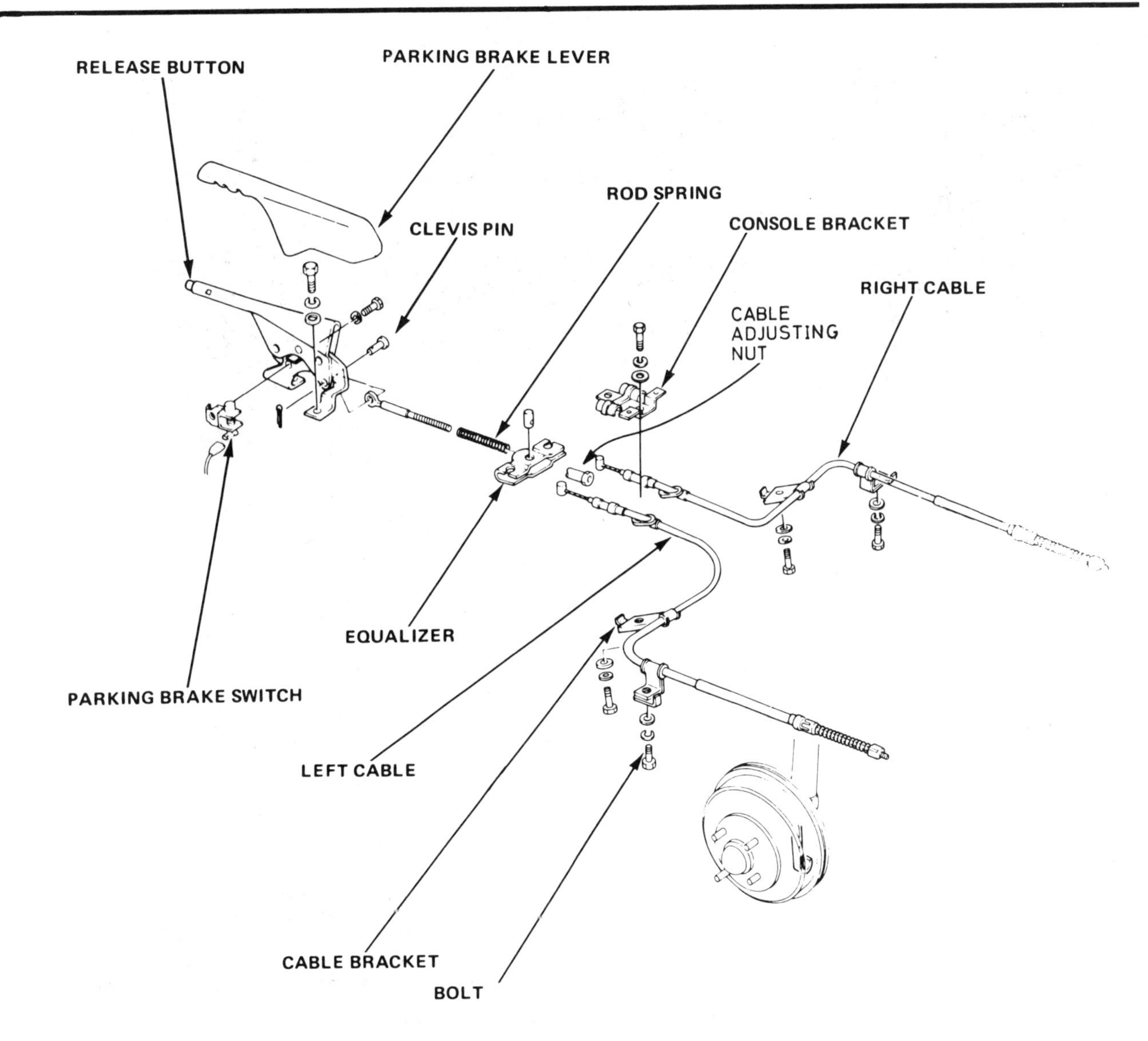

Fig. 13.194 Handbrake arrangement

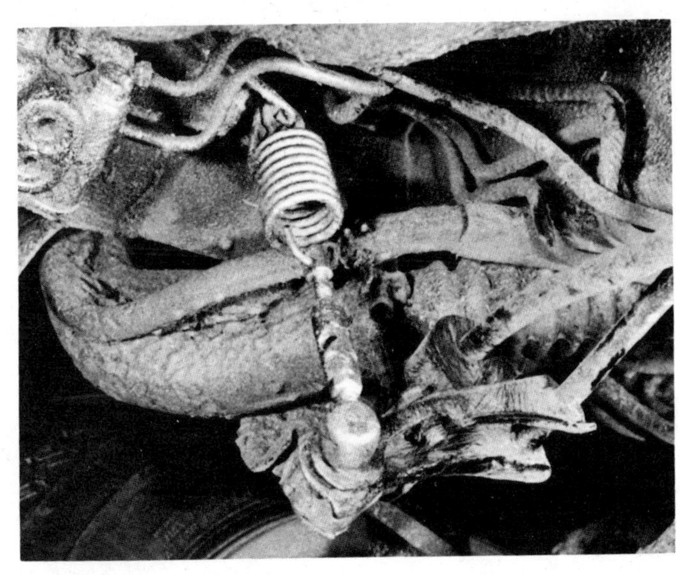

10.51 Brake load-sensing valve

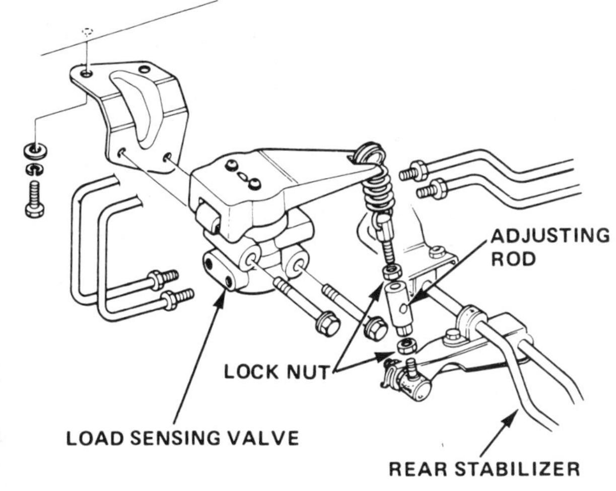

Fig. 13.195 Load sensing valve

54 Refit by reversing the removal operations and then bleed the hydraulic system.
55 Adjust the valve with the weight of the car on its roadwheels so that dimension A is 3.61 in (91.7 mm). Adjust by releasing the locknuts and turning the link rod.

Brake hydraulic system - bleeding
56 The following methods of bleeding the hydraulic system may be used in addition to that described in Chapter 9.
57 Bleed in the sequence left front, right rear, right front, left rear.
58 Unless the pressure bleeding method is being used, do not forget to keep the fluid level in the master cylinder reservoir topped up to prevent air from being drawn into the system which would make any work done worthless.

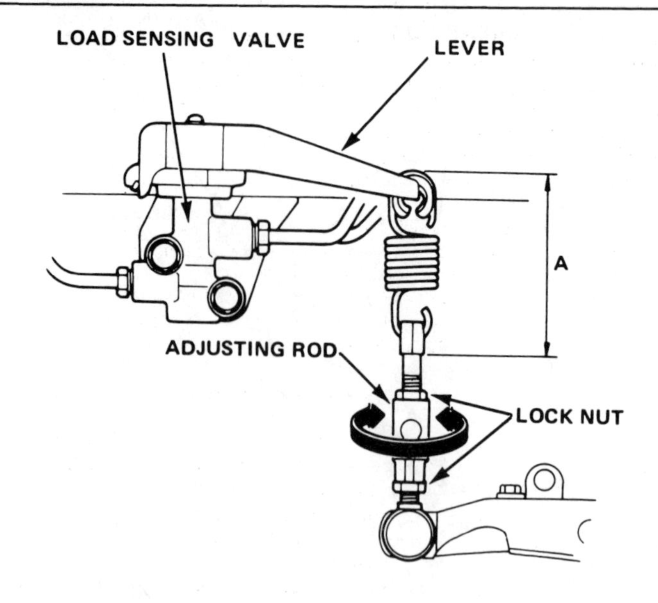

Fig. 13.196 Load sensing valve setting diagram

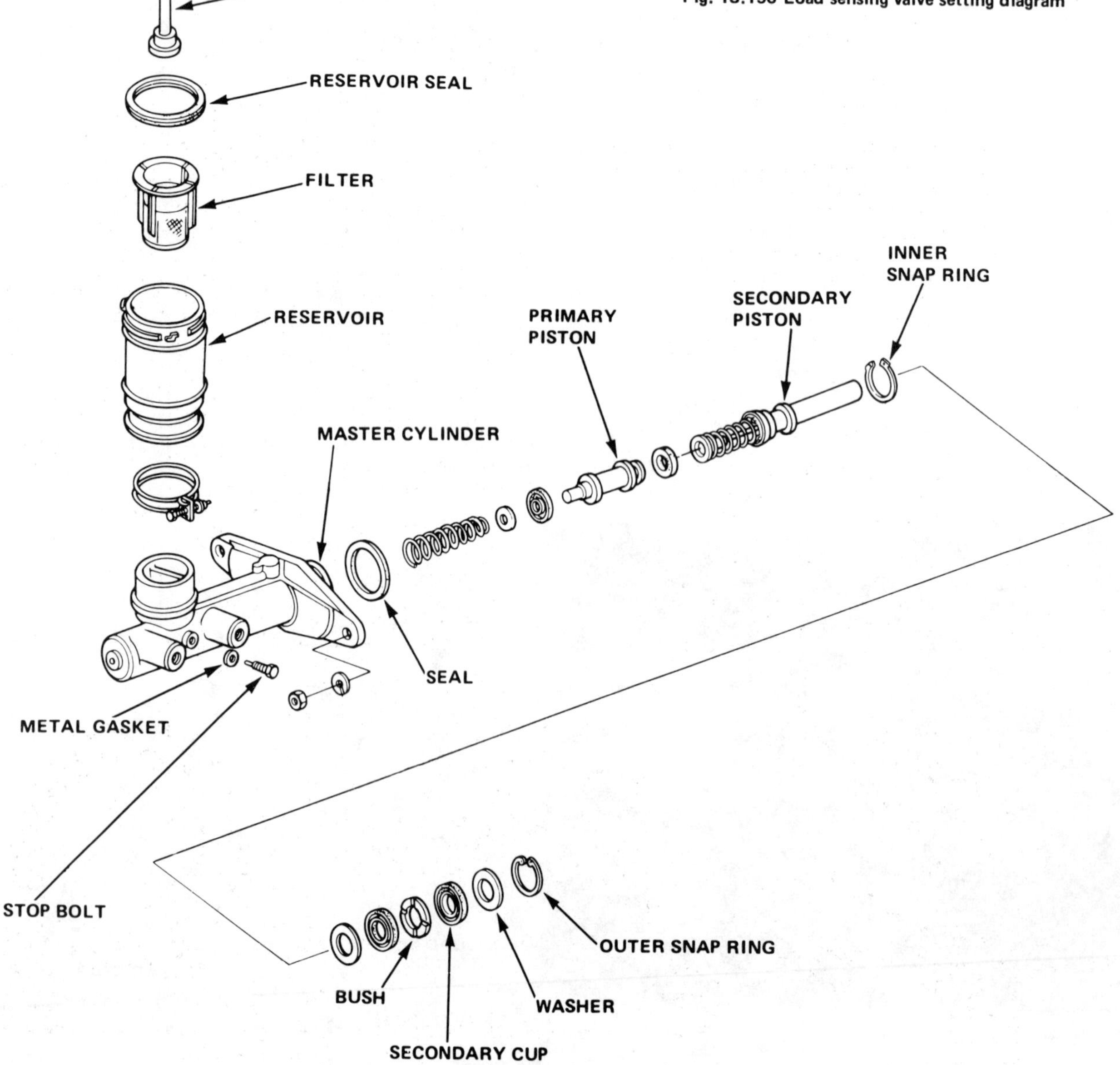

Fig. 13.197 Later type master cylinder

59 Before commencing operations, check that all system hoses and pipes are in good condition with the unions tight and free from leaks.
60 Take great care not to allow hydraulic fluid to come into contact with the vehicle paintwork as it is an effective paint-stripper. Wash off any spilled fluid immediately with cold water.
61 Destroy the vacuum in the servo by giving several applications of the brake pedal in quick succession.

Bleeding - using one-way valve kit

62 There are a number of one-man, one-way, brake bleeding kits available from motor accessory shops. It is recommended that one of these kits is used wherever possible as it will greatly simplify the bleeding operation and also reduce the risk of air or fluid being drawn back into the system quite apart from being able to do the work without the help of an assistant.
63 To use the kit, connect the tube to the bleed screw and open the screw one half a turn.
64 Depress the brake pedal fully and slowly release it. The one-way valve in the kit will prevent expelled air from returning at the end of each pedal downstroke. Repeat this operation several times to be sure of ejecting all air from the system. Some kits include a translucent container which can be positioned so that the air bubbles can actually be seen being ejected from the system.
65 Tighten the bleed screw, remove the tube and repeat the operations on the remaining brakes.
66 On completion, depress the brake pedal. If it still feels spongy repeat the bleeding operation as air must still be trapped in the system.

Bleeding - using a pressure bleeding kit

67 These kits too are available from motor accessory shops and are usually operated by air pressure from the spare tyre.
68 By connecting a pressurised container to the master cylinder fluid reservoir, bleeding is then carried out by simply opening each bleed screw in turn and allowing the fluid to run out, rather like turning on a tap, until no air is visible in the expelled fluid.
69 By using this method, the large reserve of hydraulic fluid provides a safeguard against air being drawn into the master cylinder during bleeding which often occurs if the fluid level in the reservoir is not maintained.
70 Pressure bleeding is particularly effective when bleeding 'difficult' systems or when bleeding the complete system at time of routine fluid renewal.

All methods

71 When bleeding is completed, check and top up the fluid level in the master cylinder reservoir.
72 Check the feel of the brake pedal. If it feels at all spongy, air must still be present in the system and further bleeding is indicated. Failure to bleed satisfactorily after a reasonable repetition of the bleeding operations may be due to worn master cylinder seals.
73 Discard brake fluid which has been expelled. It is almost certain to be contaminated with moisture, air and dirt making it unsuitable for further use. Clean fluid should always be stored in an airtight container as it absorbs moisture readily (hygroscopic) which lowers its boiling point and could affect braking performance under severe conditions.

10.76 Brake hose bracket and clip

Master cylinder

74 The later type master cylinder has been modified in detail, but the removal, overhaul and refitting procedures remain as described originally in Chapter 9.

Cautionary note

75 It will be observed from Fig. 13.197 that the positions of the primary and the secondary pistons are not as annotated or identified using the accepted method for other master cylinders. The reversed terminology used by Honda has been retained in order to maintain consistency with Honda servicing and parts literature.

Brake flexible hoses

76 The flexible hose end fittings are secured to their support brackets by spring clips. To remove a clip, prise it out with a screwdriver (photo).

11 Electrical system

Description

1 The majority of changes to the electrical system concern the lamps. The headlamps on later models are of single rectangular type instead of the twin round ones used previously.
2 Circuit diagrams for later models have been modified.

Headlamp bulb - renewal

3 Open the bonnet and disconnect the wiring plug from the rear of the headlamp (photo).
4 Pull off the dust excluding cover (photo).
5 Prise up the bulbholder spring clips and withdraw the bulbholder (photos).

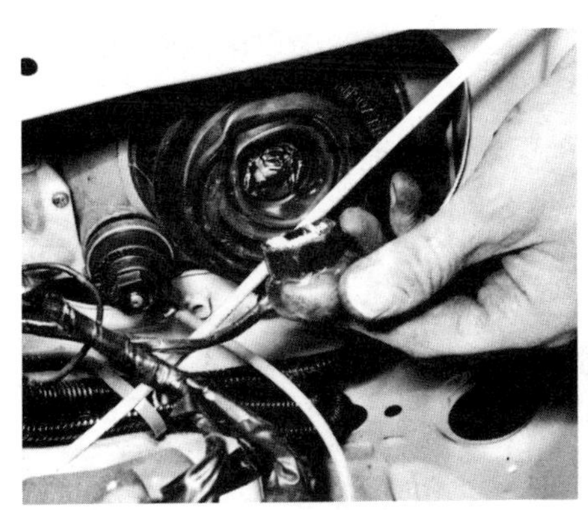

11.3 Headlamp wiring plug

11.4 Headlamp dust excluding cover

11.5A Headlamp bulb retaining spring clips

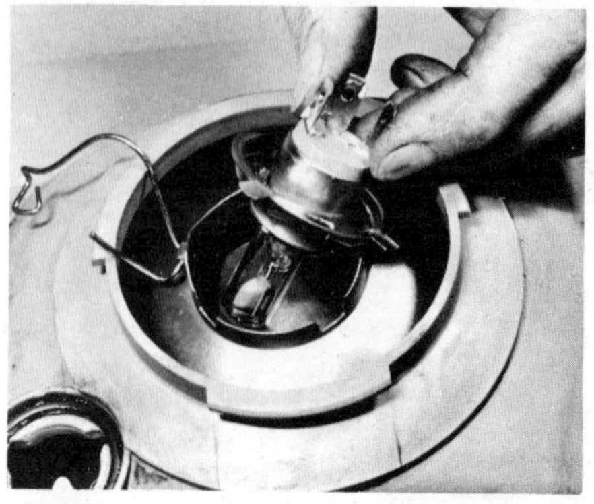

11.5B Removing headlamp bulb

11.10A Unscrewing headlamp bolt

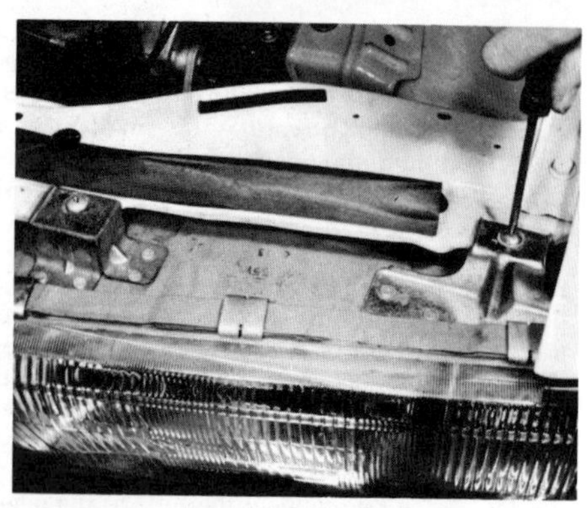
11.10B Unscrewing headlamp screw

6 When fitting the new bulb, do not handle the glass with the fingers. If it is inadvertently touched, clean it with methylated spirit.
7 Make sure that the bulbholder pip and notch are correctly engaged before fitting the retaining spring clips.
8 Fit the dust cover and reconnect the plug.

Headlamp - removal and refitting

9 Open the bonnet and disconnect the headlamp wiring plug.
10 Unscrew the two bolts and the two screws which secure the headlamp (photos).
11 Withdraw the headlamp and support it in a horizontal attitude. Now release the hydraulic load-level adjuster device plunger by twisting the unit through 90° and pulling it (photo).
12 The headlamp may now be withdrawn.
13 Refitting is a reversal of removal.

Headlamp beam - adjustment

14 The headlamp beams may be adjusted by engaging a long cross-head type screwdriver in the horizontal or vertical adjuster gearboxes. Holes are provided in the body panel for insertion of the screwdriver (photos). On models fitted with headlamp beam (load) adjuster device, the setting of the facia-mounted control knob should be carried out in accordance with the following guide.

Setting	Load
0	Driver and passenger, no luggage
1	Three to five occupants, no luggage
2	Three to five occupants, luggage 150 to 260 kg
3	Driver and passenger, luggage 315 to 350 kg

Note: If the hydraulic load-level adjuster is faulty, it cannot be repaired, and should be renewed as a complete unit.

Exterior lamps - bulb renewal

Front parking lamp

15 The bulbs are located in the headlamp casing and can be removed by twisting them from their locations (photos).

Front direction indicator lamp

16 The lamps are located in the front bumper and the bulbs are accessible after removing the lamp lens (two screws). Side repeater lamps are fitted, the bulbs being accessible after removal of the lens (photos).

11.11 Headlamp beam load adjuster hydraulic unit

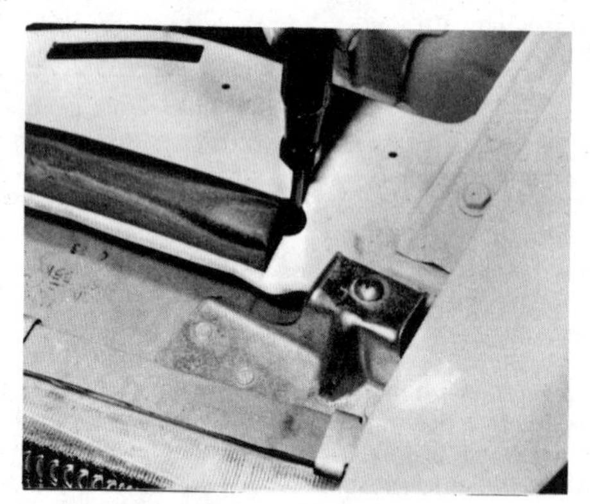
11.14A Adjusting headlamp beam

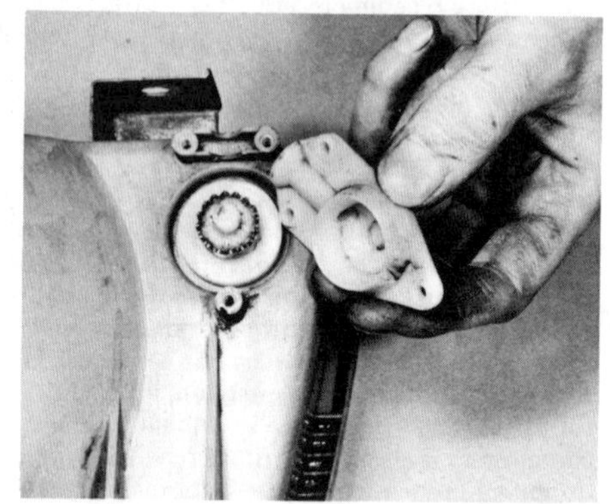
11.14B Headlamp beam adjuster gear cover

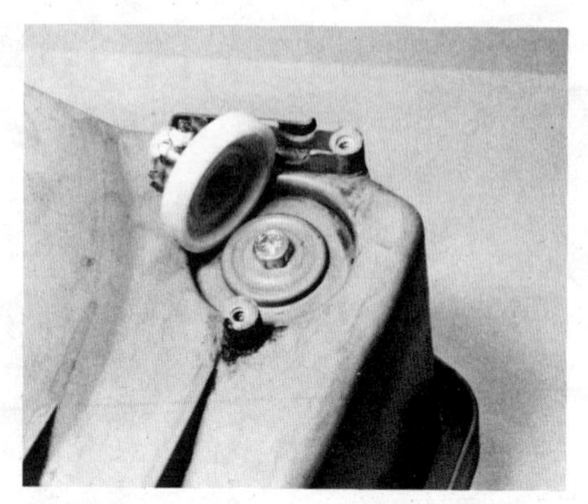
11.14C Headlamp beam adjuster drivegear

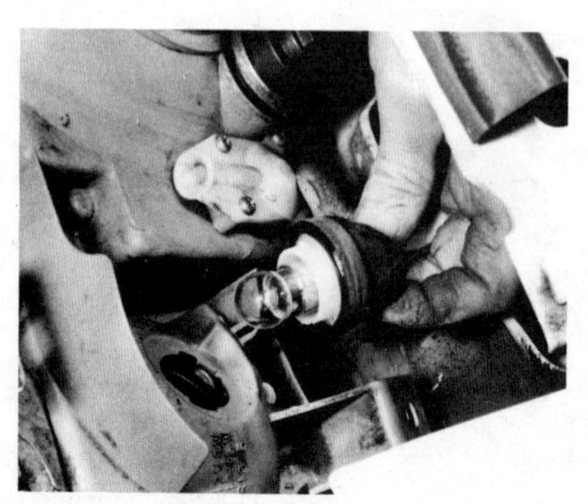
11.15 Front parking lamp bulb

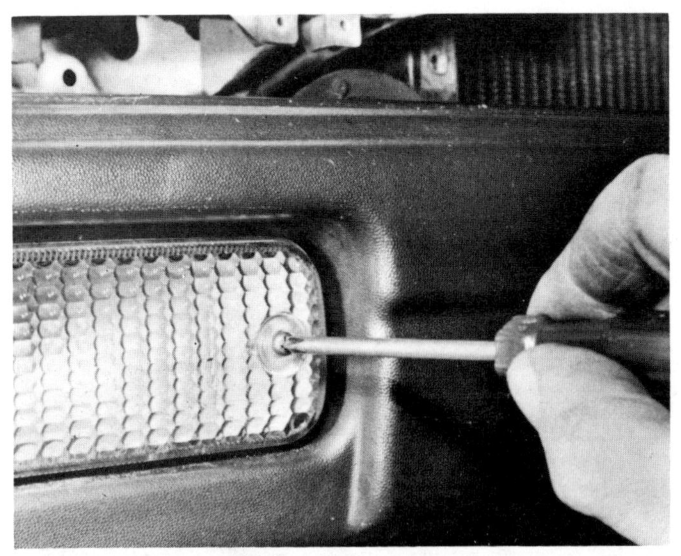

11.16A Extracting front direction indicator lamp lens screw

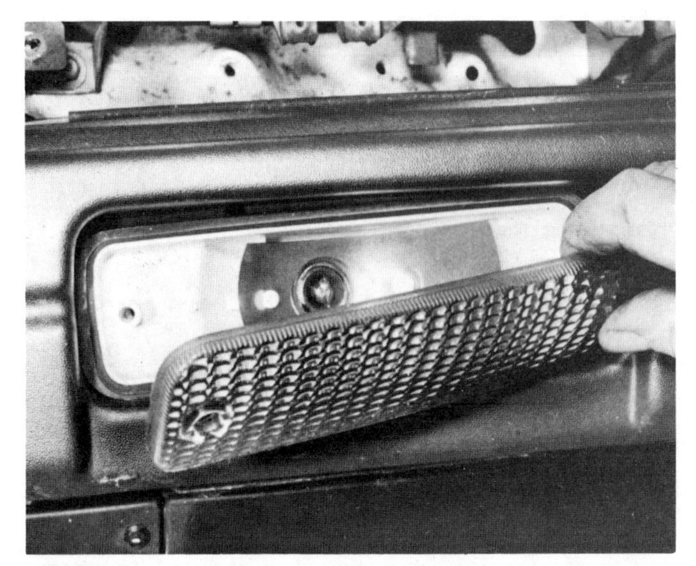

11.16B Removing front direction indicator lamp lens

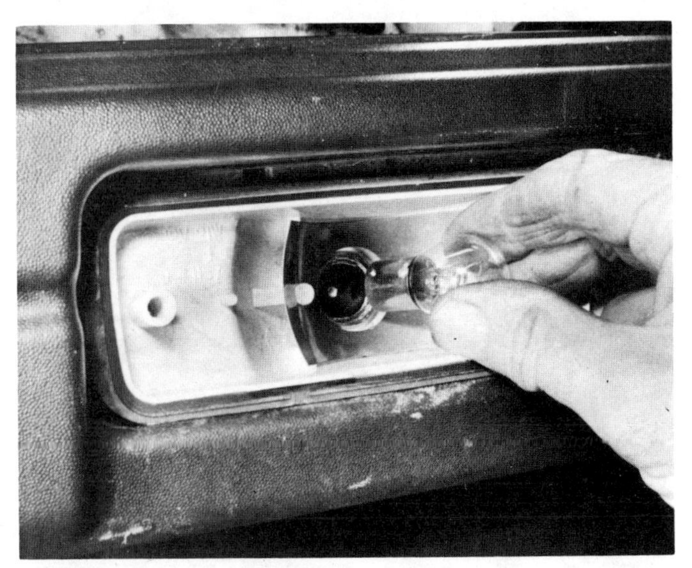

11.16C Removing front direction indicator lamp bulb

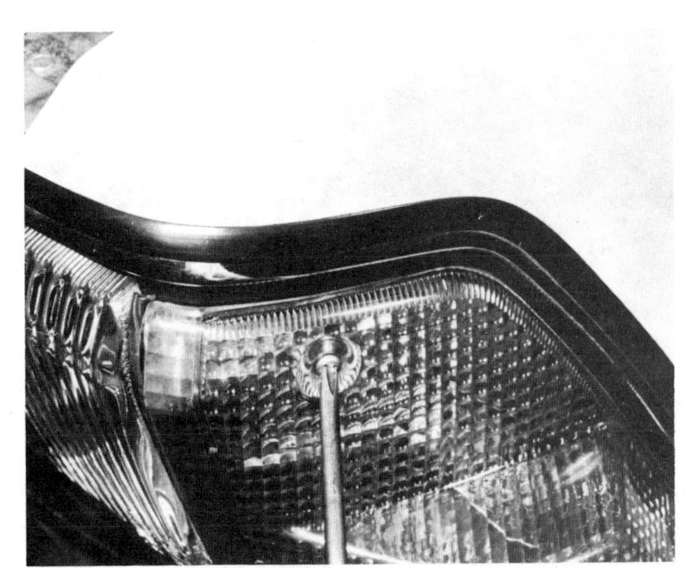

11.16D Extracting front side repeater lamp lens screw

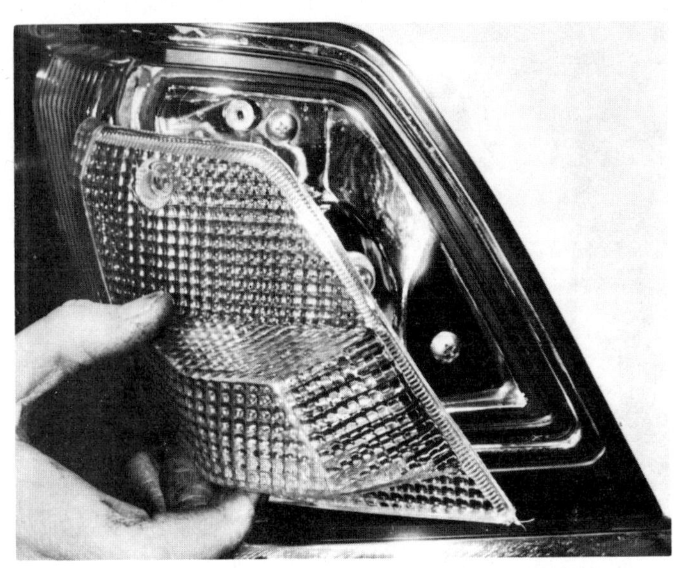

11.16E Removing front side repeater lamp lens screw

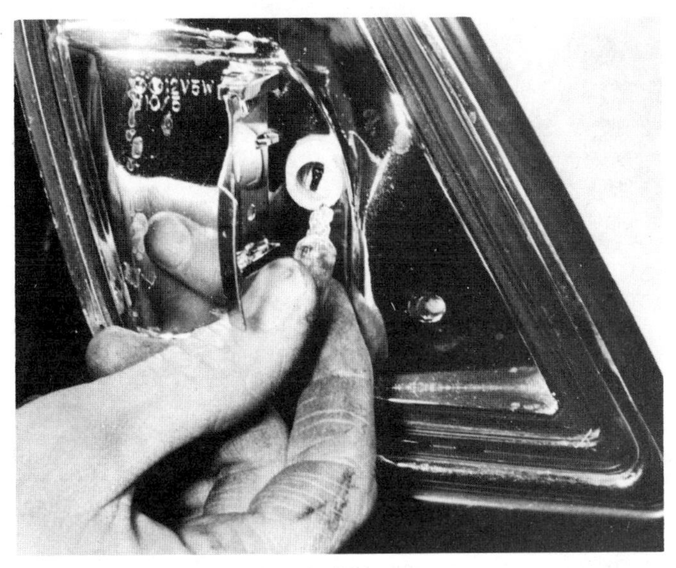

11.16F Front side repeater lamp bulb

Rear foglamp

17 The lamps are located in the rear bumper and the bulbs are accessible after removing the lamp lens (two screws) (photos).

Rear number plate lamp

18 Prise the lamp from the rear bumper and then pull the bulbholder from the lamp. The bulb is now accessible (photo).

Rear lamps

19 Open the tailgate or the boot lid and pull off the rear lamp cover flap.

20 Pull off the lamp holder cover to expose the bulbholder. The car wheel-changing jack is stored in the left-hand rear lamp cluster compartment (photo).

Interior lamps - bulb renewal

Interior light

21 The lens is held in place by a lug in the centre of each of the long sides of the lens. Press in one of the long sides to unclip the lens, then swing it downwards and remove it.

22 Remove the defective festoon lamp and fit a new one, if necessary bending the lamp contacts inwards to ensure that the bulb is held firmly.

11.18 Rear number plate lamp bulb

11.17A Extracting rear foglamp lens screw

11.20A Rear lamp bulbholder cover and jack location (Hatchback)

11.17B Removing rear foglamp bulb

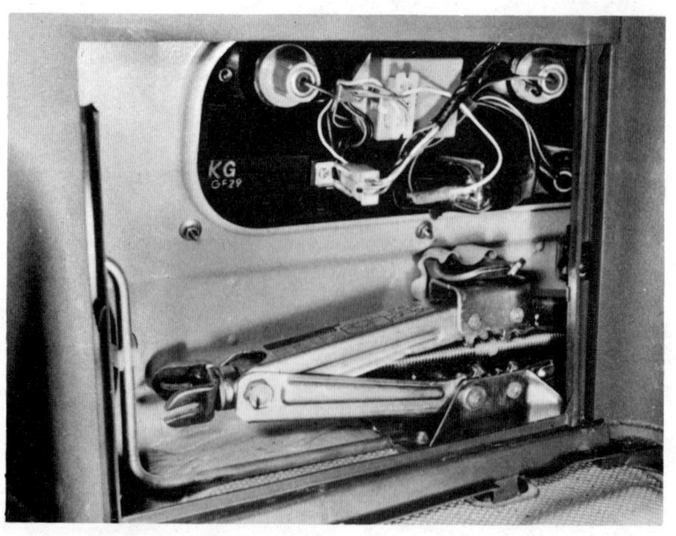

11.20B Rear lamp cluster, cover removed

Glove box light

23 The bulb is held in a rubber sleeve which fits into a hole in the ceiling of the glove box.

24 Open the glove box and pull the rubber moulding out from its hole in the ceiling of the glove box. Roll back the rubber sleeve until the bulb can be gripped and removed.

Ashtray lights

25 The ashtrays in the passenger door and the two rear doors have a light which should be illuminated if the car lights are turned on and the ashtray is open.

26 To remove the bulb, open the ashtray, press down on its top clip and remove the ashtray, exposing the two fixing screws. Remove the two fixing screws and pull the ashtray holder out of the door.

27 Pull the lamp holder out of the rear of the ashtray holder to gain access to the bulb.

Boot light (Saloon) Luggage area light (Hatchback)

28 Although it is necessary to remove the rear seat cushion, the seat back and the rear tray in order to remove the boot light assembly on Saloon models, the bulb can be removed from inside the boot or luggage area (Hatchback).

29 Open the boot and using a screwdriver, push in one of the notched tangs of the boot light lens. Lever the lens out to gain access to the bulb (photo).

Safety indicator bulb check circuit

30 A bulb check switch is mounted on the steering column, its purpose being to illuminate all safety lamps when it is depressed with the ignition switched on.

31 If there is any fault in one circuit, then the particular safety indicator lamp will come on as soon as the ignition switch is turned or whenever a danger situation occurs.

32 Pictorial type safety indicator lamps are used to monitor an unfastened door, luggage boot or hatchback and the stop lamp operation.

33 Pilot lamps are fitted to monitor the choke when in use, brake hydraulic pressure, engine oil level and pressure, alternator charging circuit, headlamp high beam, low fuel level and hazard warning.

34 Access to the bulbs is obtained by extracting the two screws from the small printed circuit on the rear of the instrument panel and withdrawing the printed circuit board.

Windscreen wiper blades

35 On later models, the wiper blades are connected to the wiper arm by two small screws (photo).

36 The wiper blade on the driver's side is fitted with an anti-flutter plate and the wiper arm fixing nut covers are removable (photo).

Relays and voltage regulator

37 The voltage regulator for the charging system and the relays are located under the washer fluid reservoir support within the engine compartment.

38 Access to the regulator and relays is obtained by sliding the reservoir upwards off its mounting and placing it to one side and then unbolting the reservoir supports. Do not damage the fusible link (photo).

39 Depending upon the equipment fitted, the relays may include those for the power window circuit, sunroof and intermittent wiper/washer.

Electrically-operated aerial - removal and refitting

40 Turn the ignition switch to the ACC position.

41 Turn the aerial switch to the 'raise' position and switch off when the aerial plinth is extended.

42 Working at the motor location, pull off the cable guide securing clips.

43 Remove the aerial drive motor mounting nuts.

44 Gently pull the aerial drive cable and then turn the ignition switch to ACC and the aerial switch to ON. The motor will turn and eject the drive cable.

45 Pull the aerial upwards and remove it.

46 To refit, have the aerial fully extended with the feeder cord taped to the drive cable conduit and the end of the conduit taped up.

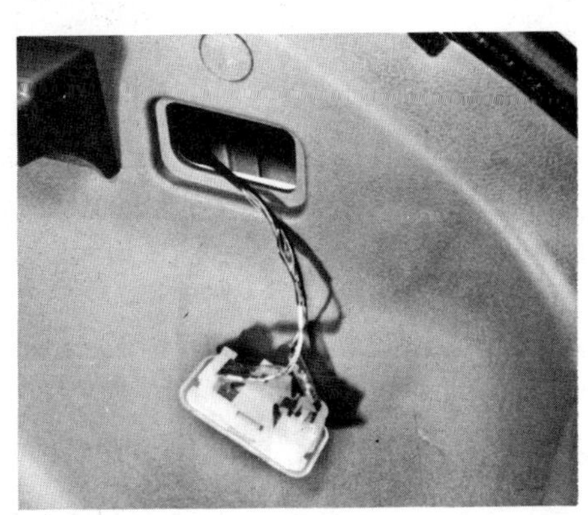

11.29 Luggage compartment lamp (Hatchback)

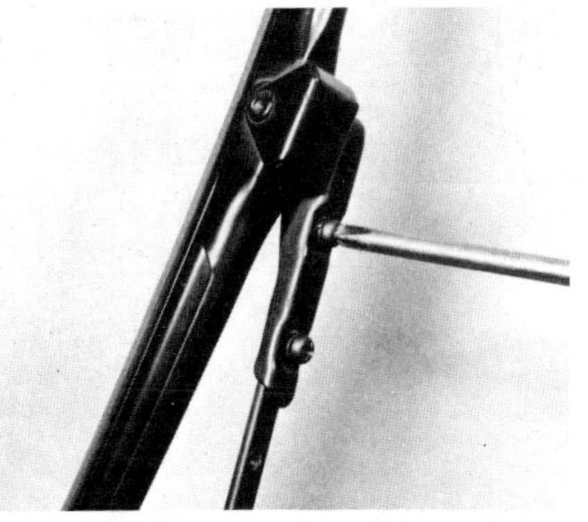

11.35 Disconnecting wiper blade from arm

11.36 Wiper arm nut cover

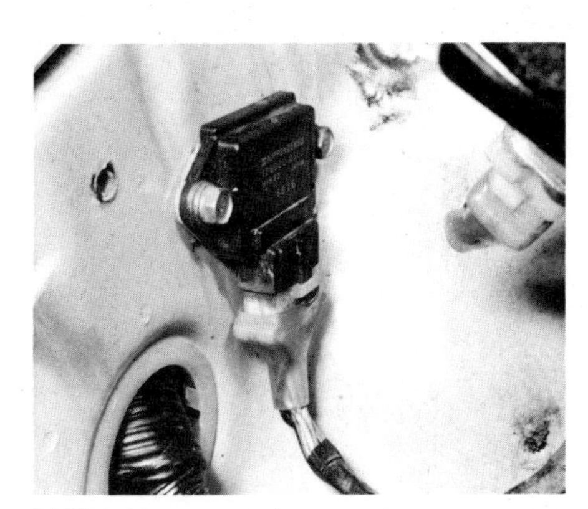

11.37A Alternator voltage regulator

11.37B Relay

11.38 Fusible link

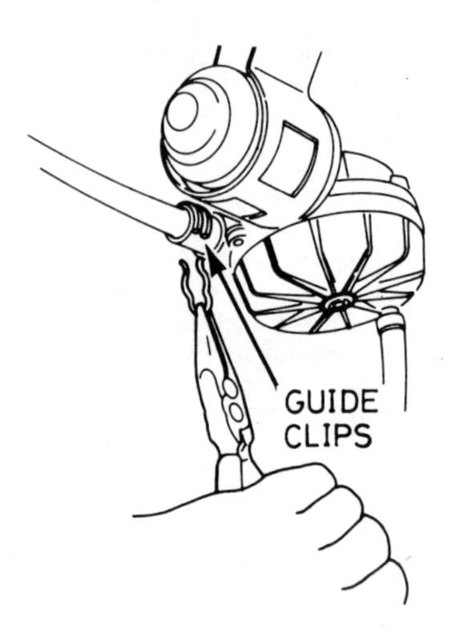

Fig. 13.198 Extracting aerial cable guide clips

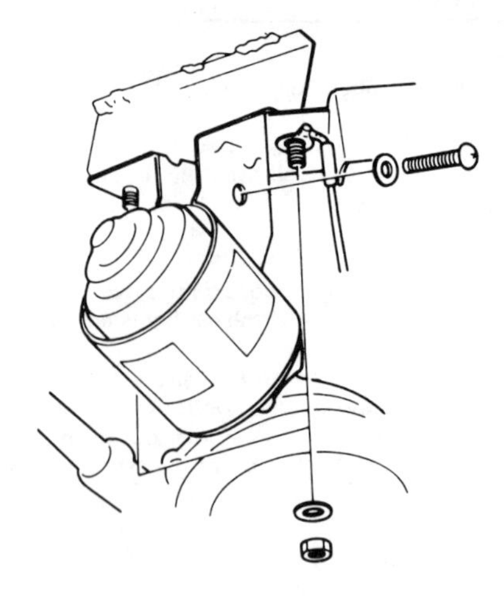

Fig. 13.199 Aerial motor mounting screws

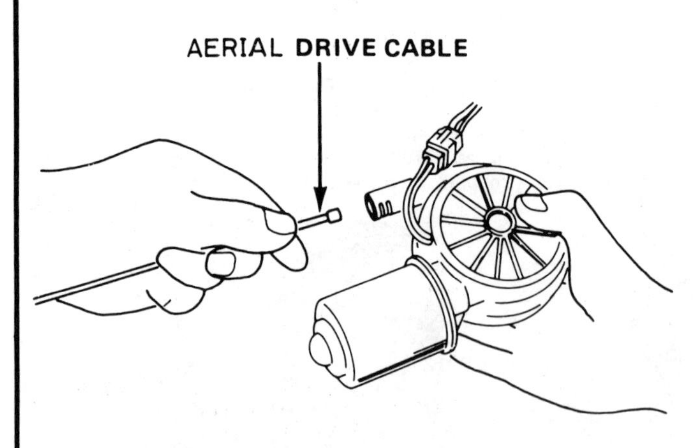

Fig. 13.200 Releasing aerial drive cable

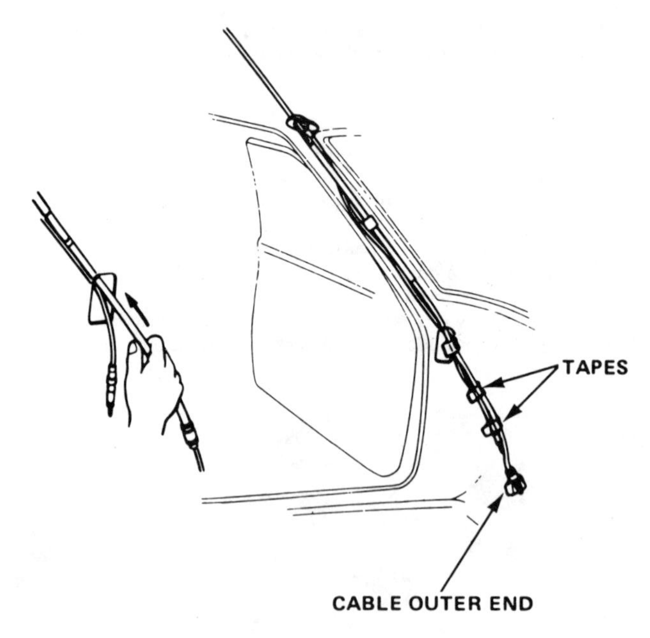

Fig. 13.201 Feeding aerial cable into position

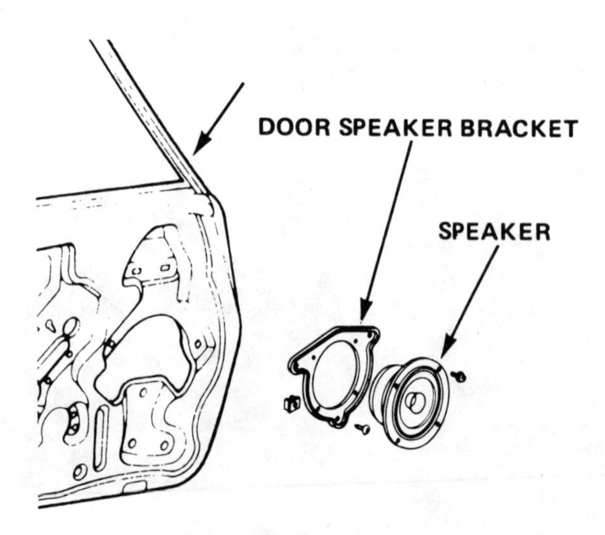

Fig. 13.202 Door speaker

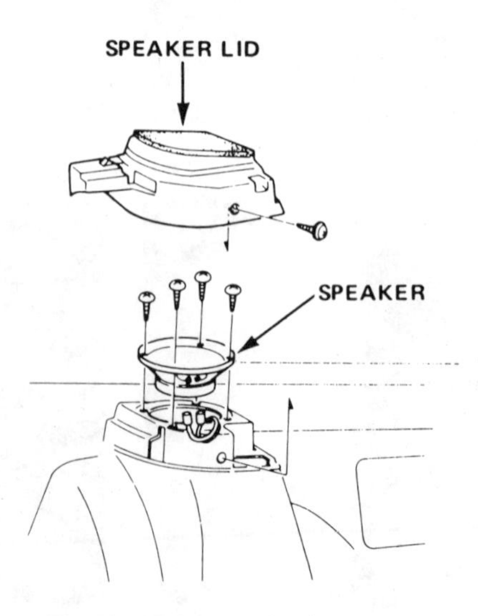

Fig. 13.203 Rear speaker (Hatchback)

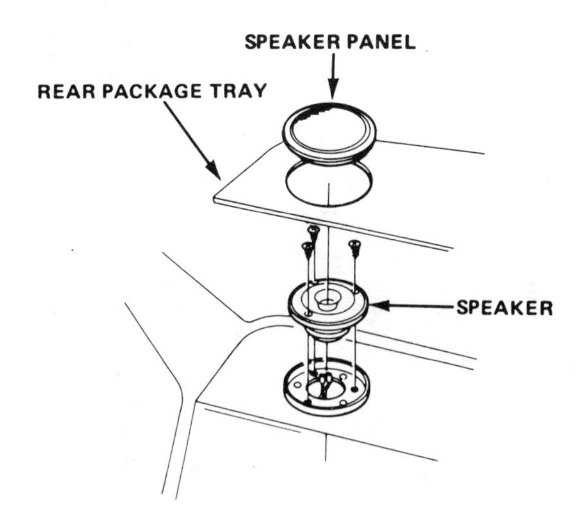

Fig. 13.204 Rear speaker (Saloon)

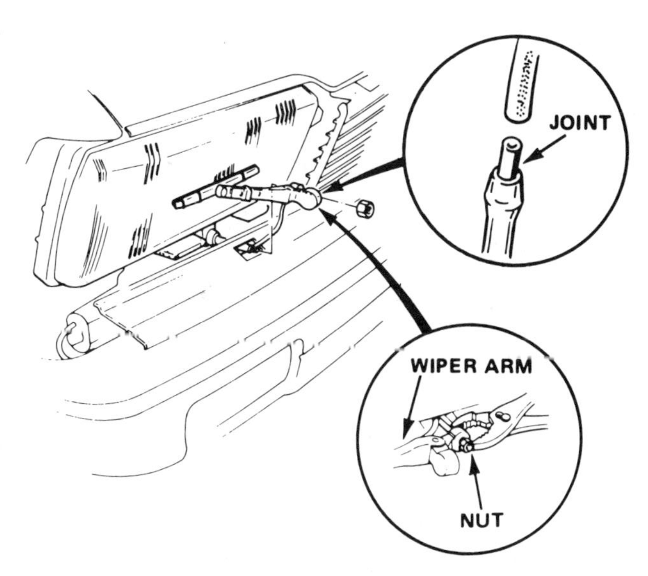

Fig. 13.205 Headlamp wiper arm

47 Insert the aerial assembly into the pillar at the roof end.
48 When the cables appear at the footwell, remove the temporary tapes and slide the cable conduit up to expose the drive cable which should then be passed through the guide.
49 Insert the drive cable into the motor, turn the ignition switch to ACC and the motor switch OFF. The drive cable will be retracted by the motor.
50 Once the drive cable is retracted, fit the cable guide to the motor and cable conduit and fit the clips.
51 Turn the ignition switch off and re-mount the motor on its bracket.

Radio speaker - removal and refitting

52 Later models may have the speakers located in the front doors, rear corner mouldings (Hatchback) or the rear parcels tray (Saloon).

Door speaker

53 Remove the door trim panel (Chapter 12), pull off the speaker wires and extract the mounting screws. Do not allow metallic objects to contact the speaker magnets.

Rear speaker (Hatchback)

54 Extract the corner moulding screws and take off the moulding. Extract the mounting screws, lift the speaker and pull off the connecting wires.

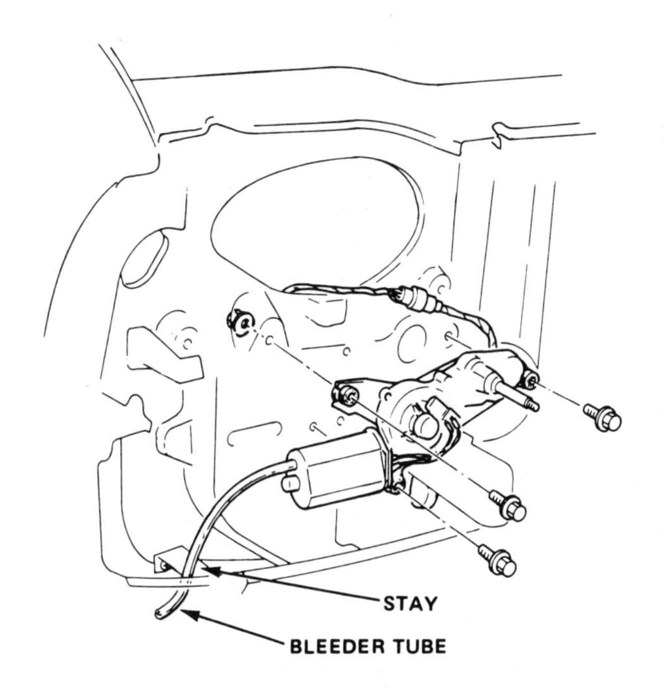

Fig. 13.206 Headlamp wiper motor

11.61 Horn location

Rear speaker (Saloon)

55 Remove the rear parcels shelf finisher, extract the speaker fixing screws, lift the speaker and disconnect the wires.
56 Refitting in all cases is a reversal of removal.

Headlamp wash/wipe assembly - removal and refitting

57 Disconnect the washer hoses at the connecting joints.
58 Loosen the wiper arm nuts.
59 Remove the arm from the wiper motor using a pair of pliers as a pressure clamp.
60 Remove the radiator grille and bumper moulding strip as described later in this Supplement.
61 Remove the horns, now exposed, and disconnect the wiper motor wiring plug (photo).

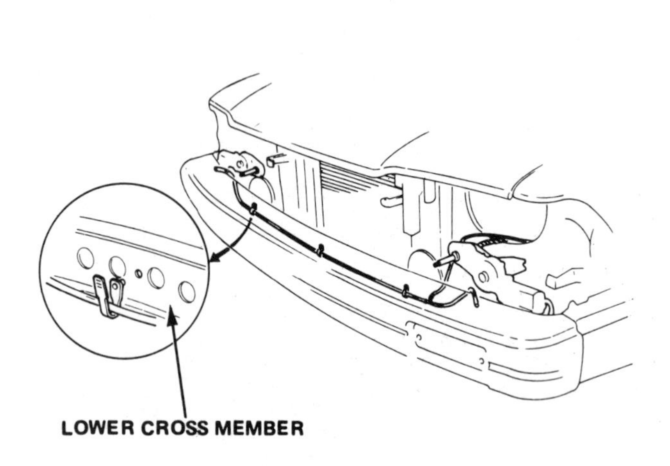

Fig. 13.207 Headlamp washer tube routing

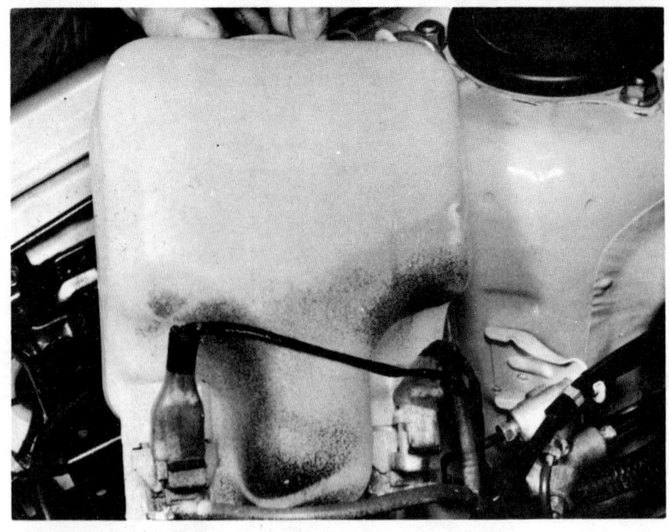

11.64 Washer fluid reservoir and pumps

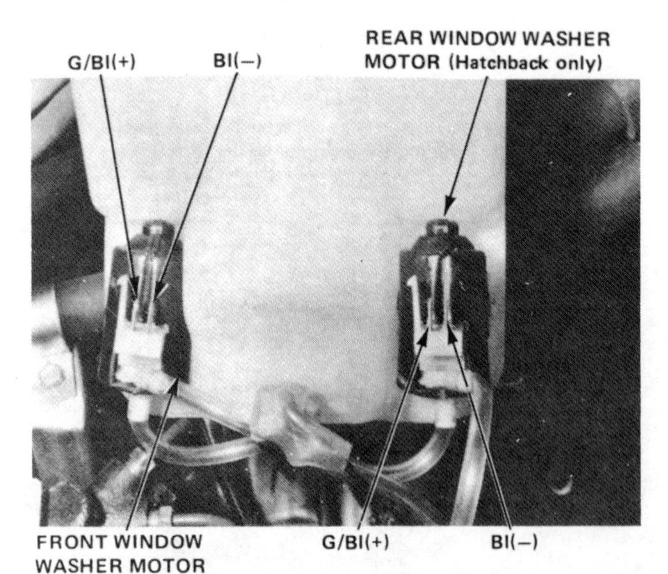

Fig. 13.208 Washer fluid reservoir and pumps

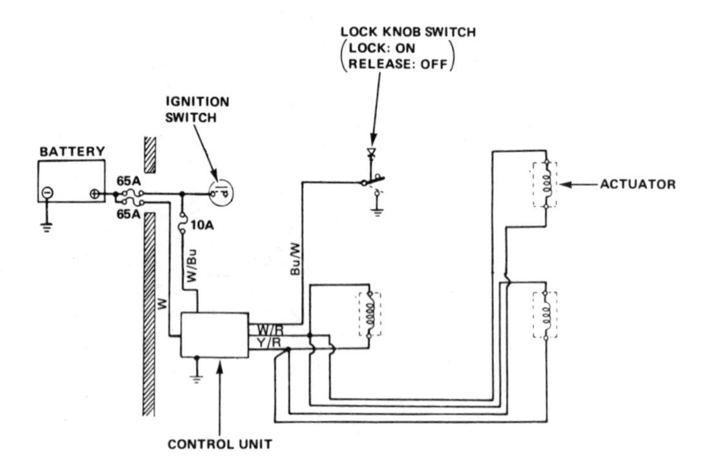

Fig. 13.209 Central door locking wiring diagram

62 Unbolt and remove the wiper motor.
63 Refitting is a reversal of removal.

Windscreen and tailgate washer pumps

64 Separate pumps are used both being located on the lower face of the fluid reservoir (photo).

Central door locking system

65 Some Saloon models are equipped with this system. All doors can be locked or unlocked using the plunger at the driver's door.
66 The lock actuator is located within each door cavity. Any failure of the system is most likely due to a faulty wire or loose connections at the switch or actuator.

Power-operated windows

67 These are fitted to certain models and can be operated independently of each other using the appropriate switch. A main overriding switch must first be actuated before the passenger and rear window switches become energised.
68 Access to the regulator and motor is obtained after removal of the door trim panel.

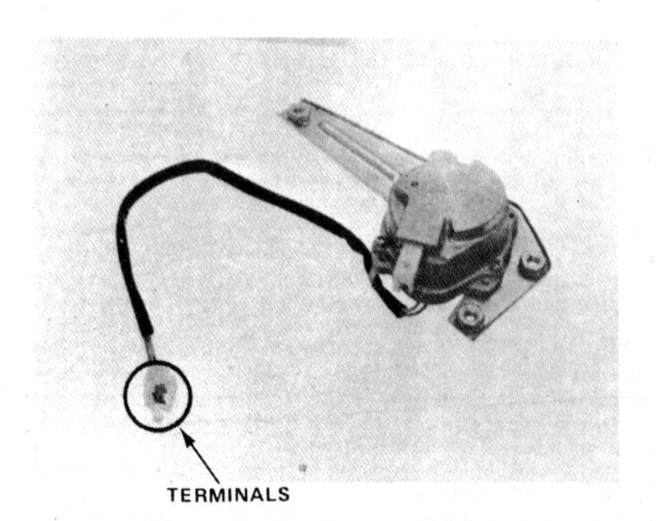

Fig. 13.210 Central door locking actuator

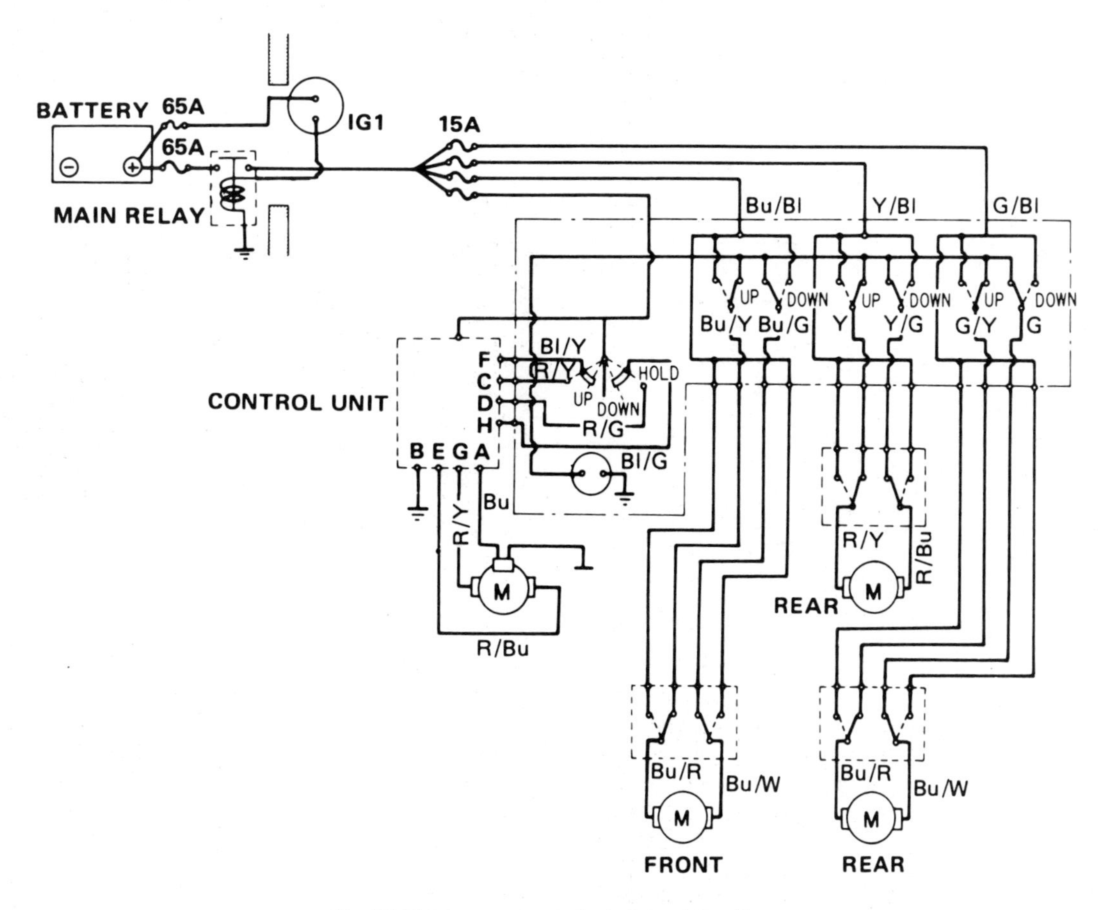

Fig. 13.211 Power-operated window wiring diagram

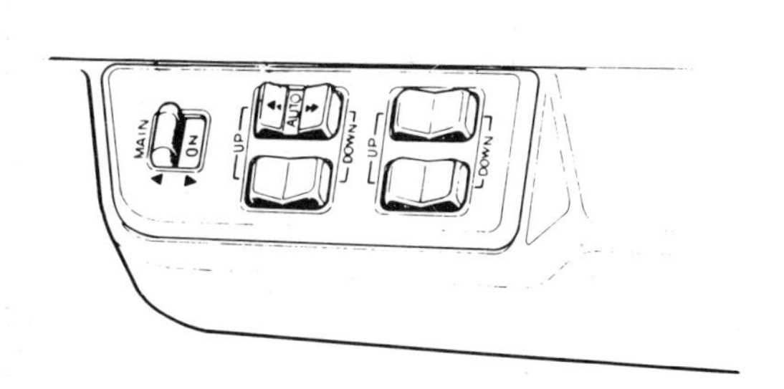

Fig. 13.212 Power-operated window switches

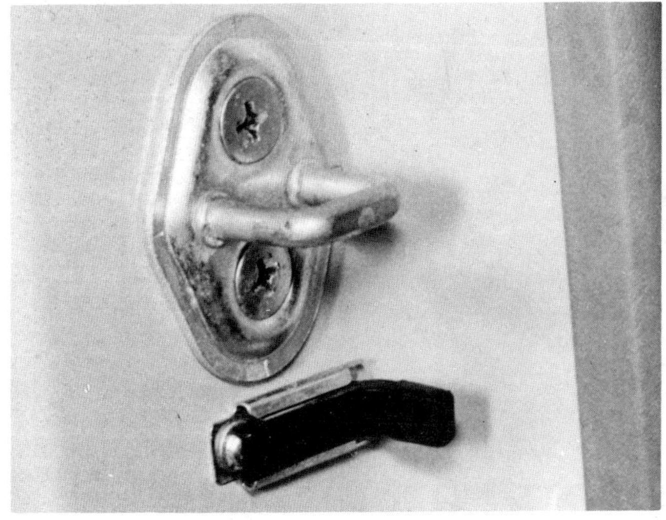

11.75 Courtesy lamp switch

Fuses

69 The fuses on later models consist of the following:

1	*Main fuse*	*55A*
1	*Circuit fuse*	*20A*
5	*Circuit fuses*	*15A*
10	*Circuit fuses*	*10A*

70 The circuits protected are indicated on the fuse box lid.

Instrument panel - removal and refitting

71 The instrument panel hood on later models is secured by three screws.

72 The steering column need only be lowered not removed, by releasing its mounting bracket bolts for the instrument panel hood to be withdrawn and the wiring disconnected.

73 Extract the four screws from the instrument panel and withdraw the panel until the wiring plugs and the speedometer cable can be disconnected. Remove the panel.

74 Refitting is a reversal of removal.

Courtesy lamp switch

75 A slide type switch is located adjacent to the door striker and is retained by one screw (photo).

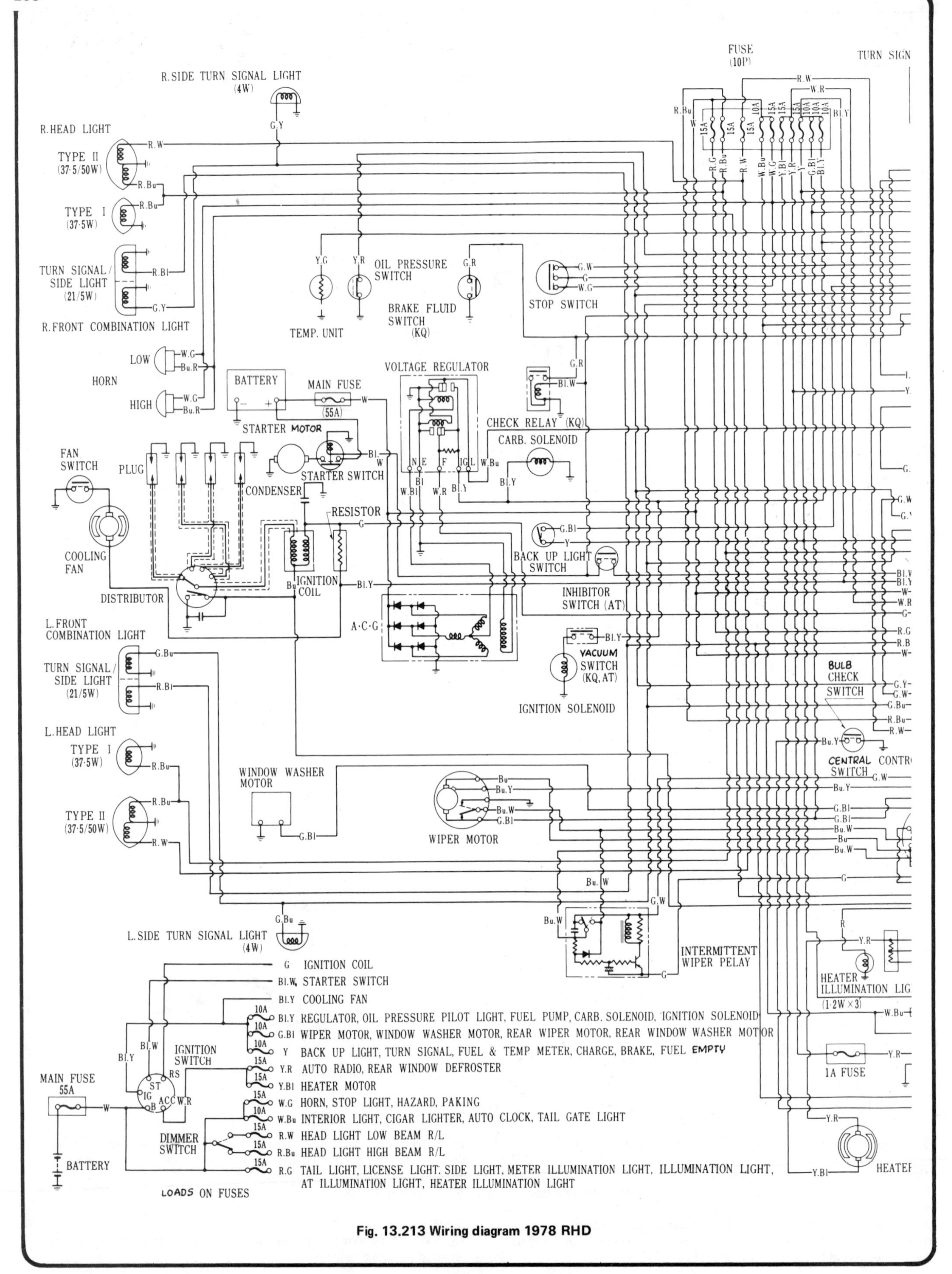

Fig. 13.213 Wiring diagram 1978 RHD

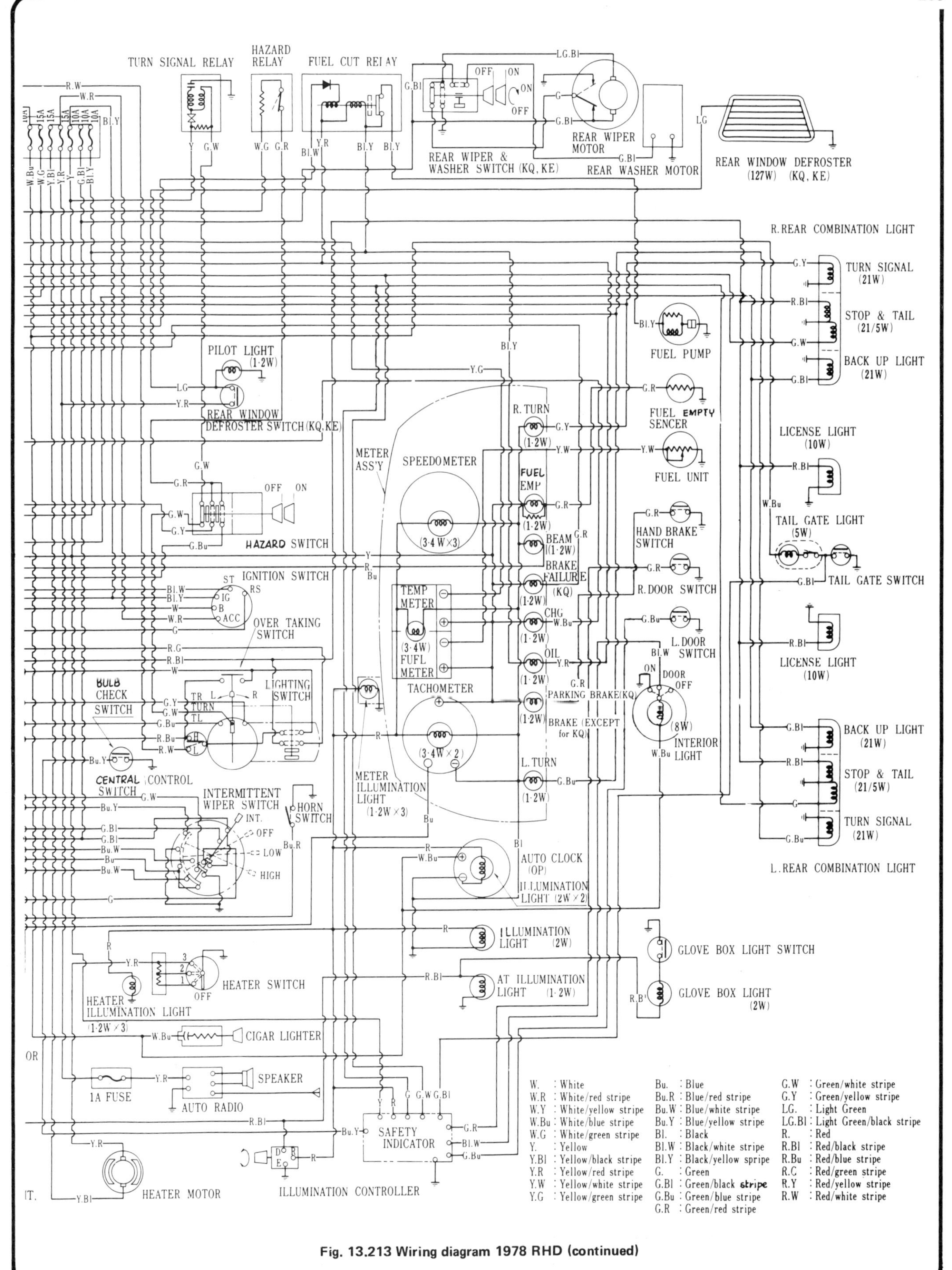

Fig. 13.213 Wiring diagram 1978 RHD (continued)

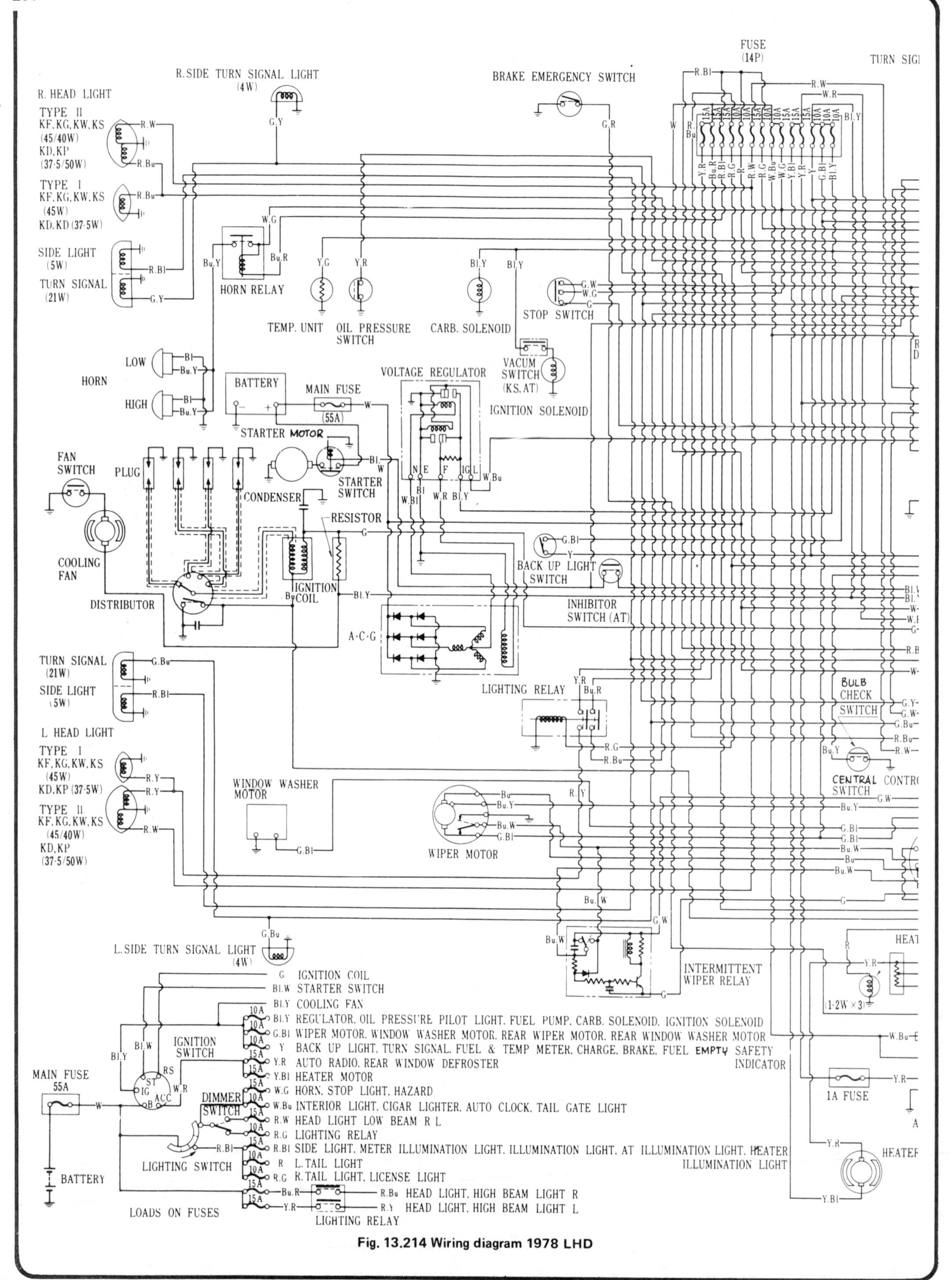

Fig. 13.214 Wiring diagram 1978 LHD

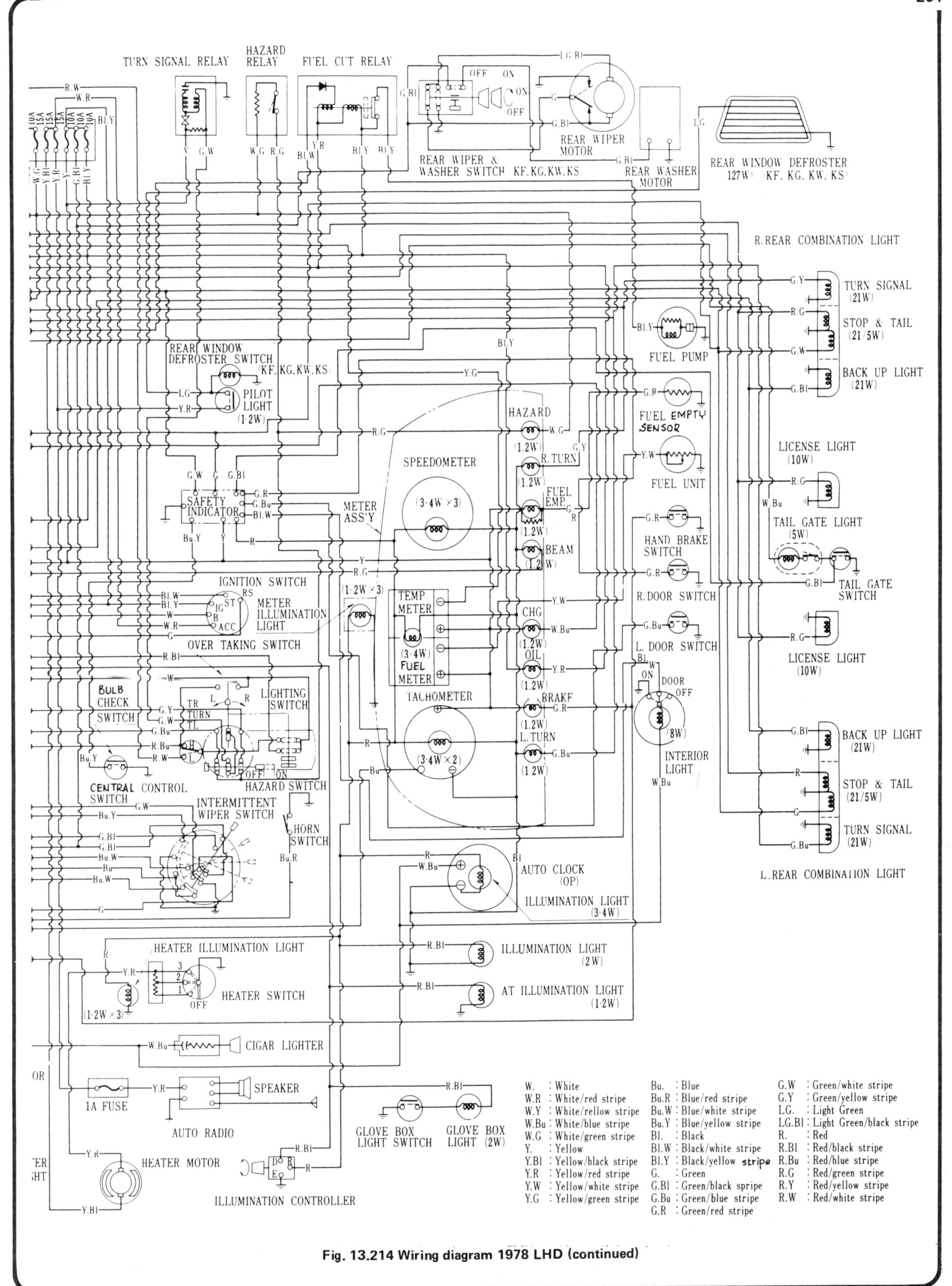

Fig. 13.214 Wiring diagram 1978 LHD (continued)

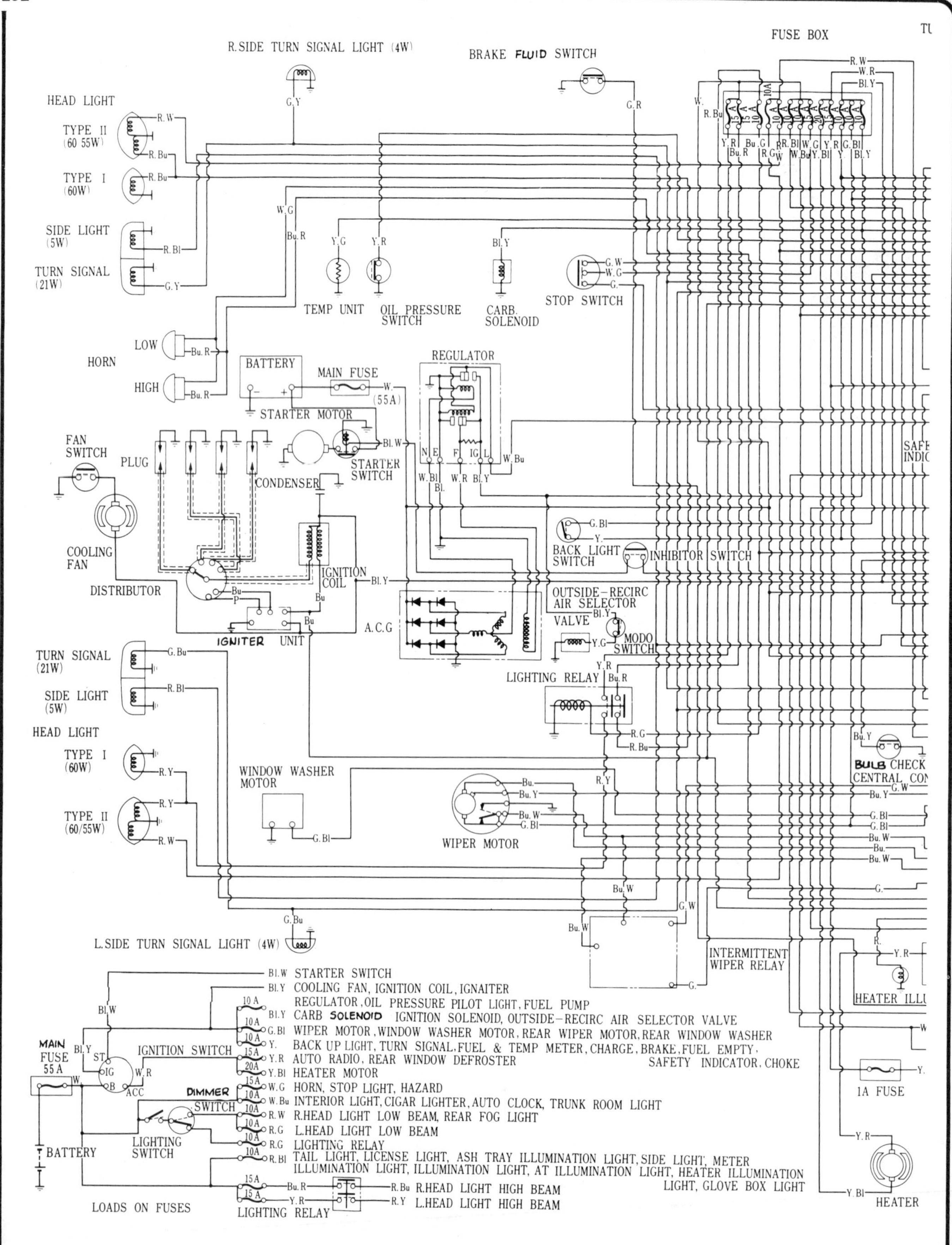

Fig. 13.215 Wiring diagram 1979 to 81 RHD

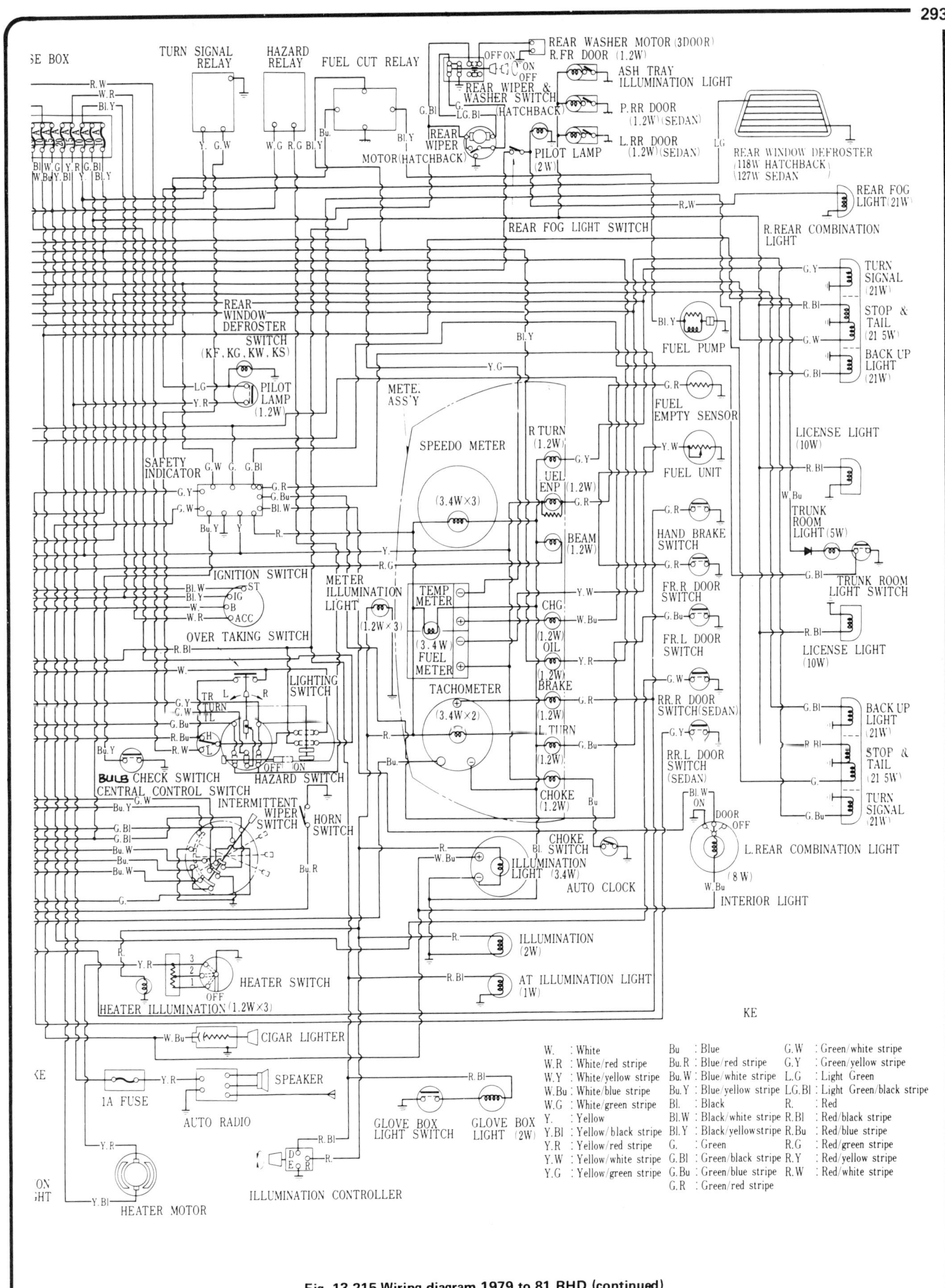

Fig. 13.215 Wiring diagram 1979 to 81 RHD (continued)

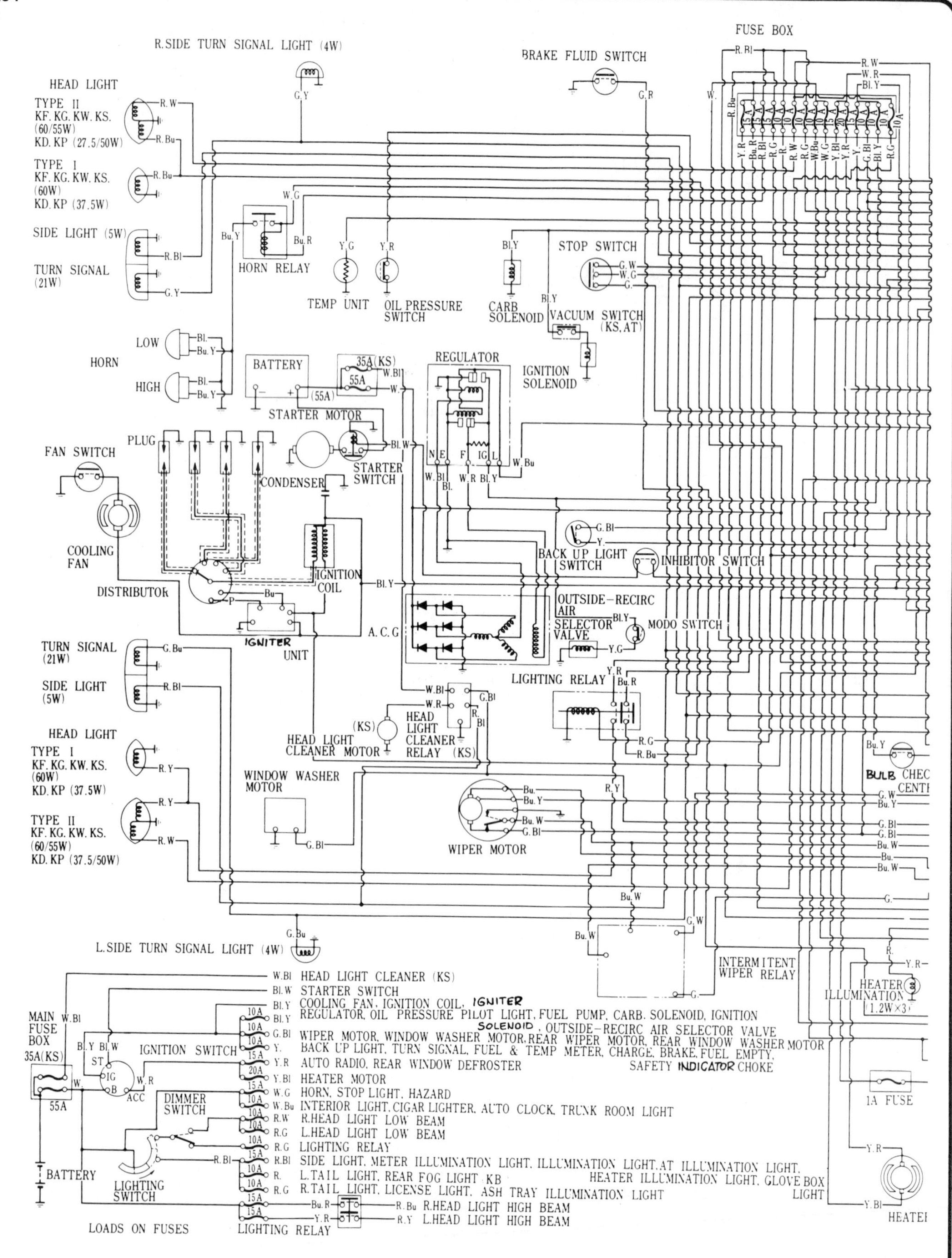

Fig. 13.216 Wiring diagram 1979 to 81 LHD

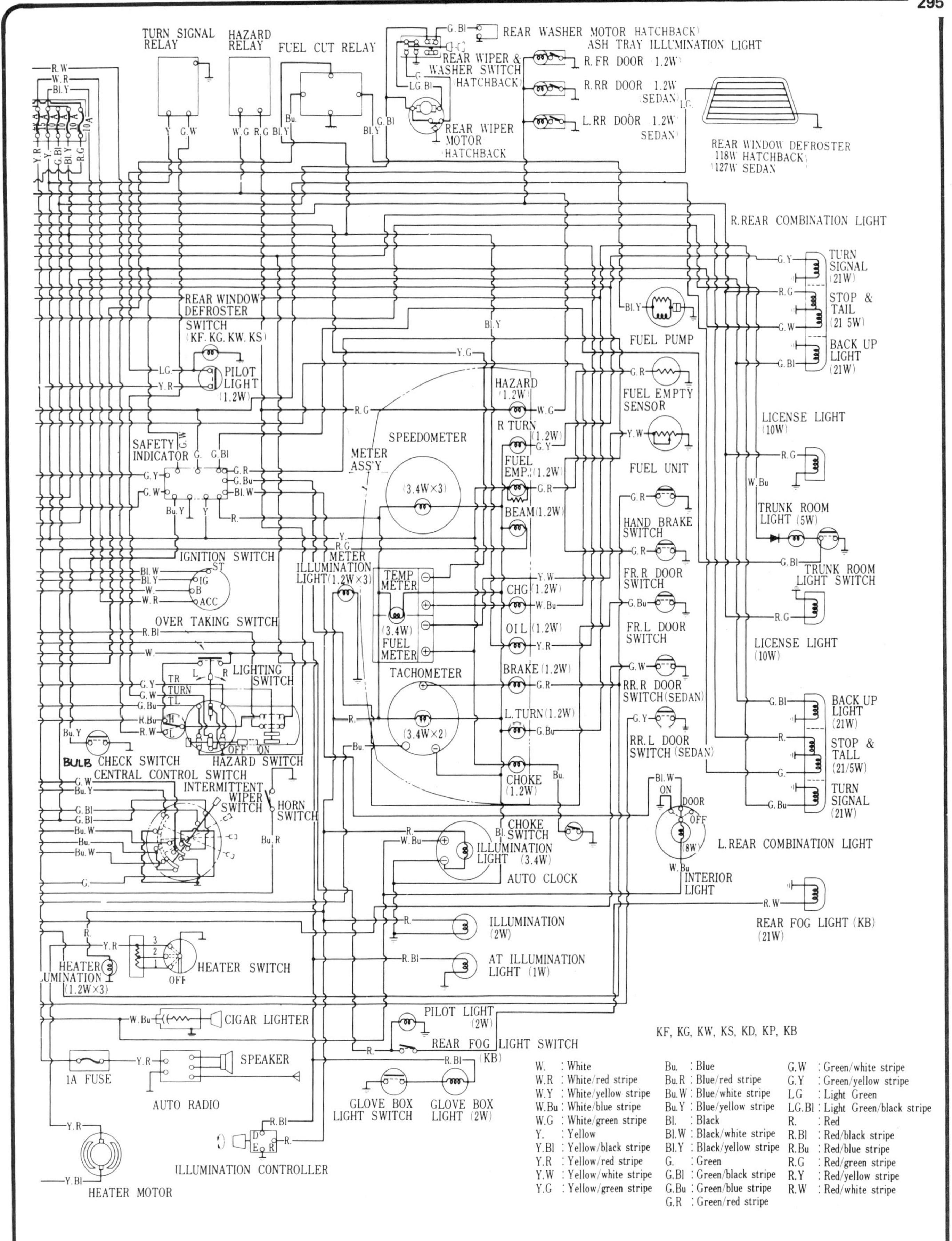

Fig. 13.216 Wiring diagram 1979 to 81 LHD

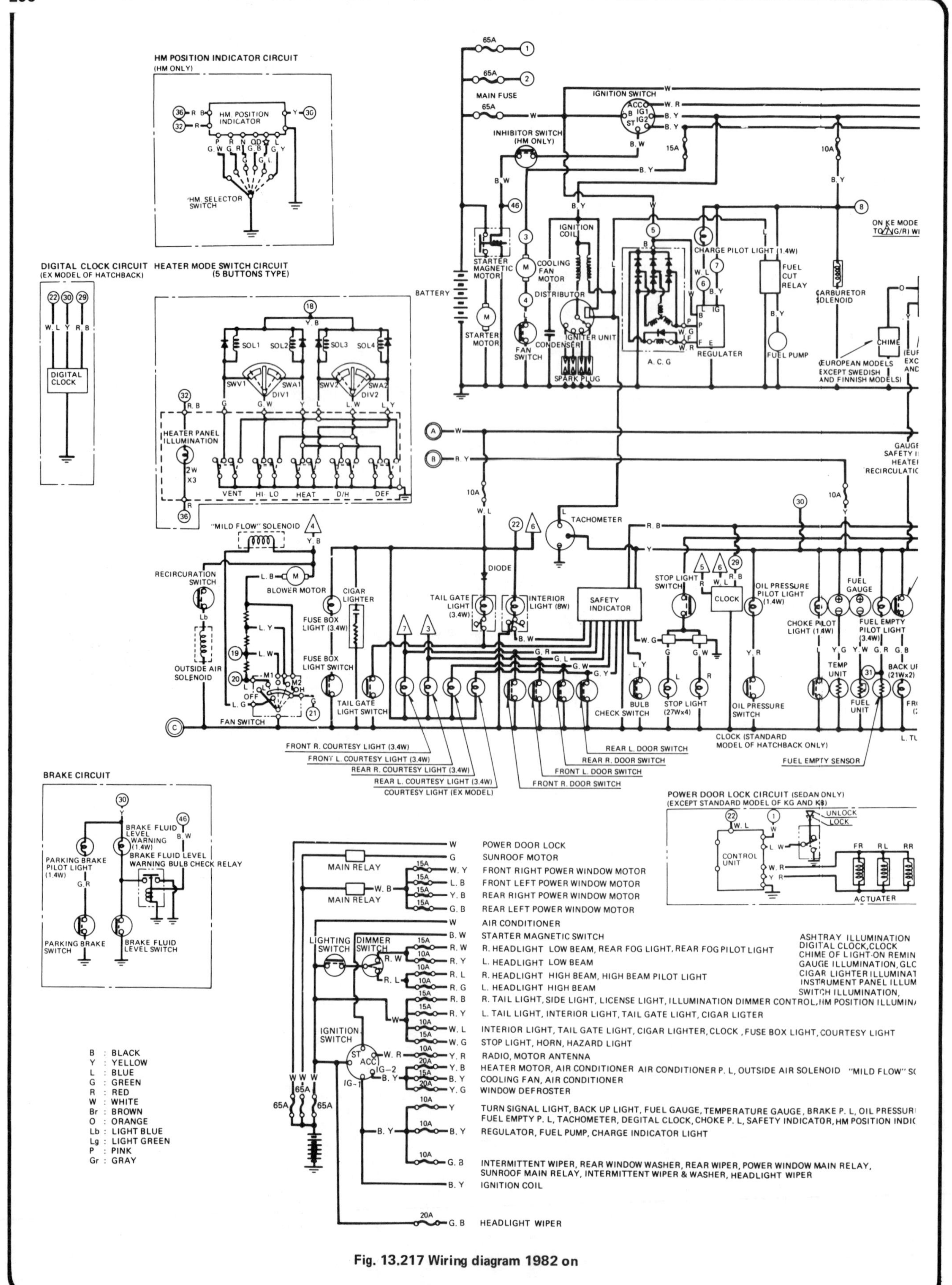

Fig. 13.217 Wiring diagram 1982 on

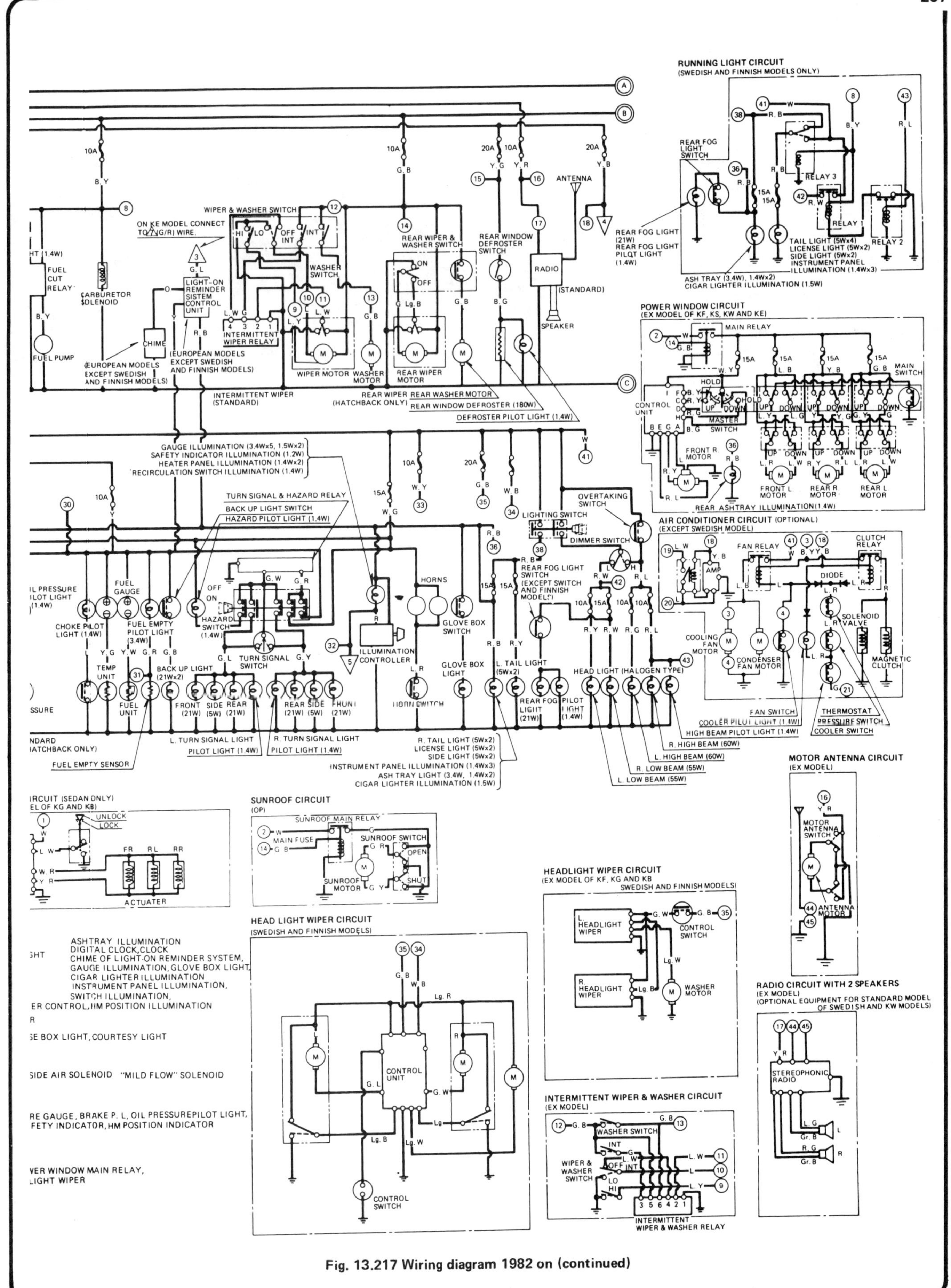

Fig. 13.217 Wiring diagram 1982 on (continued)

12.2A Rear anti-roll bar end attachment

12.2B Rear anti-roll bar clamp

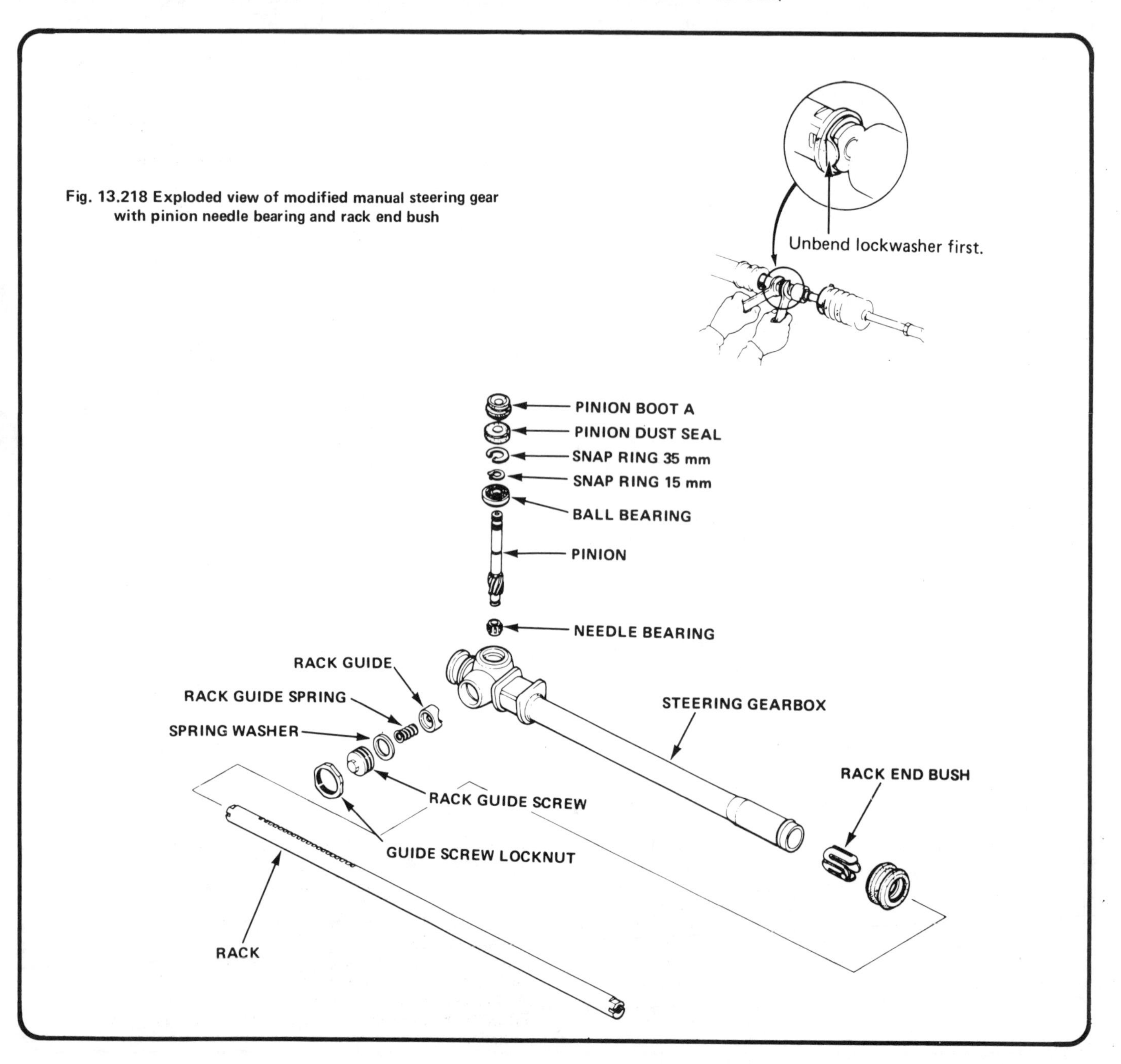

Fig. 13.218 Exploded view of modified manual steering gear with pinion needle bearing and rack end bush

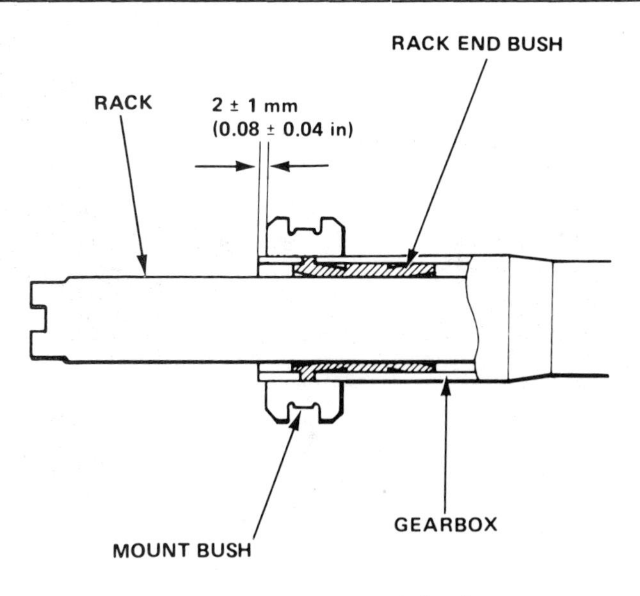

Fig. 13.219 Rack end bush fitted

12 Suspension and steering

Rear anti-roll bar - removal and refitting

1 The rear anti-roll bar fitted to later models, is attached to the lower control arms at its outer ends and to the body by rubber insulated clamps.
2 Remove by unscrewing the fixing bolts (photo).
3 Refitting is a reversal of removal.

Manual steering gear - modification (1982 on)

4 The pinion shaft is fitted with a needle bearing at its base and a new bush is used on the end of the rack.
5 When installing the rack end bush, lightly grease its inside surface but do not fill its slots with grease as they serve as air passages. Align the round projections on the bush with the holes in the gearbox, then slide the mount bush onto the gearbox.

Power steering

6 A valve body mounted on the lower part of the steering pinion shaft and a hydraulic cylinder and piston are mounted at each end of the steering rack. An engine driven pump supplies hydraulic fluid at a constant pressure to the system. Movement of the steering wheel causes movement of the spool valve in the valve body which then allows fluid to flow to one of the pistons attached to the steering rack and causes movement of the rack. The hydraulic circuit incorporates a speed sensor, which is a trochoid rotor hydraulic pump, driven by the speedometer gear shaft. This sensor controls the sensitivity of the spool valve in such a way that maximum power assistance is given to the steering when the car is moving slowly, but as car speed increases the spool valve sensitivity is decreased.

Fluid level check

7 Check the fluid level in the reservoir with the engine cold and the car parked on a level surface.
8 The fluid should be between the upper and lower marks. Add fluid of specified type if necessary, but do not fill above the upper mark.

Fluid - removal

9 This should only be necessary if the system has been dismantled or if the fluid has become discoloured or contaminated.
10 Disconnect the return hose from the reservoir by releasing the hose clip and pulling the pipe off. Then put the end of the pipe into a container which will hold a quart.
11 Start the engine and with the engine running at fast idling speed, turn the steering wheel from lock to lock several times, until fluid no longer runs out of the hose. Switch the engine off.
12 Discard the fluid which has been expelled from the system. Reconnect the return hose to the reservoir. Fill the reservoir to the FULL

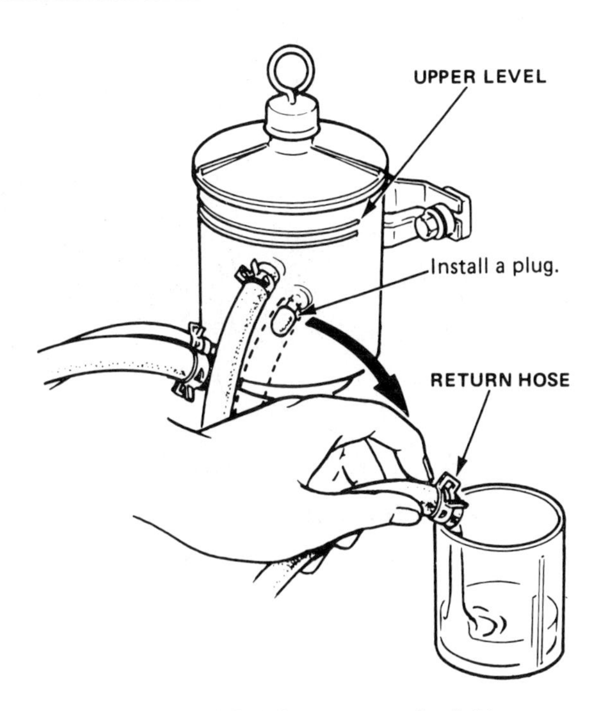

Fig. 13.220 Draining power steering fluid

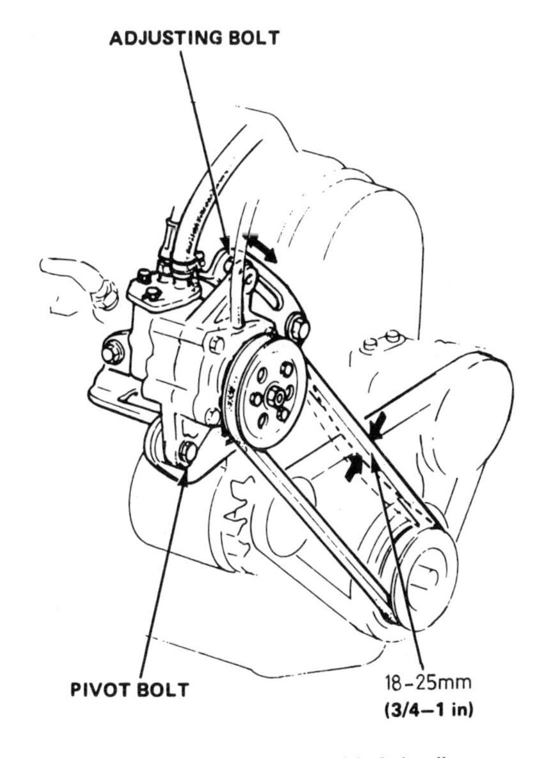

Fig. 13.221 Power steering pump drivebelt adjustment

mark on the dipstick using fresh fluid. Run the engine at a fast idling speed and turn the steering wheel from lock to lock several times to bleed all the air from the system. Switch off the engine.

Pump belt - adjustment and renewal

13 The belt is correctly tensioned when it can be deflected at the mid-point between the two pulleys by between 0.75 and 1.0 in (18.0 to 25.4 mm) using moderate thumb pressure.
14 If adjustment is required, loosen the pivot and adjustment bolts and swivel the pump until the tension is correct and then retighten the bolts.

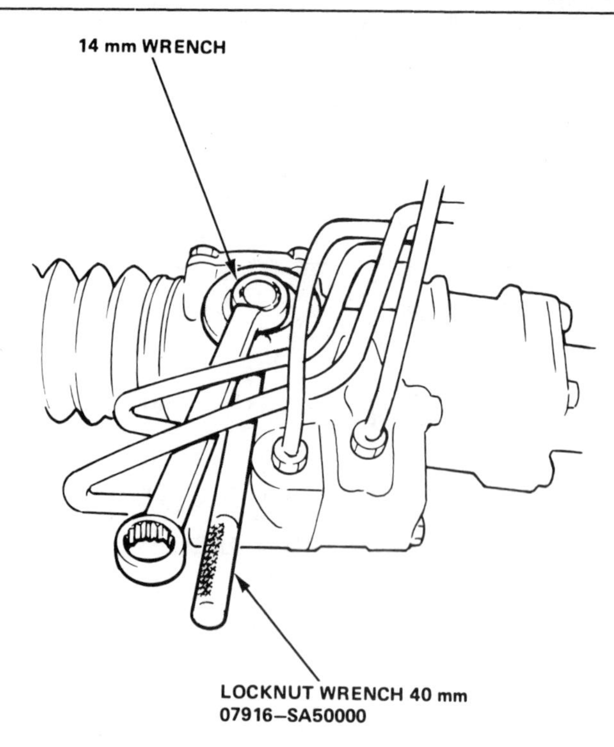

Fig. 13.222 Releasing rack guide adjuster screw and locknut

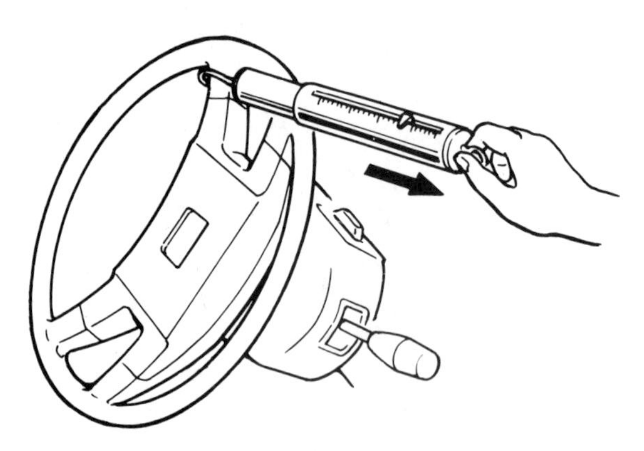

Fig. 13.223 Checking steering wheel turning force

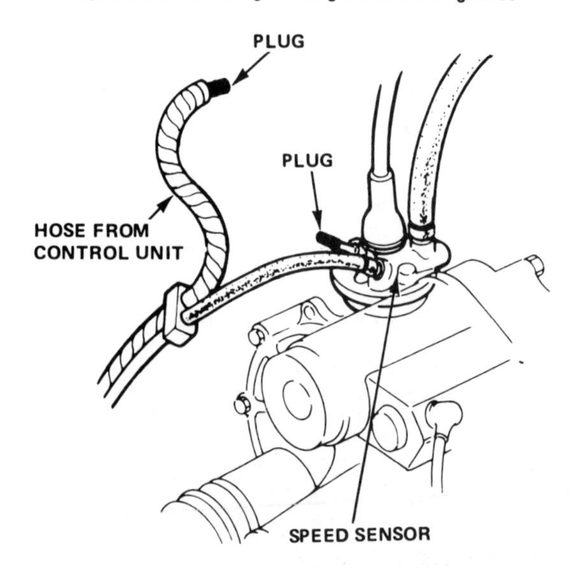

Fig. 13.224 Speed sensor

15 To renew the belt, release the bolts and push the pump towards the crankshaft pulley as far as it will go. Prise the belt over the pulley rim using the fingers only.

Rack guide - adjustment

16 Loosen the guide screw locknut using a 40.0 mm wrench.
17 Tighten the guide screw until it compresses the spring and can be felt to seat on the guide. Loosen the screw, retighten it finger tight then unscrew it one tenth of a complete turn.
18 Tighten the locknut without moving the position of the screw.

Power steering speed sensor - testing

19 If it is noticed that there is little or no power assistance at speeds below 30 mph (50 kmh) and the power steering fluid level and pump belt tension have been checked, carry out the following test.
20 Have the engine at normal operating temperature and idling.
21 Attach a spring balance to a steering wheel spoke and record the force required to turn the wheel.
22 Disconnect and plug the large diameter hose which runs between the power steering gear and the speed sensor.
23 Now attempt to turn the steering wheel by pulling on the spring balance. Record the force required to turn the wheel.
24 If the second reading is less than the first, then the speed sensor is faulty and must be renewed.
25 If the second reading is more than the first, then there is a fault in the steering gear or pump.

Power steering speed sensor - renewal

26 Slide the speedometer drive cable dust excluding boot up the cable, release the securing clip and disconnect the cable.
27 Disconnect and plug all the hoses from the speed sensor.
28 Unscrew the speedometer gear lock bolt and pull the speed sensor from its recess.
29 Install the new sensor and reconnect the hoses and speedometer cable.
30 Start the engine, let it idle and turn the steering wheel from lock to lock, to bleed the air from the system as described in earlier Sections.
31 Top-up the fluid level in the pump reservoir.

Power steering shaft - adjustment

32 If power assistance is evident in one direction only or the car tends to pull to one side by the steering gear not maintaining a self-centering action, first check that none of the fluid lines are pinched or bent at acute angles, as this might restrict fluid flow.
33 With the engine off, turn the steering wheel. A steering system in good condition will make a clunking noise and the movement will feel rough. As the wheel is turned to the left the clearance between the steering wheel hub and the rim of the column shroud should decrease by at least 0.04 in (1.0 mm) and when turned to the right increase by the same amount proving that the spool valve is operating correctly.
34 This clearance is axial movement (in and out). Where it is discovered that the movement occurs in one direction only, then carry out the following operations. Remove the steering wheel and signal switch sleeve.
35 Fit a special tool (07973-6920001) on top of the steering shaft making sure that it is fully seated.
36 Remove the boot from the base of the steering column and loosen the top bolt of the shaft coupling. Make sure that all the steering column bolts are tight.
37 Apply downward pressure to the upper half of the shaft coupling while the top bolt is fully tightened. The legs of the special tool should be seated on the body of the direction indicator switch.
38 Refit the boot and steering wheel with switch cancelling sleeve.
39 If the faults still persist, the steering assembly must be thoroughly overhauled or renewed.

Power steering pump shaft seal - renewal

40 If oil is seen to be leaking from the shaft at the rear of the pump pulley, this is probably due to a defective seal which can be renewed without having to remove the pump or disconnect the fluid lines.
41 Release the pump mounting and adjustment link bolts, push the pump in towards the engine and slip off the drivebelt.
42 Unbolt and remove the pulley. To do this, the pulley will have to be held stationary while the nut is unscrewed. Engage an old drivebelt in the pulley groove and grip the belt as close to the pulley as possible in the jaws of a vice.

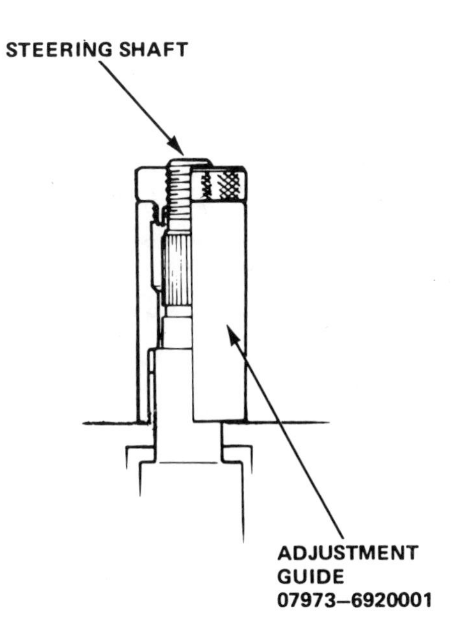

Fig. 13.225 Special tool fitted to steering column shaft

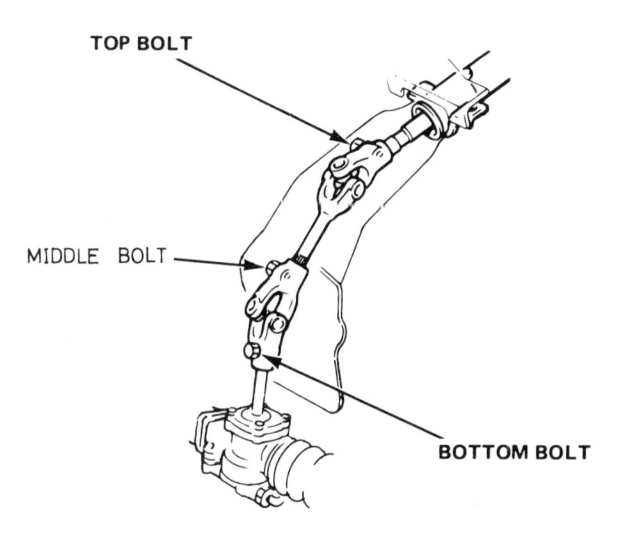

Fig. 13.226 Steering shaft coupling bolts

43 Unscrew the shaft nut and withdraw the triangular pulley mounting plate. A puller may be required for this. *Do not lever it off or the pump shaft may be distorted.*
44 Pick out the old seal using a sharp tool.
45 Coat the new seal with clean fluid and install it squarely.
46 Refit the mounting plate and pulley, tightening the bolts and nuts to the specified torque.
47 Reconnect the drivebelt and tension it as previously described.

Power steering gear - removal and refitting

48 Turn the steering wheel to full left-hand lock, then remove the boot from the base of the steering column.
49 Loosen the steering shaft coupling top and bottom bolts and slide the coupling up off the pinion shaft.
50 Drain the power steering fluid as previously described.
51 Remove the rack housing shield.
52 Clean away all external dirt.
53 Remove the front roadwheels.
54 Unscrew the nuts from the tie-rod balljoint taper pin nuts and disconnect them from the steering arms using a suitable tool.

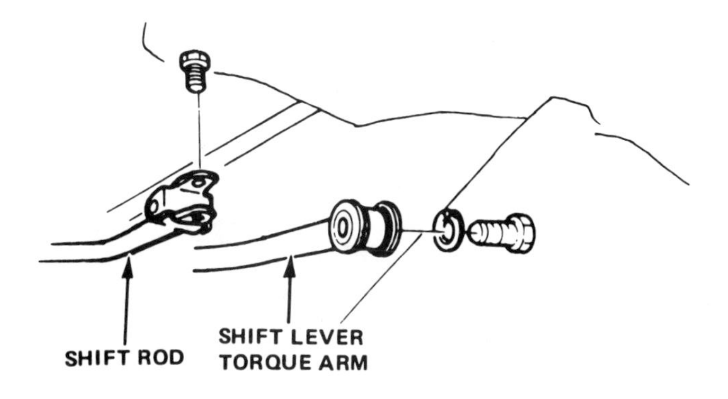

Fig. 13.227 Shift rod and shift lever torque arm (5-speed)

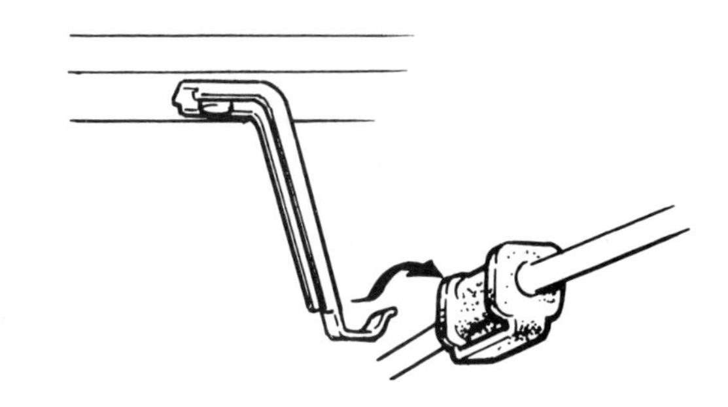

Fig. 13.228 Control cable bracket and cable insulator (Hondamatic)

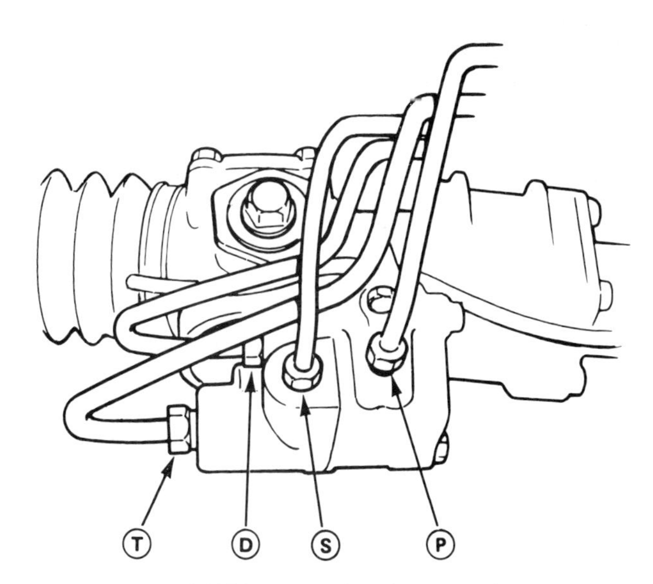

Fig. 13.229 Power steering pipe connections

D *To reservoir through speed sensor*
P *From pump*
S *To speed sensor*
T *To reservoir through control valve*

55 Unbolt and remove the centre beam.
56 On cars equipped with a five-speed manual transmission, select 1st or 3rd gear and unscrew the bolt from the shift rod clevis and disconnect the shift rod. Now disconnect the shift lever torque arm from the transmission.
57 On cars equipped with Hondamatic transmission, push the moulded rubber cushion on the control cable up and out of its support bracket.
58 Disconnect the exhaust downpipe from the manifold.
59 Disconnect the fluid pipes from the rack and pinion housing.

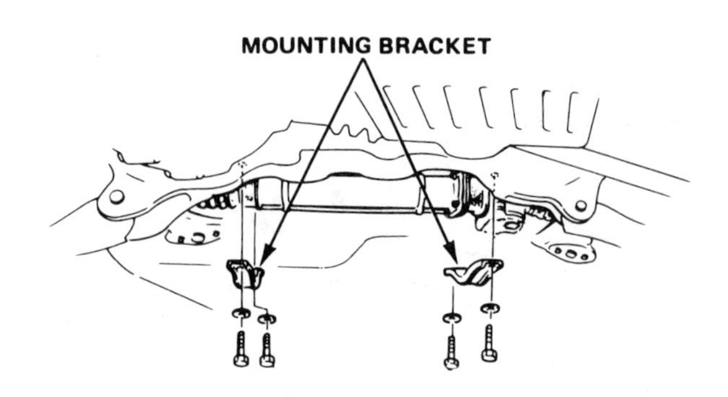

Fig. 13.230 Rack housing mounting bolts

60 Unbolt the rack and pinion housing mounting brackets.
61 Pull the rack and pinion housing downwards and remove it sideways out of the car.
62 Refitting is a reversal of removal, tighten all nuts and bolts to the specified torque. Adjust the steering shaft and fill and bleed the system as described earlier.

Power steering pump - removal and refitting
63 Drain the fluid as previously described.
64 Disconnect all the pump hoses.
65 Release the pump pivot and adjustment bolts and remove the drivebelt.
66 Remove the pivot and adjustment bolts and withdraw the pump.
67 Refitting is a reversal of removal. Tighten the bolts to the specified torque after having tensioned the drivebelt. Fill and bleed the system as previously described.

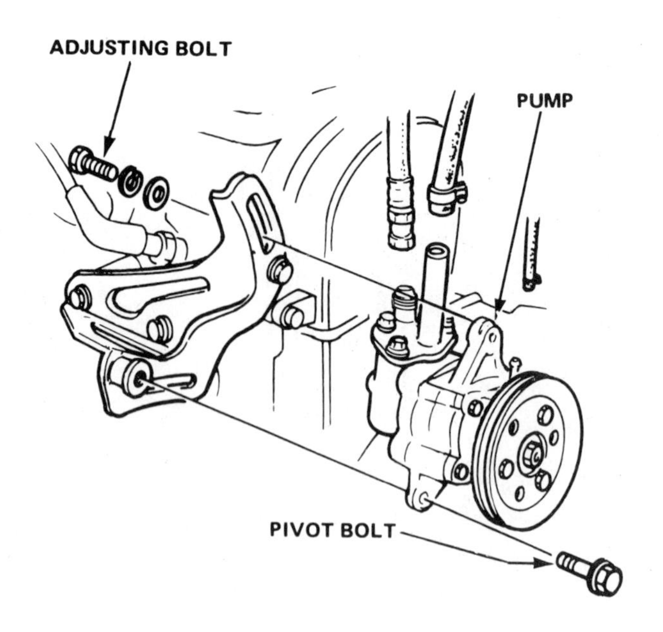

Fig. 13.231 Power steering pump and bracket

Front hub bearings
68 Commencing with 1980 models, the sealed bearings used on the front hubs were changed for bearings having detachable bearing races.
69 Removal and refitting of the bearing inner and outer tracks will necessitate the use of a press and a bearing puller. It is therefore recommended that this job is left to your dealer.

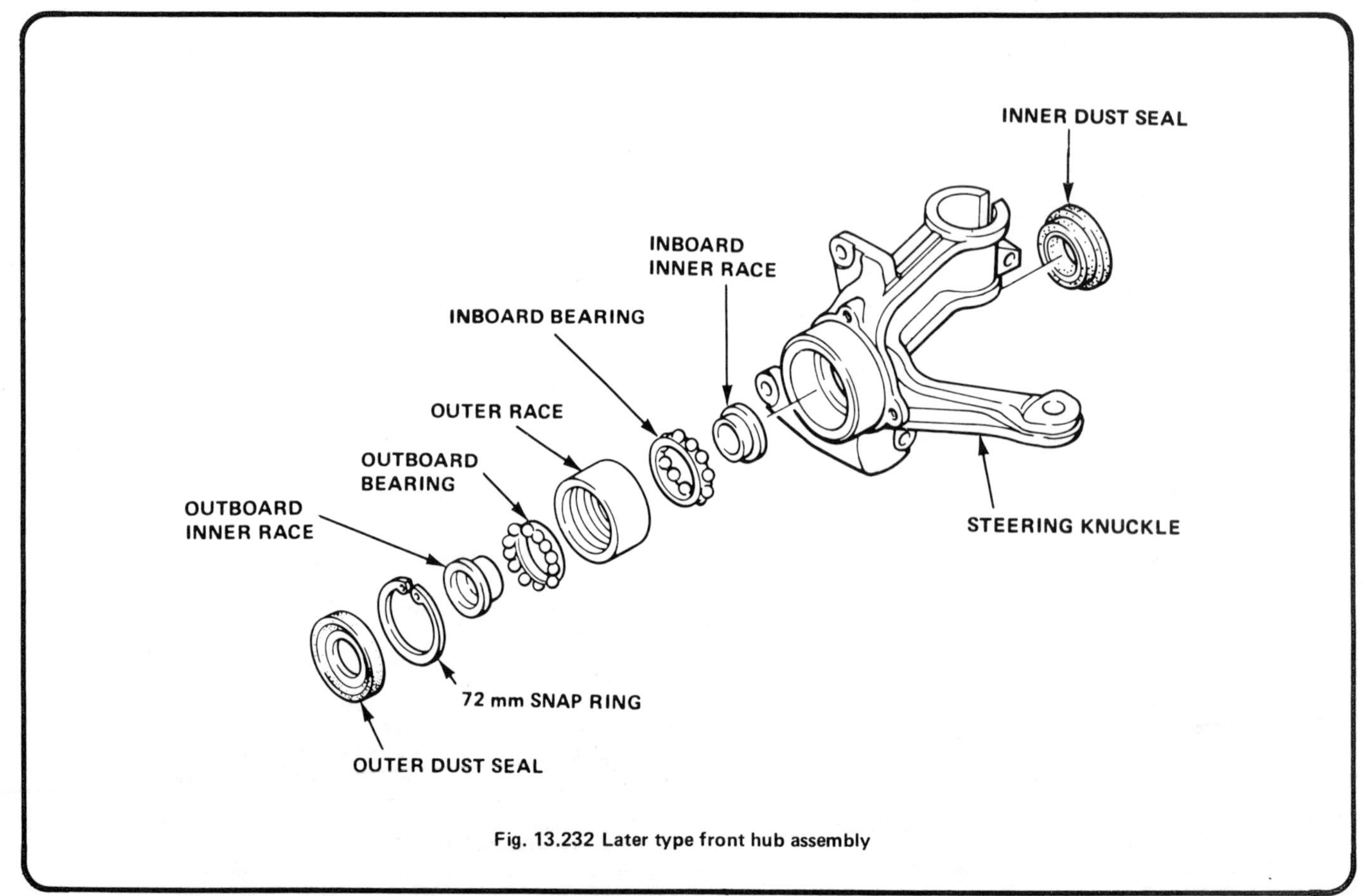

Fig. 13.232 Later type front hub assembly

13 Bodywork

PART A - BODY COMPONENTS

Bumpers - removal and refitting

1 Before removing the front or rear bumper disconnect the electrical leads from the direction indicator lamps or rear number plate lamps as appropriate.

2 The bumpers are mounted on brackets which in turn are bolted to the body members. Removal is simply a matter of unscrewing and removing the fixing bolts.

Radiator grille - removal and refitting

3 Remove the five screws and two top clips which are all accessible from the front of the car (photos).

13A.3A Extracting radiator grille screw

13A.3B Extracting radiator grille screw

13A.3C Radiator grille clip

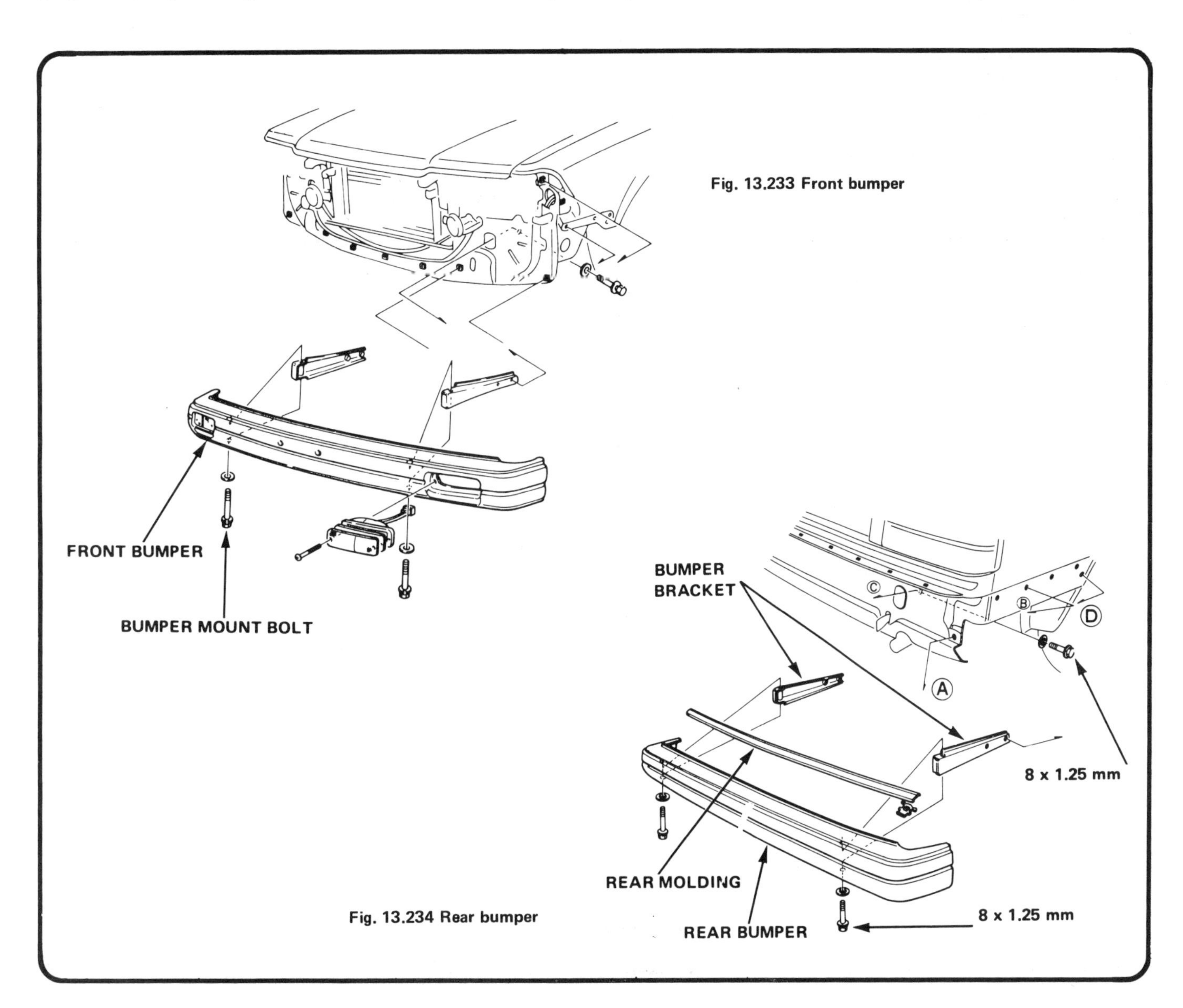

Fig. 13.233 Front bumper

Fig. 13.234 Rear bumper

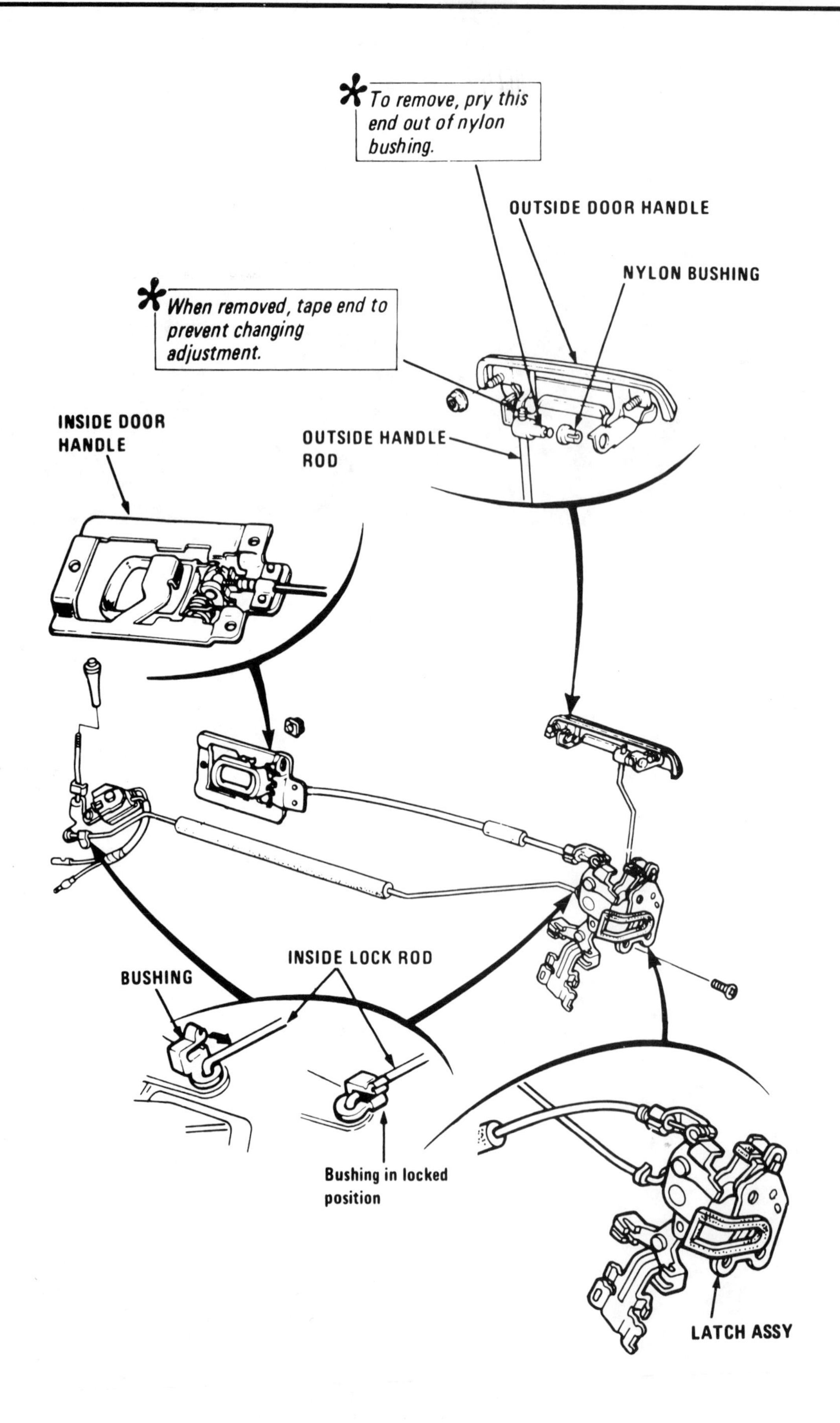

Fig. 13.235 Rear door latch components (Saloon)

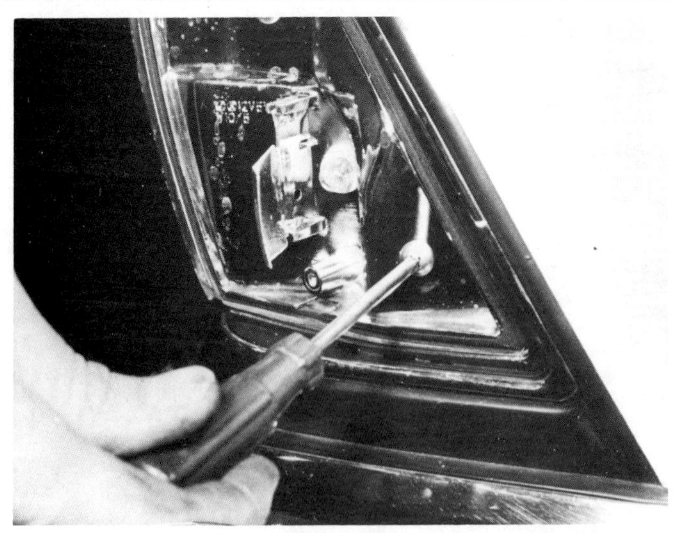
13A.4 Front side repeater lamp base screw

13A.5A Removing radiator grille

13A.5B Bonnet hinge bolts

4 Remove the front side repeater lamp lens and then extract the two screws from the lamp base (photo).
5 Gently prise the front wing chrome strips outwards until the radiator grille can be released and removed. It is recommended that the grille is removed for better access to the hinge bolts whenever the bonnet must be removed from later models (photos).

Rear doors (Saloon)

6 The components of the rear doors are shown in Figs. 13.235. For information on the removal and refitting of the door, glass, lock and latch refer to Sections 14 and 15 of Chapter 12.
7 When refitting the window regulator handle, fully engage the spring retaining clip in the handle, locate the handle on the splined shaft of the regulator and then drive the handle onto the shaft by striking it with the hand. With the glass fully up, set the handle on the shaft as shown.

Power-operated windows - door dismantling

8 On cars fitted with this system, unbolt the regulator assembly and withdraw it through the door panel aperture until the electrical leads can be disconnected.
9 If the motor must be unbolted from the regulator, take great care as the spring will be released and the regulator arm will snap back to the UP position.
10 Before refitting the power-operated type regulator to the door, connect its leads to a battery and move it to its 'glass down' position.
11 When installed, clamp the breather pipe as shown.

Central door locking system - door dismantling

12 On cars fitted with this system, unbolt the actuator and remove the lock switch if the driver's door is being dismantled.

Luggage boot lid (Saloon) - removal and refitting

13 With an assistant supporting the boot lid mark the position of the hinge attachment brackets on the boot lid and then remove the two bolts attaching the hinge to the lid.
14 Lift the lid clear, taking care not to damage the paintwork and retrieve the interlocking plates from the hinges.
15 To remove the hinges and torsion bars, first remove the tension on the torsion bars by unhooking their ends from their restrainers.
16 Remove the rear shelf and then remove the four nuts securing the hinges.
17 If the torsion bars are removed, be careful that they are not interchanged. The one which fits on the left-hand side is identified by having a white paint mark on it.
18 Lateral and longitudinal adjustment of the boot lid is achieved by loosening the hinge fixing bolts, adjusting the lid to the required position and tightening the bolts.
19 The height of the boot lid is adjusted by loosening the bolts and fitting suitable packing pieces beneath the interlocking plates.

Luggage boot lid latch (Saloon) - removal and refitting

20 Pull out the snap-connector which connects the boot light switch to the wiring harness.

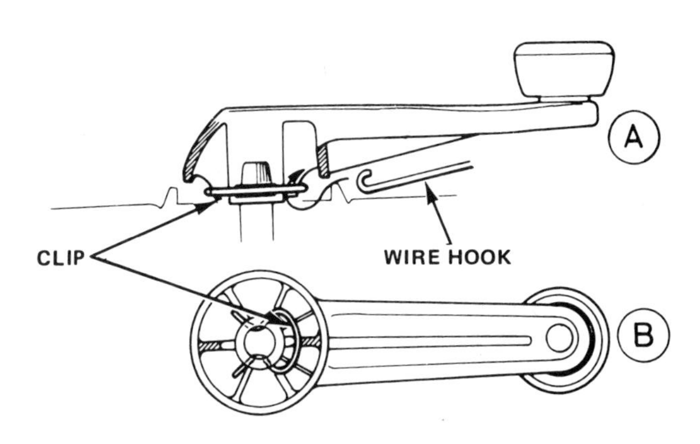

Fig. 13.236 Window regulator handle

A Removing clip B Clip ready for fitting handle to shaft

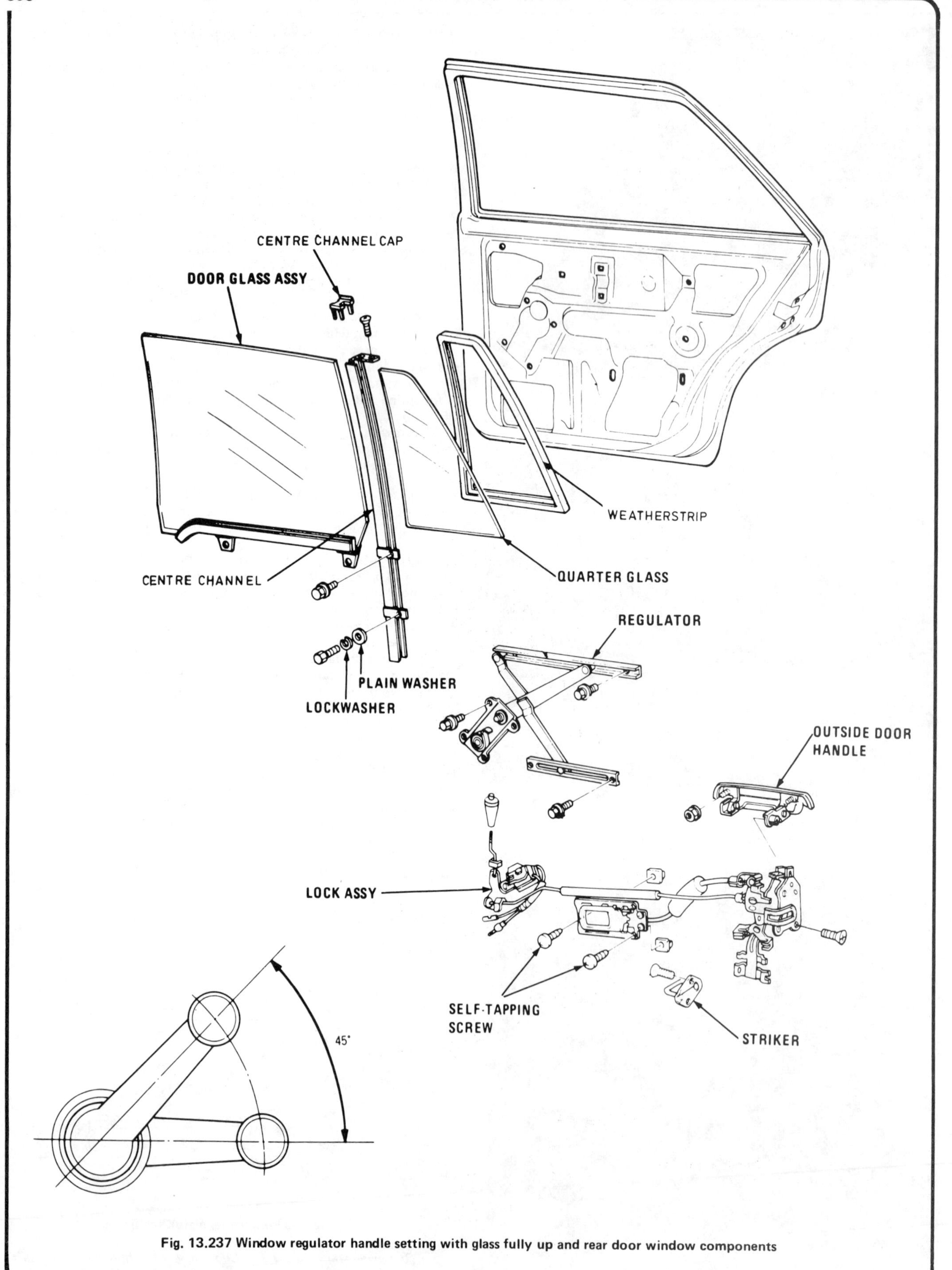

Fig. 13.237 Window regulator handle setting with glass fully up and rear door window components

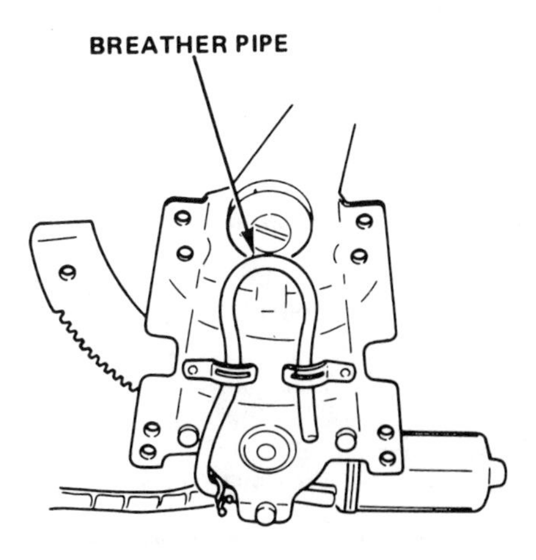

Fig. 13.238 Power-operated window regulator

Fig. 13.239 Power door lock actuator

Fig. 13.240 Power door lock switch

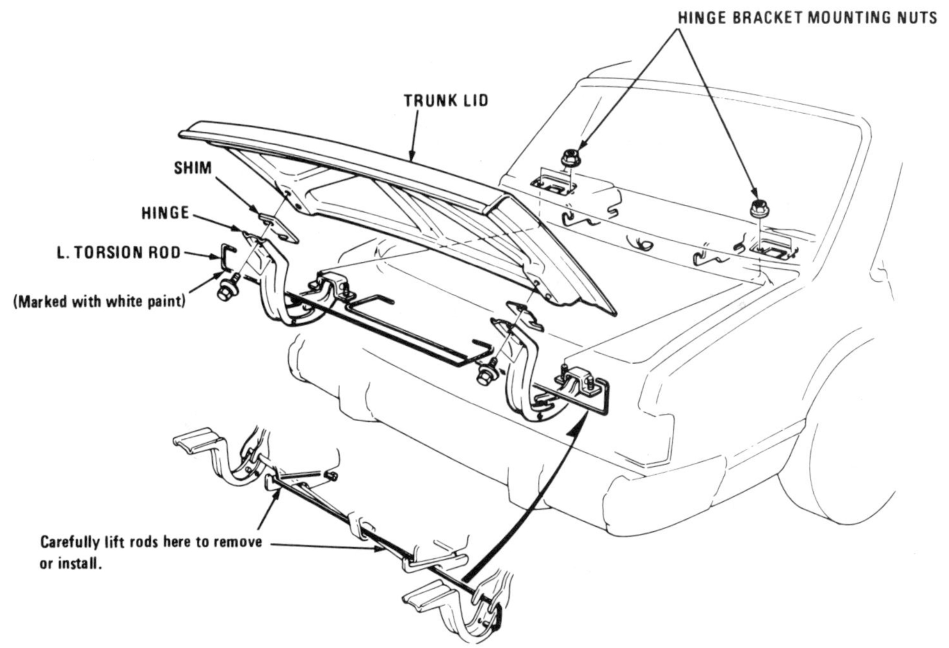

Fig. 13.241 Luggage boot lid

21 Remove the latch fixing bolts and lift the latch assembly away from the boot rear panel to gain access to the rear of the latch assembly.
22 Unclip the latch outer cable from its clip on the latch body and then release the ferrule on the end of the inner cable.
23 To remove the boot lock, slide out the clip which secures the lock cylinder.
24 If the operating cable is to be renewed, tie a cord to its end so that the new one can be drawn into position.
25 Release the locknut and turn the adjuster at the latch to adjust the cable.

Fuel filler lid lock and control lever

26 The control lever is located together with the one for the luggage boot lid beside the driver's seat.
27 To dismantle the control levers, first prise off their plastic covers.
28 Prise out the small blanking plate from the top of the moulded cover and extract the screw which is now exposed.
29 Unscrew the two fixing bolts, lift the control lever assembly and disconnect the cables.
30 To remove the lock unit, depress and turn it in a clockwise direction as shown.

Front seat - removal and refitting

31 Push the seat fully to the rear and unscrew the front mounting bolts (photo).
32 Push the seat fully forward, take off the mounting bolt plastic covers and unscrew the bolts. Remove the seat (photo).
33 Refitting is a reversal of removal.

Rear seat (Saloon) - removal and refitting

34 Lift up the two plastic clips at the bottom of the front edge of the seat, taking care not to break the clips.
35 When both clips have been lifted, pull the rear seat forward and lift it out.

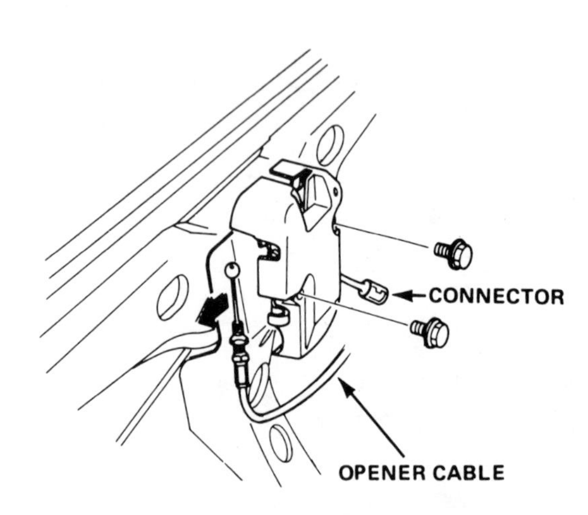

Fig. 13.242 Luggage boot lid latch

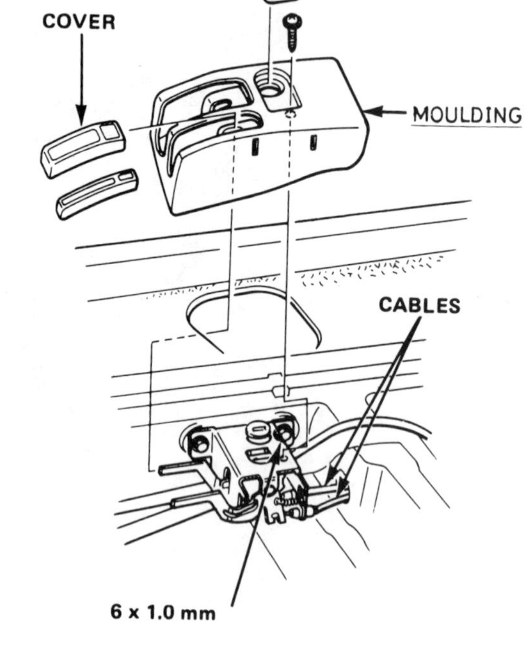

Fig. 13.244 Luggage boot and fuel filler lock remote control

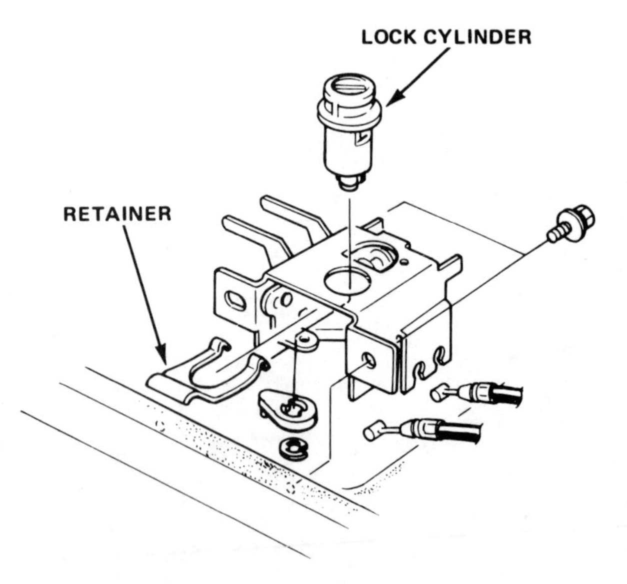

Fig. 13.243 Luggage boot cylinder lock

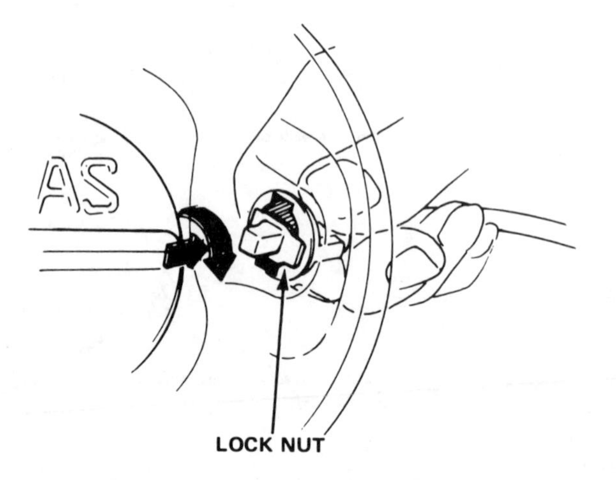

Fig. 13.245 Fuel filler cap lock unit

13A.31 Front seat front mounting

13A.32 Front seat rear mounting

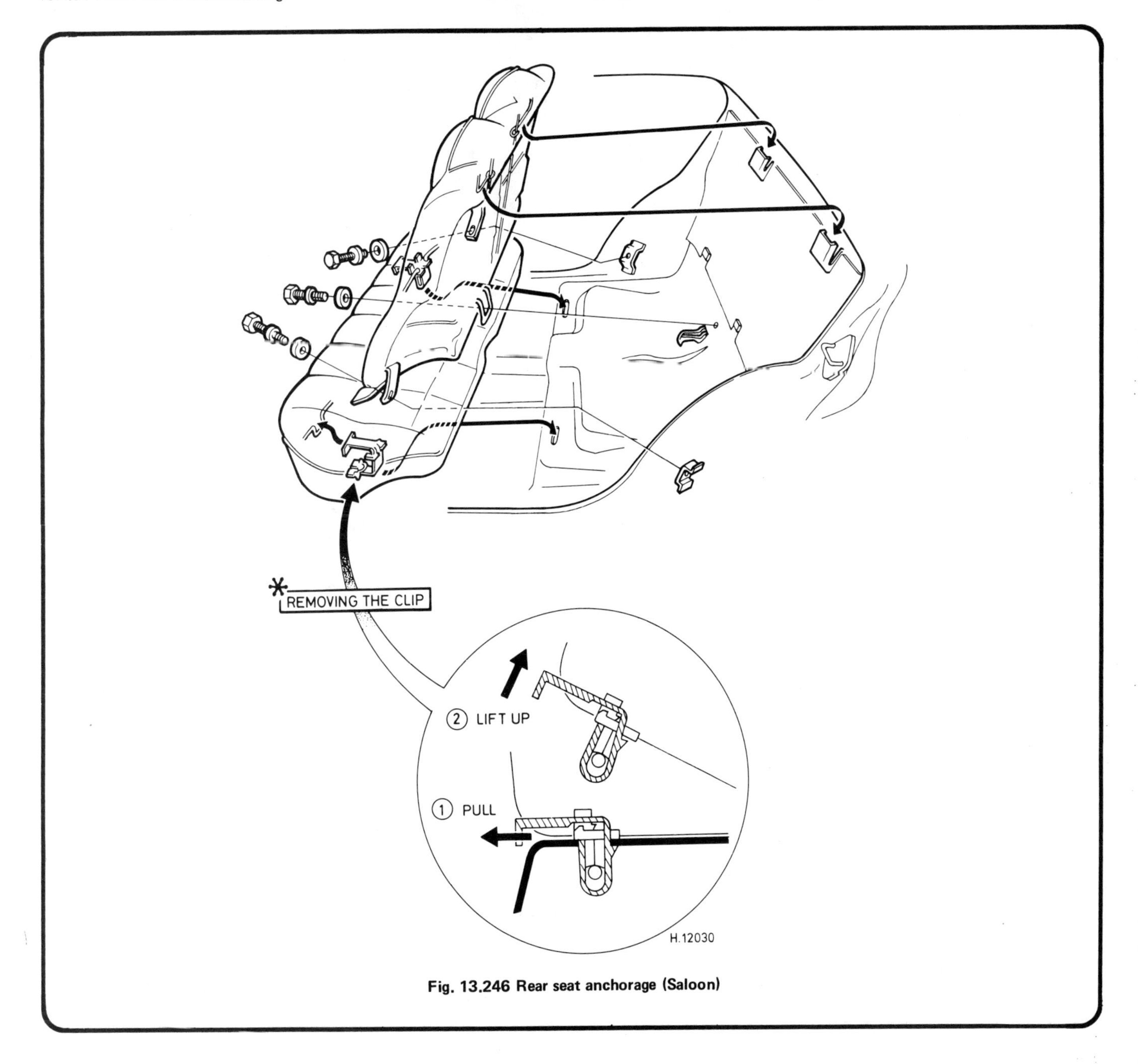

Fig. 13.246 Rear seat anchorage (Saloon)

13A.39A Rear seat pivot spacer

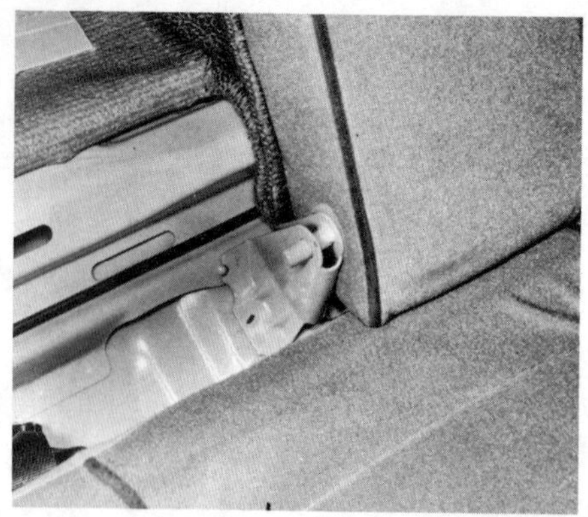

13A.39B Rear seat back pivot

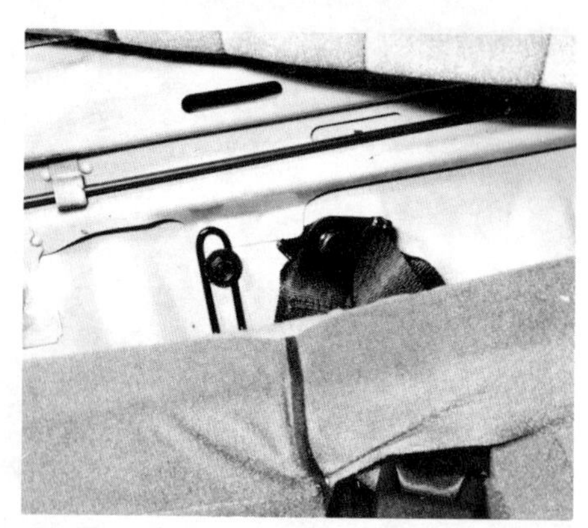

13A.40A Rear seat cushion retainer and seat belt anchorage

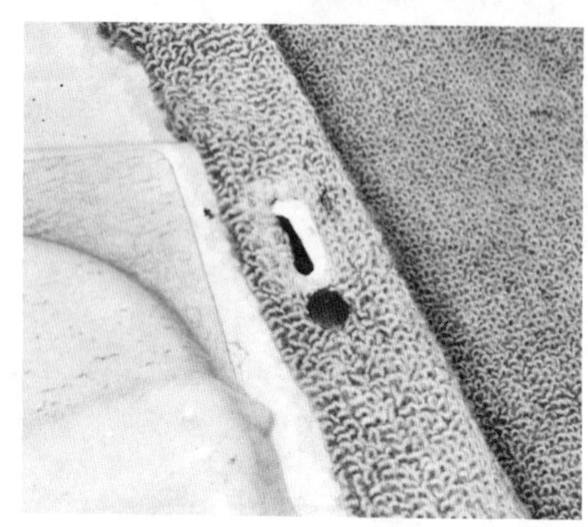

13A.40B Rear seat cushion front clip aperture

13A.40C Rear seat cushion front clip

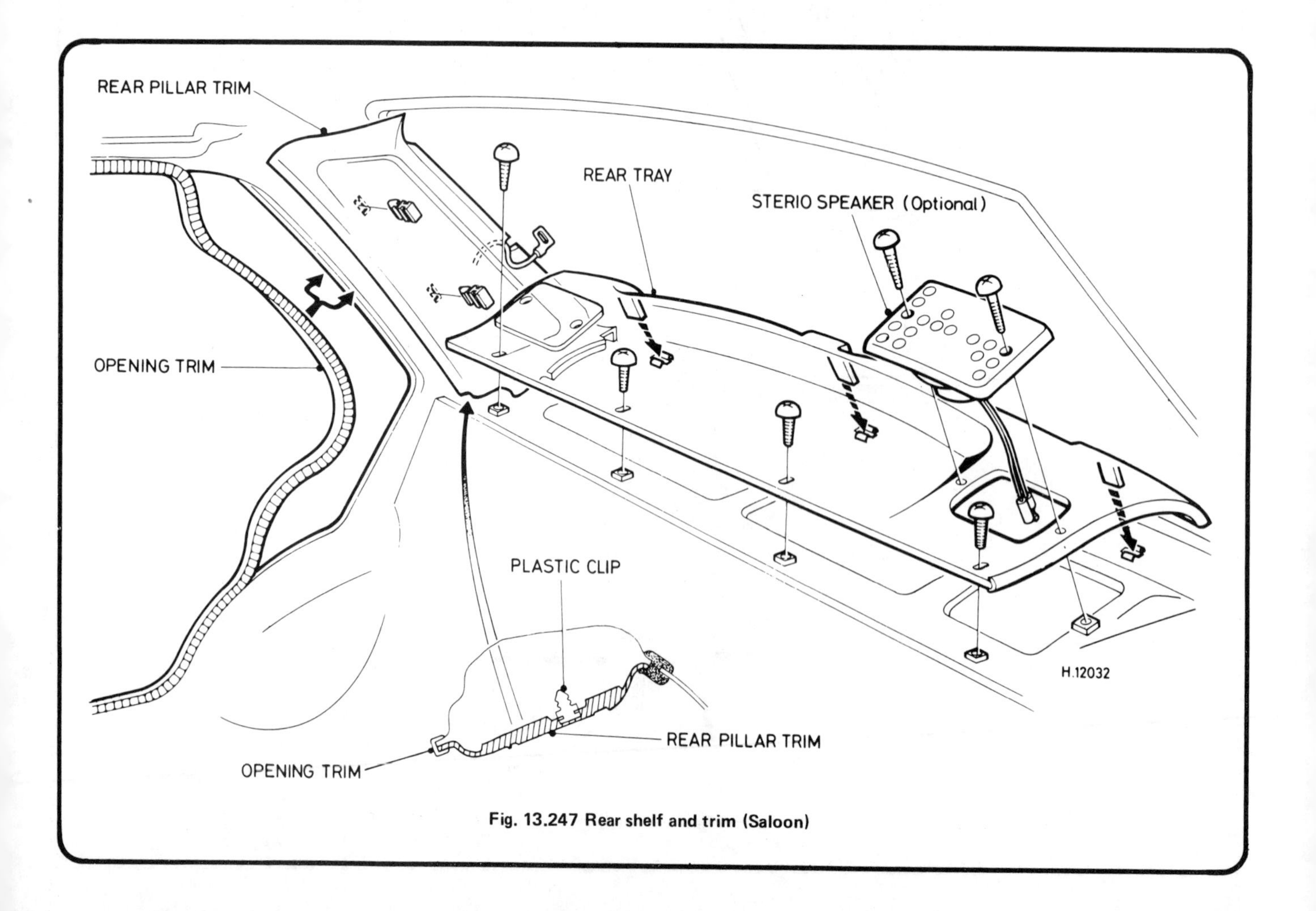

Fig. 13.247 Rear shelf and trim (Saloon)

36 Remove the three bolts which secure the brackets on the bottom of the seat back to the car body and lift the seat back to release it from its top fixings.
37 Refitting is a reversal of removal.

Rear seat (Hatchback) - removal and refitting

38 Release the carpet from the seat back.
39 Remove the spacer clip from the pivot and then slide the split seat-back section sideways off the pivots and remove it (photos).
40 Release the seat cushion retainer now exposed and tilt the cushion forward at the same time feeding the rear seat bolts through the slits in the cushion (photos).
41 Refitting is a reversal of removal.

Rear shelf and pillar trim - removal and refitting

42 Remove the back of the rear seat, as described previously.
43 If stereo speakers are fitted, remove the two fixing screws from each of the speaker grilles and pull out the speaker lead snap-connectors.
44 Remove the four fixing screws from the front edge of the rear shelf and lift the shelf out.
45 Remove the pillar trim by first pulling away the door opening trim and then levering out the two plastic fixing clips, before pulling the trim from under the rear weatherstrip.
46 Refitting is a reversal of removal.

Seat belts - maintenance, removal and refitting

47 Periodically inspect the seat belts for fraying or other damage.
4ᴄ To clean the belts use only warm water and detergent, nothing else.
49 If the belts must be removed, note that the front belt upper anchorage bolt is covered by a small blanking plate which must be prised out for access (photos).
50 When refitting a belt, make sure to retain the original sequence of fitting of the anchor components. Tighten bolts to the specified torque.

Rear view mirrors - removal and refitting

Interior

51 Pull off the rubber damper.
52 Push the mirror stem towards the windscreen and tilt it to release it from its base.
53 The base is secured by two screws.
54 When refitting the base, the cut-out must be towards the screen.
55 Fit the mirror to its base by engaging its hooks and pressing it rearwards and upwards.

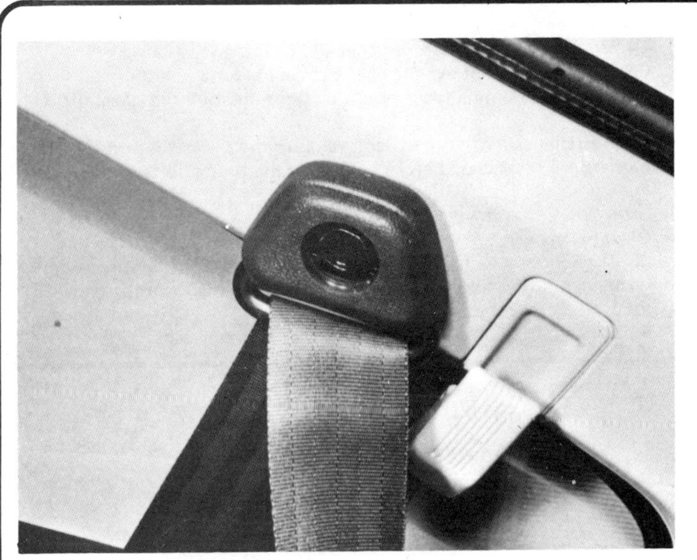

13A.49A Seat belt upper anchorage

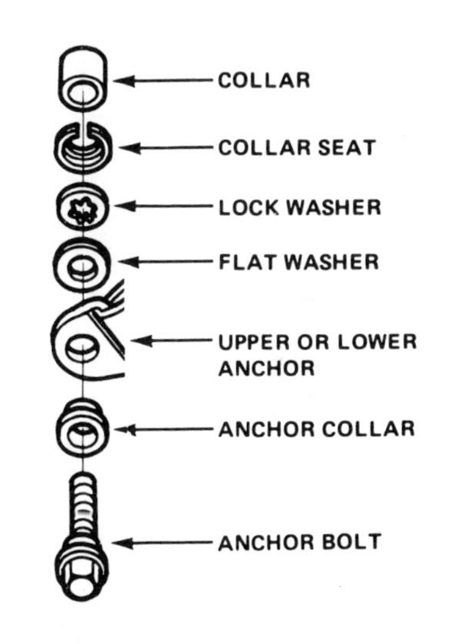

Fig. 13.248 Seat belt anchorage

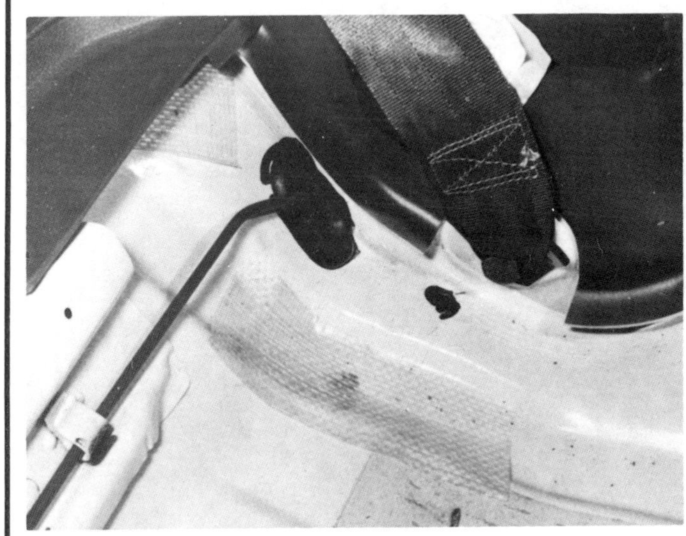

13A.49B Rear seat belt side anchorage

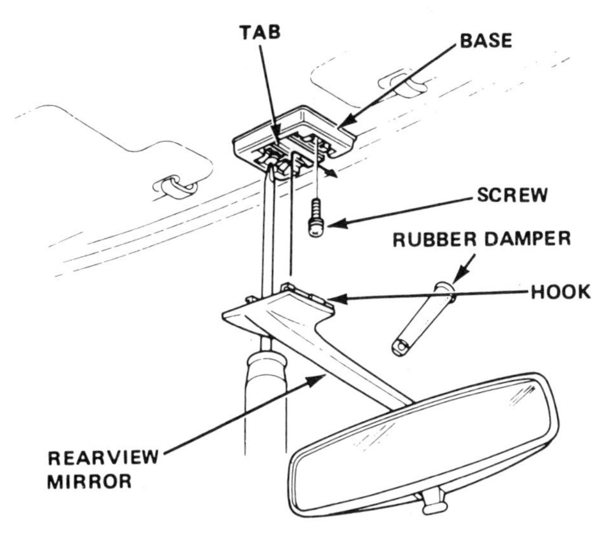

Fig. 13.249 Interior rear view mirror

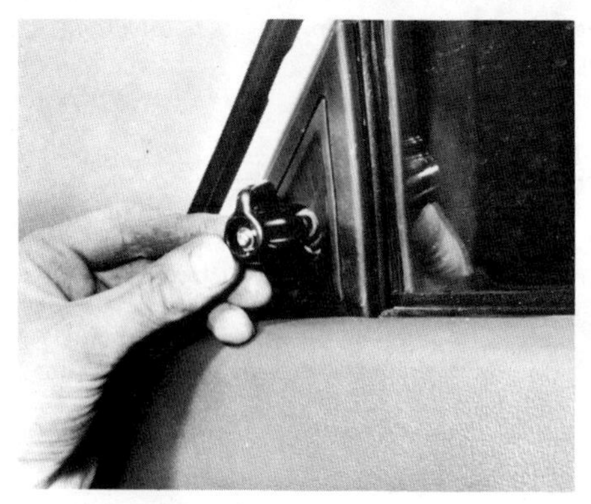

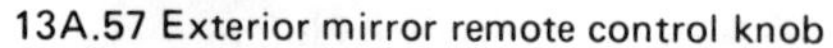

13A.57 Exterior mirror remote control knob

13A.58A Exterior mirror mounting cover plate

13A.58B Exterior mirror mounting screws

Exterior (remotely-controlled type)

56 Prise out the plate from the centre of the knob.

57 Extract the screw now exposed and pull off the knob (photo).

58 Prise out the triangular cover plate to expose the mirror mounting screws. Remove the screws and the mirror. Refitting is a reversal of removal (photos).

Facia panel - removal and refitting

59 Remove the lower covers from under the facia panel. Also remove the fuse box cover.

60 Remove the steering column mounting bolts and lower the column.

61 Remove the fuse box mounting bolts and move the fuse box away from the facia.

62 Remove the instrument panel as described in Section 11 of this Supplement.

63 Remove the heater control panel and extract the control panel frame screws.

64 Remove the facia centre panel and clock.

65 Remove the ashtray, the choke cable holder and knob.

66 Unscrew the nine facia mounting bolts and pull the panel off its guide pin.

67 Refitting is a reversal of removal, but make sure that the wiring harness is not pinched before tightening the fixing bolts.

Sunroof - adjustments

Glass height

68 If the glass weatherstrip is not level with the roof all the way round its edge, pull the sunshade back and prise the plug from the glass mounting bracket cover.

69 Extract the screw and slide the cover off rearwards.

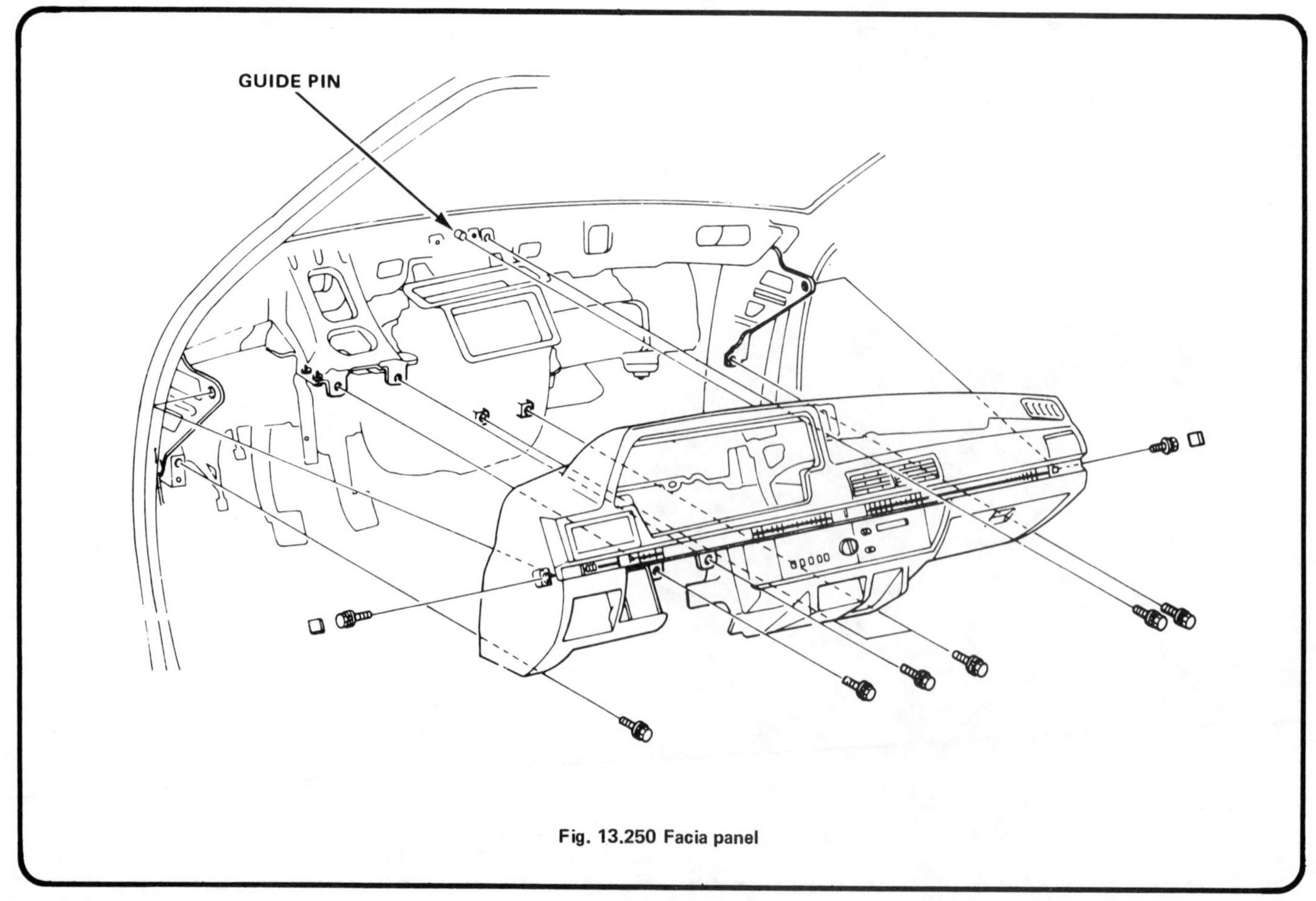

Fig. 13.250 Facia panel

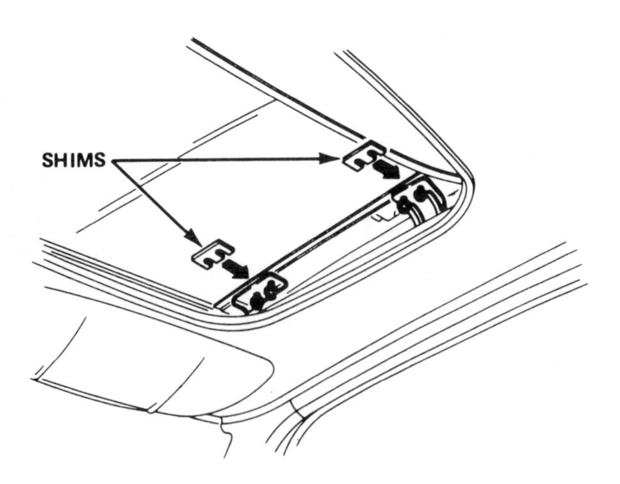

Fig. 13.251 Sunroof glass height adjustment shims

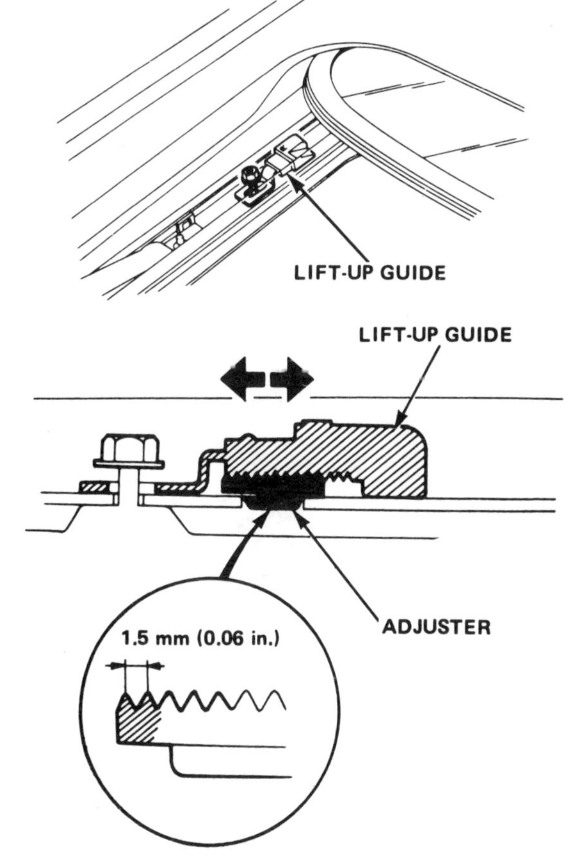

Fig. 13.252 Sunroof rear edge closing adjustment diagram

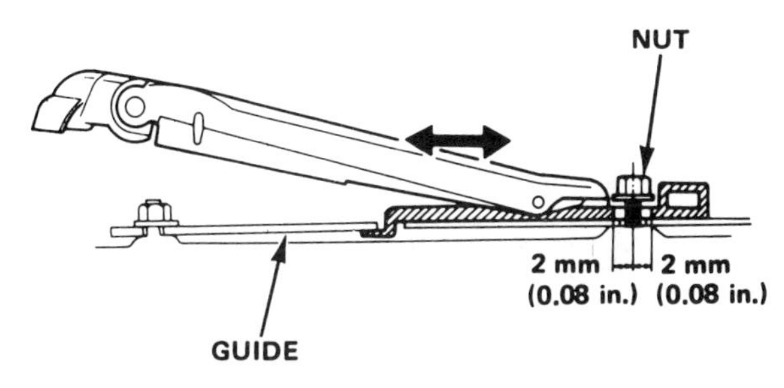

Fig. 13.253 Wind deflector adjustment diagram

70 Loosen the mounting bracket nuts and insert shims between the glass frame and the bracket - as necessary.

Glass side clearance

71 Binding on one side can be corrected by loosening the mounting bracket nuts as described in earlier paragraphs and moving the glass to left or right as necessary.

Rear edge closing adjustment

72 Open the glass about 12.0 in (305.0 mm) and then close it to check the point where the rear edge begins to rise.

73 If the glass rises too soon or too late, open the glass fully, remove the rail covers from both sides and release the lift-up guide nuts.

74 Move the guides forwards or backwards as necessary to achieve the correct lift.

Wind deflector - adjustment

75 The wind deflector should be adjusted so that the edge of its seal contacts the roof evenly otherwise wind noise will develop.

76 The deflector can be adjusted forward or backwards by 0.08 in (2.0 mm), but its height cannot be altered.

Sunroof and shade - removal and refitting

77 Move the sunshade to the fully open position.

78 Prise the plugs from the bracket covers, extract the screw and remove the cover.

79 Close the glass and remove the mounting nuts.

80 Remove the glass by raising and pulling it forward.

81 Remove the guide rail mounting nuts, raise and spread the ends of the rails and slide the sunshade out.

82 Refitting is a reversal of removal, adjust as previously described.

PART B - HEATING AND AIR CONDITIONING

Heater - removal, overhaul and refitting

1 Drain the cooling system.

2 Disconnect the heater hoses at the engine compartment rear bulkhead.

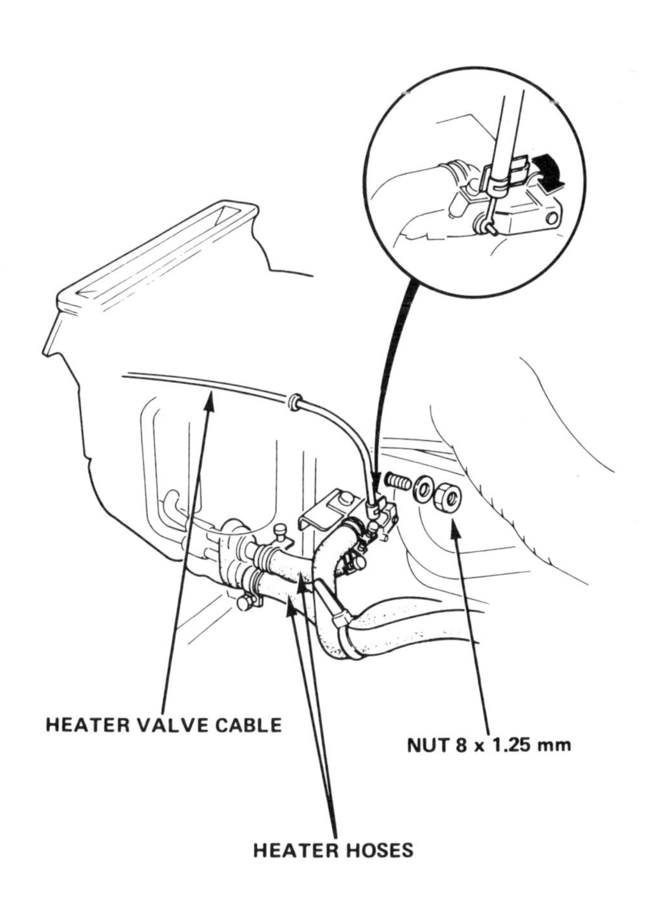

Fig. 13.254 Heater hose and coolant valve cable

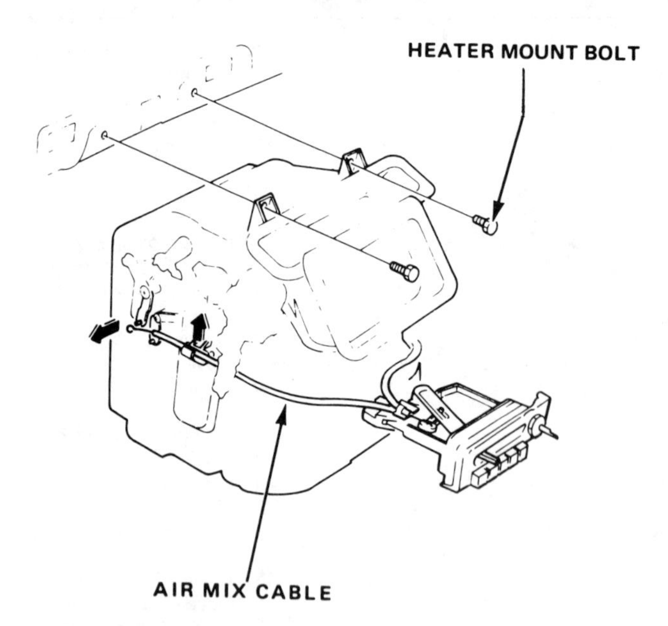

Fig. 13.255 Heater air mix cable

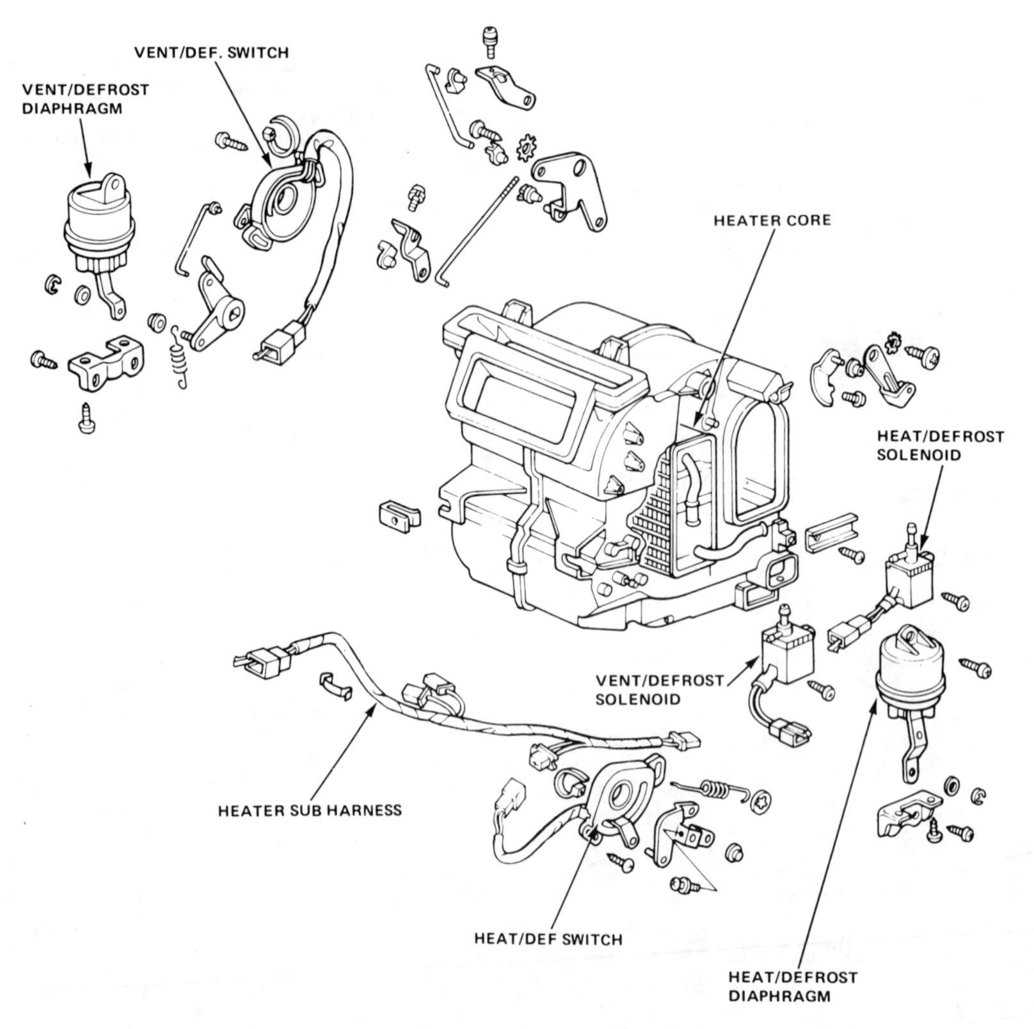

Fig. 13.256 Heater external components

3 Disconnect the control cable from the heater valve.
4 Remove the heater lower mounting nut.
5 Remove the facia panel as previously described.
6 Remove the heater duct.
7 On models with lever type heater controls, disconnect the airflow direction lever cable.
8 Disconnect the air mix cable from the heater.
9 Prise off the clip and remove the floor duct from the passenger side.
10 Prise off the clip and remove the floor duct from the driver's side.
11 Remove the two remaining heater mounting bolts and pull the heater away from the body.
12 Disconnect the vacuum hose and remove the heater from the car.
13 The heater can be dismantled by prising off the heater casing clips.
14 Refitting is a reversal of removal. Check the adjustment of the controls, fill and bleed the cooling system.

Heater blower - removal, overhaul and refitting

15 Remove the glove box.
16 Remove the floor duct and the moulded insulator pad.
17 Remove the blower duct.
18 Remove the three mounting bolts and lower the blower to the floor.
19 Disconnect the wiring plug and the vacuum hose from the rear of the blower and remove the blower from the car.
20 The blower can be dismantled by prising off the casing clips.
21 Refitting is a reversal of removal.

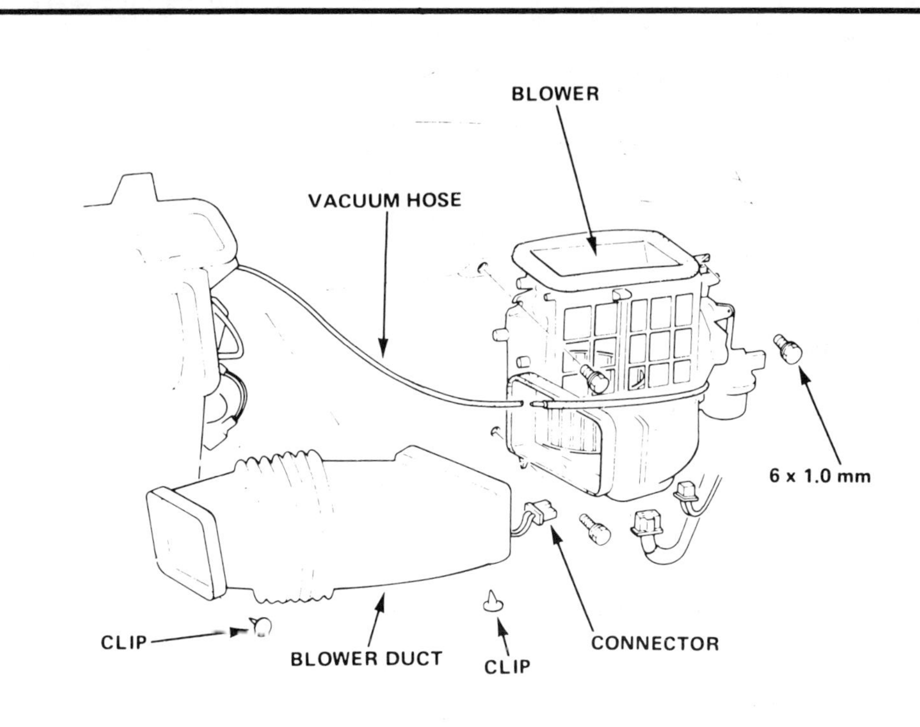

Fig. 13.257 Heater blower

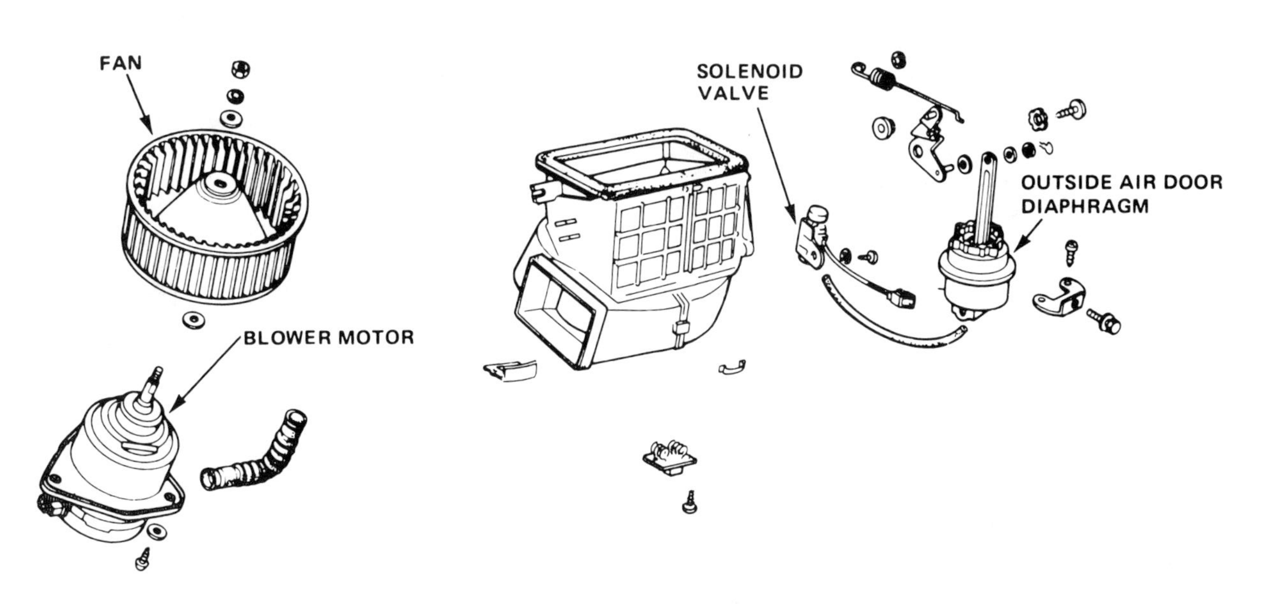

Fig. 13.258 Heater blower dismantled

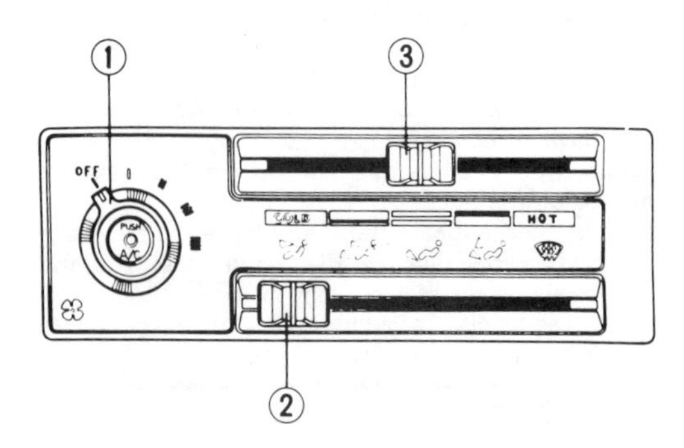

Fig. 13.259 Heater slide lever type controls

1 *Blower switch*
2 *Air direction (function) lever*
3 *Temperature lever*

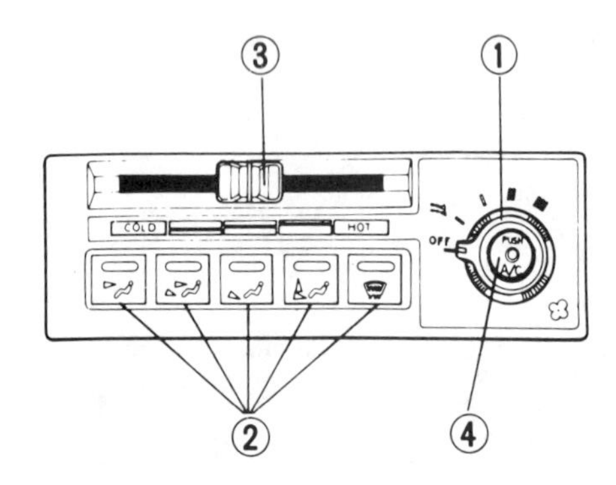

Fig. 13.260 Heater push-button type controls

1 *Blower switch*
2 *Air direction (function) buttons*
3 *Temperature lever*
4 *Air conditioner switch (option)*

Heater controls - description

22 The heater controls may be of lever or push-button type according to model.

23 The controls will vary the directional flow to the car interior, vary the heat and select fresh or recirculated air.

24 The system is of flow-through type with vents for extracting the stale air either behind the rear quarter window (Saloon) or in the tailgate (Hatchback).

Heater control cables - adjustment

Air mix cable

25 Slide the temperature lever to HOT. Release the cable conduit spring clamp.

26 Pull the arm of the air mix door (which is located in front of the heater matrix) upwards.

27 Slide the cable conduit away from the end of the inner cable to eliminate any slack, but not enough to move the control lever. Secure the conduit with the clamp.

Heater coolant valve cable

28 Slide the temperature control lever to COLD.

29 Close the heater valve with the fingers.

30 Release the cable conduit spring clamp.

31 Clamp the cable conduit with the spring clamp.

'Mild flow' cable

32 Close the air flap fully, release the cable clamp screw.

33 Slide the cable conduit away from the end of the inner cable to eliminate any slack then tighten the cable clamp screw.

Function (air distribution) cable

34 Slide the function lever to VENT.

35 Release the cable clamp.

36 Set the control arm on the heater to VENT.

37 Clamp the cable.

Lever type heater control panel - removal and refitting

38 Pull off the control knobs.

39 Prise the heater control panel escutcheon out with a screwdriver. Release the cable clips.

40 Disconnect the wiring plugs and remove the panel fixing screws. Remove the panel.

41 Refitting is a reversal of removal.

Push-button type heater control panel - removal and refitting

42 Pull off the control knobs.

43 Prise out the control panel escutcheon with a screwdriver.

44 Extract the fixing screws, disconnect the wiring plugs and the cable clamps and withdraw the control panel.

45 Refitting is a reversal of removal.

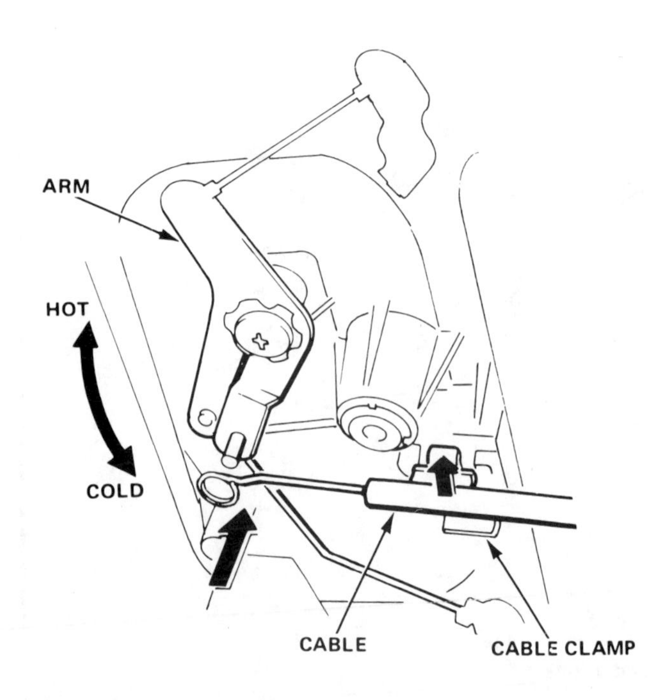

Fig. 13.261 Air mix cable

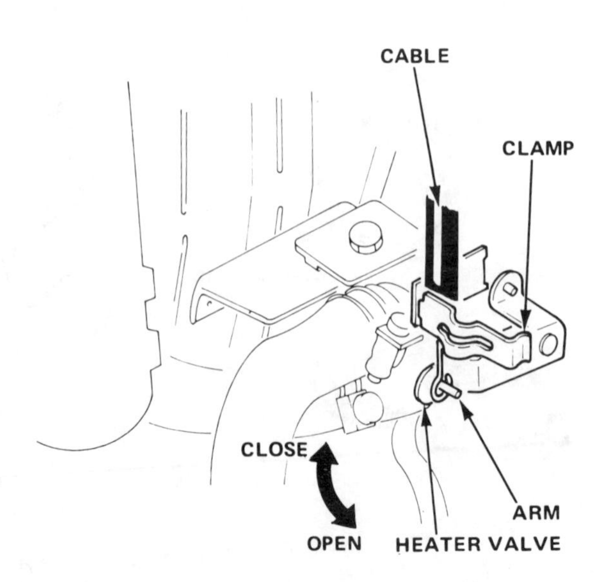

Fig. 13.262 Heater coolant valve cable

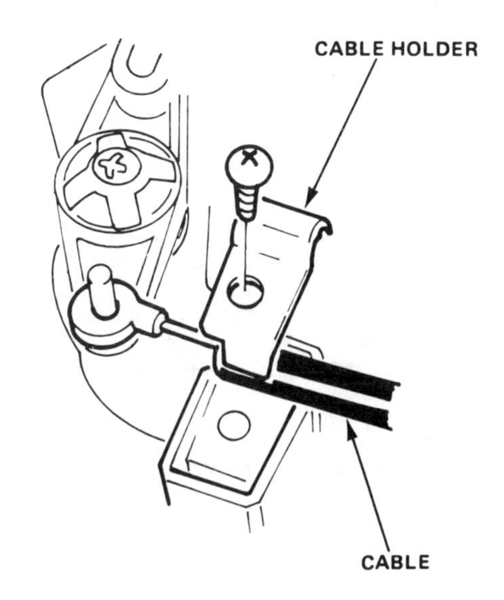

Fig. 13.263 'Mild flow' cable

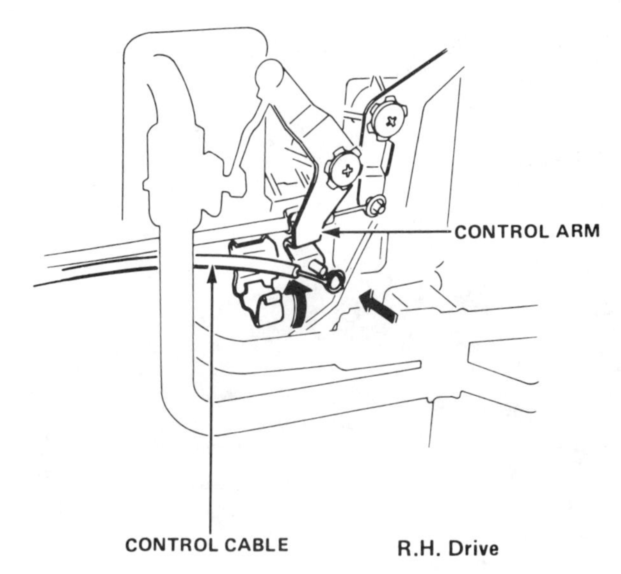

Fig. 13.264 Heater function cable at heater casing

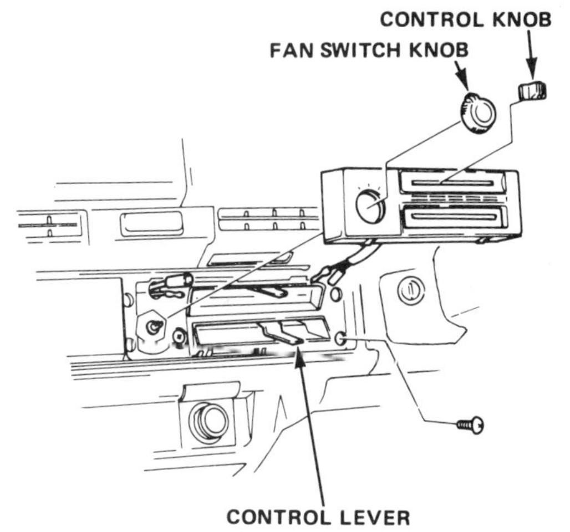

Fig. 13.265 Lever type control panel escutcheon

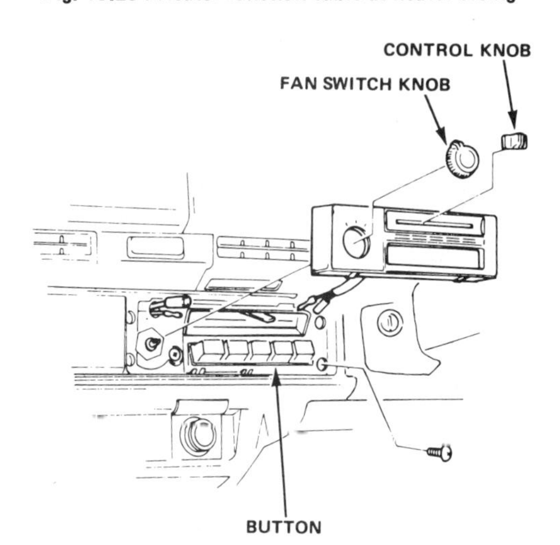

Fig. 13.266 Push-button control panel escutcheon

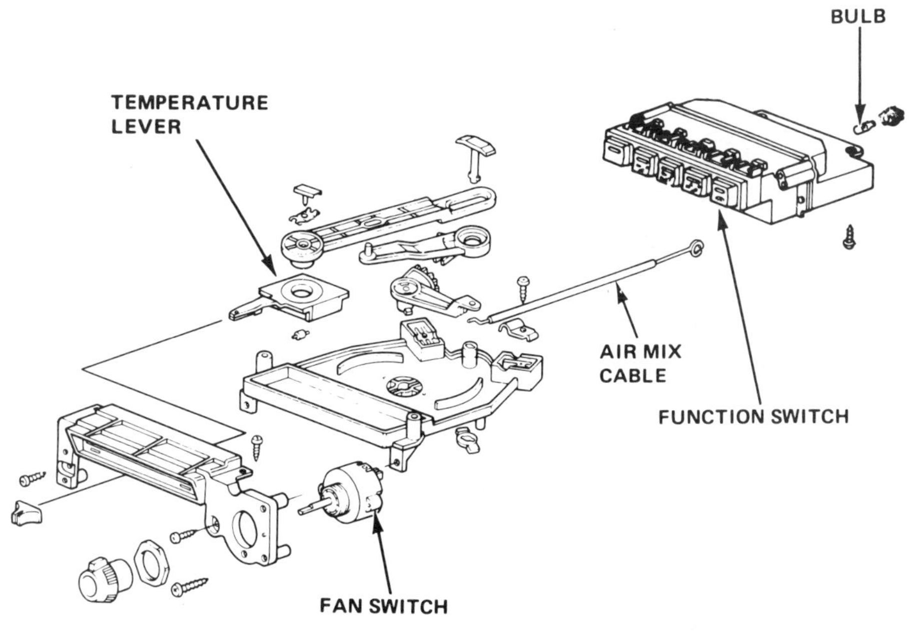

Fig. 13.267 Push-button control panel components

13B.47 Heater control vacuum tank

Vacuum-operated function control

46 An essential component of the heater control system is the vacuum circuit. This uses vacuum from the intake manifold to operate the diaphragm units within the system.

47 A vacuum reservoir tank with non-return valve is located under the scuttle grille just in front of the windscreen (photo).

Air conditioner - description and maintenance

48 The air conditioner is available as a factory-fitted option on certain models. The main components consist of a compressor, a condensor, an evaporator and a receiver/dryer.

49 It is not recommended that the system is discharged by the home mechanic - refer to the Warning Note in Chapter 1, Section 3.

50 Once the system has been discharged professionally, however, there is no reason why the individual components cannot be removed and new ones fitted provided the open lines or ports are sealed immediately after disconnection. The seals on new units should not be removed until just before they are to be connected to the system. These precautions are to prevent the admission of moisture.

51 To keep the system in perfect order, carry out the following maintenance items.

52 Regularly brush the fins of the condensor free from dirt and flies.

53 Keep the compressor drivebelt in good condition and correctly tensioned with a deflection of 0.47 to 0.63 in (12.0 to 16.0 mm) at the mid-point of the belt run.

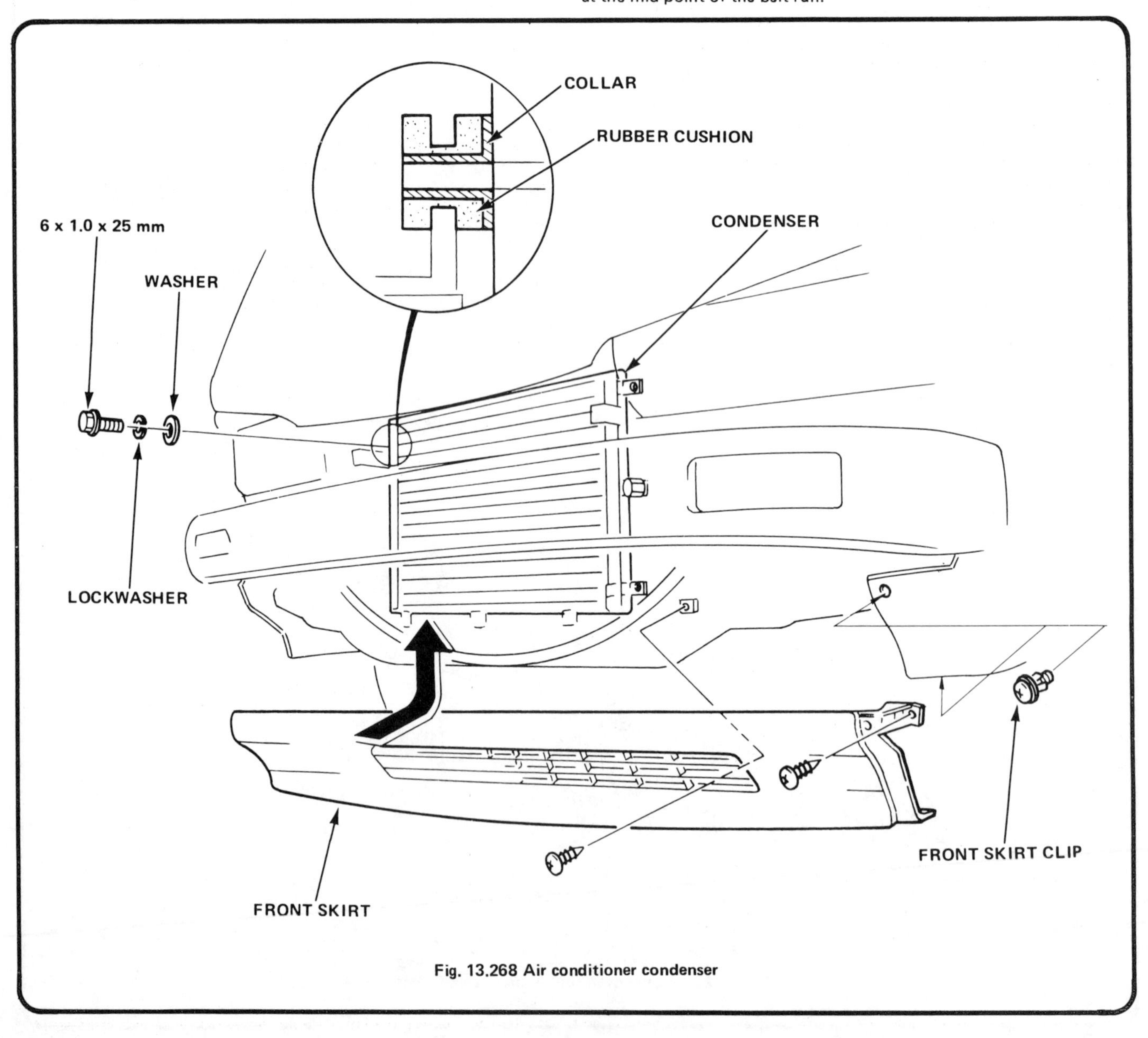

Fig. 13.268 Air conditioner condenser

54 Occasionally, start the engine and allow it to run at fast idle for a few minutes while looking through the sight glass on the receiver dryer. The appearance of continuous bubbles or foam indicates a low refrigerant level which should be rectified by your dealer or refrigeration engineer.
55 During the winter months, operate the air conditioner for ten minutes once a week to lubricate the seals and the interior of the compressor.

Compressor - removal and refitting
56 Start the engine, allow it to idle and switch on the air conditioner for a few minutes.
57 Switch off the engine and air conditioner and disconnect the lead from the battery negative terminal.
58 Disconnect the compressor clutch lead.
59 Have the system discharged by your dealer or a competent refrigeration engineer.
60 Disconnect the suction and discharge hoses from the compressor. Cap all openings immediately.
61 Loosen the compressor adjusting and mounting bolts and remove the belt cover.
62 Remove the compressor drivebelt.
63 Remove the mounting bolts and lift the compressor from its mountings.
64 Refit by reversing the removal operations. If a new compressor is being fitted, pour 0.95 fl. oz. (30.0 cc) through the suction port on the compressor. Tighten all fixings on the specified torque.
65 Adjust the drivebelt and have the system recharged.

Condenser - removal and refitting
66 Disconnect the negative lead from the battery.
67 Have the system discharged professionally.
68 Disconnect the pipeline and hose from the condenser. Cap the openings immediately.
69 Extract the fixing screws and remove the front skirt.
70 Remove the condenser mounting bolts and withdraw the condenser downwards.
71 Refitting is a reversal of removal, but if a new condenser is being fitted, pour 0.3 fl. oz. (10.0 cc) of refrigerant oil into it.
72 Tighten all fixings to the specified torque. Have the system recharged.

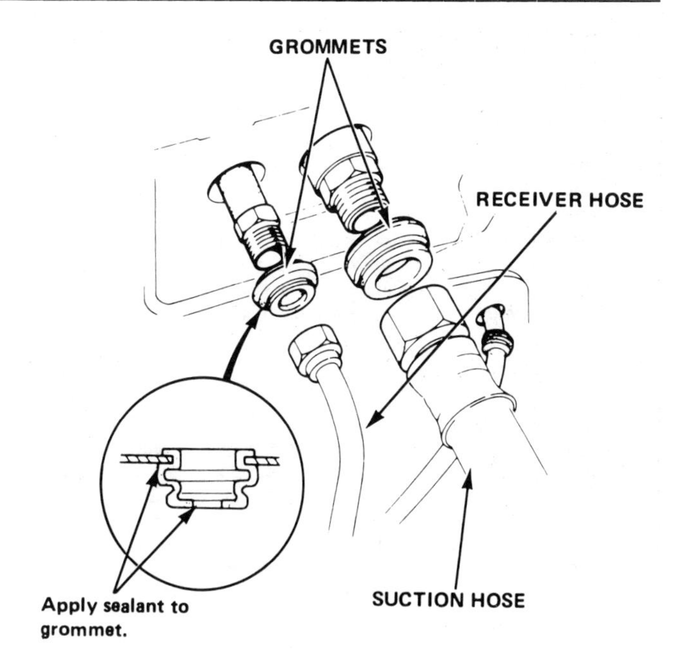

Fig. 13.269 Evaporator hose connections

Evaporator - removal and refitting
73 Disconnect the lead from the battery negative terminal.
74 Have the system discharged professionally.
75 Disconnect the pipe line and hose from the evaporator and immediately cap all openings.
76 Remove the grommets.
77 Remove the glove box and its frame.
78 Unscrew the three evaporator mounting bolts.
79 Refitting is a reversal of removal. Make sure the sealing bands are securely fitted, tighten all fixings to the specified torque.
80 Have the system recharged.

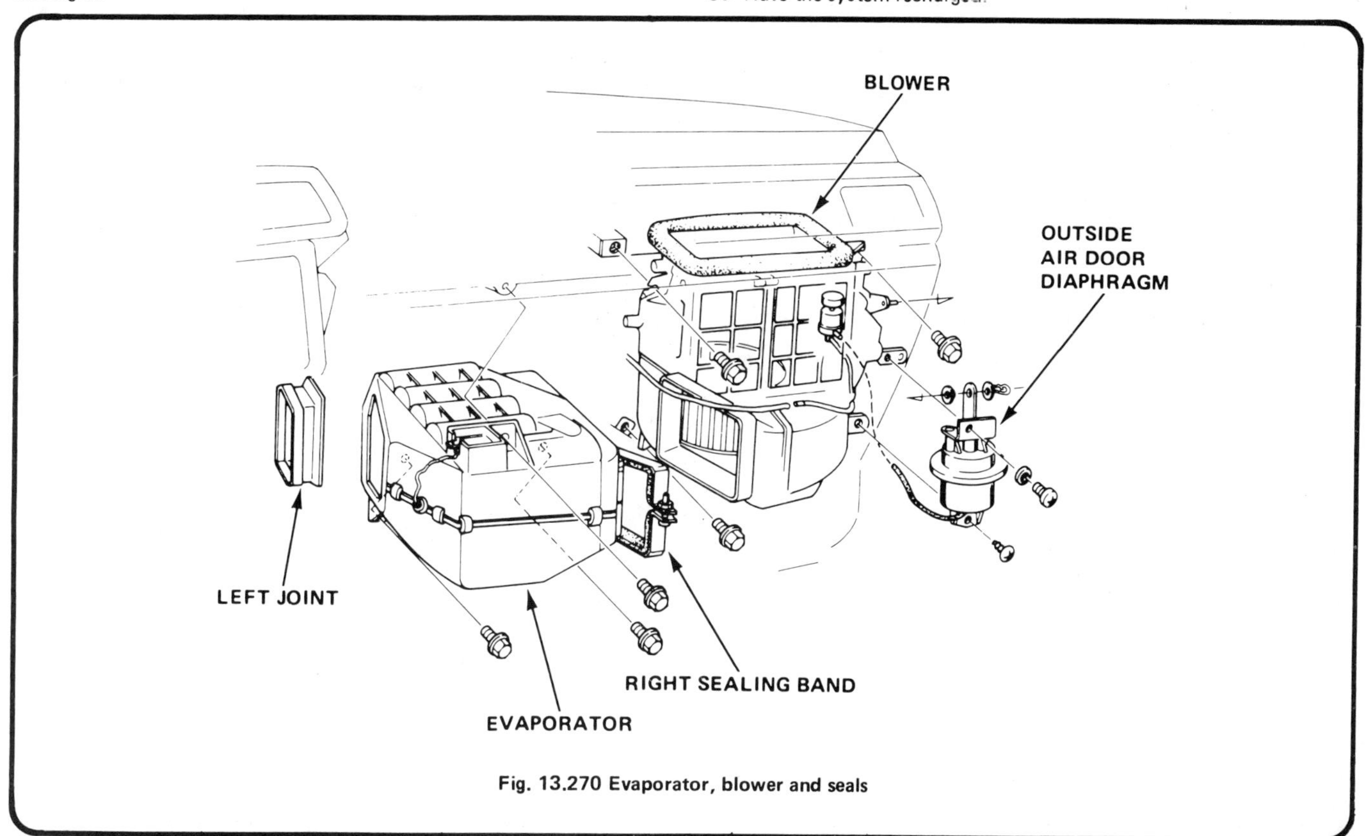

Fig. 13.270 Evaporator, blower and seals

Safety first!

Professional motor mechanics are trained in safe working procedures. However enthusiastic you may be about getting on with the job in hand, do take the time to ensure that your safety is not put at risk. A moment's lack of attention can result in an accident, as can failure to observe certain elementary precautions.

There will always be new ways of having accidents, and the following points do not pretend to be a comprehensive list of all dangers; they are intended rather to make you aware of the risks and to encourage a safety-conscious approach to all work you carry out on your vehicle.

Essential DOs and DON'Ts

DON'T rely on a single jack when working underneath the vehicle. Always use reliable additional means of support, such as axle stands, securely placed under a part of the vehicle that you know will not give way.
DON'T attempt to loosen or tighten high-torque nuts (e.g. wheel hub nuts) while the vehicle is on a jack; it may be pulled off.
DON'T start the engine without first ascertaining that the transmission is in neutral (or 'Park' where applicable) and the parking brake applied.
DON'T suddenly remove the filler cap from a hot cooling system – cover it with a cloth and release the pressure gradually first, or you may get scalded by escaping coolant.
DON'T attempt to drain oil until you are sure it has cooled sufficiently to avoid scalding you.
DON'T grasp any part of the engine, exhaust or catalytic converter without first ascertaining that it is sufficiently cool to avoid burning you.
DON'T allow brake fluid or antifreeze to contact vehicle paintwork.
DON'T syphon toxic liquids such as fuel, brake fluid or antifreeze by mouth, or allow them to remain on your skin.
DON'T inhale dust – it may be injurious to health (see *Asbestos* below).
DON'T allow any spilt oil or grease to remain on the floor – wipe it up straight away, before someone slips on it.
DON'T use ill-fitting spanners or other tools which may slip and cause injury.
DON'T attempt to lift a heavy component which may be beyond your capability – get assistance.
DON'T rush to finish a job, or take unverified short cuts.
DON'T allow children or animals in or around an unattended vehicle.
DO wear eye protection when using power tools such as drill, sander, bench grinder etc, and when working under the vehicle.
DO use a barrier cream on your hands prior to undertaking dirty jobs – it will protect your skin from infection as well as making the dirt easier to remove afterwards; but make sure your hands aren't left slippery.
DO keep loose clothing (cuffs, tie etc) and long hair well out of the way of moving mechanical parts.
DO remove rings, wristwatch etc, before working on the vehicle – especially the electrical system.
DO ensure that any lifting tackle used has a safe working load rating adequate for the job.
DO keep your work area tidy – it is only too easy to fall over articles left lying around.
DO get someone to check periodically that all is well, when working alone on the vehicle.
DO carry out work in a logical sequence and check that everything is correctly assembled and tightened afterwards.
DO remember that your vehicle's safety affects that of yourself and others. If in doubt on any point, get specialist advice.
IF, in spite of following these precautions, you are unfortunate enough to injure yourself, seek medical attention as soon as possible.

Asbestos

Certain friction, insulating, sealing, and other products – such as brake linings, brake bands, clutch linings, torque converters, gaskets, etc – contain asbestos. *Extreme care must be taken to avoid inhalation of dust from such products since it is hazardous to health.* If in doubt, assume that they *do* contain asbestos.

Fire

Remember at all times that petrol (gasoline) is highly flammable. Never smoke, or have any kind of naked flame around, when working on the vehicle. But the risk does not end there – a spark caused by an electrical short-circuit, by two metal surfaces contacting each other, by careless use of tools, or even by static electricity built up in your body under certain conditions, can ignite petrol vapour, which in a confined space is highly explosive.

Always disconnect the battery earth (ground) terminal before working on any part of the fuel or electrical system, and never risk spilling fuel on to a hot engine or exhaust.

It is recommended that a fire extinguisher of a type suitable for fuel and electrical fires is kept handy in the garage or workplace at all times. Never try to extinguish a fuel or electrical fire with water.

Fumes

Certain fumes are highly toxic and can quickly cause unconsciousness and even death if inhaled to any extent. Petrol (gasoline) vapour comes into this category, as do the vapours from certain solvents such as trichloroethylene. Any draining or pouring of such volatile fluids should be done in a well ventilated area.

When using cleaning fluids and solvents, read the instructions carefully. Never use materials from unmarked containers – they may give off poisonous vapours.

Never run the engine of a motor vehicle in an enclosed space such as a garage. Exhaust fumes contain carbon monoxide which is extremely poisonous; if you need to run the engine, always do so in the open air or at least have the rear of the vehicle outside the workplace.

If you are fortunate enough to have the use of an inspection pit, never drain or pour petrol, and never run the engine, while the vehicle is standing over it; the fumes, being heavier than air, will concentrate in the pit with possibly lethal results.

The battery

Never cause a spark, or allow a naked light, near the vehicle's battery. It will normally be giving off a certain amount of hydrogen gas, which is highly explosive.

Always disconnect the battery earth (ground) terminal before working on the fuel or electrical systems.

If possible, loosen the filler plugs or cover when charging the battery from an external source. Do not charge at an excessive rate or the battery may burst.

Take care when topping up and when carrying the battery. The acid electrolyte, even when diluted, is very corrosive and should not be allowed to contact the eyes or skin.

If you ever need to prepare electrolyte yourself, always add the acid slowly to the water, and never the other way round. Protect against splashes by wearing rubber gloves and goggles.

When jump starting a car using a booster battery, for negative earth (ground) vehicles, connect the jump leads in the following sequence: First connect one jump lead between the positive (+) terminals of the two batteries. Then connect the other jump lead first to the negative (–) terminal of the booster battery, and then to a good earthing (ground) point on the vehicle to be started, at least 18 in (45 cm) from the battery if possible. Ensure that hands and jump leads are clear of any moving parts, and that the two vehicles do not touch. Disconnect the leads in the reverse order.

Mains electricity

When using an electric power tool, inspection light etc, which works from the mains, always ensure that the appliance is correctly connected to its plug and that, where necessary, it is properly earthed (grounded). Do not use such appliances in damp conditions and, again, beware of creating a spark or applying excessive heat in the vicinity of fuel or fuel vapour.

Ignition HT voltage

A severe electric shock can result from touching certain parts of the ignition system, such as the HT leads, when the engine is running or being cranked, particularly if components are damp or the insulation is defective. Where an electronic ignition system is fitted, the HT voltage is much higher and could prove fatal.

Fault diagnosis

Introduction

The vehicle owner who does his or her own maintenance according to the recommended schedules should not have to use this section of the manual very often. Modern component reliability is such that, provided those items subject to wear or deterioration are inspected or renewed at the specified intervals, sudden failure is comparatively rare. Faults do not usually just happen as a result of sudden failure, but develop over a period of time. Major mechanical failures in particular are usually preceded by characteristic symptoms over hundreds or even thousands of miles. Those components which do occasionally fail without warning are often small and easily carried in the vehicle.

With any fault finding, the first step is to decide where to begin investigations. Sometimes this is obvious, but on other occasions a little detective work will be necessary. The owner who makes half a dozen haphazard adjustments or replacements may be successful in curing a fault (or its symptoms), but he will be none the wiser if the fault recurs and he may well have spent more time and money than was necessary. A calm and logical approach will be found to be more satisfactory in the long run. Always take into account any warning signs or abnormalities that may have been noticed in the period preceding the fault – power loss, high or low gauge readings, unusual noises or smells, etc – and remember that failure of components such as fuses or spark plugs may only be pointers to some underlying fault.

The pages which follow here are intended to help in cases of failure to start or breakdown on the road. There is also a Fault Diagnosis Section at the end of each Chapter which should be consulted if the preliminary checks prove unfruitful. Whatever the fault, certain basic principles apply. These are as follows:

Verify the fault. This is simply a matter of being sure that you know what the symptoms are before starting work. This is particularly important if you are investigating a fault for someone else who may not have described it very accurately.

Don't overlook the obvious. For example, if the vehicle won't start, is there petrol in the tank? (Don't take anyone else's word on this particular point, and don't trust the fuel gauge either!) If an electrical fault is indicated, look for loose or broken wires before digging out the test gear.

Cure the disease, not the symptom. Substituting a flat battery with a fully charged one will get you off the hard shoulder, but if the underlying cause is not attended to, the new battery will go the same way. Similarly, changing oil-fouled spark plugs for a new set will get you moving again, but remember that the reason for the fouling (if it wasn't simply an incorrect grade of plug) will have to be established and corrected.

Don't take anything for granted. Particularly, don't forget that a 'new' component may itself be defective (especially if it's been rattling round in the boot for months), and don't leave components out of a fault diagnosis sequence just because they are new or recently fitted. When you do finally diagnose a difficult fault, you'll probably realise that all the evidence was there from the start.

Electrical faults

Electrical faults can be more puzzling than straightforward mechanical failures, but they are no less susceptible to logical analysis if the basic principles of operation are understood. Vehicle electrical wiring exists in extremely unfavourable conditions – heat, vibration and chemical attack – and the first things to look for are loose or corroded connections and broken or chafed wires, especially where the wires pass through holes in the bodywork or are subject to vibration.

All metal-bodied vehicles in current production have one pole of the battery 'earthed', ie connected to the vehicle bodywork, and in nearly all modern vehicles it is the negative (–) terminal. The various electrical components – motors, bulb holders etc – are also connected to earth, either by means of a lead or directly by their mountings. Electric current flows through the component and then back to the battery via the bodywork. If the component mounting is loose or corroded, or if a good path back to the battery is not available, the circuit will be incomplete and malfunction will result. The engine and/or gearbox are also earthed by means of flexible metal straps to the body or subframe; if these straps are loose or missing, starter motor, generator and ignition trouble may result.

Assuming the earth return to be satisfactory, electrical faults will be due either to component malfunction or to defects in the current supply. Individual components are dealt with in Chapters 10 and 13. If supply wires are broken or cracked internally this results in an open-circuit, and the easiest way to check for this is to bypass the suspect wire temporarily with a length of wire having a crocodile clip or suitable connector at each end. Alternatively, a 12V test lamp can be used to verify the presence of supply voltage at various points along the wire and the break can be thus isolated.

If a bare portion of a live wire touches the bodywork or other earthed metal part, the electricity will take the low-resistance path thus formed back to the battery: this is known as a short-circuit. Hopefully a short-circuit will blow a fuse, but otherwise it may cause burning of the insulation (and possibly further short-circuits) or even a fire. This is why it is inadvisable to bypass persistently blowing fuses with silver foil or wire.

Spares and tool kit

Most vehicles are supplied only with sufficient tools for wheel changing; the *Maintenance and minor repair* tool kit detailed in *Tools and working facilities,* with the addition of a hammer, is probably sufficient for those repairs that most motorists would consider attempting at the roadside. In addition a few items which can be fitted without too much trouble in the event of a breakdown should be carried. Experience and available space will modify the list below, but the following may save having to call on professional assistance:

Spark plugs, clean and correctly gapped
HT lead and plug cap – long enough to reach the plug furthest from the distributor
Distributor rotor, condenser and contact breaker points
Drivebelt(s) – emergency type may suffice
Spare fuses
Set of principal light bulbs
Tin of radiator sealer and hose bandage

Exhaust bandage
Roll of insulating tape
Length of soft iron wire
Length of electrical flex
Torch or inspection lamp (can double as test lamp)
Battery jump leads
Tow-rope
Ignition waterproofing aerosol
Litre of engine oil
Sealed can of hydraulic fluid
Emergency windscreen
Worm drive clips
Tube of filler paste

If spare fuel is carried, a can designed for the purpose should be used to minimise risks of leakage and collision damage. A first aid kit and a warning triangle, whilst not at present compulsory in the UK, are obviously sensible items to carry in addition to the above.

When touring abroad it may be advisable to carry additional spares which, even if you cannot fit them yourself, could save having to wait while parts are obtained. The items below may be worth considering:

Clutch and throttle cables
Cylinder head gasket
Alternator brushes
Fuel pump repair kit
Tyre valve core

One of the motoring organisations will be able to advise on availability of fuel etc in foreign countries.

Engine will not start

Engine fails to turn when starter operated
Flat battery (recharge, use jump leads, or push start)
Battery terminals loose or corroded
Battery earth to body defective
Engine earth strap loose or broken
Starter motor (or solenoid) wiring loose or broken
Automatic transmission selector in wrong position, or inhibitor switch faulty
Ignition/starter switch faulty
Major mechanical failure (seizure)
Starter or solenoid internal fault (see Chapter 10)

Starter motor turns engine slowly
Partially discharged battery (recharge, use jump leads, or push start)
Battery terminals loose or corroded
Battery earth to body defective
Engine earth strap loose
Starter motor (or solenoid) wiring loose
Starter motor internal fault (see Chapter 10)

Starter motor spins without turning engine
Flat battery
Starter motor pinion sticking on sleeve
Flywheel gear teeth damaged or worn
Starter motor mounting bolts loose

Engine turns normally but fails to start
Damp or dirty HT leads and distributor cap (crank engine and check for spark)
Dirty or incorrectly gapped distributor points (if applicable)
No fuel in tank (check for delivery at carburettor)
Excessive choke (hot engine) or insufficient choke (cold engine)
Fouled or incorrectly gapped spark plugs (remove, clean and regap)
Other ignition system fault (see Chapter 4)
Other fuel system fault (see Chapter 3)
Poor compression (see Chapter 1)
Major mechanical failure (eg camshaft drive)

Engine fires but will not run
Insufficient choke (cold engine)
Air leaks at carburettor or inlet manifold
Fuel starvation (see Chapter 3)
Ballast resistor defective, or other ignition fault (see Chapter 4)

Engine cuts out and will not restart

Engine cuts out suddenly – ignition fault
Loose or disconnected LT wires
Wet HT leads or distributor cap (after traversing water splash)
Coil or condenser failure (check for spark)
Other ignition fault (see Chapter 4)

Engine misfires before cutting out – fuel fault
Fuel tank empty
Fuel pump defective or filter blocked (check for delivery)
Fuel tank filler vent blocked (suction will be evident on releasing cap)
Carburettor needle valve sticking
Carburettor jets blocked (fuel contaminated)
Other fuel system fault (see Chapter 3)

Engine cuts out – other causes
Serious overheating
Major mechanical failure (eg camshaft drive)

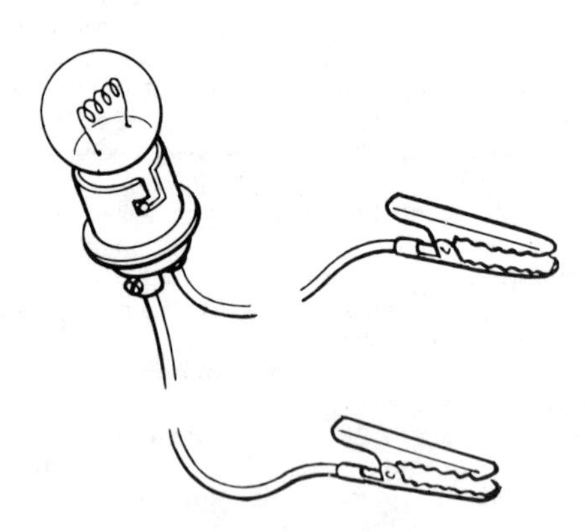

A simple test lamp is useful for tracing electrical faults

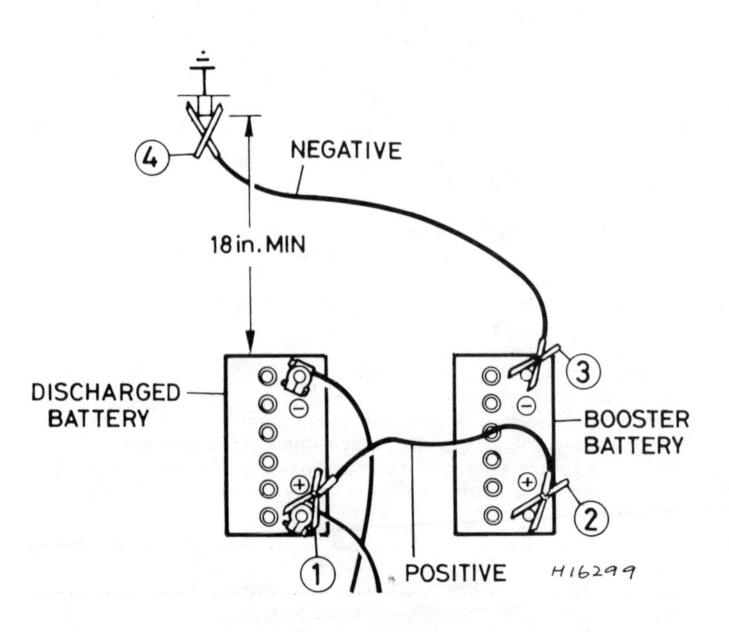

Jump start lead connections for negative earth vehicles - connect leads in order shown

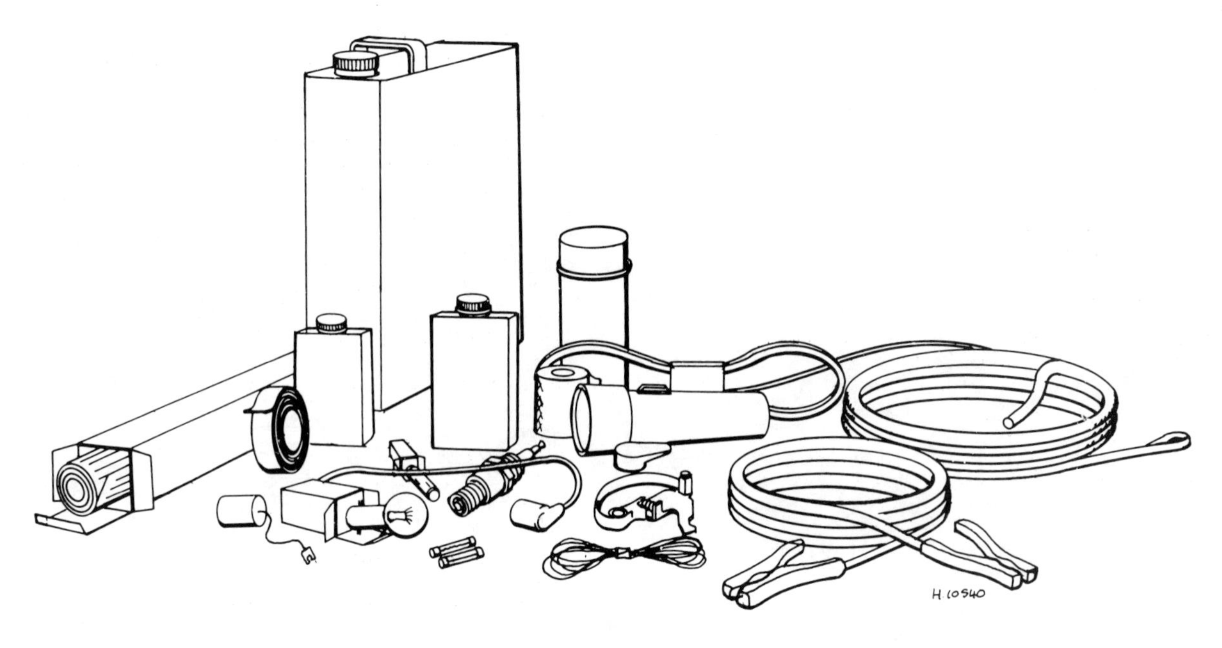

Carrying a few spares can save you a long walk!

Engine overheats

Ignition (no-charge) warning light illuminated

Slack or broken drivebelt – retension or renew (Chapter 2)

Ignition warning light not illuminated

Coolant loss due to internal or external leakage (see Chapter 2)
Thermostat defective
Low oil level
Brakes binding
Radiator clogged externally or internally
Electric cooling fan not operating correctly
Engine waterways clogged
Ignition timing incorrect or automatic advance malfunctioning
Mixture too weak

Note: *Do not add cold water to an overheated engine or damage may result*

Low engine oil pressure

Gauge reads low or warning light illuminated with engine running

Oil level low or incorrect grade
Defective gauge or sender unit
Wire to sender unit earthed
Engine overheating
Oil filter clogged or bypass valve defective
Oil pressure relief valve defective
Oil pick-up strainer clogged
Oil pump worn or mountings loose
Worn main or big-end bearings

Note: *Low oil pressure in a high-mileage engine at tickover is not necessarily a cause for concern. Sudden pressure loss at speed is far more significant. In any event, check the gauge or warning light sender before condemning the engine.*

Engine noises

Pre-ignition (pinking) on acceleration

Incorrect grade of fuel
Ignition timing incorrect
Distributor faulty or worn

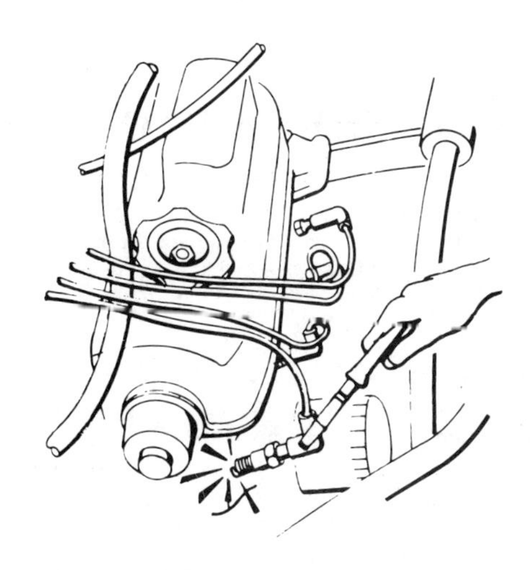

Crank engine and check for spark. Note use of insulated tool!

Worn or maladjusted carburettor
Excessive carbon build-up in engine

Whistling or wheezing noises

Leaking vacuum hose
Leaking carburettor or manifold gasket
Blowing head gasket

Tapping or rattling

Incorrect valve clearances
Worn valve gear
Worn timing chain or belt
Broken piston ring (ticking noise)

Knocking or thumping

Unintentional mechanical contact (eg fan blades)
Peripheral component fault (generator, water pump etc)
Worn big-end bearings (regular heavy knocking, perhaps less under load)
Worn main bearings (rumbling and knocking, perhaps worsening under load)
Piston slap (most noticeable when cold)

General repair procedures

Whenever servicing, repair or overhaul work is carried out on the car or its components, it is necessary to observe the following procedures and instructions. This will assist in carrying out the operation efficiently and to a professional standard of workmanship.

Joint mating faces and gaskets

Where a gasket is used between the mating faces of two components, ensure that it is renewed on reassembly, and fit it dry unless otherwise stated in the repair procedure. Make sure that the mating faces are clean and dry with all traces of old gasket removed. When cleaning a joint face, use a tool which is not likely to score or damage the face, and remove any burrs or nicks with an oilstone or fine file.

Make sure that tapped holes are cleaned with a pipe cleaner, and keep them free of jointing compound if this is being used unless specifically instructed otherwise.

Ensure that all orifices, channels or pipes are clear and blow through them, preferably using compressed air.

Oil seals

Whenever an oil seal is removed from its working location, either individually or as part of an assembly, it should be renewed.

The very fine sealing lip of the seal is easily damaged and will not seal if the surface it contacts is not completely clean and free from scratches, nicks or grooves. If the original sealing surface of the component cannot be restored, the component should be renewed.

Protect the lips of the seal from any surface which may damage them in the course of fitting. Use tape or a conical sleeve where possible. Lubricate the seal lips with oil before fitting and, on dual lipped seals, fill the space between the lips with grease.

Unless otherwise stated, oil seals must be fitted with their sealing lips toward the lubricant to be sealed.

Use a tubular drift or block of wood of the appropriate size to install the seal and, if the seal housing is shouldered, drive the seal down to the shoulder. If the seal housing is unshouldered, the seal should be fitted with its face flush with the housing top face.

Screw threads and fastenings

Always ensure that a blind tapped hole is completely free from oil, grease, water or other fluid before installing the bolt or stud. Failure to do this could cause the housing to crack due to the hydraulic action of the bolt or stud as it is screwed in.

When tightening a castellated nut to accept a split pin, tighten the nut to the specified torque, where applicable, and then tighten further to the next split pin hole. Never slacken the nut to align a split pin hole unless stated in the repair procedure.

When checking or retightening a nut or bolt to a specified torque setting, slacken the nut or bolt by a quarter of a turn, and then retighten to the specified setting.

Locknuts, locktabs and washers

Any fastening which will rotate against a component or housing in the course of tightening should always have a washer between it and the relevant component or housing.

Spring or split washers should always be renewed when they are used to lock a critical component such as a big-end bearing retaining nut or bolt.

Locktabs which are folded over to retain a nut or bolt should always be renewed.

Self-locking nuts can be reused in non-critical areas, providing resistance can be felt when the locking portion passes over the bolt or stud thread.

Split pins must always be replaced with new ones of the correct size for the hole.

Special tools

Some repair procedures in this manual entail the use of special tools such as a press, two or three-legged pullers, spring compressors etc. Wherever possible, suitable readily available alternatives to the manufacturer's special tools are described, and are shown in use. In some instances, where no alternative is possible, it has been necessary to resort to the use of a manufacturer's tool and this has been done for reasons of safety as well as the efficient completion of the repair operation. Unless you are highly skilled and have a thorough understanding of the procedure described, never attempt to bypass the use of any special tool when the procedure described specifies its use. Not only is there a very great risk of personal injury, but expensive damage could be caused to the components involved.

Conversion factors

Length (distance)						
Inches (in)	X	25.4	= Millimetres (mm)	X	0.0394	= Inches (in)
Feet (ft)	X	0.305	= Metres (m)	X	3.281	= Feet (ft)
Miles	X	1.609	= Kilometres (km)	X	0.621	= Miles

Volume (capacity)						
Cubic inches (cu in; in^3)	X	16.387	= Cubic centimetres (cc; cm^3)	X	0.061	= Cubic inches (cu in; in^3)
Imperial pints (Imp pt)	X	0.568	= Litres (l)	X	1.76	= Imperial pints (Imp pt)
Imperial quarts (Imp qt)	X	1.137	= Litres (l)	X	0.88	= Imperial quarts (Imp qt)
Imperial quarts (Imp qt)	X	1.201	= US quarts (US qt)	X	0.833	= Imperial quarts (Imp qt)
US quarts (US qt)	X	0.946	= Litres (l)	X	1.057	= US quarts (US qt)
Imperial gallons (Imp gal)	X	4.546	= Litres (l)	X	0.22	= Imperial gallons (Imp gal)
Imperial gallons (Imp gal)	X	1.201	= US gallons (US gal)	X	0.833	= Imperial gallons (Imp gal)
US gallons (US gal)	X	3.785	= Litres (l)	X	0.264	= US gallons (US gal)

Mass (weight)						
Ounces (oz)	X	28.35	= Grams (g)	X	0.035	= Ounces (oz)
Pounds (lb)	X	0.454	= Kilograms (kg)	X	2.205	= Pounds (lb)

Force						
Ounces-force (ozf; oz)	X	0.278	= Newtons (N)	X	3.6	= Ounces-force (ozf; oz)
Pounds-force (lbf; lb)	X	4.448	= Newtons (N)	X	0.225	= Pounds-force (lbf; lb)
Newtons (N)	X	0.1	= Kilograms-force (kgf; kg)	X	9.81	= Newtons (N)

Pressure						
Pounds-force per square inch (psi; lbf/in^2; lb/in^2)	X	0.070	= Kilograms-force per square centimetre (kgf/cm^2; kg/cm^2)	X	14.223	= Pounds-force per square inch (psi; lbf/in^2; lb/in^2)
Pounds-force per square inch (psi; lbf/in^2; lb/in^2)	X	0.068	= Atmospheres (atm)	X	14.696	= Pounds-force per square inch (psi; lbf/in^2; lb/in^2)
Pounds-force per square inch (psi; lbf/in^2; lb/in^2)	X	0.069	= Bars	X	14.5	= Pounds-force per square inch (psi; lbf/in^2; lb/in^2)
Pounds-force per square inch (psi; lbf/in^2; lb/in^2)	X	6.895	= Kilopascals (kPa)	X	0.145	= Pounds-force per square inch (psi; lbf/in^2; lb/in^2)
Kilopascals (kPa)	X	0.01	= Kilograms-force per square centimetre (kgf/cm^2; kg/cm^2)	X	98.1	= Kilopascals (kPa)

Torque (moment of force)						
Pounds-force inches (lbf in; lb in)	X	1.152	= Kilograms-force centimetre (kgf cm; kg cm)	X	0.868	= Pounds-force inches (lbf in; lb in)
Pounds-force inches (lbf in; lb in)	X	0.113	= Newton metres (Nm)	X	8.85	= Pounds-force inches (lbf in; lb in)
Pounds-force inches (lbf in; lb in)	X	0.083	= Pounds-force feet (lbf ft; lb ft)	X	12	= Pounds-force inches (lbf in; lb in)
Pounds-force feet (lbf ft; lb ft)	X	0.138	= Kilograms-force metres (kgf m; kg m)	X	7.233	= Pounds-force feet (lbf ft; lb ft)
Pounds-force feet (lbf ft; lb ft)	X	1.356	= Newton metres (Nm)	X	0.738	= Pounds-force feet (lbf ft; lb ft)
Newton metres (Nm)	X	0.102	= Kilograms-force metres (kgf m; kg m)	X	9.804	= Newton metres (Nm)

Power						
Horsepower (hp)	X	745.7	= Watts (W)	X	0.0013	= Horsepower (hp)

Velocity (speed)						
Miles per hour (miles/hr; mph)	X	1.609	= Kilometres per hour (km/hr; kph)	X	0.621	= Miles per hour (miles/hr; mph)

*Fuel consumption**						
Miles per gallon, Imperial (mpg)	X	0.354	= Kilometres per litre (km/l)	X	2.825	= Miles per gallon, Imperial (mpg)
Miles per gallon, US (mpg)	X	0.425	= Kilometres per litre (km/l)	X	2.352	= Miles per gallon, US (mpg)

Temperature

Degrees Fahrenheit = (°C x 1.8) + 32

Degrees Celsius (Degrees Centigrade; °C) = (°F - 32) x 0.56

**It is common practice to convert from miles per gallon (mpg) to litres/100 kilometres (l/100km), where mpg (Imperial) x l/100 km = 282 and mpg (US) x l/100 km = 235*

Index

D

E

I

J

L

M

O

P

R

S